CONTACTS
2012

101st EDITION
Published by Spotlight, 7 Leicester Place, London WC2H 7RJ
T 020 7437 7631   **F** 020 7437 5881
E questions@spotlight.com   **W** www.spotlight.com

What is Contacts?

Contacts is the essential handbook for everyone working or wanting to work in the entertainment industry. It has been published by Spotlight since 1947. It contains over 5000 listings for companies, services and individuals across all branches of Television, Stage, Film and Radio. These are updated annually to bring you the most accurate information available.

Also watch out for the 'information and advice pages', designed to tell you more about those listed and why you might want to contact them. They include valuable advice from key industry figures - especially helpful if you are just starting out in the industry.

As ever, please send any feedback or suggestions for the next edition to contacts@spotlight.com

How can I / my company appear in the next edition of Contacts?

Contacts is published annually. If you would like to appear in the next edition, either with an advert or a free, text-only listing, please visit: www.contactshandbook.com

How do I buy copies of Contacts?

To purchase copies of Contacts, visit www.contactshandbook.com, email sales@spotlight.com or call 020 7440 5026. It is also available from most good bookshops.

Mixed Sources
FSC

Designed by Consider. www.considercreative.co.uk
Printed and bound in Great Britain by MPG books.

SPOTLIGHT

Partners
Nigel Seale, Ben Seale, Emma Smith, Philippa Burton

Editor
Kate Poynton

Design & Edition Layout
Kathy Norrish

Accounts
Nas Fokeerchand – Head of Accounts
Amelia Barnham
Tanya Doganci
Laura Ruocco

Client Relations
Pippa Harrison – Head of Client Relations
Joe Bates
Emma Dyson
Thom Hammond
Nicholas Peel
Liam Simpson
Kittie Story

Data Processing
Joanna MacLeod – Head of Data Processing
Caroline Taylor
Angie Drake
Amanda Lawrence
Emma Lear
Sharon Mulcahy
Helene Van De Langenberg

Editorial
Cindy Lemmer
Angela Cottrell - Editor, Case Studies & Information Pages
Martin Pavey

HR
Marylin Peach

IT
Dylan Beattie – Head of IT
Dave Clements
Christina Kassimatis
Richard Nienaber
Dan Woodhead

IT Development
Gary Broughton – Head of Digital

IT Systems
Paul Goldsmith - IT Systems Manager
Craig Osborne

Marketing
Laura Albery – Head of Sales, Marketing
    & Customer Relations
Sally Barnham
Elaine Compton
Frances Mordue
Joan Queva
Elinor Samuels
Kelly Taylor
Kate Tozer

Production
Neill Kennedy
Louise Fairweather
Hannah Frankel
Nick Goldfinch
David McCarthy

C →

Contents

Contents

Contents

A →

CPMA
For information regarding membership of
The Co-operative Personal Management
Association please contact:

The Secretary CPMA
c/o 62 Foulden Road, London N16 7UR
T 07876 641582
W www.cpma.coop

Members of the above organisations
are clearly marked as such in the
appropriate listings

Accountants, Insurance & Law

Why might I need this section?

This section contains listings for a number of companies and services which exist to help performers with the day-to-day administration of their working lives. Performers need to manage their business affairs personally, in ways that those in 'normal' jobs do not. For example, unlike most employees, a performer does not have an accounts department to work out their tax and national insurance, or an HR department to take care of contracts or health insurance on their behalf. On top of which, performers can often be away on tour or on set for many months and unable to attend to these matters themselves.

Areas covered in this section include:

Accountants and other financial services

Dedicated companies exist which can help you to manage key financial issues, including national insurance, taxation, benefits, savings and pensions. Specialist mortgage companies also exist for performers and other self-employed workers within the entertainment industry. Specific information about accountancy services is also provided in this section's case study. If you are a member of Equity, the main actors' union in the UK, you can also ask them for free financial advice. An Equity pension scheme exists into which the BBC, ITV, PACT, TV companies and West End Theatre producers will pay when you have a main part with one of them. Similar schemes also exist for dancers and other performers.

Insurance

Performers may often need specialist insurance for specific jobs, as well as the standard life and health insurance policies held by most people. A number of specialist insurers are listed in this section. Equity also offers a specialist backstage/accident and public liability insurance policy to all of its members.

Legal

There may be times in a performer's career when he/she needs specialist legal advice or representation. This could be because of a performer's high profile, complicated contractual details, or international employment issues. Legal advisors and solicitors are listed in this section. In addition, as part of their membership, Equity performers can also obtain free legal advice regarding professional engagements or personal injury claims.

How should I use these listings?

As when looking to hire any company or individual, contact a number of different companies and carefully compare the services they offer. Ask others in the industry for recommendations. If you are an Equity member, don't forget to check first that the service isn't already available free of charge, as part of your annual membership. For information about joining Equity, visit www.equity.org.uk or see their case study in the 'Unions' section.

Accountants, Insurance & Law

CASE STUDY

MGM are chartered certified accountants who provide professional personalised solutions for each of their clients. They offer advice and guidance on a wide variety of situations.

MGM's partners have over 25 years of experience in dealing with the music, media and entertainment industries which we use to assist any clients who work within these areas. If you fall into these categories then you can feel secure in the knowledge that we have specialist experience and knowledge that could make a difference to you and your tax position.

If you are new to the industry it is important you start as you mean to go on and ensure that you set up your business correctly. If you are happy to be self-employed make sure you register as such with HMRC within 3 months of starting by calling 0845 915 4515, otherwise you could face a fine of £100. HMRC will also want you to pay Class 2 NIC at a rate of £2.50 per week.

If all of this seems a bit daunting, we would recommend consulting an accountant as setting up correctly can save a lot of time and money in the long run.

Bookkeeping

An accountant can show you how to keep your bookkeeping up-to-date in a variety of ways: on accounting software, on spreadsheets, or even manually. We have designed simple spreadsheets ready for most clients that can be tailored to individual needs and require little or no accounting knowledge, removing the need to purchase expensive software.

We will guide you on what you can and cannot claim as expenses, as well as always being there on the end of the phone and/or e-mail to help you with any issues or questions you have. Our main goal is to help you understand your tax position and to try and do this in the easiest and most approachable way possible. Alternatively, your accountant will be happy to handle all your bookkeeping for you.

Self Assessment

Some people are happy to complete all the necessary bookkeeping and accounting for themselves. However, despite HMRC calling it 'Self Assessment', we believe the complexities involved in completing what is required of you to be both arduous and sometimes unnecessarily complicated.

As well as completing your Self Assessment tax return, an accountant will complete all necessary tax computations and tax returns, calculate your tax liability and advise you how much tax you need to pay and when to pay it.

To be or not to be....Limited

Not everybody is aware that depending on your level of turnover and profit you have a choice of trading entity open to you. Initially most people automatically register as self-employed and continue in this guise until they are told otherwise. However it is often much more tax-efficient for them to incorporate, thereby becoming a limited company.

We have suggested this change and implemented it for many of our clients who are all now benefiting from paying less tax and retaining more of their hard-earned income. The idea of incorporating can sound very daunting and a little 'pie in the sky' for many people but the reality is that we will guide you through the issues and potential problems, whilst ensuring you take advantage of the tax-saving advantages.

Epilogue

Here at MGM we would never dream of attempting stand-up comedy, acting (at any level), and certainly not dancing (although vague imitations have been known...) when we realise there are people far more accomplished to perform such tasks! We hope that when it comes to your bookkeeping and tax affairs, you consider hiring an accountant as the best and most cost-effective solution.

For more information about MGM Accountancy contact Mark Livermore:
T 020 7379 9202
E admin@mgmaccountancy.co.uk
W www.mgmaccountancy.co.uk

ALEXANDER JAMES & CO   T 020 8398 4447
Contact: Andrew Nicholson
Admirals Quarters
Portsmouth Road
Thames Ditton, Surrey KT7 0XA
F 020 8398 9989
E actors@alexanderjames.co.uk
W www.alexanderjames.co.uk

AON LTD /ALBERT G. RUBEN   T 01753 785859
Insurance Brokers
Pinewood Studios, Pinewood Road
Iver, Bucks SL0 0NH
W www.aon.co.uk

BAMBRIDGE ACCOUNTANTS   T 020 7839 2163
12 Bray House
Duke of York Street, London SW1Y 6JX
E alistair@bambridgeaccountants.co.uk
W www.bambridgeaccountants.co.uk

BLACKMORE, Lawrence   T 020 7240 1817
Production Accountant
Suite 5, 26 Charing Cross Road
London WC2H 0DG

BLAKE LAPTHORNE   T 020 7405 2000
Solicitors
Watchmaker Court
33 St John's Lane, London EC1M 4DB
F 020 7814 9421
E info@bllaw.co.uk
W www.bllaw.co.uk

BLINKHORNS   T 020 7636 3702
27 Mortimer Street, London W1T 3BL
E info@blinkhorns.co.uk
W www.blinkhorns.co.uk

BOWKER ORFORD   T 020 7636 6391
Chartered Accountants
15-19 Cavendish Place, London W1G 0DD
F 020 7580 3909
E mail@bowkerorford.com
W www.bowkerorford.com

BREBNERS   T 020 7734 2244
Chartered Accountants
180 Wardour Street, London W1F 8LB
F 020 7287 5315
E partners@brebners.com
W www.brebners.com

BRECKMAN & COMPANY LTD   T 020 7499 2292
Chartered Certified Accountants
49 South Molton Street
London W1K 5LH
E info@breckmanandcompany.co.uk
W www.breckmanandcompany.co.uk

CARNE, Charlie & CO   T 020 8742 2001
49 Windmill Road, London W4 1RN
E info@charliecarne.com

CARR, Mark & CO LTD   T 020 7717 8474
Chartered Accountants
Garrick House, 26-27 Southampton Street
Covent Garden, London WC2E 7RS
T 01273 778802
E mark@markcarr.co.uk
W www.markcarr.co.uk

CHARTERED ACCOUNTANTS

Will Advise on Tax, Self Assessment, Accounts, Finance, Limited Companies etc **First meeting Free**

H And S Accountants LTD. Argo House, Kilburn Park Road, London NW6 5LF

T: 020 7644 0534 **F:** 020 7788 2984 **E:** dsummersfca@hotmail.com

CBW (CARTER BACKER WINTER LLP) T 020 7309 3800
Business Advisers. Chartered Accountants
Enterprise House
21 Buckle Street, London E1 8NN
F 020 7309 3801
E info@cbw.co.uk
W www.cbw.co.uk

CENTRE STAGE CHARTERED ACCOUNTANTS T 0161 655 2000
Hampton House
Oldham Road, Middleton
Manchester M24 1GT
E accounts@mbrookes.co.uk
W www.centrestage-accountants.com

COLLINS & COMPANY T 020 8427 1888
Chartered Accountants
2nd Floor
116 College Road
Harrow
Middlesex HA1 1BQ
F 020 8863 0068
E hq@collins116.com

COUNT & SEE LTD T 020 8767 7882
Tax, Accountancy & Book-keeping Services
219 Macmillan Way
London SW17 6AW
F 0845 0043454
E info@countandsee.com
W www.countandsee.com

DUB & CO T 020 7284 8686
7 Torriano Mews
London NW5 2RZ
F 020 7284 8687
E office@dub.co.uk
W www.dub.co.uk

EQUITY INSURANCE SERVICES T 01245 357854
131-133 New London Road
Chelmsford
Essex CM2 0QZ
F 01245 491641
E enquiries@equity-ins-services.com
W www.equity-ins-services.com

FISHER BERGER & ASSOCIATES T 020 8732 5501
Chartered Accountants
Devonshire House
582 Honeypot Lane, Stanmore HA7 1JS
F 020 8732 5500
E nik@fisherberger.com

FISHER BERGER & ASSOCIATES T 020 8732 5501
Chartered Accountants
Simia Wall
178 Bishopsgate, London EC2M 4NJ
F 020 8732 5500
E nik@fisherberger.com

FORD, Jonathan & CO T 0151 426 4512
Chartered Accountants
The Coach House
31 View Road, Rainhill
Merseyside L35 0LF
E info@jonathanford.co.uk
W www.jonathanford.co.uk

GLOBAL MOBILITY LAW T 07798 695112 (UK)
Contact: Julia de Cadenet. Transatlantic Legal & Immigration Services. Consultancy Advice on all aspects of Work Visas & US Green Cards for Members of Performing Arts & Associated Industries. Advisory work in Media Contracts & Intellectual Property & Copyright Matters in Europe & USA. Lawyers offices in London, Paris & California. Discounts for Equity Members
T 00 33 1 626218858 (Paris)
E info@legalbrain.eu
W www.globalmobilitylaw.com

H & S ACCOUNTANTS LTD T 020 7644 0534
Chartered Accountants
Argo House, Kilburn Park Road
London NW6 5LF
F 020 7788 2984
E dsummersfca@hotmail.com
W www.dsummers.co.uk

HARDWICKE BUILDING T 07720 294667
Media Law
Lincoln's Inn, London WC2A 3SB
F 020 7691 1234
E mark.engleman@hardwicke.co.uk
W www.hardwicke.co.uk

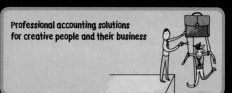

HARVEY MEAD & CO LTD   T 01892 891572
Accountants
The Old Winery
Lamberhurst Vineyard
Lamberhurst, Kent TN3 8EW
F 01892 891892
E lynnette@harveymead.co.uk

HILL DICKINSON LLP   T 0151 600 8000
1 St Paul's Square
Old Hall Street, Liverpool L3 9SJ
E mediateam@hilldickinson.com
W www.hilldickinson.com

HOOD, Karl LLP   T 07916 971998
9 Beechwood Avenue
Sunbury, Middlesex TW16 7QL
E karl@karlhoodtax.co.uk
W www.karlhoodtax.co.uk

HW LEE ASSOCIATES LLP   T 020 7025 4600
New Derwent House
69-73 Theobalds Road
London WC1X 8TA
F 020 7025 4666
E enquiries@hw-lee.com
W www.hw-lee.com

**LA PLAYA MEDIA
& PRODUCTION**   T 01223 200673
Insurance
The Stables, Manor Farm
Milton Road, Impington, Cambridge CB24 9NG
E stuart.osborne@laplayainsurance.com
W www.laplayainsurance.com

**LACHMAN SMITH
ACCOUNTANTS**   T 020 8731 1700
16B North End Road
Golders Green, London NW11 7PH
E accounts@lachmansmith.co.uk
W www.lachmansmith.eu

**LARK INSURANCE
BROKING GROUP**   T 020 7543 2800
Ibex House
42-47 Minories, London EC3N 1DY
F 020 7543 2801
E mailbox@larkinsurance.co.uk
W www.larkinsurance.co.uk

MACINTYRE HUDSON LLP   T 020 7429 4100
Media & Entertainment Accountants
New Bridge Street House
30-34 New Bridge Street
London EC4V 6BJ
F 020 7248 8939
E entertainment@mhllp.co.uk
W www.macintyrehudson.co.uk

MARTIN GREENE RAVDEN LLP   T 020 7625 4545
Chartered Accountants
55 Loudoun Road
St John's Wood, London NW8 0DL
F 020 7625 5265
E info@mgr.co.uk
W www.mgr.co.uk

MEDIA INSURANCE BROKERS   T 0141 229 6480
3rd Floor, St George's Buildings
5 St Vincent Place, Glasgow G1 2DH
F 0141 229 6489
E david.johnstone@mediainsurance.com
W www.mediainsurance.com

MGM ACCOUNTANCY LTD   T 020 7379 9202
3rd Floor
20 Bedford Street, London WC2E 9HP
E admin@mgmaccountancy.co.uk
W www.mgmaccountancy.co.uk

**MONEYWISE
INVESTMENTS PLC**   T 020 8552 5521
Insurance Brokers
440-442 Romford Road
London E7 8DF
E aadatia@moneywiseplc.co.uk
W www.moneywiseplc.co.uk

NYMAN LIBSON PAUL   T 020 7433 2400
Chartered Accountants
Regina House
124 Finchley Road, London NW3 5JS
F 020 7433 2401
E entertainment@nlpca.co.uk
W www.nlpca.co.uk

O'DRISCOLL, G. & CO   T 01621 893888
2 Catchpole Lane
Great Totham
Maldon, Essex CM9 8PY
T 07780 662544
E info@godriscoll.co.uk
W www.godriscoll.co.uk

PLANISPHERES   T/F 020 7602 2038
Business & Legal Affairs
Sinclair House, 2 Sinclair Gardens
London W14 0AT
E info@planispheres.com
W www.planispheres.com

**REES ASTLEY
INSURANCE BROKERS LTD**   T 01686 626019
Mostyn House, Market Street
Newtown, Powys SY16 2PQ
F 01686 628457
E performingarts@reesastley.co.uk
W www.insurance4performingarts.co.uk

1984 PERSONAL MANAGEMENT LTD   T 020 7251 8046
CPMA Member. Contact: David Meyer.
By Post. Accepts Showreels. 25 Performers
Suite 508, Davina House
137 Goswell Road, London EC1V 7ET
F 020 7250 3031
E info@1984pm.com
W www.1984pm.com

21ST CENTURY ACTORS MANAGEMENT LTD   T 020 7278 3438
CPMA Member. Contact: By e-mail.
18 Performers. Commercials.
Film. Stage. Television.
206 Panther House, 38 Mount Pleasant
London WC1X 0AN
E mail@21stcenturyactors.co.uk
W www.21stcenturyactors.co.uk

2MA LTD   T 023 8074 1354
Sports. Stunts
Spring Vale, Tutland Road
North Baddesley, Hants SO52 9FL
F 023 8074 1355
E mo.matthews@2ma.co.uk
W www.2ma.co.uk

A & B PERSONAL MANAGEMENT LTD   T 020 7794 3255
Personal Manager. Contact: By e-mail
PO Box 64671
London NW3 9LH
E billellis@aandb.co.uk

A & J MANAGEMENT   T 020 8342 0542
242A The Ridgeway, Botany Bay, Enfield EN2 8AP
T 020 8367 7139
E jo@ajmanagement.co.uk
W www.ajmanagement.co.uk

A-LIST LOOKALIKES & ENTERTAINMENTS LTD   T 0113 253 0563
Top Floor, Crank Mills
New Bank Street, Morley, Leeds LS27 8NT
E info@alistlookalikes.co.uk
W www.alistlookalikes.co.uk

AARDVARK CASTING AGENCY   T 07791 839294
E beth@aardvarkcasting.com
W www.aardvarkcasting.com

ABA (ABACUS ADULTS)   T 01306 877144
The Studio, 4 Bailey Road, Dorking, Surrey RH4 3QS
F 01306 877813
E aba@abacusagency.co.uk
W www.abacusaba.com

ABAKPORO, Chris   T 07986 416540
47 Chatsworth Road, Stratford, London E15 1RB
T 07903 192413
E chrisabak@hotmail.co.uk
W www.christheagent.com

ACCESS ARTISTE MANAGEMENT LTD   T 020 7866 5444
Contact: Sarah Bryan. By Post/e-mail. Accepts Showreels
11-15 Betterton Street, Covent Garden
London WC2H 9BP
E mail@access-uk.com
W www.access-uk.com

Agents & Personal Managers

Who are agents and personal managers?

There are hundreds of agents and personal managers in the UK, representing thousands of actors and artists. It is their job to promote their clients to casting opportunities and negotiate contracts on their behalf. In return they take commission ranging from 10-15%. Larger agencies can have hundreds of clients on their books; smaller ones may only have a handful. Agents usually try to represent a good range of artists (age, gender, type) to fill the diverse role types required by casting directors. A personal manager is someone who manages an artist's career on a more one-on-one basis.

What is a co-operative agency?

Co-operative agencies are staffed by actors themselves, who take turns to handle the administrative side of the agency and promote themselves to casting opportunities as a team. If you want more control over your career and can handle the pressures and responsibility that an agent takes away from you, then you might consider joining a co-operative agency. However it is very important that you think carefully about what you are signing up for.

You will be responsible for the careers of others as well as yourself, so you must first of all be able to conduct yourself well when speaking to casting professionals. You will also have to commit some of your time to administrative jobs. You must be prepared to deal with finances and forms – all the boring paperwork you usually hand over to your agent! You must also be aware that the other actors in the agency will want to interview you and, if you are successful, to give you a trial period working with them. The Co-operative Personal Management Association (CPMA) offers advice about joining a co-operative agency on their website www.cpma.coop

Why do I need an agent?

A good agent will have contacts and authority in the entertainment industry that you, as an individual actor, would find more difficult to acquire. Agents, if you want them to, can also deal with matters such as Equity and Spotlight membership renewal. They can offer you advice on which headshot would be best to send out to casting directors, what to include or exclude in your CV as you build on your

skills and experience, what a particular casting director might expect when you are invited to an audition, and so on.

How should I use these listings?

If you are an actor getting started in the industry, or looking to change your agent, the following listings will supply you with up-to-date contact details for many of the UK's leading agencies. Every company listed is done so by written request to us. Members of the Personal Managers' Association (PMA) and the Co-operative Personal Management Association (CMPA) have indicated their membership status under their name.

Some agencies have also chosen to list other information such as relevant contact names, their preferred method of contact from new applicants, whether or not they are happy to receive showreels and/or voicereels with a prospective client's CV and headshot, the number of performers represented by the agency, the number of agents working for the company, and/or a description of the performance areas they cover. Use this information to narrow down your search for a suitable agent.

How do I choose a new agent?

When writing to agencies, try to research the different companies instead of just sending a 'blanket' letter to every single one. This way you can target your approaches to the most suitable agencies and avoid wasting their time (and yours). As well as using the listing information provided here, look at agency websites and ask around for personal recommendations.

Unfortunately Spotlight is not able to offer personalised advice on choosing an agent, nor is it in a position to handle any financial or contractual queries or complaints, but we have prepared some useful career advice on our website: www.spotlight.com/artists/advice. Click on our Frequently Asked Questions page for general guidance regarding agents, or you may wish to try consulting our list of Independent Advisory Services, if you want one-to-one tailored advice. You can also contact The Agents Association www.agents-uk.com or The Personal Managers' Association (PMA) www.thepma.com. If you are a member of Equity www.equity.org.uk then you can contact their legal and welfare department with general information about issues including commissions, fees and contracts. However, Equity is not able to recommend specific agencies or agents.

How do I approach agencies?

Once you have made a list of suitable agencies, consult the listings again. Some agencies have indicated their preferred method of initial contact, whether by post, e-mail or telephone. Do not e-mail them, for example, if they have stated that they wish to receive your headshot, CV and covering letter by post. If they have not given a preference, you should send your CV by post as this is the traditional method of contacting agents. You should **always** include a stamped-addressed envelope (SAE) big enough to contain your 10 x 8 photo and with sufficient postage. This will increase your chances of getting a reply. Write your name and telephone number on the back of your headshot in case it gets separated from your CV.

Remember that agents receive hundreds of letters and e-mails each week, so try to keep your communication concise, and be professional at all times. We also recommend that your covering letter has some kind of focus: perhaps you can tell them about your next showcase, or where they can see you currently appearing on stage. This should always be addressed to an individual, not "To whom it may concern" or "Dear Sir or Madam". Some agents have indicated a specific contact to whom you can direct correspondence in their listing, otherwise check the agency's website or give them a call and find out who you should address your letter or e-mail to.

Some agents have indicated that they are happy to receive a showreel and/or voicereel with your CV, but it would be best to exclude these from your correspondence if they are not mentioned. Point out in your covering letter that one is available and the agent can contact you if they want to find out more.

Should I pay an agent to join their books? Or sign a contract?

Equity (the actors' trade union) does not recommend that artists pay an agent to join their client list. Before signing a contract, you should be very clear about the terms and commitments involved. For advice on both of these issues, or if you experience any problems with a current agent, we recommend that you contact Equity

www.equity.org.uk. They also produce the booklet *You and your Agent* which is free to all Equity members and available from their website's members' area.

How do I become an agent?

Budding agents will need to get experience of working in an agent's office; usually this is done by working as an assistant. It can be extremely hard work, and you will be expected to give up a lot of your evenings to attend productions. There are two organisations you may find it useful to contact: the Agents' Association www.agents-uk.com and the Personal Managers' Association www.thepma.com

Agents & Personal Managers

CASE STUDY

Kelly Andrews has been an agent for over eighteen years. She began her career with JAA Ltd., moved to Markham & Froggatt Ltd. (now Markham, Froggatt & Irwin Ltd.) for several years before opening Andrews Hamilton Ltd. In 2008 she joined Brown & Simcocks. Founded by Barry Brown in 1978, the company is now owned and operated by Carrie Simcocks. Brown & Simcocks is an active member of the Personal Managers' Association and both Carrie and Kelly are members of BAFTA.

I am often asked "What does an agent do?" When I was asked to write an advice page for Contacts readers I thought I'd answer this question.

The biggest part of every agent's day is, and should always be, 'suggesting' their clients for work, primarily by responding to 'breakdowns'. Each casting director will prepare a synopsis of plot and character requirements for each production. This is always a combination of physical and character markers that they, in consultation with the director, feel are needed for the role. These 'breakdowns' are then posted to a live, secure website (designed, hosted and facilitated by Spotlight) to which all agents with clients in Spotlight have access.

The first and most obvious filters are those of physicality (age, height etc.) and skill (instruments, languages etc.). These are commonly non-negotiable requirements and consequently dramatically limit your suggestion pool. Then comes required experience (sometimes a 'known' face, sometimes a 'new' face). Occasionally, this is negotiable but ultimately this, too, will have reduced the possible submission pool further – leaving you with perhaps 20% of your list. The final submission will be determined by the agent's experience. It will be based on a combination of his/her knowledge of the project, an understanding of the director's voice, a familiarity with the casting director's style, and most importantly the progression of the actor's career. The physical process of suggesting is simply a matter of selecting the checkbox next to the client's name and adding supporting remarks. The actor's Spotlight entry is then available for the casting director to view at their end of the live, secure website.

Other suggestions can be achieved, after reading a script, in verbal or email consultation with the casting director. Script reading is more commonly used in feature film casting, or for leading roles in new TV series.

The rest of an agent's day is spent largely on three other tasks.

The first is emailing and chatting to casting directors and producers to follow up on suggestions, encouraging them to meet actors they have not met before, or re-think their opinions about 'type-cast' actors.

The second task is negotiating deals and reading contracts before forwarding them to actors for signature. This element is becoming increasingly complex and time consuming. In the current climate of funding and budgetary constraints, an agent must fight to maintain fee levels and needs to be doubly vigilant to ensure that all clauses adhere to the collective bargaining agreements drawn up by Equity, the actors' union. As a result, agents can spend large parts of each day liaising with Equity, with independent lawyers, and with each other to achieve the best terms for actors. All agents are engaged in these conversations no matter how big or small their agency is.

The third is relaying appointment details to actors. Nothing can derail the day more than this. Many hours of every day can be lost arranging, and rearranging, meetings for clients who have not kept you informed of their availability.

I have overlooked the fourth task each day… a scramble from the office to get to the theatre by 7.30pm – all the time hoping that your professional guest has not cancelled!

Please visit www.brownandsimcocks.co.uk for further information.

Pete Bartlett *Photography*

Check out my online video tutorial: **"How to get a great headshot"**

petebartlettheadshots.co.uk   info@petebartlett.com   07971 653994

ACROBAT PRODUCTIONS   T 01923 518989
Advisors. Artists
2 The Grove, Whippendell
Chipperfield
Kings Langley, Herts WD4 9JF
E roger@acrobatproductions.com
W www.acrobatproductions.com

ACT IN AMERICA LTD   T 07798 695112
Personal Management. Immigration. IP. Offices in London,
Paris & California
25 Wimpole Street
London W1
T 00 33 1 626218858
E info@actinamerica.com
W www.actinamerica.com

ACTING ASSOCIATES   T/F 020 7607 3562
Personal Manager. Contact: Fiona Farley. By Post. Accepts
Showreels/Voicereels. 1 Agent represents 40 Performers.
Commercials. Corporate. Film. Musicals. Radio. Stage. TV
71 Hartham Road, London N7 9JJ
E fiona@actingassociates.co.uk
W www.actingassociates.co.uk

ACTOR-MUSICIANS @ ACCESS   T 020 7866 5444
Personal Manager. Contact: Sarah Bryan. By Post/e-mail.
Specialises in Actor-Musicians
c/o Access Artiste Management Ltd
11-15 Betterton Street
Covent Garden, London WC2H 9BP
E mail@access-uk.com
W www.access-uk.com

Rhys Rusbatch

Ingrid Lacey

ROBERT WORKMAN Superb casting photographs
Tel: 020 7385 5442   www.robertworkman.demon.co.uk

ACTORS AGENCY T 0131 228 4040
1 Glen Street, Tollcross
Edinburgh EH3 9JD
F 0131 228 4645
E info@stivenchristie.co.uk
W www.stivenchristie.co.uk

**ACTORS AGENCY OF
SWEDEN THE** T 00 46 8 56305409
Gamla Brogatan 44
111 20 Stockholm
Sweden
E info@actorsagency.se
W www.actorsagency.se

ACTORS ALLIANCE T/F 020 7407 6028
*CPMA Member. Contact: By Post. Commercials. Corporate.
Film. Stage. Stills. Television*
Disney Place House
14 Marshalsea Road, London SE1 1HL
E actors@actorsalliance.co.uk
W www.actorsalliance.co.uk

ACTORS' CREATIVE TEAM T 020 7278 3388
CPMA Member
Panther House, 38 Mount Pleasant
London WC1X 0AN
F 020 7833 5086
E office@actorscreativeteam.co.uk
W www.actorscreativeteam.co.uk

ACTORS DIRECT LTD T/F 0161 237 1904
Gainsborough House, 109 Portland Street
Manchester M1 6DN
E info@actorsdirect.org.uk
W www.actorsdirect.org.uk

ACTORS FILE THE T 020 7278 0087
*Personal Manager. Co-operative. CPMA Member.
Contact: By Post/e-mail*
Spitfire Studios
63-71 Collier Street
London N1 9BE
E mail@theactorsfile.co.uk
W www.theactorsfile.co.uk

ACTORS' GROUP THE (TAG) T/F 0161 834 4466
Personal Manager. CPMA Member
21-31 Oldham Street, Manchester M1 1JG
E enquiries@theactorsgroup.co.uk
W www.theactorsgroup.co.uk

ACTORS IN SCANDINAVIA T 00 358 4 00540640
Jääkärinkatu 10
00150 Helsinki, Finland
E laura@actorsinscandinavia.com
W www.actorsinscandinavia.com

ACTORS INTERNATIONAL LTD T 020 7025 8777
18 Soho Square, London W1D 3QL
F 020 7900 6800
E mail@actorsinternational.co.uk

ACTORS IRELAND T 028 9077 1450
11 Whitewell Crescent
Newtownabbey, Belfast BT36 7HH
E actorsireland@aol.com
W www.actorsireland.net

ACTOR'S TEMPLE THE T 020 3004 4537
13 Warren Street, London W1T 5LG
T 07771 734670
E info@actorstemple.com
W www.actorstemple.com

SHEILA BURNETT

P H O T O G R A P H Y

Simon Pegg

Imelda Staunton

Patsy Palmer

Ewan McGregor

020 7289 3058

www.sheilaburnett-headshots.com

Student Rates

ACTORS WORLD CASTING T 07960 332846
13 Briarbank Road, London W13 0HH
T 07870 594388
E katherine@actors-world-production.com
W www.actors-world-production.com

ACTORUM LTD T 020 7636 6978
Personal Manager
9 Bourlet Close, London W1W 7BP
F 020 7636 6975
E info@actorum.com
W www.actorum.com

**ADA (ACTORS DIRECT
ASSOCIATES)** T 07951 477015
2 Hawthorn Way, Sawtry
Huntingdon, Cambridgeshire PE28 5QB
E casting@actorsdirectassociates.net
W www.actorsdirectassociates.net

AFA ASSOCIATES T 020 7682 3677
Unit 101, Business Design Centre
52 Upper Street, London N1 0QH
E afa-associates@hotmail.com

AFFINITY MANAGEMENT T 01342 715275
The Coach House, Down Park
Turners Hill Road, Crawley Down
West Sussex RH10 4HQ
E jstephens@affinitymanagement.co.uk

AGENCY LTD THE T 00 353 1 6618535
Contact: Teri Hayden, Karl Hayden
9 Upper Fitzwilliam Street, Dublin 2
Ireland **F** 00 353 1 6766615
E admin1@tagency.ie
W www.the-agency.ie

AHA
See HOWARD, Amanda ASSOCIATES LTD

**AIM (ASSOCIATED INTERNATIONAL
MANAGEMENT)** T 020 7831 9709
PMA Member
Fairfax House, Fulwood Place, London WC1V 6HU
F 020 7242 0810
E info@aimagents.com
W www.aimagents.com

**AIRCRAFT CIRCUS ENTERTAINMENT
(ACE) AGENCY** T 07946 472329
Circus Artists only
7A Melish House, Harrington Way
London SE18 5NR
E lucy@aircraftcircus.com
W www.aircraftcircus.com

ALEXANDER PERSONAL MANAGEMENT LTD
See APM ASSOCIATES

**ALL TALENT -
THE SONIA SCOTT AGENCY** T 0141 418 1074
*Contact: Sonia Scott Mackay. By Post/e-mail/Telephone.
Accepts Showreels/Voicereels. 2 Agents represent 40
Performers. Film. Modelling. Television. Voice Overs.
Walk-on & Supporting Artists*
Unit 325, 95 Morrison Street
Glasgow G5 8BE
T 07971 337074
E enquiries@alltalentuk.co.uk
W www.alltalentuk.co.uk

**ALLISTON & FOSTER
ARTIST MANAGEMENT** T 020 3390 4321
Suite 404 Albany House
324-326 Regent Street, London W1B 3HH
E contact@allistonandfoster.com
W www.allistonandfoster.com

ALLSORTS AGENCY T 020 8989 0500
Suite 3, Marlborough Business Centre
96 George Lane, London E18 1AD
F 020 8989 5600
E bookings@allsortsagency.com
W www.allsortsagency.com

**ALLSORTS DRAMA
FOR CHILDREN** T/F 020 8969 3249
In Association with Sasha Leslie Management
34 Crediton Road, London NW10 3DU
E sasha@allsortsdrama.com

ALLSTARS CASTING T 0151 707 2100
66 Hope Street, Liverpool L1 9BZ
T 07739 359737
E sylvie@allstarscasting.co.uk
W www.allstarscasting.co.uk

**ALPHA PERSONAL
MANAGEMENT** T 020 7241 0077
Co-operative. CPMA Member
Studio B4, 3 Bradbury Street
London N16 8JN
F 020 7241 2410
E alpha@alphaactors.com
W www.alphaactors.com

ALPHABET MANAGEMENT T 020 7252 4343
Nice Business Park
19-35 Sylvan Grove, London SE15 1PD
F 020 7252 4341
E contact@alphabetmanagement.co.uk
W www.alphabetmanagement.co.uk

**ALRAUN, Anita
REPRESENTATION** T 01253 343784
PMA Member. Contact: By Post only (SAE)
1A Queensway, Blackpool
Lancashire FY4 2DG
T 07946 630986
E anita@cjagency.demon.co.uk

**ALTARAS, Jonathan
ASSOCIATES LTD** T 020 7836 8722
PMA Member
11 Garrick Street, Covent Garden
London WC2E 9AR
F 020 7836 6066
E info@jaalondon.com

ALW ASSOCIATES T 020 7388 7018
Contact: Carol Paul
1 Grafton Chambers, Grafton Place
London NW1 1LN
E alw_carolpaul@talktalk.net

**AMAZON ARTISTS
MANAGEMENT** T/F 020 8350 4909
27 Inderwick Road, Crouch End, London N8 9LB
T 07957 358767
E amazonartists@gmail.com

**AMBER PERSONAL
MANAGEMENT LTD** T 0161 228 0236
PMA Member
Room A, 2nd Floor, Plumtree House
21-31 Oldham Street
Manchester M1 1JG
Einfo@amberltd.co.uk
W www.amberltd.co.uk

**AMBER PERSONAL
MANAGEMENT LTD** T 020 7734 7887
PMA Member
London
E info@amberltd.co.uk
W www.amberltd.co.uk

LDW HEADSHOTS
www.ldwheadshots.com
photography@ldwheadshots.com
07504 696164
Crouch End, London   Student Rates Available

AMC MANAGEMENT   T 01438 714652
Contact: Anna McCorquodale, Tricia Howell
31 Parkside, Welwyn
Herts AL6 9DQ
F 01438 718669
E anna@amcmanagement.co.uk
W www.amcmanagement.co.uk

AMCK MANAGEMENT LTD   T 020 7524 7788
125 Westbourne Studios
242 Acklam Road
Notting Hill, London W10 5JJ
F 020 7524 7789
E info@amck.tv
W www.amck.tv

AMERICAN AGENCY THE   T 020 7485 8883
Contact: By Post.
3 Agents represent 70-80 Performers. Commercials.
Corporate. Film. Musicals. Stage. Television. Voice Overs
(American)
14 Bonny Street
London NW1 9PG
E americanagency@btconnect.com
W www.americanagency.tv

**AMG - ARTISTS
MANAGEMENT GUILD**   T 020 7603 6555
Actors. Film Directors. Film Producers.
Script Writers. Visual Artists
The Studio, 28 Royal Crescent Mews
Holland Park, London W11 4SY
T 07889 241283
E kyra@amguild.com
W www.amguild.com

**ANA
(ACTORS NETWORK AGENCY)**   T 020 7735 0999
Personal Manager. Co-operative.
CPMA Member
55 Lambeth Walk,
London SE11 6DX
F 020 7735 8177
E info@ana-actors.co.uk
W www.ana-actors.co.uk

**ANDERSON SAUNDERS
ASSOCIATES**   T 020 8806 6361
4 Geldeston Road
London E5 8RQ
E belanderson@talktalk.net

Alistair McGowan   Rachel Weisz

CAROLE LATIMER Photography
T: 020 7727 9371   www.carolelatimer.com   E: carole@carolelatimer.com

ANDREWS, Amanda AGENCY   T/F 01782 393889
30 Caverswall Road, Blythe Bridge
Stoke-on-Trent, Staffordshire ST11 9BG
T 07711 379770
E amanda.andrews.agency@tesco.net
W www.amandaandrewsagency.org.uk

**ANGEL, Susan &
FRANCIS, Kevin LTD**   T 020 7439 3086
PMA Member
1st Floor, 12 D'Arblay Street
London W1F 8DU
F 020 7437 1712
E agents@angelandfrancis.co.uk
W www.angelandfrancis.co.uk

**ANTONY, Christopher
ASSOCIATES**   T 020 8994 9952
The Old Dairy, 164 Thames Road, London W4 3QS
F 020 8742 8066
E info@christopherantony.co.uk
W www.christopherantony.co.uk

APM ASSOCIATES   T 01753 639204
Contact: Linda French. By Post/e-mail. Accepts Showreels/
Voicereels. 3 Agents represent 80 Performers
Pinewood Studios, Pinewood Road
Iver Heath, Bucks SL0 0NH
F 01753 639205
E apm@apmassociates.net
W www.apmassociates.net

ARAENA/COLLECTIVE   T/F 020 8428 0037
10 Bramshaw Gardens, South Oxhey
Herts WD19 6XP
E info@collectivedance.co.uk

A.R.C. ENTERTAINMENTS   T 01740 631292
Contact: By e-mail. 1 Agent represents
500 Active Performers
10 Church Lane, Redmarshall
Stockton on Tees, Cleveland TS21 1EP
E arcents@hotmail.com
W www.arcents.co.uk

ARCADIA ASSOCIATES   T/F 020 7937 0264
18B Vicarage Gate, London W8 4AA
E info.arcadia@btopenworld.com

**ARENA ENTERTAINMENT
(UK) LTD**   T 0113 239 2222
Regent's Court, 39 Harrogate Road
Leeds LS7 3PD
F 0113 239 2016
E info@arenaentertainment.co.uk
W www.arenaentertainment.co.uk

**ARENA PERSONAL
MANAGEMENT LTD**   T/F 020 7278 1661
Co-operative
Room 11, East Block, Panther House
38 Mount Pleasant, London WC1X 0AP
E arenapmltd@aol.com
W www.arenapmltd.co.uk

**A R G
(ARTISTS RIGHTS GROUP LTD)**   T 020 7436 6400
PMA Member
4 Great Portland Street, London W1W 8PA
F 020 7436 6700
E argall@argtalent.com

ARGYLE ASSOCIATES   T 07905 293319
Personal Manager. Contact: Richard Argyle. By Post (SAE)
43 Clappers Lane, Fulking, West Sussex BN5 9ND
E argyle.associates@me.com

ARTEMIS STUDIOS LTD   T 01344 429403
30 Charles Square, Bracknell
Berkshire RG12 1AY
E agency@artemis-studios.co.uk
W www.agency.artemis-studios.co.uk

ARTIST MANAGEMENT UK LTD   T 0151 523 6222
PO Box 96, Liverpool L9 8WY
T 07948 793552
E chris@artistmanagementuk.com
W www.artistmanagementuk.com

ARUN, Jonathan   T 020 7840 0123
Personal Manager. PMA Member. Contact: Jonathan Arun,
Jeff Guerrera
Studio 9, 33 Stannary Street, London SE11 4AA
E info@jonathanarun.com
W www.jonathanarun.com

ASHCROFT MANAGEMENT LTD   T 01422 883090
Dean Clough Mills, Halifax HX3 5AX
E ashcroftmanagement@gmail.com
W www.ashcroftmanagement.co.uk

ASQUITH & HORNER   T 020 8466 5580
Including Elspeth Cochrane Personal Management.
Personal Manager. Contact: By Telephone/Post (SAE)
The Studio, 14 College Road, Bromley, Kent BR1 3NS
T 07770 482144
E asquith@dircon.co.uk

ASSOCIATED ARTS   T 020 8856 4958
Designers. Directors. Lighting & Sound Designers
8 Shrewsbury Lane, London SE18 3JF
F 020 8856 8189
E karen@associated-arts.co.uk
W www.associated-arts.co.uk

JOHN CLARK

London's leading headshot photographer
actors - children - dancers

Annie Cooper: Hollyoaks

Matt Di Angelo: The Hustle

Jamie Borthwick: EastEnders

Charlie Brooks

Cherie Lunghi

07702 627 237
0208 854 4069

Book online at www.johnclarkphotography.com
info@johnclarkphotography.com

ASSOCIATED SPEAKERS T 020 8848 9048
Lecturers & Celebrity Speakers
24A Park Road, Hayes, Middlesex UB4 8JN

ASTON MANAGEMENT T 07742 059762
Aston Farm House, Remenham Lane
Henley on Thames, Oxon RG9 3DE
E astonagent@yahoo.co.uk
W www.astonmanagement.org

ASTRAL ACTORS
MANAGEMENT T 020 8728 2782
7 Greenway Close, London NW9 5AZ
E info@astralactors.com
W www.astralactors.com

AVALON MANAGEMENT
GROUP LTD T 020 7598 8000
4A Exmoor Street, London W10 6BD
F 020 7598 7300
E enquiries@avalonuk.com
W www.avalonuk.com

AVENUE ARTISTES LTD T 023 8076 0930
PO Box 1573, Southampton SO16 3XS
E info@avenueartistes.com
W www.avenueartistes.com

AVIEL TALENT
MANAGEMENT INC T 001 514 288 8885
1117 St Catherine Street West
Suite 718, Montreal, Quebec, Canada H3B 1H9
F 001 514 288 0768
E aviel@canadafilm.com

AWA - ANDREA WILDER AGENCY T 07919 202401
23 Cambrian Drive, Colwyn Bay
Conwy LL28 4SL
F 07092 249314
E andreawilder@fastmail.fm
W www.awagency.co.uk

AXM (ACTORS EXCHANGE
MANAGEMENT) T 020 7837 3304
Co-operative
308 Panther House, 38 Mount Pleasant
London WC1X 0AN
F 020 7837 7215
E info@axmgt.com
W www.axmgt.com

BALLROOM, LONDON
THEATRE OF T 020 8722 8798
Contact: Paul Harris®. Ballroom/Social Dancers for Film,
Stage & Television
24 Montana Gardens, Sutton, Surrey SM1 4FP
T 07958 784462
E office@londontheatreofballroom.com
W www.londontheatreofballroom.com

B A M ASSOCIATES T 01934 852942
Benets, Dolberrow
Churchill, Bristol BS25 5NT
E casting@ebam.tv
W www.ebam.tv

BANANAFISH MANAGEMENT T 0151 708 5509
The Arts Village, 20-26 Henry Street, Liverpool L1 5BS
T 07974 206622
E info@bananafish.co.uk
W www.bananafish.co.uk

BARKER, Alexander
MANAGEMENT T 020 7183 5097
Islington Arts Factory, 2 Parkhurst Road
London N7 0SF
E info@alexanderbarker.com
W www.alexanderbarker.com

BARKER, Gavin ASSOCIATES LTD T 020 7499 4777
PMA Member. Contact: Gavin Barker, Michelle Burke
2d Wimpole Street, London W1G 0EB
F 020 7499 3777
E katie@gavinbarkerassociates.co.uk
W www.gavinbarkerassociates.co.uk

BARR, Becca MANAGEMENT T 020 3137 2980
Dorland House, 5th Floor
14-16 Regent Street, London SW1Y 4PH
E info@beccabarrmanagement.co.uk
W www.beccabarrmanagement.co.uk

BEAUS & BELLES T 07944 894889
175 Moor Lane, Chessington, Surrey KT9 2AB
E info@beausandbelles.com
W www.beausandbelles.com

BELFAST TALENT AGENCY T 028 9024 3324
The Crescent Arts Centre, 2-4 University Road
Belfast, Antrim BT7 1NH
E info@belfasttalent.com
W www.belfasttalentagency.com

BELFIELD & WARD T 020 7395 7535
PMA Member
4th Floor, 80-81 St Martin's Lane, London WC2N 4AA
F 020 3292 9382
E office@belfieldandward.com

BELFRAGE, Julian ASSOCIATES T 020 7287 8544
PMA Member
Adam House, 14 New Burlington Street
London W1S 3BQ
F 020 7287 8832

BELL, Olivia MANAGEMENT T 020 7439 3270
PMA Member. Contact: By Post. 2 Agents represent 100
Performers. Commercials. Film. Musicals. Stage. Television
189 Wardour Street, London W1F 8ZD
E info@olivia-bell.co.uk
W www.olivia-bell.co.uk

BENJAMIN MANAGEMENT LTD T 020 7766 5223
Cameo House, 11 Bear Street
London WC2H 7AS
E agent@benjaminmanagement.co.uk

BERLIN ASSOCIATES T 020 7836 1112
PMA Member. Dramatists & Technicians only
7 Tyers Gate, London SE1 3HX
F 020 7632 5296
E agents@berlinassociates.com
W www.berlinassociates.com

BETTS, Jorg ASSOCIATES T 020 7903 5300
PMA Member
Gainsborough House
81 Oxford Street, London W1D 2EU
F 020 7903 5301
E agents@jorgbetts.com

BILLBOARD PERSONAL
MANAGEMENT T 020 7735 9956
45 Lothrop Street, London W10 4JB
T 07791 970773
E billboardpm@btconnect.com
W www.billboardpm.com

BILLY MARSH DRAMA LTD
See MARSH, Billy DRAMA LTD

BIRD AGENCY T 020 8269 6862
Personal Performance Manager
The Centre, 27 Station Road
Sidcup, Kent DA15 7EB
F 020 8308 1370
E birdagency@birdcollege.co.uk
W www.birdcollege.co.uk

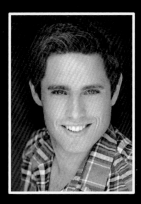  

BIZZY ADULTS AGENCY   T 0845 5200402
Bizzy Studios, 10-12 Pickford Lane
Bexleyheath, Kent DA7 4QW
F 0845 5200401
E bookings@bizzyadults.com
W www.bizzyadults.com

BLOND, Rebecca ASSOCIATES   T 020 7351 4100
PMA Member
69A Kings Road, London SW3 4NX
F 020 7351 4600
E info@rebeccablond.com

BLOOMFIELDS MANAGEMENT   T 020 7659 2001
PMA Member
77 Oxford Street
London W1D 2ES
F 020 7659 2101
E info@bloomfieldsmanagement.com
W www.bloomfieldsmanagement.com

BLUE STAR ASSOCIATES   T 020 7836 6220
Apartment 8 Shaldon Mansions
132 Charing Cross Road
London WC2H 0LA
T 020 7836 4128
E hopkinstacey@aol.com

BMA ACTORS & PRESENTERS   T 01442 878878
Personal Manager. Contact: Alex Haddad. By e-mail. 1200
Performers. Children. Commercials. Corporate. Dancers.
Film. Modelling. Presenters. Singers. Television. Walk-on &
Supporting Artists
346 High Street, Marlow House
Berkhamsted, Hertfordshire HP4 1HT
F 01442 879879
E info@bmamodels.com
W www.bmamodels.com

BODENS AGENCY   T 020 8447 0909
Personal Manager. Contact: Adam Boden,
Katie McCutcheon, Sarah Holder. By Post/e-mail/
Telephone. 3 Agents represent 400 Performers. Children.
Commercials. Film. Television. Walk-on & Supporting Artists
Bodens Studios & Agency
99 East Barnet Road
New Barnet, Herts EN4 8RF
T 07545 696888
E info@bodens.co
W www.bodens.co

BODY LONDON   T 020 3441 9878
Studio 1, Fairbanks Studios 2
65-69 Lots Road
Chelsea, London SW10 0RN
E info@bodylondon.com
W www.bodylondon.com

BODYWORK AGENCY   T 07792 851972
25-29 Glisson Road, Cambridge CB1 2HA
F 01223 568231
E agency@bodyworkds.co.uk

**BOSS CREATIVE
ENTERTAINMENT**   T 020 8299 0478
Office 1, 6 Lordship Lane
Zenoria Street, London SE22 8HN
F 020 8516 1867
E enquiries@bosscreativeentertainment.com
W www.bosscreativeentertainment.com

BOSS CREATIVES   T 0161 237 0100
Fourways House
57 Hilton Street, Manchester M1 2EJ
F 0161 236 1237
E info@bossmodels.co.uk
W www.bossmodelmanagement.co.uk

BOSS LIFESTYLE MODELS   T 0161 237 0100
Fourways House, 57 Hilton Street, Manchester M1 2EJ
F 0161 236 1237
E info@bossmodels.co.uk
W www.bossmodelmanagement.co.uk

**BOSS MODEL
MANAGEMENT LTD**   T 0161 237 0100
Fourways House, 57 Hilton Street
Manchester M1 2EJ
E info@bossmodels.co.uk
W www.bossmodelmanagement.co.uk

BOYCE, Sandra MANAGEMENT   T 020 7923 0606
PMA Member
1 Kingsway House, Albion Road, London N16 0TA
F 020 7241 2313
E info@sandraboyce.com
W www.sandraboyce.com

**BRAIDMAN, Michelle
ASSOCIATES LTD**   T 020 7237 3523
PMA Member
2 Futura House, 169 Grange Road, London SE1 3BN
F 020 7231 4634
E info@braidman.com
W www.braidman.com

**BRAITHWAITE'S
THEATRICAL AGENCY**   T 020 8954 5638
8 Brookshill Avenue, Harrow Weald
Middlesex HA3 6RZ

**BREAK A LEG
MANAGEMENT LTD**   T 020 7359 3594
Units 2/3 The Precinct
Packington Square, London N1 7UP
F 020 7359 3660
E agency@breakalegman.com
W www.breakalegman.com

**BRIDGES:
THE ACTORS' AGENCY**   T 0131 226 6433
St George's West, 58 Shandwick Place
Edinburgh EH2 4RT
E admin@bridgesactorsagency.com
W www.bridgesactorsagency.com

BROADCASTING AGENCY   T 020 7490 4225
3rd Floor, Block A, Morelands
5-23 Old Street, London EC1V 9HL
E info@broadcastingagency.co.uk
W www.broadcastingagency.co.uk

BROOD MANAGEMENT   T 020 8699 1757
Contact: By e-mail. 1 Agent represents 40 Performers
High Street Buildings, 134 Kirkdale
London SE26 4BB
F 020 8699 8787
E broodmanagement@aol.com
W www.broodmanagement.com

BROOK, Dolly AGENCY   T 01371 875767
PO Box 5436, Dunmow CM6 1WW
F 01371 875996
E dollybrookcasting@btinternet.com

BROOK, Jeremy LTD   T 020 7434 0398
37 Berwick Street, London W1F 8RS
F 020 7287 8016
E info@jeremybrookltd.co.uk
W www.jeremybrookltd.co.uk

BROOK, Valerie AGENCY   T 0161 486 1631
10 Sandringham Road, Cheadle Hulme
Cheshire SK8 5NH
T 07973 434953
E colinbrook@freenetname.co.uk

Caroline Summers

Digital or Film
Session includes make-up
Short notice possible

020 7223 7669   07931 301234

carolinesummers@me.com
www.carolinesummers.co.uk

BROWN & SIMCOCKS   T 020 7928 1229
PMA Member
1 Bridgehouse Court
109 Blackfriars Road
London SE1 8HW
F 020 7928 1909
E mail@brownandsimcocks.co.uk

BRUNO KELLY LTD   T 020 7183 7331
4th Floor
Albany House
324-326 Regent Street
London W1B 3HH
F 020 7183 7332
E info@brunokelly.com
W www.brunokelly.com

BRUNSKILL MANAGEMENT LTD   T 020 7581 3388
Personal Manager. PMA Member. Contact: Aude Powell.
By Post only. Accepts Showreels/Voicereels. Commercials.
Corporate. Film. Musicals. Radio. Stage. TV. Voice Overs
Suite 8A, 169 Queen's Gate, London SW7 5HE
F 020 7589 9460
E contact@brunskill.com

BRUNSKILL MANAGEMENT LTD   T 01768 881430
Personal Manager. PMA Member. Contact: Aude Powell.
By Post only. Accepts Showreels/Voicereels. Commercials.
Corporate. Film. Musicals. Radio. Stage. TV. Voice Overs
The Courtyard, Edenhall
Penrith, Cumbria CA11 8ST
F 01768 881850
E aude@brunskill.com

Liz Peters

James Harwood

*Online black & white web gallery

*Additional colour gallery option

natasha merchant photographer
07932 618 111

natashamerchant.com

natashamerchant@mac.com

BSA LTD
See HARRISON, Penny BSA LTD

**BUCHANAN, Bronia
ASSOCIATES LTD**   T 020 7395 1400
PMA Member
1st Floor, 23 Tavistock Street, London WC2E 7NX
F 020 7379 5560
E info@buchanan-associates.co.uk
W www.buchanan-associates.co.uk

BURNETT CROWTHER LTD   T 020 7437 8008
PMA Member. Contact: Barry Burnett, Lizanne Crowther
3 Clifford Street, London W1S 2LF
F 020 7287 3239
E associates@bcltd.org
W www.bcltd.org

BWH AGENCY LTD THE   T 020 7240 5299
PMA Member
117 Shaftesbury Avenue, London WC2H 8AD
F 020 7240 2287
E info@thebwhagency.co.uk
W www.thebwhagency.co.uk

BYRAM, Paul ASSOCIATES   T 020 3137 3385
13 Embassy Court, 24 Inglis Road
London W5 3RL
F 020 3468 7450
E admin@paulbyram.com
W www.paulbyram.com

BYRON'S MANAGEMENT   T 020 7242 8096
*Contact: By Post/e-mail. Accepts Showreels. Commercials.
Film. Musicals. Stage. Television*
180 Drury Lane, London WC2B 5QF
E byronsmanagement@aol.com
W www.byronsmanagement.co.uk

C.A. ARTISTES MANAGEMENT   T 020 8834 1608
26-28 Hammersmith Grove, London W6 7BA
E casting@caartistes.com
W www.caartistes.com

**CAMBELL JEFFREY
MANAGEMENT**   T 01838 200707
Set, Costume, Lighting Designers
6 Glenview, Dalmally
Argyll, Scotland PA33 1BE
E cambell@theatricaldesigners.co.uk

**CAMPBELL, Alison MODEL & PROMOTION
AGENCY**   T 028 9080 9809
381 Beersbridge Road, Belfast BT5 5DT
F 028 9080 9808
E info@alisoncampbellmodels.com
W www.alisoncampbellmodels.com

CAPITAL VOICES   T 01372 466228
*Contact: Anne Skates. Film. Session Singers.
Stage. Studio. Television*
PO Box 364, Esher
Surrey KT10 9XZ
F 01372 466229
E capvox@aol.com
W www.capitalvoices.com

**CARAVANSERAI
ASSOCIATES LTD**   T 05601 534892
*Contact: By e-mail. Accepts Showreels. 3 Agents represent
30 Performers. Commercials. Corporate. Film. Stage.
Television*
Basement, Townsend House
22-25 Dean Street, London W1D 3RX
T 07552 162909
E info@cserai.co.uk

CAREY, Roger ASSOCIATES   T 01932 582890
Personal Manager. PMA Member
Suite 909, The Old House, Shepperton Film Studios
Studios Road, Shepperton, Middlesex TW17 0QD
F 01932 569602
E info@rogercareyassociates.com
W www.rogercareyassociates.com

CARNEY, Jessica ASSOCIATES   T 020 7434 4143
Personal Manager. PMA Member
4th Floor, 23 Golden Square
London W1F 9JP
F 020 7434 4173
E info@jcarneyassociates.co.uk
W www.jessicacarneyassociates.co.uk

CAROUSEL EVENTS   T 0844 2250465
Entertainment for Corporate & Private Events
Incentive House, 23 Castle Street
High Wycombe, Bucks HP13 6RU
F 01494 511501
E info@carouselentertainments.co.uk
W www.carouselentertainments.co.uk

CARR, Norrie AGENCY   T 020 7253 1771
Holborn Studios, 49-50 Eagle Wharf Road
London N1 7ED
F 020 7253 1772
E info@norriecarr.com
W www.norriecarr.com

CASA MANAGEMENT   T 0161 612 0082
Alison House, 5 Highfield Road
Mellor, Stockport, Cheshire SK6 5AL
F 0161 880 2056
E casamgmt@aol.com
W www.casamanagement.co.uk

NICK BRIMBLE

CATHERINE SHAKESPEARE LANE

PHOTOGRAPHER

020 7226 7694   www.csl-art.co.uk

John Colclough Advisory

Practical independent guidance for actors and actresses

t: 020 8873 1763   e: john@johncolclough.org.uk   www.johncolclough.co.uk

---

CASAROTTO MARSH LTD   T 020 7287 4450
Film Technicians
Waverley House, 7-12 Noel Street
London W1F 8GQ
F 020 7287 9128
E info@casarotto.co.uk
W www.casarotto.co.uk

**CASTAWAY
ACTORS AGENCY**   T 00 353 1 6719264
30-31 Wicklow Street, Dublin 2, Ireland
F 00 353 1 6719133
E castaway@clubi.ie
W www.irish-actors.com

CASTCALL   T 01582 456213
Casting & Consultancy Service
106 Wilsden Avenue, Luton LU1 5HR
F 08721 156975
E casting@castcall.co.uk
W www.castcall.co.uk

CASTING DEPARTMENT THE   T 020 8582 5523
277 Chiswick Village, London W4 3DF
E jillscastingdpt@aol.com
W www.thecastingdept.co.uk

CAVAT AGENCY   T 020 8651 1099
3, 97 Wardour Street, London W1F 0UF
E enquiries@cavatagency.co.uk
W www.cavatagency.co.uk

C B A INTERNATIONAL   T 00 33 1 45263342
Contact: Cindy Brace
c/o C.M.S. Experts Associés
149 Boulevard Malesherbes
75017 Paris, France
E c_b_a@club-internet.fr
W www.cindy-brace.com

C B A INTERNATIONAL   T 07789 991032
166 Waverley Avenue
Twickenham TW2 6DL
E cba_office@yahoo.co.uk

CBL MANAGEMENT   T 01273 321245
Artistes. Creatives
20 Hollingbury Rise, Brighton, East Sussex BN1 7HJ
T 07956 890307
E enquiries@cblmanagement.co.uk
W www.cblmanagement.co.uk

C C A MANAGEMENT   T 020 7630 6303
Personal Manager. PMA Member. Contact: By Post.
Actors. Technicians
Garden Level, 32 Charlwood Street
London SW1V 2DY
F 020 7630 7376
E actors@ccamanagement.co.uk
W www.cca-management.co.uk

CCM   T 020 7278 0507
CPMA Member
Panther House, 38 Mount Pleasant
London WC1X 0AP
E ccmactors@btconnect.com
W www.ccmactors.co.uk

CDA   T 020 7373 3323
PMA Member. Contact: Belinda Wright, Theresa Hickey
125 Gloucester Road, London SW7 4TE
F 020 7373 1110
E cda@cdalondon.com
W www.cdalondon.com

CELEBRITY GROUP THE   T 0871 2501234
12 Connaught Square, London W2 2BE
E info@celebrity.co.uk
W www.celebrity.co.uk

CENTER STAGE AGENCY   T 00 353 1 4533599
Personal Manager. Contact: By e-mail. Accepts Showreels.
Commercials. Film. Singers. Stage. Television
7 Rutledge Terrace, South Circular Road
Dublin 8, Ireland
E geraldinecenterstage@eircom.net
W www.centerstageagency.com

CENTRAL LINE   T 0115 941 2937
Personal Manager. Co-operative. CPMA Member.
Contact: By Post
11 East Circus Street
Nottingham NG1 5AF
E centralline@btconnect.com
W www.the-central-line.co.uk

**CENTURY MODELS
MANAGEMENT**   T 020 3086 9031
United Consortium, 24 Greville Street
Farringdon, London EC1N 8SS
T 07792 339801
E models@centurym.com
W www.century.com

CHAMBERS MANAGEMENT   T 020 7796 3588
Comedians. Comic Actors
39-41 Parker Street, London WC2B 5PQ
F 020 7831 8598
E hannah@chambersmgt.com
W www.chambersmgt.co.uk

**CHARLESWORTH,
Peter & ASSOCIATES**   T 020 7792 4600
67 Holland Park Mews, London W11 3SS
F 020 7792 1893
E info@petercharlesworth.co.uk

CHATTO & LINNIT LTD   T 020 7352 7722
123A Kings Road, London SW3 4PL
F 020 7352 3450
E info@chattolinnit.com

CHP ARTIST MANAGEMENT   T 01844 345630
Meadowcroft Barn
Crowbrook Road, Askett
Princes Risborough
Buckinghamshire HP27 9LS
E contact@chproductions.org.uk
W www.chproductions.org.uk

CHRYSTEL ARTS AGENCY   T 01494 773336
6 Eunice Grove, Chesham
Bucks HP5 1RL
T 07799 605489
E chrystelarts@waitrose.com

Peter Simpkin
PHOTOGRAPHY

020 8364 2634
07973 224 084
petersimpkin@aol.com
www.petersimpkin.co.uk

Robert Powell

Katya Virshilas

CINEL GABRAN MANAGEMENT   T 029 2066 6600
*Personal Manager. PMA Member. Contact: By Post.
Accepts Showreels. 60 Performers. Commercials.
Corporate. Film. Musicals. Presenters. Radio. Stage.
Television. Voice Overs*
PO Box 5163, Cardiff CF5 9BJ
F 0845 0666601
E info@cinelgabran.co.uk   **W** www.cinelgabran.co.uk

CINEL GABRAN MANAGEMENT   T 0845 0666605
*Personal Manager. PMA Member. Contact: By Post.
Accepts Showreels. 60 Performers. Commercials.
Corporate. Film. Musicals. Presenters. Radio. Stage.
Television. Voice Overs*
PO Box 101, Whitby, North Yorkshire YO21 3WT
F 0845 0666601
E mail@cinelgabran.co.uk   **W** www.cinelgabran.co.uk

**CIRCUIT PERSONAL
MANAGEMENT LTD**   T 01782 285388
*Co-operative. Contact: By Post/e-mail. Accepts Showreels.
Commercials. Corporate. Film. Stage. Television*
Suite 71 S.E.C.
Bedford Street, Shelton
Stoke-on-Trent, Staffs ST1 4PZ
F 01782 206821
E mail@circuitpm.co.uk
W www.circuitpm.co.uk

CITY ACTORS' MANAGEMENT   T 020 7793 9888
Personal Manager. CPMA Member. Contact: Nikki Everson
Oval House, 52-54 Kennington Oval
London SE11 5SW
E info@cityactors.co.uk
W www.cityactors.co.uk

BE NOTICED MORE

Michael Wharley
PHOTOGRAPHY
07961 068759
Student Concs
MICHAELWHARLEY.COM

Penelope Rawlins

Dugald Bruce-Lockhart

Drew Hart
Photography
+44 (0) 7824 810 474
info@drewhartphotography.com
www.drewhartphotography.com

CLARKE & JONES LTD
T 020 8438 0185
28 Fordwych Court, Shoot Up Hill, London NW2 3PH
F 0870 1313391
E mail@clarkeandjones.plus.com

CLASS - CARLINE LUNDON ASSOCIATES
T 07853 248957
25 Falkner Square, Liverpool L8 7NZ
E clundon@googlemail.com

CLAYMAN, Tony PROMOTIONS LTD
T 020 7368 3336
Vicarage House, 58-60 Kensington Church Street
London W8 4DB
F 020 7368 3338
E tony@tonyclayman.com
W www.tonyclayman.com

alex pielak photography | headshots & portraiture

t: 078177 50560
e: alex@alexpielak.com
w: www.alexpielak.com

CLAYPOLE MANAGEMENT
T 0845 6501777
PO Box 123, DL3 7WA
E info@claypolemanagement.co.uk
W www.claypolemanagement.co.uk

CLIC AGENCY
T 01248 354420
7 Ffordd Seion, Bangor
Gwynedd LL57 1BS
E clic@btinternet.com
W www.clicagency.co.uk

CLOUD NINE AGENCY
T/F 020 7278 0029
96 Tiber Gardens, Treaty Street
London N1 0XE
T 07957 268971
E email@cloudnineagency.co.uk
W www.cloudnineagency.co.uk

COCHRANE, Elspeth PERSONAL MANAGEMENT
See ASQUITH & HORNER

COLE KITCHENN PERSONAL MANAGEMENT LTD
T 020 7427 5681
PMA Member
212 Strand, London WC2R 1AP
F 020 7353 9639
E stuart@colekitchenn.com
W www.colekitchenn.com

COLLINS, Shane ASSOCIATES
T 020 7826 8560
PMA Member
45 Beech Street, London EC2Y 8AD
F 0870 4601983
E info@shanecollins.co.uk
W www.shanecollins.co.uk

COLLIS MANAGEMENT LTD
T 020 8767 0196
PMA Member
182 Trevelyan Road, London SW17 9LW
T 07850 435303
E marilyn@collismanagement.co.uk

COMEDY CLUB LTD THE
T 0845 4595656
2nd Floor, 28-31 Moulsham Street
Chelmsford, Essex CM2 0HX
F 01245 255507
E info@hahaheehee.com
W www.hahaheehee.com

COMIC VOICE MANAGEMENT
T 0845 4595656
Comedians
2nd Floor, 28-31 Moulsham Street
Chelmsford, Essex CM2 0HX
F 01245 255507
E info@comicvoice.com
W www.comicvoice.com

COMMERCIAL AGENCY THE
See TCA (THE COMMERCIAL AGENCY)

COMMERCIALS@BBA
T 020 7395 1402
Commercials. Corporate
1st Floor, 23 Tavistock Street
London WC2E 7NX
E commercials@buchanan-associates.co.uk
W www.commercialsatbba.co.uk

CONTI, Italia AGENCY LTD
T 020 7608 7500
PMA Member. Contact: By Post/Telephone
Italia Conti House, 23 Goswell Road
London EC1M 7AJ
F 020 7253 1430
E agency@italiaconti.co.uk

CONWAY, Clive CELEBRITY PRODUCTIONS LTD
T 01865 514830
32 Grove Street, Oxford OX2 7JT
F 01865 514409
E info@celebrityproductions.org
W www.celebrityproductions.info

Nick Gregan
PHOTOGRAPHY

The easiest and probably the best headshot you'll ever have by one of London's premier theatrical photographers

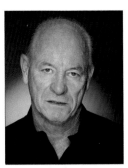  

For headshots that open doors & get you noticed, call Nick now
Tel: 020 8533 3003 Mobile: 07774 421878 www.nickgregan.com
email: info@nickgregan.com
Special rates for theatre schools and groups

CONWAY VAN GELDER GRANT LTD T 020 7287 0077
Personal Manager. PMA Member
3rd Floor, 8-12 Broadwick Street
London W1F 8HW
E info@conwayvg.co.uk

COOKE, Howard ASSOCIATES T 020 7591 0144
PMA Member. Contact: Howard Cooke. By Post.
2 Agents represent 50 Performers. Commercials. Film.
Stage. Television
19 Coulson Street, Chelsea, London SW3 3NA
F 020 7591 0155

COOPER, Tommy MAGICAL AGENCY T 07860 290437
Comedy. Magicians
21 Streatham Court, Ashley Cross
Poole, Dorset BH14 0EX
E clive@tommycoopershow.co.uk
W www.tommycooperremembered.co.uk

COOPER & CHAND TALENT MANAGEMENT T 020 8450 3901
69 Teignmouth Road, London NW2 4EA
E agents@cooperandchand.com
W www.cooperandchand.com

CORNER, Clive ASSOCIATES T 01305 860267
Contact: Duncan Stratton. By Post. Accepts Showreels.
2 Agents represent 40 Performers. Commercials. Film.
Musicals. Stage. Television
'The Belenes', 60 Wakeham
Portland DT5 1HN
E cornerassociates@btconnect.com

CORNISH, Caroline MANAGEMENT LTD T 020 8743 7337
Technicians only
12 Shinfield Street, London W12 0HN
T 07725 555711
E carolinecornish@me.com
W www.carolinecornish.co.uk

CORONA MANAGEMENT T 020 8758 2553
3 Thameside Centre, Kew Bridge Road
Brentford, Middlesex TW8 0HF
E info@coronatheatreschool.com
W www.coronatheatreschool.com

COULSON, Lou ASSOCIATES LTD T 020 7734 9633
PMA Member
1st Floor, 37 Berwick Street, London W1F 8RS
F 020 7439 7569
E info@loucoulson.co.uk

COULTER MANAGEMENT AGENCY LTD T 0141 357 6666
PMA Member. Contact: Anne Coulter
PO Box 2830, Glasgow G61 9BQ
E coultermanagement@ntlworld.com
W www.coultermanagement.com

COVENT GARDEN MANAGEMENT T 07944 283659
5 Denmark Street
London WC2H 8LP
E admin@splatsentertainment.com
W www.coventgardenmanagement.com

CPA MANAGEMENT T 01708 766444
The Studios, 219B North Street
Romford, Essex RM1 4QA
F 01708 766077
E info@cpamanagement.co.uk
W www.cpastudios.co.uk

CRAWFORDS T 020 8947 9999
PO Box 56662
London W13 3BH
E cr@wfords.com
W www.crawfords.tv

CREATIVE ARTISTS MANAGEMENT (CAM) T 020 7292 0600
PMA Member. Contact: By e-mail only
4th Floor, 111 Shoreditch High Street
London E1 6JN
E reception@cam.co.uk
W www.cam.co.uk

CREATIVE BLAST AGENCY T 020 8123 6386
The Training Centre, Radford Way
Billericay, Essex CM12 0DX
T 07545 009830
E info@cbagency.co.uk
W www.cbagency.co.uk

CREATIVE MEDIA MANAGEMENT T 020 8584 5363
PMA Member. No Actors. Film, TV & Theatre Technical
Personnel only
Ealing Studios, Ealing Green
London W5 5EP
F 020 8566 5554
E enquiries@creativemediamanagement.com
W www.creativemediamanagement.com

CREDITS ACTORS AGENCY LTD T 020 7737 0735
29 Lorn Road
London SW9 0AB
E credits@actors29.freeserve.co.uk

Management

Established in 1995
JPA Management offers
personal management to
professional actors for work in
all aspects of the entertainment
industry including Television,
Film, Theatre, Musical Theatre,
Radio & Commercials.

Visit our website:
www.jpamanagement.co.uk

Address: 30 Daws Hill Lane,
High Wycombe, HP11 1PW
Tel: 01494 520 978

paulcable
photography & design

www.paulcable.com
info@paulcable.com
07958 932 764

CRESCENT MANAGEMENT   T 020 8987 0191
Personal Manager. Co-operative. CPMA Member.
Contact: By Post. Accepts Showreels
10 Barley Mow Passage, Chiswick, London W4 4PH
F 020 8987 0207
E mail@crescentmanagement.co.uk
W www.crescentmanagement.co.uk

CROI8 ACTORS AGENCY   T 00 353 85 1420683
Town Hall Theatre, Galway
Co. Galway, Ireland
E croiactorsagency@yahoo.co.uk
W www.croiproductions.webs.com

**CRUICKSHANK
CAZENOVE LTD**   T 020 7735 2933
PMA Member. Contact: Harriet Cruickshank. By Post.
1 Agent. Choreographers, Designers & Directors only
97 Old South Lambeth Road, London SW8 1XU
F 020 7582 6405
E harriet@ccagents.co.uk

CS MANAGEMENT   T 020 8886 4264
The Croft, 7 Cannon Road
Southgate, London N14 7HE
F 020 8886 7555
E carole@csmanagementuk.com
W www.csmanagementuk.com

**C.S.A. (CHRISTINA
SHEPHERD ADVERTISING)**   T 020 7499 7534
4th Floor, 45 Maddox Street
London W1S 2PE
F 020 7499 7535
E csa@shepherdmanagement.co.uk

CURTIS BROWN GROUP LTD   T 020 7393 4400
PMA Member
Haymarket House, 28-29 Haymarket
London SW1Y 4SP
F 020 7393 4401
E actorsagents@curtisbrown.co.uk
W www.curtisbrown.co.uk

CWC   T 0113 245 9664
Top Floor, 67 St Pauls Street, Leeds LS1 2TE
F 0113 245 9665
E info@cwc-uk.net
W www.cwc-uk.net

DAA (DEBI ALLEN ASSOCIATES   T 020 7255 6123
PMA Member. Contact: Debi Allen
The Heals Building, 22 Torrington Place
London WC1E 7HP
F 020 7255 6128
E info@debiallenassociates.com
W www.debiallenassociates.com

DALY, David ASSOCIATES   T 020 7384 1036
Contact: David Daly, Louisa Clifton
586A King's Road, London SW6 2DX
F 020 7610 9512
E agent@daviddaly.co.uk
W www.daviddaly.co.uk

**DALY, David ASSOCIATES
(MANCHESTER)**   T 01565 631999
Contact: Mary Ramsay
16 King Street, Knutsford
Cheshire WA16 6DL
F 01565 755334
E north@daviddaly.co.uk
W www.daviddaly.co.uk

DALZELL & BERESFORD LTD   T 020 7341 9411
26 Astwood Mews, London SW7 4DE
F 020 7341 9412
E mail@dbltd.co.uk
W www.dalzellandberesford.co.uk

claire grogan
photography

Steve McFadden

Abi Hardingham

Duane Henry

Beth Kingston

Ben Richards

Tiffany Graves

Alex Humes

Lindsey Coulson

Martin Freeman

claire@clairegrogan.co.uk
www.clairegrogan.co.uk

film & digital

020 7272 1845
07932 635381

DANCERS T 020 7636 1473
1 Charlotte Street, London W1T 1RD
F 020 7637 0328
E info@features.co.uk
W www.features.co.uk

**DAVID ARTISTES MANAGEMENT
AGENCY LTD THE** T 020 8834 1615
26-28 Hammersmith Grove, London W6 7BA
E casting@davidagency.co.uk
W www.davidagency.co.uk

DAVIS, Chris MANAGEMENT LTD T 01584 819005
PMA Member
Tenbury House, 36 Teme Street
Tenbury Wells, Worcestershire WR15 8AA
F 01584 819076
E cdavis@cdm-ltd.com
W www.cdm-ltd.com

**DAVIS, Lena, BISHOP,
John ASSOCIATES** T 01604 891487
Personal Manager. Contact: By Post. 2 Agents
Cotton's Farmhouse, Whiston Road
Cogenhoe, Northants NN7 1NL
E admin@cottonsfarmhouse.org

DAVIS-PRIOR ASSOCIATES T 020 7635 7083
Unit 2, The Wheelwright Building
125 Pomeroy Street, London SE14 5BT
E info@davis-prior.co.uk
W www.davis-prior.co.uk

DEALERS AGENCY BELFAST T 028 9020 9761
Cathedral House, 22-31 Waring Street
Belfast BT1 2DX
T 07834 774330
E info@dealersagency.co.uk
W www.dealersagency.co.uk

**DENMARK STREET
MANAGEMENT** T 020 7700 5200
*Personal Manager. Co-operative. CPMA Member. Contact:
By e-mail (include Spotlight View PIN)*
Suite 4, Clarendon Buildings
25 Horsell Road, Highbury N5 1XL
E mail@denmarkstreet.net
W www.denmarkstreet.net

DEREK'S HANDS AGENCY T 020 8834 1609
Hand & Foot Modelling
26-28 Hammersmith Grove
London W6 7BA
E casting@derekshands.com
W www.derekshands.com

DEVINE ARTIST MANAGEMENT T 0844 8844578
145-157 St John Street
London EC1V 4PW
E mail@devinemanagement.co.uk
W www.devinemanagement.co.uk

de WOLFE, Felix T 020 7242 5066
*Personal Manager. PMA Member. Contact: By Post.
Accepts Showreels. 3 Agents. Film. Musicals. Radio.
Stage. Television*
Kingsway House
103 Kingsway
London WC2B 6QX
F 020 7242 8119
E info@felixdewolfe.com
W www.felixdewolfe.com

DIAMOND MANAGEMENT T 020 7631 0400
PMA Member
31 Percy Street, London W1T 2DD
F 020 7631 0500
E agents@diman.co.uk

GENUINE ARAB CASTING

Represents authentic, talented performers for stage, screen and radio
from everywhere across the Arabic Speaking World

Arab Actors - Arab Voices - Arab Presenters & Translators

Recent Clients:
Paramount Films "WWZ" - Strike Back 2 - Circle Creative - BBDO
McCann Erikson - The Edge - ORTV International - Stink Productions
BBC "Spooks" - Channel 4 "The Promise" - TV DR - Perform Group UK - SRI

Please contact us for "Anything Arabic" - we have the cultural expertise!

Tel: +44 (0)1895 437787   Mobile: 07748737374
info@genuinearabcasting.com   www.genuinearabcasting.com

DIESTENFELD, Lily T 07957 968214
Personal Manager. Over 50+ ages. No unsolicited Post/e-mails/Calls from Actors
28B Alexandra Grove, London N12 8HG
E lilyd@talk21.com

**DIRECT PERSONAL
MANAGEMENT** T/F 020 8694 1788
Co-operative. CPMA Member. Contact: Daphne Franks. By Post/e-mail. Commercials. Corporate. Film. Stage. Television
St John's House, 16 St John's Vale
London SE8 4EN
E daphne.franks@directpm.co.uk
W www.directpm.co.uk

**DIRECT PERSONAL
MANAGEMENT** T/F 0113 266 4036
Co-operative. CPMA Member. Contact: Daphne Franks. By Post/e-mail. Commercials. Corporate. Film. Stage. Television
Park House, 62 Lidgett Lane
Leeds LS8 1PL
E daphne.franks@directpm.co.uk
W www.directpm.co.uk

DOE, John MANAGEMENT T 01543 300689
262 Beacon Street, Lichfield WS13 7BH
T 07957 114175
E casting@johndoemgt.com
W www.johndoemgt.com

**DOUBLE ACT CELEBRITY
LOOK ALIKES** T 020 8381 0151
PO Box 25574, London NW7 3GB
F 020 8201 1795
E info@double-act.co.uk
W www.double-act.co.uk

DOUBLEFVOICES T 01580 830071
Singers
1 Hunters Lodge, Bodiam, East Sussex TN32 5UE
T 07976 927764
E rob@doublefvoices.com

**DOWNES PRESENTERS
AGENCY** T 020 8304 0541
96 Broadway, Bexleyheath, Kent DA6 7DE
E downes@presentersagency.com
W www.presentersagency.com

DP MANAGEMENT T 07837 138892
Contact: Danny Pellerini. By Post. Accepts Showreels/ Voicereels. 1 Agent represents 60 Performers
Argyle House, 29-31 Euston Road
London NW1 2SD
E danny@dpmanagement.org
W www.dpmanagement.org

DQ MANAGEMENT T 01273 721221
27 Ravenswood Park, Northwood
Middlesex HA6 3PR
T 07713 984633
E dq.management1@gmail.com
W www.dqmanagement.com

**DRAGON PERSONAL
MANAGEMENT** T 029 2075 4491
20 Nantfawr Road, Cyncoed, Cardiff CF23 6JR
T 020 7183 5362
E casting@dragon-pm.com
W www.dragon-pm.com

DRAKE, Simon MANAGEMENT T 020 7183 8995
9 Golden Square, London W1F 9HZ
F 020 7183 9013
E admin@simondrakemanagement.co.uk
W www.simondrakemanagement.co.uk

DREW, Bryan LTD T 020 7823 2346
31 Oakley House, 103 Sloane Street
London SW1X 9PP
E bryan@bryandrewltd.com

DS PERSONAL MANAGEMENT T 020 8743 7777
PO Box 118, 43 Bedford Street, London WC2E 9HA
T 07711 245848
E ds@denisesilvey.com

**DYSON, Louise at
VisABLE PEOPLE** T 01905 776631
Contact: Louise Dyson. Artists with Disabilities
E louise@visablepeople.com
W www.visablepeople.com

**EARLE, Kenneth
PERSONAL MANAGEMENT** T 020 7274 1219
214 Brixton Road, London SW9 6AP
F 020 7274 9529
E kennethearle@agents-uk.com
W www.entertainment-kennethearle.co.uk

**EARNSHAW, Susi
MANAGEMENT** T 020 8441 5010
Personal Manager
The Bull Theatre, 68 High Street
Barnet, Herts EN5 5SJ
F 020 8364 9618
E casting@susiearnshaw.co.uk
W www.susiearnshawmanagement.com

ED & JAMES T 020 7047 1969
T 07540 724522
E info@edandjames.co.uk
W www.edandjames.co.uk

**EDEN, Shelly
ASSOCIATES LTD** T/F 020 8558 3536
The Old Factory, Minus One House
Lyttelton Road, London E10 5NQ
E shellyeden@aol.com

EJA ASSOCIATES T 020 7564 2688
Incorporating Simply Singers International
PO Box 63617, London SW9 1AN
T 07891 632946
E ejaassociates@aol.com

EKA ACTOR MANAGEMENT T 01925 761088
Personal Manager. Contact: By Post/e-mail. Accepts Showreels. 6 Agents. Commercials. Film. TV. Voice Overs
The Warehouse Studios, Glaziers Lane
Culcheth, Warrington, Cheshire WA3 4AQ
F 01925 767563
E castings@eka-agency.com
W www.eka-agency.com

ELITE TALENT LTD T 07787 342221
Studio 14, 3rd Floor, M One Studios
8 Lower Ormond Street, Manchester M1 5QF
E eliteactors@yahoo.com
W www.elite-talent.net

ELLIOTT AGENCY LTD THE T 01273 454111
10 High Street, Shoreham-by-Sea BN43 5DA
E elliottagency@btconnect.com
W www.elliottagency.co.uk

ELLIS, Bill LTD
See A & B PERSONAL MANAGEMENT LTD

ELLITE MANAGEMENT T 0845 6525361
Contact: By Post/e-mail. Accepts Showreels. 3 Agents represent 40 Performers. Dancers
'The Dancer', 8 Peterson Road, Wakefield WF1 4EB
T 07957 631510
E enquiries@ellitemanagement.co.uk
W www.elliteproductions.co.uk

TITUS POWELL PHOTOGRAPHY

£99 HEADSHOTS PACKAGE
HAPPINESS GUARANTEED

07970 972675
WWW.TITUSPOWELL.COM

EMPTAGE HALLETT　　　　T 020 7436 0425
PMA Member
14 Rathbone Place, London W1T 1HT
F 020 7580 2748
E mail@emptagehallett.co.uk

EMPTAGE HALLETT　　　　T 029 2034 4205
PMA Member
2nd Floor, 3-5 The Balcony
Castle Arcade, Cardiff CF10 1BU
F 029 2034 4206　　　E cardiff@emptagehallett.co.uk

ENCORE UK CASTING　　　T 01626 211040
PO Box 251, Newton Abbot, Devon TQ12 1AL
F 01626 202989
E hannah@encorecasting.co.uk
W www.encorecasting.co.uk

ENGERS, Emma
ASSOCIATES LTD　　　　T 020 7278 9980
56 Russell Court, Woburn Place, London WC1H 0LW
T 07790 011920
E emma@emmaengersassociates.com
W www.emmaengersassociates.com

ENGLISH, Doreen '95　　　T/F 01243 825968
Contact: By Post/Telephone
4 Selsey Avenue, Aldwick, Bognor Regis
West Sussex PO21 2QZ

EPSTEIN, June ASSOCIATES　　T 020 7328 0864
Contact: By Post/e-mail
Flat 1, 62 Compayne Gardens, London NW6 3RY
F 020 7328 0684
E june@june-epstein-associates.co.uk

HEADSHOTS by phil stewart

Emma Georgia Murphy · Nigel Harman · Olivia Sloyan · Michael McKell

07884 005014   www.headshotsbyphilstewart.co.uk   philheadshots@yahoo.co.uk

ESSANAY   T 020 8998 0007
Personal Manager. PMA Member. Contact: By Post
PO Box 56662, London W13 3BH
E info@essanay.co.uk

ESTALL, Jane AGENCY THE   T 07703 550006
37 Madeira Drive, Hastings
East Sussex TN34 2NH
E thejaneestallagency@gmail.com

ETHNICS ARTISTE AGENCY   T 020 8523 4242
86 Elphinstone Road, Walthamstow, London E17 5EX
F 020 8523 4523
E info@ethnicsaa.co.uk

EUROKIDS CASTING AGENCY   T 01925 761088
Contact: Amy Musker. By Post/e-mail. Accepts Showreels.
6 Agents. Children & Teenagers. Commercials. Film.
Television. Walk-on & Supporting Artists
The Warehouse Studios, Glaziers Lane
Culcheth, Warrington, Cheshire WA3 4AQ
F 01925 767563
E castings@eka-agency.com
W www.eka-agency.com

EVANS, Jacque
MANAGEMENT LTD   T 020 8699 1202
Top Floor Suite, 14 Holmesley Road, London SE23 1PJ
F 020 8699 5192
W www.jacqueevansltd.com

EVANS, Stephanie
ASSOCIATES   T/F 0870 6092629
Rivington House, 82 Great Eastern Street
London EC2A 3JF
E steph@stephanie-evans.com
W www.stephanie-evans.com

EVANS & REISS   T 020 8871 0788
100 Fawe Park Road, London SW15 2EA
E janita@evansandreiss.co.uk

EVOLUTION TALENT
MANAGEMENT   T 020 7749 9187
The Truman Brewery Building, Studio 21
91 Brick Lane, London E1 6QL
T 020 7770 6128
E info@evolutionmngt.com
W www.evolutionmngt.com

EXCESS ALL AREAS   T/F 020 7737 5300
Contact: Paul L. Martin (Director). Cabaret, Circus & Variety
Entertainment
1st & 2nd Floors, 20 Stansfield Road
Stockwell, London SW9 9RZ
E info@excessallareas.co.uk
W www.excessallareas.co.uk

EXPERTS MANAGEMENT
SERVICES LTD   T 01625 858556
T/A Jane Hughes Management
PO Box 200, Stockport, Cheshire SK12 1GW
T 07766 130604
E gill@jhm.co.uk

EXPRESSIONS
CASTING AGENCY   T 01623 424334
3 Newgate Lane, Mansfield
Nottingham NG18 2LB
F 01623 647337
E expressions-uk@btconnect.com
W www.expressionsperformingarts.co.uk

EXTRA MILE AGENCY THE   T 07792 047328
40 Bowling Green Lane
London EC1R 0NE
E sheila@theextramileagency.com
W www.theextramileagency.com

EYE AGENT MANAGEMENT   T 07986 416540
T 07903 192413
E chris_abakporo@yahoo.co.uk
W www.eyeagentmanagement.co.uk

EYE MODELS THE   T 020 7377 7500
1st Floor, 92 Commercial Street
Spitalfields, London E1 6LZ
E bayo@theeyecasting.com
W www.theeyecasting.com

FARINO, Paola   T 020 7207 0858
Actors
109 St Georges Road, London SE1 6HY
E info@paolafarino.co.uk
W www.paolafarino.co.uk

FARNES, Norma MANAGEMENT   T 020 7727 1544
9 Orme Court
London W2 4RL
F 020 7792 2110

FAWKES, Irene MANAGEMENT   T 020 7729 8559
Contact: Irene Fawkes. By Post. Accepts Showreels.
1 Agent represents 40 Performers. Commercials. Film.
Musicals. Stage. Television
2nd Floor, 91A Rivington Street
London EC2A 3AY
F 020 7613 0769
E irenefawkes@btconnect.com

FBI AGENCY   T 07050 222747
PO Box 250, Leeds LS1 2AZ
T 07515 567309
E casting@fbi-agency.co.uk
W www.fbi-agency.co.uk

FD MANAGEMENT T 07730 800679
Sandhill, Sandhill Lane
Crawley Down Village RH10 4LE
E vivienwilde@mac.com

**FEA MANAGEMENT
(FERRIS ENTERTAINMENT)** T 0845 4724725
London. Belfast. Cardiff
Number 8, 132 Charing Cross Road
London WC2H 0LA
E info@ferrisentertainment.com
W www.ferrisentertainment.com

FEAST MANAGEMENT LTD T 020 7354 5216
PMA Member
1st Floor, 34 Upper Street
London N1 0PN
F 020 7354 8995
E office@feastmanagement.co.uk

**FEATURED & BACKGROUND
CASTING LTD** T 01628 522688
Contact: Lois Ward, Suzanne Johns
13A Waldeck House, Waldeck Road
Maidenhead, Berkshire SL6 8BR
T 07808 781167
E info@fabcastingagency.com
W www.fabcastingagency.com

FEATURES T 020 7637 1487
1 Charlotte Street, London W1T 1RD
F 020 7637 0328
E info@features.co.uk
W www.features.co.uk

FIELD, Alan ASSOCIATES T 020 8441 1137
*Personal Manager. Contact: By e-mail. Celebrities.
Composers. Musicals. Presenters. Singers*
3 The Spinney, Bakers Hill
Hadley Common, Herts EN5 5QJ
T 07836 555300
E alan@alanfield.com

FILM CAST CORNWALL & SW T 01326 311419
T 07811 253756
E enquiries@filmcastcornwall.co.uk
W www.filmcastcornwall.co.uk

FILM RIGHTS LTD T 020 7316 1837
Personal Manager. Contact: By Post
Suite 306, Belsize Business Centre
258 Belsize Road, London NW6 4BT
F 020 7624 3629

FINCH & PARTNERS T 020 7851 7140
Top Floor, 35 Heddon Street
London W1B 4BR
F 020 7287 6420
E reception@finchandpartners.com
W www.finchandpartners.com

**FIRST & FOREMOST
ENTERTAINMENT LTD** T 07505 565635
*Bespoke Entertainment Consultants. Acts.
Performers. Shows*
90 Longridge Avenue, Brighton
East Sussex BN2 8RB
E info@firstandforemostentertainment.com
W www.firstandforemostentertainment.com

FIRST CALL MANAGEMENT T 00 353 1 6798401
29-30 Dame Street, Dublin 2, Ireland
F 00 353 1 6798353
E fcm@indigo.ie

FISHER T 020 7993 6042
Studio 125, 77 Beak Street, London W1F 9DB
E fisher@castinguk.com

Paul Merton

Katy Rooke

FITZGERALD, Sheridan
MANAGEMENT   T 0845 5390504
Contact: Edward Romfourt. By Post (SAE). No Phone Calls
16 Pond Lane, Brandon
Suffolk IP27 0LA
W www.sheridanfitzgerald.com

FLAIR TALENT   T 020 7766 5212
Cameo House, 13-17 Bear Street
London WC2H 7AS
E bookings@flairtalent.com
W www.flairtalent.com

FLETCHER ASSOCIATES   T 020 8361 8061
Personal Manager. Contact: Francine Fletcher. Corporate
Speakers. Experts for Radio & Television. Stage
25 Parkway, London N20 0XN
F 020 8361 8866
W www.fletcherassociates.net

FLETCHER JACOB   T 020 7617 7181
Artist Management
162-168 Regent Street, London W1B 5TD
T 020 7038 3707
E info@fletcherjacob.co.uk
W www.fletcherjacob.co.uk

FLP   T 020 7371 0300
136-144 New Kings Road, Fulham
London SW6 4LZ
F 020 7371 8707
E info@formulaliveproductions.com
W www.formulaliveproductions.com

FOCUS TALENT   T 020 3240 1064
Personal Manager. Representing Actors in Feature Films,
Television, Theatre & Commercials. Existing Clients only
81 Sutherland Avenue, London W9 2HG
T 07532 158818
E info@focustalent.co.uk
W www.focustalent.co.uk

FOLEY, Kerry MANAGEMENT LTD T 07747 864001
Communications House, 26 York Street
London W1U 6PZ
E contact@kfmltd.com

FOSTER, Sharon MANAGEMENT   T 0121 443 4865
15A Hollybank Road, Birmingham B13 0RF
E mail@sharonfoster.co.uk
W www.sharonfoster.co.uk

FOX, Clare ASSOCIATES   T/F 020 7328 7494
Set, Lighting & Sound Designers
9 Plympton Road, London NW6 7EH
E cimfox@yahoo.co.uk
W www.clarefox.co.uk

FOX, Julie ASSOCIATES   T/F 01628 777853
Personal Manager. Contact: Julie Fox.
By e-mail only. Accepts Showreels/Voicereels.
2 Agents represent 50 Performers
E agent@juliefoxassociates.co.uk
W www.juliefoxassociates.co.uk

FRENCH, Linda
See APM ASSOCIATES

FRESH AGENTS LTD   T 01273 711777
Suite 5, Saks House
19 Ship Street,
Brighton BN1 1AD
T 0845 4080998
E info@freshagents.co.uk
W www.freshagents.co.uk

FRESH PARTNERS LTD   T 020 7198 8478
1 Hardwick's Square
Wandsworth
London SW18 4AW
E hello@fresh-partners.com
W www.fresh-partners.com

FRONTLINE ACTORS
AGENCY DUBLIN   T 00 353 1 6359882
30-31 Wicklow Street
Dublin 2, Ireland
E frontlineactors@eircom.net
W www.frontlineactors.com

FUNKY BEETROOT
CELEBRITY MANAGEMENT LTD   T 01227 751549
Personal Manager. Actors. Television Celebrities
PO Box 143, Faversham
Kent ME13 9LP
F 01227 752300
E info@funky-beetroot.com
W www.funky-beetroot.com

FUNNY SIDE ARTIST
MANAGEMENT THE   T 0844 4780404
Comedy
Number 1, 63 Mount Ephraim
Tunbridge Wells, Kent TN4 8BG
E contact@thefunnysideagency.com
W www.thefunnysideagency.com

GADBURY PERSONAL
MANAGEMENT   T 01942 635556
5 Bolton Road, Atherton
Manchester M46 9JQ
T 07791 737306
E vicky@gadbury-casting.co.uk
W www.gadburycasting.co.uk

PHOTOGRAPHY · DIGITAL · FILM · COLOUR · BLACK & WHITE

Steve Lawton

WWW.STEVELAWTON.COM · 07973 307487 · STUDENT RATES

Dev Patel · Kerry Ellis · Adam-Joe Florentino · Anna Walton · Robert Kazinsky · Natalie Cox · Steven Webb · Natalie Anderson · Douglas Booth

GAELFORCE 10 MANAGEMENT   T 0845 6031266
14 Beaumont Gardens, Dowanhill
Glasgow G12 9LR
T 07778 296002
E info@gaelforce10.com
W www.gaelforce10.com

GAGAN, Hilary ASSOCIATES   T 020 7404 8794
Personal Manager. PMA Member
187 Drury Lane, London WC2B 5QD
F 020 7430 1869
E hilary@hgassoc.co.uk

GALLOWAYS   T 020 7636 7770
16 Percy Street, London W1T 1DT
F 020 7636 7761
E info@gallowaysagency.com
W www.gallowaysagency.com

GANNON, Kay   T/F 0141 221 8622
Central Chambers
93 Hope Street
Glasgow G2 6LD
E kay@revolutiontalentmanagement.com
W www.revolutiontalentmanagement.com

GARDNER HERRITY LTD   T 020 7388 0088
PMA Member. Contact: Andy Herrity, Nicky James
24 Conway Street, London W1T 6BG
F 020 7388 0688
E info@gardnerherrity.co.uk
W www.gardnerherrity.co.uk

GARRICKS   T 020 7738 1600
PMA Member
Angel House, 76 Mallinson Road, London SW11 1BN
F 020 7801 0088
E info@garricks.net

GAY, Noel   T 020 7836 3941
PMA Member
19 Denmark Street
London WC2H 8NA
F 020 7287 1816
E info@noelgay.com
W www.noelgay.com

GDA MANAGEMENT   T 020 8677 5395
Contact: By e-mail only. No Post
338C Streatham High Road, London SW16 6HH
T 07974 680439
E info@gdamanagment.co.uk

GENESIS PERSONAL MANAGEMENT LTD   T 01225 706883
Actors only
6B New Broughton Road, Melksham, Wiltshire SN12 8BS
W www.genesismanagement.co.uk

GENUINE CASTING   T 01895 437787
78 York Street, London W1H 1DP
T 07748 737374
E info@genuinecasting.com
W www.genuinecasting.com

GFI MANAGEMENT   T 020 8943 1120
Personal Manager
Green Gables, 47 North Lane
Teddington, Middlesex TW11 0HU
T 07956 646412
E agency@goforitcentre.com
W www.goforitcentre.com

GIELGUD MANAGEMENT   T 01444 447020
PMA Member
The Old Cinema, 1st Floor, 59-61 The Broadway
Haywards Heath, West Sussex RH16 3AS
F 01444 447030
E info@gielgudmanagement.co.uk
W www.gielgudmanagement.co.uk

GILBERT & PAYNE   T 020 7734 7505
Room 236, 2nd Floor, Linen Hall
162-168 Regent Street, London W1B 5TB
F 020 7494 3787
E ee@gilbertandpayne.com

GILLMAN, Geraldine ASSOCIATES   T 01634 263344
Malcolm House, Malcolm Primary School
Malcolm Road, Penge, London SE20 8RH
T 07799 791586
E geraldi.gillma@btconnect.com

WINTERSONS

- **Frequent client contact**
- **Long term career strategy**
- **Contractual protection**

Wintersons Talent Management

59 St Martin's Lane
London WC2N 4JS
T: 020 7836 7849
www.nikiwinterson.com

Agent
Niki Winterson   niki@nikiwinterson.com

Assistant
Becky Barrett   becky@nikiwinterson.com

Accounts
Mithra Harding   mithra@nikiwinterson.com

Members of the Personal Managers' Association

Niki Winterson ltd trading as WINTERSONS.
Registered in England at 50 Seymour Street, London W1H 7JG, Company No. 07413069

GLASS, Eric LTD   T 020 7229 9500
25 Ladbroke Crescent, Notting Hill
London W11 1PS
F 020 7229 6220
E eglassltd@aol.com

GLOBAL7   T/F 020 7281 7679
PO Box 56232, London N4 4XP
T 07956 956652
E global7castings@gmail.com
W www.global7casting.com

GLOBAL ARTISTS   T 020 7839 4888
PMA Member. Contact: By Post/e-mail.
Accepts Showreels/Voicereels. 5 Agents
23 Haymarket, London SW1Y 4DG
F 020 7839 4555
E info@globalartists.co.uk
W www.globalartists.co.uk

GLYN MANAGEMENT   T 01449 737695
The Old School House, Brettenham
Ipswich IP7 7QP
F 01449 736117
E glyn.management@tesco.net

GMM (GREGG MILLARD
MANAGEMENT)   T 07710 562774
38 Barton House, Sable Street, London N1 2AF
E greggmillard.gmm@gmail.com

GO ENTERTAINMENTS LTD   T 01260 276627
Circus Artistes. Chinese State Circus. Cirque Surreal.
Bolshoi Circus "Spirit of The Horse"
The Arts Exchange, Congleton
Cheshire CW12 1LA
F 01260 270777
E info@arts-exchange.com
W www.arts-exchange.com

GOLD ARTISTES
TALENT MANAGEMENT   T 020 7873 2356
2 Alric Avenue, London NW10 8RB
E goldartistes@live.co.uk
W www.goldartistes.com

GOLDMANS MANAGEMENT   T 01323 472391
E casting@goldmansmanagement.co.uk
W www.goldmansmanagement.co.uk

GORDON & FRENCH   T 020 7734 4818
PMA Member. Contact: By Post
12-13 Poland Street, London W1F 8QB
F 020 7734 4832
E mail@gordonandfrench.net

GRAHAM, David PERSONAL MANAGEMENT
(DGPM)   T/F 020 7241 6752
The Studio, 107A Middleton Road
London E8 4LN
E info@dgpmtheagency.com

GRANT, James MEDIA   T 020 8742 4950
94 Strand On The Green, Chiswick
London W4 3NN
F 020 8742 4951
E enquiries@jamesgrant.co.uk
W www.jamesgrant.co.uk

GRANTHAM-HAZELDINE LTD   T 020 7038 3737
PMA Member
Suite 315, The Linen Hall
162-168 Regent Street, London W1B 5TD
F 020 7038 3739
E agents@granthamhazeldine.com

GRAY, Darren MANAGEMENT   T 023 9269 9973
Specialising in representing/promoting Australian Artists
2 Marston Lane, Portsmouth, Hampshire PO3 5TW
F 023 9267 7227
E darren.gray1@virgin.net
W www.darrengraymanagement.co.uk

GREEN & UNDERWOOD   T 020 8998 0007
In association with Essanay. Personal Manager.
Contact: By Post
PO Box 56662, London W13 3BH
E ny@greenandunderwood.com

GRESHAM, Carl GROUP   T 01274 735880
PO Box 3, Bradford, West Yorkshire BD1 4QN
F 01274 827161
E gresh@carlgresham.co.uk
W www.carlgresham.com

GRIDMODELS UK LTD   T 020 7993 6512
Contact: Rosie Beasley. By e-mail/Telephone. 2 Agents
represent 300 Performers. Modelling
45 Garth Close, Morden
Surrey SM4 4NN
E enquiries@gridmodels.com
W www.gridmodelsfashionandcommercialsagency.com

GRIFFIN, Sandra
MANAGEMENT LTD   T 020 8891 5676
6 Ryde Place, Richmond Road
East Twickenham, Middlesex TW1 2EH
F 020 8744 1812
E office@sandragriffin.com
W www.sandragriffin.com

GROUNDLINGS THEATRE
COMPANY   T 023 9273 7370
The Old Beneficial School, Kent Street
Portsea, Hampshire PO1 3BS
E richard@groundlings.co.uk
W www.groundlings.co.uk

GROVES, Rob PERSONAL
MANAGEMENT   T 020 3174 0501
Contact: By e-mail
4th Floor, 33 Glasshouse Street, London W1B 5DG
F 07092 873538
E rob@robgroves.co.uk
W www.robgroves.co.uk

GUBBAY, Louise ASSOCIATES   T 01959 573080
26 Westmore Road, Tatsfield, Kent TN16 2AX
E louise@louisegubbay.com
W www.louisegubbay.com

GUBBAY, Louise
ASSOCIATES (LA)   T 001 424 230 7896
1680 North Vine, Suite 611
Hollywood, CA 90028
E louise@louisegubbay.com
W www.louisegubbay.com

GURNETT J. PERSONAL MANAGEMENT LTD   T 020 7440 1850
12 Newburgh Street
London W1F 7RP
F 020 7287 9642
E mail@jgpm.co.uk
W www.jgpm.co.uk

HALL JAMES PERSONAL MANAGEMENT   T 020 8429 8111
PO Box 604, Pinner
Middlesex HA5 9GH
F 020 8868 5825
E agents@halljames.co.uk
W www.halljames.co.uk

HALLY, Yvette MANAGEMENT   T 00 353 1 4933685
121 Grange Road
Rathfarnham
Dublin 14
Ireland
F 00 353 1 4933076
E yhmgt@eircom.net

HAMBLETON, Patrick MANAGEMENT   T 020 7226 0947
Top Floor
136 Englefield Road
London N1 3LQ
E info@phm.uk.com

HAMILTON HODELL LTD   T 020 7636 1221
PMA Member
5th Floor, 66-68 Margaret Street, London W1W 8SR
F 020 7636 1226
E info@hamiltonhodell.co.uk
W www.hamiltonhodell.co.uk

HARRIS AGENCY LTD THE   T 01923 211644
71 The Avenue, Watford
Herts WD17 4NU
E theharrisagency@btconnect.com

HARRISON, Penny BSA LTD   T 020 8672 0136
Trinity Lodge, 25 Trinity Crescent
London SW17 7AG
E harrisonbsa@aol.com

HARVEY VOICES   T 020 7952 4361
58 Woodlands Road, London N9 8RT
W www.harveyvoices.co.uk

HAT MANAGEMENT   T 0161 370 8648
Contact: Neil Howarth
24 Thornley Rise, Audenshaw
Manchester M34 5JX
T 07775 744438
E hat.mgmt@hotmail.co.uk

HATTON McEWAN   T 020 7253 4770
Personal Manager. PMA Member. Contact: Stephen Hatton,
Aileen McEwan, James Penford. By Post
Unit 3, Chocolate Studios
7 Shepherdess Place, London N1 7LJ
F 020 7251 9081
E mail@hattonmcewan.com
W www.hattonmcewan.com

H C A
See COOKE, Howard ASSOCIATES

HEADNOD TALENT AGENCY   T 020 7502 9478
63 Redchurch Street, London E2 7DJ
E info@headnodagency.com
W www.headnodagency.com

HENRIETTA RABBIT CHILDREN'S
ENTERTAINMENT AGENCY   T 0333 000 4567
Children's Entertainers. Balloonologists. Close-up Magicians.
Clowns. Face Painters. Jugglers. Punch & Judy. Stiltwalkers
The Warren, 12 Eden Close
York YO24 2RD
E info@henriettarabbit.co.uk
W www.henriettarabbit.co.uk

HICKS, Jeremy
ASSOCIATES LTD   T 020 7734 7957
Personal Manager. Contact: By Post/e-mail. Accepts
Showreels. 2 Agents represent 25 Performers. Chefs.
Comedians. Presenters. Writers
3 Richmond Buildings, London W1D 3HE
F 020 7734 6302
E info@jeremyhicks.com
W www.jeremyhicks.com

HILTON, Elinor ASSOCIATES   T 020 7240 2555
1 Goodwin's Court, London WC2H 4LL
E info@elinorhilton.com
W www.elinorhilton.com

HIRED HANDS   T 020 7267 9212
12 Cressy Road, London NW3 2LY
E hiredhandsagency@aol.com
W www.hiredhandsmodels.com

HOBBART & HOBBART   T 07595 260208
24 Kelvedon Road, London SW6 5BS
E braathen@hobbart.no
W www.hobbart.co.uk

HOBBS, Liz GROUP LTD   T 0870 0702702
65 London Road, Newark, Notts NG24 1RZ
F 01636 703343
E casting@lizhobbsgroup.com
W www.lizhobbsgroup.com

HOBSONS COMMERCIALS
& CORPORATES   T 020 8995 3628
62 Chiswick High Road, Chiswick
London W4 1SY
F 020 8996 5350
E actors@hobsons-international.com
W www.hobsons-international.com

HOLLOWOOD, Jane
ASSOCIATES LTD   T 0161 237 9141
Apartment 17, 113 Newton Street, Manchester M1 1AE
T 020 8291 5702
E janehollowood@btconnect.com
W www.janehollowood.co.uk

HOLMES, Kim SHOWBUSINESS
ENTERTAINMENT AGENCY LTD   T 0115 930 5088
8 Charles Close, Ilkeston
Derbyshire DE7 5AF
F 0115 944 0390
E kimholmesshowbiz@hotmail.co.uk

HOPE, Sally ASSOCIATES   T 020 7613 5353
PMA Member
108 Leonard Street, London EC2A 4XS
F 020 7613 4848
E casting@sallyhope.biz
W www.sallyhope.biz

HORSEY, Dick
MANAGEMENT LTD   T 01923 710614
Personal Manager. Contact: By Post/e-mail/Telephone.
Accepts Showreels/Voicereels. 2 Agents represent 40
Performers. Corporate. Musicals. Stage. Television
Suite 1, Cottingham House, Chorleywood Road
Rickmansworth, Herts WD3 4EP
T 07850 112211
E roger@dhmlimited.co.uk
W www.dhmlimited.co.uk

HOWARD, Amanda
ASSOCIATES LTD   T 020 7287 9277
PMA Member. Contact: By Post
21 Berwick Street, London W1F 0PZ
F 020 7287 7785
E mail@amandahowardassociates.co.uk
W www.amandahowardassociates.co.uk

HOWELL, Philippa
See PHPM
(PHILIPPA HOWELL PERSONAL MANAGEMENT)

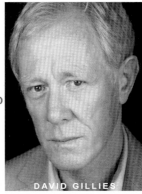
HOXTON STREET MANAGEMENT   T 020 7503 5131
Hoxton Hall, 130 Hoxton Street, London N1 6SH
T 07411 479077
E lucy@hoxtonstreetmanagement.co.uk
W www.hoxtonstreetmanagement.co.uk

HRCA   T 020 3286 8830
Contact: By e-mail only
18 Soho Square, London W1D 3QL
E agent@hrca.eu
W www.hrca.eu

HUDSON, Nancy ASSOCIATES LTD   T 020 7499 5548
16 Hanover Square, Mayfair, London W1S 1HT
E agents@nancyhudsonassociates.com
W www.nancyhudsonassociates.com

HUNTER, Bernard ASSOCIATES   T 020 8878 6308
13 Spencer Gardens, London SW14 7AH
F 020 8392 9334

HUNWICK HUGHES LTD   T 0131 225 3585
Personal Manager
Suite 2F, 45A George Street, Edinburgh EH2 2HT
F 0131 225 4535
E maryam@hunwickhughes.com
W www.hunwickhughes.com

I-MAGE CASTINGS   T 020 7725 7003
Regent House Business Centre
Suite 22, 24-25 Nutford Place
Marble Arch, London W1H 5YN
F 020 7725 7004
E jane@i-mage.uk.com
W www.i-mage.uk.com

alexruoccophotography
Tel: 07732293231
www.alexruoccophotography.co.uk

**I.A.G. (IDENTITY
AGENCY GROUP)**   T 020 7470 8711
Black Actors
11-15 Betterton Street, Covent Garden
London WC2H 9BP
E casting@identityagencygroup.com
W www.identityagencygroup.com

ICON ACTORS MANAGEMENT   T 0161 273 3344
Tanzaro House, Ardwick Green North
Manchester M12 6FZ
F 0161 273 4567
E info@iconactors.net
W www.iconactors.net

I.M.L.   T/F 020 7587 1080
Personal Manager. CPMA Member
The White House
52-54 Kennington Oval, London SE11 5SW
E info@iml.org.uk
W www.iml.org.uk

**IMPACT INTERNATIONAL
MANAGEMENT**   T 07941 269849
*Personal Manager. Contact: Colin Charles. By e-mail.
Accepts Showreels/Voicereels. 1 Agent represents 10
Performers. Cruises. Musical Theatre. Speciality
Acts & Events*
310 Cascades Tower, 4 Westferry Road
London E14 8JL
E colin.charles310@gmail.com
W www.impact-london.co.uk

IMPACT MEDIA MANAGEMENT   T 020 3397 2269
Studio F7, Battersea Studios
80 Silverthorne Road, London SW8 3HE
E tiffany@impactmediamanagement.com
W www.impactmediamanagement.com

**IMPERIAL PERSONAL
MANAGEMENT LTD**   T 0113 244 3222
102 Kirkstall Road, Leeds, West Yorkshire LS3 1JA
T 07890 387758
E katie@ipmcasting.com
W www.ipmcasting.com

IMPERIUM MANAGEMENT   T 020 8351 3152
179 Muswell Hill Broadway, London N10 3RS
E info@imperium-management.com
W www.imperium-management.com

**INDEPENDENT TALENT
GROUP LTD**   T 020 7636 6565
Formerly ICM, London. PMA Member
Oxford House, 76 Oxford Street, London W1D 1BS
F 020 7323 0101
W www.independenttalent.com

**INDEPENDENT THEATRE
WORKSHOP THE**   T 00 353 1 2600831
8 Terminus Mills, Clonskeogh, Dublin 6, Ireland
E info@independent-theatre-workshop.com
W www.independent-theatre-workshop.com

INSPIRATION MANAGEMENT   T 020 7704 0440
Co-operative. CPMA Member. Est 1986
Room 227, Aberdeen Centre
22-24 Highbury Grove, London N5 2EA
E mail@inspirationmanagement.org.uk
W www.inspirationmanagement.org.uk

INSPIRE ACADEMY   T 0115 9881 800
The Attic Studio, 3rd Floor
46-48 Carrington Street, Nottingham NG1 7FG
E admin@inspireacademy.co.uk
W www.inspireacademy.co.uk

INTER-CITY CASTING   T/F 01942 321969
*Personal Manager. Contact: By Post. Accepts Showreels.
2 Agents represent 60 Performers*
27 Wigan Lane, Wigan
Greater Manchester WN1 1XR
E intercitycasting@btconnect.com

INTERNATIONAL ARTISTES LTD T 020 7025 0600
PMA Member
4th Floor, Holborn Hall
193-197 High Holborn, London WC1V 7BD
F 020 7404 9865
E reception@internationalartistes.com
W www.internationalartistes.com

**INTERNATIONAL COLLECTIVE
ARTIST MANAGEMENT**   T 020 7557 6650 ext 201
9-13 Grape Street, Covent Garden
London WC2H 8ED
F 020 7557 6656
E mel@international-collective.com
W www.internationalcollective.com

**INTERNATIONAL MODEL
MANAGEMENT LTD**   T 020 7610 9111
Incorporating Yvonne Paul Management
Elysium Gate, Unit 15
126-128 New Kings Road, London SW6 4LZ
F 020 7736 2221
E info@immmodels.com
W www.immmodels.com

**INTERNATIONAL MODELS &
TALENT AGENCY**   T 001 310 461 1550
1901 Avenue of The Stars, Suite 200
Century City, CA 90067
F 001 310 461 1304
E int.talent@hotmail.com

IRISH ACTORS LONDON   T 020 3318 5732
2 Bloemfontein Road
London W12 7BX
E irishactorslondon@gmail.com
W www.irishactorslondon.co.uk

IT&M MANAGEMENT   T 020 7470 8786
*Personal Manager. Contact: Piers Chater Robinson. By
Post/e-mail. Accepts Voicereels. 2 Agents represent 32
Performers. Dancers. Musicals. Singers. Writers*
Garden Studios, 11-15 Betterton Street
Covent Garden, London WC2H 9BP
F 020 7379 0801
E info@it-m.co.uk
W www.it-m.co.uk

JAA
See ALTARAS, Jonathan ASSOCIATES LTD

JABBERWOCKY AGENCY   T 01580 714306
*Contact: Christina Yates. By e-mail. 4 Agents represent
135 Performers. Children. Teenagers*
Glassenbury Hill Farm
Glassenbury Road
Cranbrook, Kent TN17 2QF
F 01580 714346
E info@jabberwockyagency.com
W www.yt93.co.uk

JAFFREY MANAGEMENT LTD   T 01708 732350
*Personal Manager. Contact: By Post/e-mail. Accepts
Showreels/Voicereels (SAE). 60 Performers. Commercials.
Film. Stage. Television*
74 Western Road, Romford, Essex RM1 3LP
E mail@jaffreyactors.co.uk
W www.jaffreymanagement.com

JAM AGENCY   T 020 7269 7923
Holborn Hall, 193-197 High Holborn
London WC1V 7BD
F 020 7831 7267
E info@jamagency.co.uk

JAM2000 AGENCY   T 01895 624755
The Windmill Studio Centre, 106A Pembroke Road
Ruislip, Middlesex HA4 8NW
E info@jam2000.co.uk
W www.jam2000.co.uk

JAMES, Susan
See SJ MANAGEMENT

JAMESON, Joy LTD   T/F 020 7359 2581
Personal Manager
PO Box 68182, London N1P 2BN
E joy@jote.freeuk.com

ANNA MOMCILOVIC

RULA LENSKA

SARAH HAMPSON

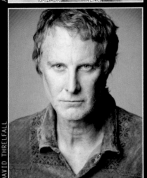
DAVID THRELFALL

MATT KENNEDY

NEED AMERICAN ACTORS?
The North American Actors Association is *the* source
for genuine professional American and Canadian actors, based
in the UK without permit restrictions. Get in touch today!
e: admin@naaa.org.uk   web: www.naaa.org.uk

JB ASSOCIATES   T 0161 237 1808
Personal Manager. PMA Member. Contact: John Basham.
By Post/e-mail. Accepts Showreels/Voicereels. 2 Agents
represent 60 Performers. Commercials. Radio. Stage.
Television
PO Box 173, Manchester M19 0AR
F 0161 249 3666
E info@j-b-a.net
W www.j-b-a.net

JEFFREY & WHITE
MANAGEMENT LTD   T 01462 433752
Personal Manager. PMA Member
2 Ladygrove Court, Hitchwood Lane
Preston, Hitchin, Hertfordshire SG4 7SA
E info@jeffreyandwhite.co.uk
W www.jeffreyandwhite.co.uk

JERMIN, Mark MANAGEMENT   T 01792 458855
Contact: By Post/e-mail. Accepts Showreels. 2 Agents
8 Heathfield, Swansea SA1 6EJ
F 01792 458844
E info@markjermin.co.uk
W www.markjermin.co.uk

JLM PERSONAL MANAGEMENT   T 020 7025 0630
Personal Manager. PMA Member. Contact: Sharon Henry.
By Post. Accepts Showreels. 2 Agents. Commercials. Film.
Radio. Stage. Television
4th Floor, Holborn Hall
193-197 High Holborn
London WC1V 7BD
F 020 7404 9865
E info@jlmpm.co.uk

J.M. MANAGEMENT   T 020 8908 0502
Personal representation to a small number of
Actors/Actresses in film work
20 Pembroke Road, North Wembley
Middlesex HA9 7PD

JOHNSON WHITELEY LTD   T 020 7348 0163
12 Argyll Mansions, Hammersmith Road
London W14 8QG
F 020 7348 0164
E johnsonwhiteley@btconnnect.com

JOHNSTON & MATHERS
ASSOCIATES LTD   T/F 020 8449 4968
PO Box 3167, Barnet EN5 2WA
E johnstonmathers@aol.com
W www.johnstonandmathers.com

JOYCE, Michael MANAGEMENT   T 020 3178 7190
3rd Floor, 33 Glasshouse Street
London W1B 5DG
T 07903 324405
E info@michaeljoyce.tv
W www.michaeljoycemanagement.com

JPA MANAGEMENT   T 01494 520978
30 Daws Hill Lane, High Wycombe
Bucks HP11 1PW
F 01494 510479
E jackie.palmer@btinternet.com
W www.jpamanagement.co.uk

K TALENT ARTIST
MANAGEMENT   T 020 7430 0882
Personal Manager. Contact: By Post/e-mail. Accepts
Showreels/Voicereels. 4 Agents represent approx 100
Performers. Children. Commercials. Dancers. Film.
Musicals. Singers. Stage. Television
187 Drury Lane, Covent Garden, London WC2B 5QD
T 0844 5672470
E mail@ktalent.co.uk
W www.ktalent.co.uk

KAL MANAGEMENT   T 020 8783 0039
Contact: By Post
95 Gloucester Road, Hampton, Middlesex TW12 2UW
F 020 8979 6487
E kaplan222@aol.com
W www.kaplan-kaye.co.uk

KANAL, Roberta AGENCY   T 020 8894 2277
82 Constance Road, Twickenham
Middlesex TW2 7JA
T/F 020 8894 7952
E roberta.kanal@dsl.pipex.com

KEDDIE SCOTT
ASSOCIATES LTD   T 020 7836 6802
Personal Manager. PMA Member. Contact: By Post.
Accepts Showreels/Voicereels. 4 Agents represent 145
Performers. Commercials. Corporate. Dancers. Film.
Musicals. Presenters. Radio. Singers. Stage. TV. Writers
Studio 1, 17 Shorts Gardens
Covent Garden, London WC2H 9AT
F 020 7147 1326
E london@keddiescott.com
W www.keddiescott.com

KSA - SCOTLAND   T 07973 235355
Personal Manager. PMA Member. Contact: Paul Michael.
By Post/e-mail. Accepts Showreels/Voicereels. 2 Agents
represent 45 Performers. Film. Musicals. Stage. Television
Studio 1, 17 Shorts Gardens
Covent Garden, London WC2H 9AT
F 020 7147 1326
E scotland@keddiescott.com
W www.keddiescott.com

KSA - WALES   T 07917 272298
PMA Member
Studio 1, 17 Shorts Gardens
Covent Garden, London WC2H 9AT
E wales@keddiescott.com
W www.keddiescott.com

KELLY MANAGEMENT   T 020 7402 0444
PMA Member
Studio 13, 22 Brook Mews North
London W2 3BW
E office@kelly-management.com
W www.kelly-management.com

KENIS, Steve & CO   T 020 7434 9055
PMA Member
Royalty House, 72-74 Dean Street
London W1D 3SG
F 020 7287 6328
E sk@sknco.com

AM LONDON

ACTORS HEADSHOTS

SIMON PEGG

JULIA SAWALHA

CHRIS DALEY

JOHN BARROWMAN

MATHEW HORNE

PETER SERAFINOWICZ

CATHERINE TATE

JAMES SUTTON

MODEL, DANCER & PERFORMER PORTFOLIOS

WWW.AM-LONDON.COM

PHOTOGRAPHERS CLAIRE ALEXANDER & CASEY MOORE

 STUDIO: 020 7193 1868   MOBILE: 07974 188 105

icon actors management
tel: 0161 273 3344   **fax:** 0161 273 4567
tanzaro house, ardwick green north, manchester. m12 6fz
info@iconactors.net   www.iconactors.net

KEW PERSONAL
MANAGEMENT   **T** 020 8871 3697
PO Box 679, RH1 9BT
E info@kewpersonalmanagement.com
W www.kewpersonalmanagement.com

KEYLOCK MANAGEMENT   **T** 01494 563142
Contact: By e-mail. 2 Agents represent 35 Performers.
Commercials. Film. Stage. Television
5 North Dean Cottages
Speen Road
North Dean, Bucks HP14 4NN
T 07712 579502
E agent@keylockmanagement.com
W www.keylockmanagement.com

KHANDO ENTERTAINMENT   **T** 020 3463 8492
1 Marlborough Court, London W1F 7EE
E info@khandoentertainment.com
W www.khandoentertainment.com

KIDS MANAGEMENT   **T** 01444 401595
35 Truggers, Handcross
West Sussex RH17 6DQ
E kidsmanagement@ymail.com
W www.kidsmanagement.co.uk

KING, Adrian ASSOCIATES   **T** 020 7435 4600
PMA Member. Contact: Adrian King. By Post/e-mail.
Accepts Showreels
33 Marlborough Mansions, Cannon Hill
London NW6 1JS
F 020 7435 4100
E akassocs@aol.com

K M C AGENCIES   **T** 0845 0340772
Personal Manager. Actors. Commercials. Corporate.
Dancers. Musicals
Garden Studios, 11-15 Betterton Street
London WC2H 9BP
E london@kmcagencies.co.uk

K M C AGENCIES   **T** 0161 237 3009
Personal Manager. Actors. Commercials. Corporate.
Dancers. Musicals
PO Box 122, 48 Great Ancoats Street
Manchester M4 5AB
F 0161 237 9812
E casting@kmcagencies.co.uk

KNIGHT, Nic MANAGEMENT   **T** 020 3093 5422
23 Buckler Court
Eden Grove, London N7 8EF
E enquiries@nicknightmanagement.com
W www.nicknightmanagement.com

KNIGHT, Ray CASTING   **T** 020 7722 1551
21A Lambolle Place, London NW3 4PG
E casting@rayknight.co.uk
W www.rayknight.co.uk

KNIGHT AYTON MANAGEMENT   **T** 020 7831 4400
35 Great James Street
London WC1N 3HB
F 020 7831 4455
E info@knightayton.co.uk
W www.knightayton.co.uk

KORT, Richard
MANAGEMENT LTD   **T** 01636 636686
Moat Farm, Norwell Woodhouse
Newark, Notts NG23 6NG
F 01636 636719
E richardkort@playhouseproductionsltd.co.uk
W www.richardkort.co.uk

KREATE   **T** 020 7401 9007
Unit 232, Great Guildford Business Square
30 Great Guildford Street, London SE1 0HS
F 020 7401 9008
E hello@kreate.co.uk

KREMER ASSOCIATES
See MARSH, Billy DRAMA LTD

KSA - SCOTLAND
See KEDDIE SCOTT ASSOCIATES LTD

KSA - WALES
See KEDDIE SCOTT ASSOCIATES LTD

KW PROMOTIONS LTD   **T** 07835 316639
9 College Road, Alsager
Stoke-on-Trent ST7 2SS
E dkeeno1@hotmail.com
W www.kwpromotions.co.uk

L.A. MANAGEMENT   **T** 07963 573538
10 Fairoak Close, Kenley, Surrey CR8 5LJ
E info@lamanagement.biz
W www.lamanagement.biz

LADA MANAGEMENT   **T** 020 3384 5815
Personal Manager. Contact: Richard Boschetto.
By Post/e-mail. Accepts Showreels/Voicereels.
2 Agents represent 40 Performers. Film.
Musicals. Stage. Television
23 Austin Friars, London EC2N 2QP
F 020 3384 5816
E info@ladamanagement.com
W www.ladamanagement.com

LADA MANAGEMENT   **T** 01522 837243
Personal Manager. Contact: Richard Boschetto. By
Post/e-mail. Accepts Showreels/Voicereels. 2 Agents
represent 40 Performers. Film. Musicals. Stage. Television
Sparkhouse Studios, Rope Walk
Lincoln LN6 7DQ
F 01522 837201
E info@ladamanagement.com
W www.ladamanagement.com

LADIDA   **T** 020 7379 6199
Contact: By Post. Accepts Showreels. 3 Agents represent
90 Performers. Commercials. Creatives. Film. Musicals.
Radio. Stage. Television. Writers
19 Percy Street, London W1T 1DU
F 020 7379 6198
E m@ladidagroup.com
W www.ladidagroup.com

LAINE, Betty MANAGEMENT   **T/F** 01372 721815
The Studios, East Street
Epsom, Surrey KT17 1HH
E enquiries@betty-laine-management.co.uk

martin richardson
p h o t o g r a p h y

07890 149 657
info@martinrichardsonphotography.com
www.martinrichardsonphotography.com

LAINE MANAGEMENT LTD   T 0161 789 7775
Laine House, 131 Victoria Road
Hope, Salford M6 8LF
F 0161 787 7572
E sam@lainemanagement.co.uk
W www.lainemanagement.co.uk

LANGFORD ASSOCIATES LTD   T 020 8878 7148
Personal Manager. Contact: Barry Langford.
By Post/e-mail. Commercials. Film. Stage. Television
17 Westfields Avenue, Barnes, London SW13 0AT
F 020 8878 7078
E barry.langford@btconnect.com
W www.langfordassociates.com

LAWRENCE, Tonicha
AGENCY   T/F 0113 289 3433
Now trading as TLA Boutique Management. Incorporating
Young Boutique
T 07766 415996
E tonichalawrence@gmail.com
W www.tlaboutiquemanagement.com

LAWRENCE-AGENCY   T 07883 250470
PO Box 2183, Leigh on Sea, Essex SS9 3RQ
E info@lawrence-agency.co.uk
W www.lawrence-agency.co.uk

LE BARS, Tessa MANAGEMENT   T 01689 837084
Existing Clients only
54 Birchwood Road, Petts Wood
Kent BR5 1NZ
T 07860 287255
E tessa.lebars@ntlworld.com
W www.galtonandsimpson.com

LEE, Wendy MANAGEMENT   T 020 7703 5187
E wendy-lee@btconnect.com

LEHRER, Jane ASSOCIATES   T 020 7435 9118
Personal Manager. PMA Member. Contact:
By Post/e-mail. 2 Agents
PO Box 66334, London NW6 9QT
F 020 7435 9117
E jane@janelehrer.co.uk
W www.janelehrer.co.uk

LEIGH, Mike ASSOCIATES   T 020 7935 5500
37 Marylebone Lane
London W1U 2NW
F 020 7486 5886
W www.mikeleighassoc.com

LEIGH MANAGEMENT   T 020 8951 4449
14 St David's Drive, Edgware, Middlesex HA8 6JH
E leighmanagement@aol.com

LESLIE, Sasha
MANAGEMENT   T/F 020 8969 3249
In association with Allsorts Drama for Children
34 Crediton Road, London NW10 3DU
E sasha@allsortsdrama.com

LIGHT AGENCY &
PRODUCTIONS LTD   T 020 8090 0006
Actors. Dancers
12 Molasses Row, Plantation Wharf
Battersea, London SW11 3UX
E lucy@lightproductions.tv
W www.lightproductions.tv

LIME ACTORS AGENCY
& MANAGEMENT LTD   T 0161 236 0827
Contact: Georgina Andrew. By Post. Accepts Showreels
Nemesis House, 1 Oxford Court
Bishopsgate, Manchester M2 3WQ
F 0161 228 6727
E georgina@limemanagement.co.uk
W www.limemanagement.tv

LINKSIDE AGENCY   T 020 7384 1477
Contact: By Post. 2 Agents represent 40 Performers.
Dancers. Musicals. Singers. Stage. Television
Southbank House, Black Prince Road, London SE1 7SJ
E info@linksideagency.com

LINTON MANAGEMENT   T 0161 761 2020
3 The Rock, Bury BL9 0JP
F 0161 761 1999
E carol@linton.tv

LINTON MANAGEMENT   T 020 7785 7275
27-31 Clerkenwell Close, London EC1R 0AT
F 020 7785 7276
E london@linton.tv

LONDON THEATRICAL   T 020 8748 1478
Contact: Paul Pearson
18 Leamore Street, London W6 0JZ
E agent@londontheatrical.com
W www.londontheatrical.com

LONG, Eva AGENTS   T 07736 700849
Contact: By Post/e-mail. 2 Agents represent 30 Performers.
Commercials. Corporate. Film. Musicals. Radio. Singers.
Stage. Television. Voice Overs
107 Station Road, Earls Barton, Northants NN6 0NX
F 01604 811921
E evalongagents@yahoo.co.uk
W www.evalongagents.co.uk

LONGRUN ARTISTES AGENCY   T 020 8316 6662
Contact: Gina Long. By Post. Accepts Showreels/
Voicereels. 3 Agents represent 100 Performers.
Commercials. Corporate. Dancers. Film. Musicals. Singers.
Stage. Television
Marylebone Dance Studio, 12 Lisson Grove
London NW1 6TS
E gina@longrunartistes.co.uk
W www.longrunartistes.co.uk

LOOKALIKES   T 020 7281 8029
Contact: Susan Scott
106 Tollington Park, London N4 3RB
E susan@lookalikes.info
W www.lookalikes.info

LOOKS AGENCY   T 020 8341 4477
Contact: By Post/e-mail/Telephone. 200 Performers.
Commercials. Corporate. Modelling. Presenters. Walk-on &
Supporting Artists
PO Box 42783, London N2 0UF
F 020 8442 9190
E lookslondonltd@btconnect.com
W www.lookslondon.com

LOTHERINGTON, Michelle
PERSONAL MANAGEMENT   T 07785 293806
Contact: Michelle Lotherington. By e-mail. Choreographers.
Composers. Designers. Directors. Lighting & Sound
Designers. Music Technology. Musical Directors.
Orchestrators
23 Tell Grove, London SE22 8RH
E michelle@michellelotherington.com
W www.michellelotherington.com

LOVETT LOGAN ASSOCIATES   T 0131 478 7878
Formerly PLA. PMA Member
2 York Place, Edinburgh EH1 3EP
F 0131 478 7070
E edinburgh@lovettlogan.com
W www.lovettlogan.com

LOVETT LOGAN ASSOCIATES   T 020 7495 6400
Formerly PLA. PMA Member
40 Margaret Street, London W1G 0JH
F 020 7495 6411
E london@lovettlogan.com
W www.lovettlogan.com

PHOTOGRAPHY by Henrietta Garden
Great head shots that'll get you through that door

Student rates available
07973 825 734
henri.garden@blueyonder.co.uk

LSW PROMOTIONS T/F 020 7793 9755
PO Box 31855, London SE17 3XP
E londonswo@hotmail.com

LUXFACTOR GROUP (UK) THE T 0845 3700589
Personal Manager. Contact: Michael D. Finch. By e-mail.
1 Agent represents 20+ Performers. Creatives. Presenters.
Television. Walk-on & Supporting Artists
Fleet Place, 12 Nelson Drive, Petersfield, Hants GU31 4SJ
F 0845 3700588
E info@luxfactor.co.uk W www.luxfactor.co.uk

LYNE, Dennis AGENCY T 020 7272 5020
PMA Member
503 Holloway Road, London N19 4DD
F 020 7272 4790
E info@dennislyne.com W www.dennislyne.com

MA9 MODEL MANAGEMENT T 020 7096 1191
New Bond House, 124 New Bond Street
London W1S 1DX
E info@ma9models.com W www.ma9models.com

**MACFARLANE CHARD
ASSOCIATES LTD** T 020 7636 7750
PMA Member
33 Percy Street, London W1T 2DF
F 020 7636 7751
E enquiries@macfarlane-chard.co.uk
W www.macfarlane-chard.co.uk

**MACFARLANE CHARD
ASSOCIATES IRELAND** T 00 353 1 6638646
7 Adelaide Street, Dun Laoghaire, Co Dublin, Ireland
F 00 353 1 6638649 E derick@macfarlane-chard.ie

Danielle Harold Robert H. O'Neil Helen Russell-Clark

James Davies Photography

www.jamesdaviesheadshots.com
07716 515170
Student Rates available. Quote 'Contacts' for special package.

MACFARLANE DOYLE ASSOCIATES   T/F 01244 347091
125 Hoole Road
Chester CH2 3NW
E ross.macfarlane@btinternet.com
W www.macfarlanedoyle.com

MACNAUGHTON LORD REPRESENTATION   T 020 7499 1411
PMA Member. Choreographers. Composers. Designers.
Directors. Lighting Designers. Lyricists. Musical Directors.
Writers. 44 South Molton Street, London W1K 5RT
F 020 7493 2444
E info@mlrep.com
W www.mlrep.com

MAIDA VALE SINGERS   T 020 7266 1358
Contact: Christopher Dee. Singers for Recordings, Stage,
Film, Radio & Television
7B Lanhill Road, Maida Vale, London W9 2BP
T 07889 153145
E maidavalesingers@cdtenor.freeserve.co.uk
W www.maidavalesingers.co.uk

MAITLAND MANAGEMENT   T 020 7636 7492
Personal Manager. Contact: Anne Skates
21A Harley Place, London W1G 8LZ
F 01372 466229
E maitmus@aol.com
W www.maitlandmanagement.com

MAMBAB AGENCY   T 020 7587 5225
Contact: Nichola D. Hartwell
PO Box 51261, Kennington, London SE11 4SW
T 07868 120709
E contacts@mrandmissblackandbeautiful.com
W www.mrandmissblackandbeautiful.com

Jennifer Bea

michael pollard
manchester
tel : 0161 456 7470
email : info@michaelpollard.co.uk
website : www.michaelpollard.co.uk
location and studio shoots

MANAGEMENT 2000   T/F 01352 771231
Contact: Jackey Gerling. By Post. Accepts Showreels.
1 Agent represents 40 Performers. Commercials. Film.
Radio. Stage. Television
11 Well Street
Treuddyn
Flintshire CH7 4NH
E jackey@management-2000.co.uk
W www.management-2000.co.uk

MANIC MEDIA GROUP THE   T 020 3246 0088
77A Brick Lane, London E1 6QL
F 020 3246 0081
E zach@themanicmediagroup.co.uk
W www.themanicmediagroup.co.uk

MANS, Johnny PRODUCTIONS   T 01992 470907
PO Box 196
Hoddesdon, Herts EN10 7WG
T 07974 755997
E johnnymansagent@aol.com
W www.johnnymansproductions.co.uk

MANTLE MANAGEMENT   T 01273 454111
32 Westbourne Place
Hove, East Sussex BN3 4GN
E info@mantlemanagement.co.uk
W www.mantlemanagement.co.uk

MARCUS & McCRIMMON MANAGEMENT   T 020 3012 3477
Personal Manager. Contact: By Post/e-mail.
Accepts Showreels. 2 Agents represent 80 Performers.
Film. Musicals. Stage. Television
1 Heathgate Place
75 Agincourt Road
Hampstead, London NW3 2NU
E info@marcusandmccrimmon.com
W www.marcusandmccrimmon.com

MARKHAM AGENCY THE   T 020 7836 4111
Personal Manager. PMA Member. Contact: John Markham.
By Post/e-mail. Accepts Showreels/Voicereels
405 Strand, London WC2R 0NE
F 020 7836 4222
E info@themarkhamagency.com
W www.themarkhamagency.com

MARKHAM, FROGGATT & IRWIN   T 020 7636 4412
Personal Manager. PMA Member. Contact: By Post
4 Windmill Street
London W1T 2HZ
F 020 7637 5233
E admin@markhamfroggattirwin.com
W www.markhamfroggattirwin.com

MARLOWES AGENCY   T 020 7193 7227
HMS President
Victoria Embankment
Blackfriars, London EC4Y 0HJ
E miles@marlowes.eu
W www.marlowes.eu

MARLOWES DANCERS & MUSICAL THEATRE AGENCY   T 020 7193 4484
HMS President, Victoria Embankment
Blackfriars, London EC4Y 0HJ
E mitch@marlowes.eu
W www.marlowes.eu

MARMALADE MANAGEMENT   T 07595 177154
21 Beechtree Avenue
Marlow, Buckinghamshire SL7 3NH
E info@marmalademanagement.co.uk
W www.marmalademanagement.co.uk

Ricky Whittle   Antonia Clarke   Charlie Clements

MARSH, Billy ASSOCIATES LTD   T 020 7449 6930
PMA Member
76A Grove End Road, St John's Wood, London NW8 9ND
F 020 7449 6933
E talent@billymarsh.co.uk
W www.billymarsh.co.uk

MARSH, Billy DRAMA LTD   T 020 3178 4748
Actors. Actresses
20 Garrick Street, London WC2E 9BT
F 020 3178 5488
E info@billymarshdrama.co.uk

**MARSHALL, Ronnie
AGENCY THE**   T/F 020 8368 4958
66 Ollerton Road, London N11 2LA
E ronniemarshallagency@yahoo.co.uk
W www.ronniemarshallagency.com

**MARSHALL, Scott
PARTNERS LTD**   T 020 7637 4623
*PMA Member. Contact: Amanda Evans,
Suzy Kenway, Manon Palmer*
2nd Floor
15 Little Portland Street
London W1W 8BW
F 020 7636 9728
E smpm@scottmarshall.co.uk
W www.scottmarshall.co.uk

**MARTIN, Carol
PERSONAL MANAGEMENT**   T 020 8348 0847
19 Highgate West Hill
London N6 6NP
F 020 8340 4868
E carolmartin@talktalk.net

MAY, John T 020 8962 1606
46 Golborne Road
London W10 5PR
E john@johnmaymanagement.co.uk
W www.johnmaymanagement.co.uk

MAYER, Cassie LTD T 020 7350 0880
PMA Member
5 Old Garden House, The Lanterns
Bridge Lane, London SW11 3AD
F 020 7350 0890
E info@cassiemayerltd.co.uk

**MBA / MAHONEY
BANNON ASSOCIATES** T 01273 685970
Formerly John Mahoney Management
Concorde House
18 Margaret Street, Brighton BN2 1TS
F 01273 685971
E info@mbagency.co.uk
W www.mbagency.co.uk

**McDONAGH, Melanie MANAGEMENT
(ACADEMY OF PERFORMING ARTS
& CASTING AGENCY)** T 01254 392560
14 Apple Tree Way
Oswaldtwistle
Accrington, Lancashire BB5 0FB
T 07909 831409
E mcdonaghmgt@aol.com
W www.mcdonaghmanagement.co.uk

**McKINNEY MACARTNEY
MANAGEMENT LTD** T 020 8995 4747
Technicians
Gable House
18-24 Turnham Green Terrace, London W4 1QP
E mail@mckinneymacartney.com
W www.mckinneymacartney.com

**McLEAN, Bill
PERSONAL MANAGEMENT** T 020 8789 8191
Personal Manager. Contact: By Post
23B Deodar Road, London SW15 2NP

**McLEAN-WILLIAMS
MANAGEMENT** T 020 7223 8683
PMA Member
Gainsborough House
81 Oxford Street, London W1D 2EU
F 020 7228 2386
E info@mclean-williams.com
W www.mclean-williams.com

McLEOD AGENCY LTD THE T 01482 565444
1st Floor, 6 The Square
Hessle, East Yorkshire HU13 0AA
E info@mcleodagency.co.uk
W www.mcleodagency.co.uk

McMAHON MANAGEMENT T 020 8752 0172
Formerly Morse & du Fer Management
17 Thistlefield Close
Bexley, Kent DA5 3GJ
E mcmahonmanagement@hotmail.co.uk
W www.mdm-ltd.co.uk

**McREDDIE, Ken
ASSOCIATES LTD** T 020 7439 1456
Personal Manager. PMA Member. Contact: By Post only
11 Connaught Place
London W2 2ET
F 020 7734 6530
E email@kenmcreddie.com
W www.kenmcreddie.com

**MEDIA CELEBRITY
SERVICES LTD** T 07946 531011
47 Dean Street, London W1D 5BE
T 07809 831340
E info@mcsagency.co.uk
W www.mediacelebrityservices.co.uk

MEDIA LEGAL T 01732 460592
Existing Clients only
Town House, 5 Mill Pond Close
Sevenoaks, Kent TN14 5AW

METROPOLITAN MANAGEMENT T 020 7193 5978
24 Beehive Lane
Basildon SS14 2LG
E info@dan-blumenau.com
W www.dan-blumenau.com

MGA MANAGEMENT T 0131 466 9392
The MGA Company
207 Balgreen Road
Edinburgh EH11 2RZ
E info@themgacompany.com
W www.themgacompany.com

MILAEON T 020 8993 3903
*Actors & Performers. Commercials. Corporate.
Film. Stage. Television*
333 Western Avenue, Park Royal
London W3 0RS
E info@milaeon.co.uk
W www.milaeon.co.uk

MIME THE GAP T 07970 685982
Mime Artistes. Physical Comedy Specialists
29 Elizabeth Avenue, Staines
Middlesex TW18 1JW
E richard@mimethegap.com
W www.mimethegap.com

MISKIN THEATRE AGENCY THE T 01322 629469
The Miskin Theatre, Oakfield Lane
Dartford, Kent DA1 2JT
T 07709 429354
E miskintheatreagency@yahoo.co.uk

MITCHELL MAAS McLENNAN T 020 8301 8745
MPA Offices, 29 Thomas Street
Woolwich, London SE18 6HU
T 07540 995802
E agency@mmm2000.co.uk
W www.mmm2000.co.uk

MLR
See MACNAUGHTON LORD REPRESENTATION

MONDI ASSOCIATES LTD T 07817 133349
*Personal Manager. Contact: Michelle Sykes. By Post/e-mail.
Accepts Showreels/Voicereels. 1 Agent represents 60
Performers. Children. Commercials. Corporate. Dancers.
Film. Musicals. Presenters. Radio. Singers. Stage.
Television. Voice Overs*
Unit 3 O, Cooper House, 2 Michael Road
London SW6 2AD
E info@mondiassociates.com
W www.mondiassociates.com

MONTAGU ASSOCIATES LTD T 020 7263 3883
Ground Floor, 13 Hanley Road
London N4 3DU
E montagus@btconnect.com

MOORE, Jakki MANAGEMENT T 01229 776389
Halecote, St Lukes Road
Haverigg, Cumbria LA18 4HB
T 07967 612784
E jakki@jakkimoore.com

MORELLO CHERRY ACTORS AGENCY   T 020 7993 5538
E info@mcaa.co.uk
W www.mcaa.co.uk

MORGAN, Lee MANAGEMENT   T 020 7691 8940
24-25 Macklin Street
Covent Garden
London WC2B 5NN
E lee@leemorgan.biz
W www.leemorganmanagement.co.uk

MORGAN & GOODMAN   T 020 7437 1383
271 Regent Street
London W1B 2ES
E mg1@btinternet.com

MORRIS, Andrew MANAGEMENT   T 020 7482 0451
124 Cole Green Lane
Welwyn Garden City
Herts AL7 3JD
T 01707 695849
E agentmorris1@yahoo.com

MOUTHPIECE MANAGEMENT   T 01527 850149
PO Box 145
Inkberrow
Worcestershire WR7 4ZG
T 07900 240904
E karin@mouthpiecemanagement.co.uk
W www.mouthpiecemanagement.co.uk

MPC ENTERTAINMENT   T 020 7624 1184
Contact: By e-mail/Telephone
MPC House, 15-16 Maple Mews
Maida Vale, London NW6 5UZ
F 020 7624 4220
E mpc@mpce.com
W www.mpce.com

MR MANAGEMENT   T/F 020 8674 1211
PMA Member
2nd Floor, 14 Raleigh Gardens, London SW2 1AD
E info@mrmanagement.net
W www.mrmanagement.net

MRS JORDAN ASSOCIATES   T 020 3151 0710
*PMA Member. Contact: By e-mail only. 3 Agents represent
40 Performers. Commercials. Creatives. Film.
Stage. Television*
Communications House
26 York Street, London W1U 6PZ
T 0161 401 0710
E info@mrsjordan.co.uk
W www.mrsjordan.co.uk

MUGSHOTS AGENCY   T 07880 896911
E becky@mugshots.co.uk

MURPHY, Elaine ASSOCIATES   T 020 8989 4122
Suite 1, 50 High Street, London E11 2RJ
F 020 8989 1400
E elaine@elainemurphy.co.uk

MUSIC INTERNATIONAL   T 020 7359 5183
13 Ardilaun Road, London N5 2QR
F 020 7226 9792
E neil@musicint.co.uk
W www.musicint.co.uk

MV MANAGEMENT   T 020 8889 8231
*Clients must be graduates of Mountview Academy of
Theatre Arts. Co-operative of 25 Performers*
Ralph Richardson Memorial Studios, Kingfisher Place
Clarendon Road, London N22 6XF
F 020 8829 1050
E theagency@mountview.org.uk
W www.mvmanagement.org.uk

MYERS MANAGEMENT   T/F 020 8204 8941
63 Fairfields Crescent, London NW9 0PR
E judy_hepburn@hotmail.com

**NARROW ROAD
COMPANY THE**   T 020 7379 9598
PMA Member
3rd Floor, 76 Neal Street, London WC2H 9PL
F 020 7379 9777
E agents@narrowroad.co.uk

**NARROW ROAD
COMPANY THE**   T 020 8763 9895
PMA Member
182 Brighton Road, Coulsdon, Surrey CR5 2NF
F 020 8763 2558
E richardireson@narrowroad.co.uk

**NARROW ROAD
COMPANY THE**   T/F 0161 833 1605
PMA Member
2nd Floor, Grampian House, 144 Deansgate
Manchester M3 3EE
E manchester@narrowroad.co.uk

NEALON, Steve ASSOCIATES   T 020 3178 7196
3rd Floor, 33 Glasshouse Street
London W1B 5DG
T 020 3178 7191
E admin@stevenealonassociates.co.uk
W www.stevenealonassociates.co.uk

**NELSON BROWNE
MANAGEMENT LTD**   T 020 7970 6010
PMA Member
40 Bowling Green Lane, London EC1R 0NE
T 07796 891388
E enquiries@nelsonbrowne.com
W www.nelsonbrowne.com

NEVS AGENCY   T 020 7352 4886
Regal House, 198 King's Road, London SW3 5XP
F 020 7352 6068
E getamodel@nevs.co.uk
W www.nevs.co.uk

NEW CASEY AGENCY   T 01923 823182
129 Northwood Way
Northwood HA6 1RF

NEW FACES LTD   T 020 7439 6900
*Personal Manager. Contact: Val Horton, Holly Janowski. By
Post/e-mail. Accepts Showreels. 3 Agents represent 50
Performers. Children. Commercials. Film. Stage. Television*
3rd Floor, The Linen Hall
162-168 Regent Street, London W1B 5TD
F 020 7287 5481
E info@newfacestalent.co.uk
W www.newfacestalent.co.uk

**NFD - THE FILM &
TV AGENCY**   T/F 01977 681949
PO Box 76, Leeds LS25 9AG
E info@film-tv-agency.com
W www.film-tv-agency.com

**NICHOLSON, Jackie
ASSOCIATES**   T 020 7580 4422
Personal Manager. Contact: Marvin Giles. By Post
Suite 44, 2nd Floor, Morley House
320 Regent Street, London W1B 3BD
F 020 7580 4489
E jnalondon@aol.com

NIC KNIGHT MANAGEMENT
See KNIGHT, Nic MANAGEMENT

N M MANAGEMENT   T 020 8853 4337
16 St Alfege Passage, Greenwich
London SE10 9JS
E nmmanagement@hotmail.com

NMP MANAGEMENT   T 01372 361004
*Personal Manager. Contact: By e-mail.
2 Agents represent 10 Performers. Comedians.
Corporate. Presenters. Television*
8 Blenheim Court, Brookway
Leatherhead, Surrey KT22 7NA
F 01372 374417
E management@nmp.co.uk
W www.nmpmanagement.co.uk

**NORTH OF WATFORD
ACTORS AGENCY**   T 01422 845361
Co-operative
Bridge Mill, Hebden Bridge, West Yorks HX7 8EX
F 01422 846503
E info@northofwatford.com
W www.northofwatford.com

**NORTH WEST ACTORS
- NIGEL ADAMS**   T/F 0161 724 6625
*Personal Manager. Contact: Nigel Adams.
By Post. Accepts Showreels/Voicereels.
Commercials. Film. Radio. Stage. Television*
36 Lord Street, Radcliffe
Manchester M26 3BA
E nigel.adams@northwestactors.co.uk
W www.northwestactors.co.uk

**NORTHERN LIGHTS
MANAGEMENT LTD**   T 01422 382203
Dean Clough Mills, Halifax
West Yorks HX3 5AX
F 01422 330101
E northern.lights@virgin.net

NORTHERN PROFESSIONALS   T 0191 257 8635
*Action Safety. Boat & Diving Equipment Hire.
Casting. Technicians*
21 Cresswell Avenue , North Shields
Tyne & Wear NE29 9BQ
E bill@northernprocasting.co.uk
W www.northernprocasting.co.uk

**NORTHERN STAR
ACTORS AGENCY**   T 0161 832 3535
332 Royal Exchange
Manchester M2 7BR
E mark@northernstaractors.co.uk
W www.northernstaractors.co.uk

NORTHONE MANAGEMENT   T/F 020 7359 9666
CPMA Member
HG08 Aberdeen Studios
Highbury Grove
London N5 2EA
E actors@northone.co.uk
W www.northone.co.uk

**NOTTING HILL
MANAGEMENT LTD**   T 020 7291 1050
9 Wimpole Street
London W1G 9SR
E agents@nottinghillmanagement.com
W www.nottinghillmanagement.com

NS ARTISTES MANAGEMENT   T 0121 684 5607
10 Claverdon House, Holly Bank Road
Billesley, Birmingham B13 0QY
T 07870 969577
E nsmanagement@fsmail.net
W www.nsartistes.co.uk

**NSM (NATASHA STEVENSON
MANAGEMENT LTD)**   T 020 7720 3355
*Personal Manager. PMA Member. Contact: By e-mail/
Telephone. 2 Agents. Commercials. Film. Stage. Television*
Studio 7C
Clapham North Arts Centre
Voltaire Road, London SW4 6DH
F 020 7720 5565
E inbox@natashastevenson.co.uk
W www.natashastevenson.co.uk

NUMBER ONE MODEL AGENCY   T 01675 443900
The Barn, Pasture Farm
Coventry Road, Solihull B92 0HH
E info@numberonemodelagency.co.uk
W www.numberonemodelagency.co.uk

NYLAND MANAGEMENT   T 01663 745629
93 Kinder Road
Hayfield SK22 2LE
E casting@nylandmanagement.com
W www.nylandmanagement.com

**OBJECTIVE TALENT
MANAGEMENT**   T/F 020 7202 2300
3rd Floor
Riverside Building, County Hall
Westminster Bridge Road, London SE1 7PB
E info@objectivetalentmanagement.com
W www.objectivetalentmanagement.com

OFF THE KERB PRODUCTIONS T 020 7437 0607
3rd Floor, Hammer House
113-117 Wardour Street
London W1F 0UN
F 020 7437 0647
E info@offthekerb.co.uk
W www.offthekerb.co.uk

**OH SO SMALL PRODUCTIONS LTD
& SHORT ACTORS AGENCY**   T 07787 788673
*Contact: Lisa Osmond. By e-mail/Telephone. Commercials.
Corporate. Film. Stage. Television*
6 High Street, Penarth, Cardiff CF64 1EY
F 029 2041 1244
E lisa@ohsosmallproductions.com
W www.ohsosmallproductions.com

OI OI AGENCY   T 01753 852326
*Actors, Actresses, Children & Young Performers, Dancers &
Models. Commercials. Film. Stage. Television*
Based in Pinewood Studios
F 01753 655622
E info@oioi.org.uk
W www.oioi.org.uk

**ONE MAKE UP/ONE
PHOTOGRAPHIC LTD**   T 020 7287 2311
4th Floor, 48 Poland Street, London W1F 7ND
F 020 7287 2313
E info@onemakeup.com
W www.onemakeup.com

OPERA & CONCERT ARTISTS   T 020 7328 3097
Musicals. Opera
75 Aberdare Gardens, London NW6 3AN
F 020 7372 3537
E enquiries@opera-and-concert-artists.co.uk

ORDINARY PEOPLE   T 020 7267 7007
Actors. Modelling
16 Camden Road, London NW1 9DP
F 020 7267 5677
E info@ordinarypeople.co.uk
W www.ordinarypeople.co.uk

OREN ACTORS MANAGEMENT   T 0845 4591420
CPMA Member
Chapter Arts Centre
Market Road, Cardiff CF5 1QE
E info@orenactorsmanagement.co.uk
W www.orenactorsmanagement.co.uk

**ORIENTAL CASTING
AGENCY LTD**   T 020 8660 0101
*Contact: By e-mail/Telephone.
Accepts Showreels/Voicereels.
1 Agent represents 200+ Performers. Afro/Asian Artists*
22 Wontford Road, Purley, Surrey CR8 4BL
E billiejames@btconnect.com
W www.orientalcasting.com

ORR MANAGEMENT AGENCY   T 01204 579842
1st Floor
147-149 Market Street
Farnworth
Greater Manchester BL4 8EX
E barbara@orrmanagement.co.uk
W www.orrmanagement.co.uk

**OTTO PERSONAL
MANAGEMENT LTD**   T 0114 275 2592
Personal Manager. CPMA Member
S.I.F., 5 Brown Street, Sheffield S1 2BS
E admin@ottopm.co.uk
W www.ottopm.co.uk

PADBURY, David ASSOCIATES   T 020 8883 1277
44 Summerlee Avenue
Finchley
London N2 9QP
E info@davidpadburyassociates.com

PAN ARTISTS AGENCY LTD   T 0800 6349147
Cornerways
34 Woodhouse Lane
Sale
Cheshire M33 4JX
T 07890 715115
E panartists@btconnect.com
W www.panartists.co.uk

neil waterson
PHOTOGRAPHY

07891 830471
info@neilwaterson.com   www.neilwaterson.com

PARADIGM ARTIST MANAGEMENT T 07747 612157
49 St Josephs Court, Llanelli
Carmarthenshire SA15 1NR
E info@paradigmartistagency.com
W www.paradigmartistagency.com

PARAMOUNT INTERNATIONAL MANAGEMENT T 020 8429 3179
30 Performers.International Comedians
Talbot House, 204-226 Imperial Drive
Harrow, Middlesex HA2 7HH
F 020 8868 6475
E mail@ukcomedy.com
W www.ukcomedy.com

PARKER, Cherry MANAGEMENT (RSM)
See RSM
(CHERRY PARKER MANAGEMENT)

PARSONS, Cary MANAGEMENT T 01926 735375
Set, Costume & Lighting Designers & Directors
118 Plymouth Place
Leamington Spa, Warwickshire CV31 1HW
E carylparsons@gmail.com
W www.caryparsons.co.uk

PAYNE MANAGEMENT T 020 7193 1156 (London)
Contact: Natalie Payne
T 0161 408 6715 (Manchester)
E agent@paynemanagement.co.uk
W www.paynemanagement.co.uk

P B J MANAGEMENT LTD T 020 7287 1112
Personal Manager. PMA Member. Contact: Janette Linden.
By e-mail. Accepts Showreels: 11 Agents represent 115
Performers. Comedians. Commercials. Corporate.
Presenters. Radio. Stage. Television. Voice Overs. Walk-on
& Supporting Artists. Writers
22 Rathbone Street
London W1T 1LA
F 020 7287 1191
E general@pbjmanagement.co.uk
W www.pbjmanagement.co.uk

PC THEATRICAL, MODEL & CASTING AGENCY T 020 8381 2229
Large Database of Twins
10 Strathmore Gardens
Edgware
Middlesex HA8 5HJ
F 020 8933 3418
E twinagy@aol.com
W www.twinagency.com

PELHAM ASSOCIATES T 01273 323010
Personal Manager. PMA Member. Contact: Peter Cleall
The Media Centre
9-12 Middle Street
Brighton BN1 1AL
F 01273 202492
E petercleall@pelhamassociates.co.uk
W www.pelhamassociates.co.uk

PEMBERTON ASSOCIATES LTD T 020 7734 4144
PMA Member. Contact: Barbara Pemberton.
By Post/e-mail. Showreels on request. 5 Agents represent
130 Performers. Film. Musicals. Radio. Stage. Television.
Voice Overs
51 Upper Berkeley Street
London W1H 7QW
E general@pembertonassociates.com
W www.pembertonassociates.com

PEMBERTON ASSOCIATES LTD T 0161 235 8440
PMA Member. Contact: Barbara Pemberton.
By Post/e-mail. Showreels on request. 5 Agents represent
130 Performers. Film. Musicals. Radio. Stage. Television.
Voice Overs
Express Networks
1 George Leigh Street
Manchester M4 5DL
F 0161 235 8442
E general@pembertonassociates.com
W www.pembertonassociates.com

PEOPLEMATTER.TV T 020 7415 7070
40 Bowling Green Lane
Clerkenwell
London EC1R 0NE
F 020 7415 7074
E tony@peoplematter.tv
W www.peoplematter.tv

PEPPERPOT PROMOTIONS T 020 7405 9108
Bands
Suite 20B, 20-22 Orde Hall Street
London WC1N 3JW
E chris@pepperpot.co.uk

PERFORMANCE ACTORS AGENCY T 020 7251 5716
Co-operative. CPMA Member
137 Goswell Road
London EC1V 7ET
F 020 7251 3974
E info@performanceactors.co.uk
W www.performanceactors.co.uk

PERFORMERS LEAGUE AGENCY THE T 07946 781116
Studio 55, 55 Openshaw Road
London SE2 0TB
E johnson@tpla.co.uk
W www.tpla.co.uk

PERFORMING ARTS T 020 7255 1362
Personal Manager. PMA Member. Contact:
By Post/e-mail. 2 Agents represent 30 Performers.
Creative Team Members only
6 Windmill Street
London W1T 2JB
F 020 7631 4631
E info@performing-arts.co.uk
W www.performing-arts.co.uk

PERRYMENT, Mandy   **T** 020 8941 7907
In association with Roger Carey Associates
T 07790 605191
E mail@mandyperryment.com

PERSONAL APPEARANCES   **T/F** 020 8343 7748
20 North Mount, 1147-1161 High Road
Whetstone N20 0PH
E patsy@personalappearances.biz
W www.personalappearances.biz

PHD ARTISTS   **T/F** 020 7241 6601
Contact: Paul Harris® on behalf of Pineapple Agency
24 Montana Gardens
Sutton, Surrey SM1 4FP
E office@phdartists.com
W www.phdartists.com

PHILLIPS, Frances   **T** 020 8953 0303
Personal Manager. PMA Member. Contact:
Frances Zealander-Phillips. By e-mail. 2 Agents represent
40 Performers
89 Robeson Way, Borehamwood
Hertfordshire WD6 5RY
T 07957 334328
E frances@francesphillips.co.uk
W www.francesphillips.co.uk

PHPM (PHILIPPA HOWELL PERSONAL
MANAGEMENT)   **T** 020 7836 2837
Contact: By e-mail only. Commercials. Film. Musicals.
Stage. Television
405 The Strand, London WC2R 0NE
T 07790 969024
E philippa@phpm.co.uk
W www.phpm.co.uk

PHPM (PHILIPPA HOWELL PERSONAL
MANAGEMENT)   **T** 020 7836 2837
184 Bradway Road, Sheffield S17 4QX
T 07790 969024
E philippa@phpm.co.uk
W www.phpm.co.uk

PICCADILLY MANAGEMENT   **T** 0161 953 4057
Personal Manager
23 New Mount Street, Manchester M4 4DE
F 0161 953 4001
E info@piccadillymanagement.com
W www.piccadillymanagement.com

PINEAPPLE AGENCY   **T** 020 7241 6601
Montgomery House
159-161 Balls Pond Road, London N1 4BG
F 020 7241 3006
E pineapple.agency@btconnect.com
W www.pineappleagency.com

PLA
See LOVETT LOGAN ASSOCIATES

PLAIN JANE   **T** 07813 667319
E info@plain-jane.co.uk
W www.plain-jane.co.uk

PLATER, Janet
MANAGEMENT LTD   **T** 0191 221 2490
Contact: Janet Plater. By Post/e-mail. Commercials. Film.
Radio. Stage. Television
D Floor, Milburn House, Dean Street
Newcastle upon Tyne NE1 1LF
E magpie@tynebridge.demon.co.uk
W www.janetplatermanagement.co.uk

PLATINUM ARTISTS   T 020 3006 2242
78 York Street, Marylebone
London W1H 1DP
E mail@platinumartists.co.uk
W www.platinumartists.co.uk

**PLUNKET GREENE
ASSOCIATES**   T 020 7603 2227
In conjunction with James Sharkey Associates Ltd.
Existing Clients only
PO Box 8365, London W14 0GL
F 020 7603 2221
E lyndatrapnell@compuserve.com

**POLLYANNA
MANAGEMENT LTD**   T/F 020 8530 6722
1 Knighten Street, Wapping
London E1W 1PH
E aliceharwood@talktalk.net
W www.pollyannatheatre.org

POOLE, Gordon AGENCY LTD   T 01275 463222
The Limes, Brockley, Bristol BS48 3BB
F 01275 462252
E agents@gordonpoole.com
W www.gordonpoole.com

PORTABLE COMEDY CLUB THE   T 07808 808080
14 Dover Street
Mayfair, London W1S 4LY
F 020 7281 6520
E enquiries@theportablecomedyclub.co.uk
W www.theportablecomedyclub.co.uk

**POWER MODEL MANAGEMENT
CASTING AGENCY**   T 01603 777190
PO Box 1198
Salhouse
Norwich NR13 6WD
E info@powermodel.co.uk
W www.powermodel.co.uk

POWER PROMOTIONS   T/F 0151 230 0070
PO Box 61, Liverpool L13 0EF
E tom2@powerpromotions.co.uk
W www.powerpromotions.com

PREGNANT PAUSE AGENCY   T 020 8979 8874
Pregnant Models,Dancers, Actresses
11 Matham Road
East Molesey KT8 0SX
E sandy@pregnantpause.co.uk
W www.pregnantpause.co.uk

PRESTON, Morwenna
MANAGEMENT　　　**T/F** 020 8835 8147
49 Leithcote Gardens, London SW16 2UX
E info@morwennapreston.com
W www.morwennapreston.com

PRICE GARDNER
MANAGEMENT　　　**T** 020 7610 2111
PO Box 59908, London SW16 5QH
F 020 7381 3288
E info@pricegardner.co.uk
W www.pricegardner.co.uk

PRINCIPAL ARTISTES　　**T** 020 7224 3414
Personal Manager. Contact: By Post
4 Paddington Street
Marylebone, London W1U 5QE

PROSPECTS ASSOCIATIONS　**T** 020 8555 3628
Sessions. Singers. Voice Overs for Commercials,
Film & Television
28 Magpie Close, Forest Gate, London E7 9DE
E wasegun@yahoo.co.uk

PURE ACTORS AGENCY
& MANAGEMENT LTD　　**T** 0161 832 5727
4th Floor, 20-22 High Street
Manchester M4 1QB
E enquiries@pure-management.co.uk
W www.pure-management.co.uk

PURPLESTAR CELEBRITY
MANAGEMENT　　　**T** 0800 6126637
Willow Brook, Steadfolds Lane
Rotherham, South Yorkshire S66 9LT
E questions@purplestarmedia.co.uk
W www.purplestarmedia.co.uk

PVA MANAGEMENT LTD　　**T** 01905 616100
County House, St Mary's Street
Worcester WR1 1HB
F 01905 610709
E post@pva.co.uk
W www.pva.co.uk

RAFFLES, Tim
ENTERTAINMENTS　　**T/F** 023 8046 5843
Personal Manager. 2 Agents represent 9 Performers.
Corporate. Cruise Work. Singers. Television
Victoria House
29 Swaythling Road, West End
Southampton SO30 3AG
E info@timrafflesentertainments.co.uk
W www.timrafflesentertainments.co.uk

RAGE MODELS　　　**T** 020 7262 0515
Tigris House, 256 Edgware Road, London W2 1DS
F 020 7402 0507
E ragemodels@ugly.org
W www.ugly.org

RAMA GLOBAL LTD　　**T** 0845 0540255
Contact: Rachael Pacey, Martin Arrowsmith. By Post.
Accepts Showreels. 1 Agent represents 10 Performers.
Children. Commercials. Film. Stage. Television
Huntingdon House
278-290 Huntingdon Street
Nottingham NG1 3LY
F 0115 948 3696
E admin@rama-global.co.uk
W www.rama-global.co.uk

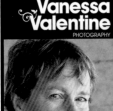

Rare Talent Actors Management is a dynamic agency with a fresh approach to acting management.

We supply professional actors to all aspects of the industry including television, film, theatre, corporate and commercials.

tanzaro house, ardwick green north, manchester, m12 6fz
t: 0161 273 4004   **f:** 0161 273 4567
info@raretalentactors.com www.raretalentactors.com

ACTORS MANAGEMENT

RAPID TALENT LTD   T 020 7734 5775
Personal Manager. Contact: Jason Nicholls, Jason Warren.
By e-mail/Telephone. 3 Agents represent 300 Performers.
Commercials. Film. Television. Walk-on & Supporting Artists
5 Vancouver Road, Sovereign Harbour
Eastbourne, East Sussex BN23 5BF
T 07980 899156
E enquiries@rapidtalent.co.uk
W www.rapidtalent.co.uk

RARE TALENT ACTORS
MANAGEMENT   T 0161 273 4004
Tanzaro House, Ardwick Green North
Manchester M12 6FZ
F 0161 273 4567
E info@raretalentactors.com
W www.raretalentactors.com

RAVENSCOURT MANAGEMENT
See CORONA MANAGEMENT

RAY KNIGHT CASTING
See KNIGHT, Ray CASTING

RAZZAMATAZZ MANAGEMENT   T 01342 301617
Personal Manager. Contact: Jill Shirley. By e-mail/Telephone.
1 Agent represents 10 Clients. Children. Dancers.
Presenters. Singers
204 Holtye Road, East Grinstead
West Sussex RH19 3ES
T 07836 268292
E razzamatazzmanagement@btconnect.com

RbA MANAGEMENT LTD   T 0151 708 7273
Personal Manager. CPMA Member. Contact: By e-mail.
Accepts Showreels/Voicereels. Approx 25 Performers
37-45 Windsor Street, Liverpool L8 1XE
E info@rbamanagement.co.uk
W www.rbamanagement.co.uk

RBM ACTORS   T 020 7630 7733
3rd Floor, 168 Victoria Street, London SW1E 5LB
F 020 7630 6549
E info@rbmactors.com
W www.rbmactors.com

RDDC MANAGEMENT AGENCY   T 01706 211161
52 Bridleway, Waterfoot
Rossendale, Lancashire BB4 9DS
T 07811 239780
E info@rddc.co.uk
W www.rddc.co.uk

RE-PM (RAIF EYLES
PERSONAL MANAGEMENT)   T 020 8953 1481
Film. Stage. Television
8 Dacre Gardens, Borehamwood WD6 2JP
T 07794 971733
E info@re-pm.co.uk
W www.re-pm.co.uk

REACH TO THE SKY
PERSONAL MANAGEMENT   T 0843 2892503
Actors. Artistes. Entertainers. Musicians
Maxet House, Liverpool Road, Luton, Beds LU1 1RS
E info@reachtothesky.com
W www.reachtothesky.com

REACTORS AGENCY   T 00 353 1 8786833
CPMA Member. Contact: By Post/e-mail.
Accepts Showreels. Co-operative of 24 Performers
1 Eden Quay, Dublin 1, Ireland
F 00 353 1 8783182
E info@reactors.ie
W www.reactors.ie

REAL PEOPLE REAL TALENT   T 0161 237 0101
Fourways House, 57 Hilton Street, Manchester M1 2EJ
F 0161 236 1237
E info@realpeople4u.com
W www.realpeople4u.com

RED CANYON MANAGEMENT   T 07931 381696
T 07939 365578
E info@redcanyon.co.uk
W www.redcanyon.co.uk

RED DOOR MANAGEMENT   T 0161 850 9989
The Pie Factory, 101 Broadway
Media City, Manchester M50 2EQ
E mail@the-reddoor.co.uk
W www.the-reddoor.co.uk

RED HOT ENTERTAINMENT   T 020 7635 0403
Contact: Nicky Raby. By e-mail. Accepts Showreels/
Voicereels. 4 Agents represent 35 Performers.
Commercials. Disabled. Film. Musicals. Stage.
Television. Writers
6 Farriers Mews, London SE15 3XP
F 020 7635 8988
E info@redhotentertainment.biz
W www.redhotentertainment.biz

REDDIN, Joan   T 01494 882729
Personal Manager. Contact: By Post
Hazel Cottage, Frogg's Island
Wheeler End Common, Bucks HP14 3NL

REDROOFS ASSOCIATES   T 01628 674092
26 Bath Road, Maidenhead, Berkshire SL6 4JT
T 01628 822982 (Holiday Times)
E agency@redroofs.co.uk
W www.redroofs.co.uk

REGAN RIMMER MANAGEMENT   T 020 8851 1414
Contact: Debbie Rimmer
17 Dallinger Road, London SE12 0TJ
F 020 8851 1517
E reganrimmer@btconnect.com

REGAN RIMMER MANAGEMENT   T 01656 841841
Contact: Leigh-Ann Regan
Ynyslas Uchaf Farm, Blackmill, Bridgend CF35 6DW
F 01656 841815
E regan-rimmer@btconnect.com

REGENCY AGENCY   T 0113 255 8980
25 Carr Road, Calverley, Leeds LS28 5NE

REPRESENTATION
UPSON EDWARDS   T 01782 827222
Voice Coaches only
23 Victoria Park Road, Tunstall
Stoke-on-Trent, Staffs ST6 6DX
F 01782 728004
E sarah.upson@voicecoach.tv
W www.voicecoach.tv

Joseph Lowe

Huw Collins

Rory Guinness

GEORGE GARNIER

LONDON STUDIO

T.020 7277 9554   WWW.GEORGEGARNIER.COM   M.07796262368

REYNOLDS, Sandra AGENCY   T 020 7387 5858
8 Agents represent 150 Performers. Children. Commercials.
Photographic Modelling. Presenters
Amadeus House, 27B Floral Street, London WC2E 9DP
F 020 7387 5848
E info@sandrareynolds.co.uk
W www.sandrareynolds.co.uk

REYNOLDS, Sandra
AGENCY (EAST ANGLIA)   T 01603 623842
8 Agents represent 150 Performers. Children. Commercials.
Photographic Modelling. Presenters
Bacon House, 35 St Georges Street, Norwich NR3 1DA
F 01603 219825
E info@sandrareynolds.co.uk
W www.sandrareynolds.co.uk

RICHARD STONE PARTNERSHIP THE
See STONE, Richard PARTNERSHIP THE

RICHARDS, Lisa
AGENCY THE   T 00 353 1 6375000
108 Upper Leeson Street
Dublin 4, Ireland
F 00 353 1 6671256
E info@lisarichards.ie
W www.lisarichards.ie

RICHARDS, Lisa AGENCY THE   T 020 7922 5799
117 Waterloo Road
London SE1 8UL
E office@lisarichards.co.uk
W www.lisarichards.co.uk

Kirsty Dillon   Roberto Giordano   Charlotte Williams   Ben Redfern   Michael D'Cruze

MARK VESSEY *HEADSHOTS.POINTANDSNAP.COM*
BRIGHTON/LONDON BASED - STUDENT RATES
07984 829078 mark@pointandsnap.com *10% OFF QUOTE MVCONTACTS*

Thornton Agency Artistes Representation
For People 5ft and Under
APT. 8 COURT ROYAL, ERIDGE ROAD, TUNBRIDGE WELLS, KENT TN4 8HT
01892 523 161   j.b.collins@btinternet.com

RICHARDS, Stella MANAGEMENT T 020 7736 7786
Contact: Stella Richards, Julia Lintott. Existing Clients only
42 Hazlebury Road, London SW6 2ND
E stellagent@aol.com
W www.stellarichards.com

RICHMOND SHARPE AGENCY T 0161 858 0049
Merricourt, Windmill Lane
Appleton, Warrington, Cheshire WA4 5JP
E info@richmondsharpe.com
W www.richmondsharpe.com

RIDGEWAY MANAGEMENT T 01992 633775
Office: 106 Hawkshead Road
Potters Bar, Hertfordshire EN6 1NG
E info@ridgewaystudios.co.uk

RIGHTS HOUSE THE T 020 3291 2929
Drury House, 34-43 Russell Street, London WC2B 5HA
E all@therightshouse.com
W www.therightshouse.com

RISQUE MODEL MANAGEMENT LTD T 0870 2283890
Rivington House, 82 Great Eastern Street
London EC2A 3JF
E info@risquemodel.co.uk
W www.risquemodel.co.uk

ROAR GLOBAL T 020 7462 9060
34-35 Eastcastle Street, London W1W 8DW
F 020 7462 9061
E info@roarglobal.com
W www.roarglobal.com

ROBERTS, Nicola MANAGEMENT T 01737 270500
9 Blackthorn Close, Reigate RH2 7NG
E info@nicolarobertsmanagement.com
W www.nicolarobertsmanagement.com

ROGUES & VAGABONDS MANAGEMENT LTD T 020 7254 8130
Personal Manager. CPMA Member
The Print House, 18 Ashwin Street, London E8 3DL
F 020 7249 8564
E rogues@vagabondsmanagement.com
W www.vagabondsmanagement.com

ROLE MODELS T 020 7284 4337
12 Cressy Road, London NW3 2LY
E info@rolemodelsagency.com
W www.rolemodelsagency.com

RONAN, Lynda PERSONAL MANAGEMENT T 020 7183 0017
Hunters House, 1 Redcliffe Road, London SW10 9NR
F 020 7183 0547
E lynda@lyndaronan.com
W www.lyndaronan.com

ROOM 3 AGENCY T 0845 5678333
The Old Chapel, 14 Fairview Drive
Redland, Bristol BS6 6PH
F 0845 5679333
E kate@room3agency.com
W www.room3agency.com

ROSEBERY MANAGEMENT LTD T 020 7684 0187
CPMA Member. Contact: Ben West (Lead Agent). By Post.
Accepts Showreels. 1 Agent represents 35 Performers.
Commercials. Film. Musicals. Stage. Television. Voice Overs
Hoxton Hall, 130 Hoxton Street
London N1 6SH
T 07805 162731
E admin@roseberymanagement.com
W www.roseberymanagement.com

ROSS, Frances MANAGEMENT T/F 01726 832395
Personal Manager. Contact: Frances Ross.
By e-mail.1 Agent represents 20 Performers.
Commercials. Corporate. Film. Stage. Television
Higher Leyonne
Golant, Fowey
Cornwall PL23 1LA
T 07918 648330
E francesross@btconnect.com
W www.francesrossmanagement.co.uk

ROSS BROWN ASSOCIATES T 07860 558033
Personal Manager
Rosedale House, Rosedale Road
Richmond, Surrey TW9 2SZ
F 020 8398 4111
E sandy@rossbrown.eu

ROSSMORE MANAGEMENT T 020 7258 1953
PMA Member
10 Wyndham Place, London W1H 2PU
F 020 7258 0124
E agents@rossmoremanagement.com
W www.rossmoremanagement.com

ROUGH HANDS AGENCY THE T 01992 578835
29 James Street, Epping
Essex, London CM16 6RR
T 07932 573228
E roughhandsagency@yahoo.co.uk

ROWE ASSOCIATES T/F 01992 308519
33 Percy Street, London W1T 2DF
T 07887 898220
E agents@growe.co.uk
W www.growe.co.uk

ROYCE MANAGEMENT T 020 8650 1096
121 Merlin Grove
Beckenham BR3 3HS
E office@roycemanagement.co.uk
W www.roycemanagement.co.uk

RPM2 T/F 0845 2415585
Studio House, Delamare Road
Cheshunt, Herts EN8 9SH
T 0845 3625456
E rhino-rpm2@hotmail.com
W www.rhino2-rpm.com

RSM (CHERRY PARKER MANAGEMENT) T 01702 522647
Contact: Cherry Parker
15 The Fairway SS9 4QN
T 07976 547066
E info@rsm.uk.net
W www.rsm.uk.net

RUDEYE DANCE AGENCY T 020 7014 3023
The Basement, 73 St John Street, London EC1M 4NJ
E info@rudeye.com
W www.rudeye.com

SAATCHI MODEL MANAGEMENT LTD
Contact: By Post/e-mail
Parkside, Chestnut Close, Ashford, Middlesex
E info@saatchimodels.co.uk
W www.saatchimodels.co.uk

SAINOU T 020 7734 6441
PMA Member
10-11 Lower John Street, London W1F 9EB
F 020 7734 1312
E office@sainou.com
W www.sainou.com

SANDERS, Loesje LTD T 01394 385260
PMA Member.
Contact: Loesje Sanders, Jo Probitts. By Post.
Choreographers. Designers. Directors.
Lighting Designers
Pound Square, 1 North Hill
Woodbridge, Suffolk IP12 1HH
F 01394 388734
E loesje@loesjesanders.org.uk
W www.loesjesanders.com

SARABAND ASSOCIATES T 020 7609 5313
Contact: Sara Randall, Bryn Newton
265 Liverpool Road, London N1 1LX
F 020 7609 2370
E brynnewton@btconnect.com

Philip Wade Photography | £125 Spotlight Package

Sophie Bleasdale — Tommy Bastow — Lee Bennett — Andrew Paul — Jay Bailey

www.philipwade.com | 07956 599 691 / 0207 226 3088 | pix@philipwade.com

SAROSI, Amanda ASSOCIATES T 020 7993 6008
1 Holmbury View, London E5 9EG
F 020 7096 2141
E amanda@asassociates.biz

SASHAZE TALENT AGENCY T 07968 762942
2 Gleannan Close, Omagh
Co. Tyrone BT79 7YA
E info@sashaze.com
W www.sashaze.com

SCA MANAGEMENT T 01932 268375
Contact: By Post
Abbey Business Centre
Wellington Way, Brooklands Business Park
Weybridge KT13 0TT
F 01932 268500
E agency@sca-management.co.uk
W www.sca-management.co.uk

SCHNABL, Peter T 01666 502133
The Barn House, Cutwell, Tetbury
Gloucestershire GL8 8EB
F 01666 502998
E peter.schnabl@virgin.net

SCHWARTZ, Marie Claude -
AGENCE CINETEA T 00 33 1 42781717
9 Rue des Trois Bornes, 75011 Paris, France
E cinetea@orange.fr
W www.cinetea.fr

SCOTT, Russell MANAGEMENT &
PRODUCTIONS LTD T 0844 5676896
Specialises in Finding, Developing & Working with Emerging
Professional Talent in Cabaret, Jazz & Musical Theatre
PO Box 729, Borehamwood
Herts WD6 9GW
E enquiry@russellscottmanagement.com
W www.russellscottmanagement.com

SCOTT, Tim T 020 7828 3824
PO Box 61776, London SW1V 3UX
E timscott@btinternet.com

SCOTT MARSHALL PARTNERS LTD
See MARSHALL, Scott PARTNERS LTD

SCOTT-NIVEN ASSOCIATES T 020 7884 0375
Lower Ground Floor Office
205 Victoria Rise
Clapham, London SW4 0PF
E theteam@scott-nivenassociates.com
W www.scott-nivenassociates.com

SCOTT-PAUL YOUNG
ENTERTAINMENTS LTD T/F 01753 693250
Artists Representation & Promotions
SPY Record Company
Northern Lights House
110 Blandford Road North
Langley, Nr Windsor, Berks SL3 7TA
E castingdirect@spy-ents.com
W www.spy-artistsworld.com

SCRIMGEOUR, Donald
ARTISTS AGENT T 020 8444 6248
Choreographers. Principal Dancers. Producers
49 Springcroft Avenue, London N2 9JH
F 020 8883 9751
E wwest@dircon.co.uk
W www.donaldscrimgeour.com

SEARS MANAGEMENT LTD T 01689 861859
Melbury House
34 Southborough Road
Bickley, Kent BR1 2EB
F 01689 862120
E linda@searsgroup.co.uk

SECOND SKIN AGENCY T/F 01494 730166
Foxgrove House
School Lane, Seer Green
Beaconsfield, Bucks HP9 2QJ
E jenny@secondskinagency.com
W www.secondskinagency.com

SEDGWICK, Dawn
MANAGEMENT T 020 7240 0404
3 Goodwins Court, Covent Garden
London WC2N 4LL
F 020 7240 0415
W www.dawnsedgwickmanagement.com

SELECT MANAGEMENT T 07956 131494
PO Box 748, London NW4 1TT
F 020 8203 2007
E mail@selectmanagement.info
W www.selectmanagement.info

SEVEN CASTING AGENCY T 0161 850 1057
Personal Manager. Children. Modelling. Television.
Walk-on & Supporting Artists
Manchester Office: 4th Floor
59 Piccadilly, Manchester M1 2AQ
T 07801 942178
E guy@7casting.co.uk
W www.7casting.co.uk

steve
ULLATHORNE PHOTOGRAPHY 07961 380 969

Miranda Hart, Clarke Peters,
Stephen Tompkinson, Michelle Collins,
Arthur Smith

www.SteveUllathorne.com

SEVEN CASTING AGENCY   T 01785 212266
Personal Manager. Children. Modelling. Television. Walk-on
& Supporting Artists
Staffordshire Office: Suite 3, Tudor House
9 Eastgate Street, Stafford ST16 2NQ
T 07801 942178
E guy@7casting.co.uk
W www.7casting.co.uk

SHAPER, Susan MANAGEMENT   T 020 7585 1023
5 Dovedale Gardens
465 Battersea Park Road, London SW11 4LR
F 020 7350 1802
E info@susanshapermanagement.com

SHELDRAKE, Peter AGENCY   T 020 8876 9572
Contact: By e-mail. 1 Agent represents 35 Performers.
Commercials. Film. Musicals. Stage. Television
139 Lower Richmond Road, London SW14 7HX
T 07758 063663
E psagent@btinternet.com
W www.petersheldrake.co.uk

SHEPHERD MANAGEMENT LTD   T 020 7495 7813
4th Floor, 45 Maddox Street
London W1S 2PE
F 020 7499 7535
E info@shepherdmanagement.co.uk
W www.shepherdmanagement.co.uk

SHEPPERD-FOX   T 07957 624601
5 Martyr Road, Guildford, Surrey GU1 4LF
E info@shepperd-fox.co.uk
W www.shepperd-fox.co.uk

SHOWSTOPPERS!   T 01376 518486
Events Management & Entertainment
42 Foxglove Close, Witham, Essex CM8 2XW
F 01376 510340
E mail@showstoppers-group.com
W www.showstoppers-group.com

SHOWTIME CASTINGS   T 020 7068 6816
112 Milligan Street
Docklands, London E14 8AS
T 07908 008364
E gemma@showtimecastings.com
W www.showtimecastings.com

SIMON & HOW ASSOCIATES   T 020 7739 8820
12-18 Hoxton Street, London N1 6NG
E info@simon-how.com
W www.simon-how.com

SIMPSON FOX ASSOCIATES LTD T 020 7434 9167
PMA Member. Set, Costume and Lighting Designers.
Directors. Choreographers
6 Beauchamp Place, London SW3 1NG
F 020 7494 2887
E info@simpson-fox.com

SINGER, Sandra ASSOCIATES   T 01702 331616
Personal Manager. Contact: By e-mail. 2 Agents represent
60 Performers. Adults. Children. Choreographers.
Commercials. Feature Film. Musicals. Television
21 Cotswold Road
Westcliff-on-Sea, Essex SS0 8AA
E sandrasingeruk@aol.com
W www.sandrasinger.com

Robert Kilroy-Silk   Ruth Shephard   Anthony Marsh   Michelle C

Howard Sayer Photographer
www.howardsayer.com   m: 07860 559891   howard@howardsayer.com

SINGERS INC T 020 7557 6650
9-13 Grape Street, Covent Garden
London WC2H 8ED
F 020 7557 6656
E chris@inc-space.com
W www.internationalcollective.com

SIRR, Peggy
See ORIENTAL CASTING AGENCY LTD

SJ MANAGEMENT T 020 7371 0441
8 Bettridge Road
London SW6 3QD
E sj@susanjames.demon.co.uk

SMART MANAGEMENT T 020 7837 8822
Contact: Mario Renzullo
PO Box 64377, London EC1P 1ND
E smart.management@virgin.net

SMEDLEY, Tom MANAGEMENT T 07515 775220
53 Waterford Road
London SW6 2DT
E tom@tomsmedleymanagement.com
W www.tomsmedleymanagement.com

SMILE TALENT T/F 01799 618809
2 Church Walk, Littlebury
Saffron Walden, Essex CB11 4TS
T/F 01799 618809
E info@smiletalent.com
W www.smiletalent.biz

SNODE, Chris
SPORTS PROMOTIONS T 020 8771 4700
Contact: By e-mail/Telephone. 300+ Performers. Actors.
Commercials. Dancers. Modelling. Sports Models
56 Church Road
Crystal Palace, London SE19 2EZ
F 020 8771 4704
E agent@sportspromotions.co.uk
W www.sportspromotions.co.uk

SOPHIE'S PEOPLE T 0870 7876446
Choreographers. Dancers
40 Mexfield Road, London SW15 2RQ
F 0870 7876447
E sophies.people@btinternet.com
W www.sophiespeople.com

S.O.S. T 020 7735 5133
85 Bannerman House, Lawn Lane
London SW8 1UA
T 07740 359770
E info@sportsofseb.com
W www.sportsofseb.com

SPEAKERS CIRCUIT LTD THE T 01892 750131
After Dinner Speakers
The Green, Frant
East Sussex TN3 9DR
F 01892 750089
E speakers-circuit@freenetname.co.uk

SPEAKERS CORNER T 020 8365 3200
Award Hosts, Comedians, Facilitators & Speakers for
Corporate Events
207 High Road, London N2 8AN
F 020 8883 7213
E info@speakerscorner.co.uk
W www.speakerscorner.co.uk

SPLITTING IMAGES
LOOKALIKES AGENCY T 020 8809 2327
25 Clissold Court, Greenway Close, London N4 2EZ
E info@splitting-images.com
W www.splitting-images.com

SPORTS OF SEB LTD T 020 7735 5133
85 Bannerman House, Lawn Lane
London SW8 1UA
T 07740 359770
E info@sportsofseb.com
W www.sportsofseb.com

SPYKER, Paul MANAGEMENT T 020 7462 0046
PO Box 48848
London WC1B 3WZ
F 020 7462 0047
E belinda@psmlondon.com

SRA PERSONAL MANAGEMENT T 01932 863194
Lockhart Road, Cobham
Surrey KT11 2AX
E agency@susanrobertsacademy.co.uk

SSA MANAGEMENT T 020 3560 7708
95 Warwick Road, London N11 2SP
T 07904 817229
E info@ssamanagement.co.uk
W www.ssamanagement.co.uk

S.T. ARTS MANAGEMENT T 0845 4082468
Contact: Tarquin Shaw-Young. Actors. Actresses
PO Box 127
Ross On Wye HR9 6WZ
F 0845 4082464
E tarquin@startsmanagement.co.uk
W www.startsmanagement.co.uk

ST. JAMES'S MANAGEMENT T 01932 860666
Personal Manager. Existing Clients only
19 Lodge Close, Stoke D'Abernon
Cobham, Surrey KT11 2SG
F 01932 863152
E jlstjames@btconnect.com

STA MANAGEMENT (SONGTIME THEATRE
ACADEMY MANAGEMENT) T 020 8133 1827
174A Merton High Street
South Wimbledon, London SW19 1AY
E info@stamanagement.co.uk
W www.stamanagement.co.uk

STAFFORD, Helen
MANAGEMENT T 020 8360 6329
Contact: Helen Stafford
14 Park Avenue, Bush Hill Park
Enfield EN1 2HP
F 020 8372 0611
E helen.stafford@blueyonder.co.uk

STAGE CENTRE
MANAGEMENT LTD T 020 7607 0872
Co-operative. CPMA Member. Contact: Lawrence
Panther-James. By e-mail/Telephone. 1 Lead Agent
represents 28 Performers. Commercials. Film. Musicals.
Stage. Television
41 North Road, London N7 9DP
E info@stagecentre.org.uk
W www.stagecentre.org.uk

STAGEWORKS
ARTIST MANAGEMENT T 020 7247 7110
32 Brookfield Road, London E9 5AH

STAGEWORKS WORLDWIDE
PRODUCTIONS T 01253 342426
Contact: By e-mail. Cirque Artistes. Corporate. Dancers.
Ice-Skaters. Musicals
525 Ocean Boulevard, Blackpool FY4 1EZ
F 01253 343702
E kelly.willars@stageworkswwp.com
W www.stageworkswwp.com

Representing actors for
Theatre | Television | Film

www.wildemanagement.co.uk

07759 567 639 | 07759 567 640

If you are interested in representation
or for any further information
please send enquiries to:

wilde.management@gmail.com

STAR POWER PRODUCTIONS T 07943 969242
23 Castalia Square, Docklands
London E14 3NG
E danny.page52@yahoo.com
W www.starpowerproductions.co.uk

STENTORIAN T 07808 353611
44 Broughton Grove
Skipton BD23 1TL
E stentorian@btinternet.com
W www.stentorian.freeuk.com

STEVENSON, Natasha MANAGEMENT LTD
See NSM
(NATASHA STEVENSON MANAGEMENT LTD)

STIRLING MANAGEMENT T 01204 848333
Contact: Glen Mortimer. By e-mail.
Accepts Showreels. 3 Agents represent 70 Performers.
Commercials. Film. Presenters. Stage. Television
490 Halliwell Road, Bolton
Greater Manchester BL1 8AN
E admin@stirlingmanagement.co.uk
W www.stirlingmanagement.co.uk

STIVEN CHRISTIE
MANAGEMENT T 0131 228 4040
Incorporating The Actors Agency of Edinburgh
1 Glen Street, Tollcross
Edinburgh EH3 9JD
F 0131 228 4645
E info@stivenchristie.co.uk
W www.stivenchristie.co.uk

STONEHOUSE, Katherine
MANAGEMENT T 020 8560 7709
Contact: Katherine Stonehouse. By e-mail.
1 Agent represents 35 Performers. Commercials.
Film. Musicals. Stage. Television
PO Box 64412
London W5 9GU
E katherine@katherinestonehouse.co.uk
W www.katherinestonehouse.co.uk

STONE, Ian ASSOCIATES T 020 8667 1627
Suite 262, Maddison House
226 High Street, Croydon CR9 1DF

STONE, Richard
PARTNERSHIP THE T 020 7497 0849
PMA Member
Suite 3, De Waldon Court
85 New Cavendish Street, London W1W 6XD
F 020 7497 0869
E all@thersp.com
W www.thersp.com

STRAIGHT LINE MANAGEMENT T 020 8393 4220
Division of Straight Line Productions
58 Castle Avenue
Epsom
Surrey KT17 2PH
F 020 8393 8079
E hilary@straightlinemanagement.co.uk

SUCCESS T 020 7734 3356
Room 236, 2nd Floor
Linen Hall
162-168 Regent Street
London W1B 5TB
F 020 7494 3787
E ee@successagency.co.uk
W www.successagency.co.uk

SUMMERS, Mark MANAGEMENT T 020 7229 8413
1 Beaumont Avenue
West Kensington, London W14 9LP
E louise@marksummers.com
W www.marksummers.com

SUPERTED.COM T 05602 406688
2 Chapel Place, Rivington Street, London EC2A 3DQ
E email@superted.com
W www.superted.com

TACT-AGENTS T 00 31 20 5708945
Palestrinastraat 10 hs, 1071 LE
Amsterdam, The Netherlands
F 00 31 20 5708989
E info@tactagents.nl
W www.tactagents.nl

TAKE2 CASTING AGENCY & TALENT MANAGEMENT T 00 353 87 2563403
28 Beech Park Road, Foxrock, Dublin 18, Ireland
E pamela@take2.ie
W www.take2.ie

TALENT4 MEDIA LTD T 020 7183 4330
Studio LG16, Shepherds Building Central
Charecroft Way, London W14 0EH
F 020 7183 4331
E enquiries@talent4media.com
W www.talent4media.com

TALENT ARTISTS LTD T 020 7923 1119
Contact: Jane Wynn Owen. No Unsolicited Enquiries
59 Sydner Road, London N16 7UF
F 020 7923 2009
E talent.artists@btconnect.com

TALENT SCOUT THE T 01924 464049
19 Edge Road, Dewsbury WF12 0QA
E connect@thetalentscout.org
W www.thetalentscout.org

TAVISTOCK WOOD T 020 7494 4767
PMA Member
45 Conduit Street, London W1S 2YN
F 020 7434 2017
E info@tavistockwood.com
W www.tavistockwood.com

TCA (THE COMMERCIAL AGENCY) T 020 7233 8100
12 Evelyn Mansions, Carlisle Place, London SW1P 1NH
F 020 7233 8110
E mail@thecommercialagency.co.uk
W www.thecommercialagency.co.uk

TCG ARTIST MANAGEMENT LTD T 020 7240 3600
Contact: Kristin Tarry (Director/Agent), Johnny Muller (Agent), Cal Griffiths (Assistant), Emma Davidson (Assistant), Jackie Davis (Office Manager), Charlie Wale (Legal/Contracts). By Post/e-mail. Accepts Showreels. Film. Musicals. Stage. Television
14A Goodwin's Court, London WC2N 4LL
F 020 7240 3606
E info@tcgam.co.uk
W www.tcgam.co.uk

TEAM PLAYERS T 00 45 20494218
Carit Etlars Vej 3, Frederiksberg
Copenhagen DK-1814, Denmark
E info@teamplayers.dk
W www.teamplayers.dk

TENNYSON AGENCY THE   T 020 8543 5939
10 Cleveland Avenue, Merton Park
London SW20 9EW
E mail@tennysonagency.co.uk

THOMAS, Lisa MANAGEMENT   T 0845 9005511
Contact: By e-mail. 5 Agents represent 30+ Performers
Unit 10, 7 Wenlock Road, London N1 7SL
F 0845 9005522
E lisa@lisathomasmanagement.com
W www.lisathomasmanagement.com

**THOMPSON, David
ASSOCIATES**   T 020 8682 3083
7 St Peter's Close, London SW17 7UH
T 07889 191093
E montefioredt@aol.com

THOMSON, Mia ASSOCIATES   T 020 7307 5939
Albany House, Suite 404
324-326 Regent Street, London W1B 3HH
F 020 7580 4729
E info@miathomsonassociates.co.uk
W www.miathomsonassociates.co.uk

**THORNTON AGENCY ARTISTES
REPRESENTATION**   T 01892 523161
For People 5ft & Under
Apt 8 Court Royal, Eridge Road
Tunbridge Wells, Kent TN4 8HT
E j.b.collins@btinternet.com

**THRELFALL, Katie
ASSOCIATES**   T 020 8543 4344
2A Gladstone Road, London SW19 1QT
F 020 8543 7545
E info@ktthrelfall.co.uk

**THRESH, Melody MANAGEMENT
ASSOCIATES LTD (MTM)**   T 0161 457 2110
2 Imperial Court, Exchange Quay
Manchester M5 3EB
E melodythreshmtm@aol.com

TILDSLEY, Janice ASSOCIATES   T 020 8521 1888
Contact: Kathryn Kirton
47 Orford Road, London E17 9NJ
F 020 8521 1174
E kathryn@janicetildsleyassociates.co.uk
W www.janicetildsleyassociates.co.uk

**TINKER, Victoria
MANAGEMENT**   T/F 01403 210653
Non-Acting. Technical
Birchenbridge House, Brighton Road
Mannings Heath, Horsham
West Sussex RH13 6HY

TOP TALENT AGENCY LTD   T 01727 855903
Film. Stage. Television
c/o Top Hat Stage & Screen School
PO Box 860, St Albans, Herts AL1 9BR
F 01727 812666
E admin@toptalentagency.co.uk
W www.toptalentagency.co.uk

TOTAL VANITY LTD   T 07710 780152
15 Walton Way, Aylesbury, Buckinghamshire HP21 7JJ
T 07739 381788
E richard.williams@totalvanity.com
W www.totalvanity.com

**TRENDS AGENCY &
MANAGEMENT LTD**   T 0871 2003343
*Contact: By e-mail. Commercials. Dancers. Musicals.
Singers. Stage*
Sullom Lodge, Sullom Side Lane, Garstang PR3 1GH
F 01253 407715
E info@squiresjohns.com
W www.squiresjohns.com

STAGEWORKS®
WORLDWIDE PRODUCTIONS

agency

SKATING
ICE DANCERS
FREE SKATERS
PAIR SKATERS
ADAGIO SKATERS
COMEDY SKATERS

DANCERS
ACTORS
SINGERS
MODELS

CIRCUS ARTISTS
SPECIALITY ACTS
MAGICIANS
ILLUSIONISTS
COSTUME CHARACTERS
STREET PERFORMERS

PROMOTIONAL PERSONNEL
HOSTS & HOSTESSES
GUEST SPEAKERS

SCRIPT WRITING

TECHNICAL STAGE MANAGEMENT

MUSIC PRODUCTION
PUBLISHING

MILLINERY AND COSTUMES

CHOREOGRAPHERS
DIRECTORS
PRODUCERS

00 44 **(0) 1253 342426**
00 44 **(0) 1253 336341**
info@stageworkswwp.com
stageworkswwp.com

TROIKA T 020 7336 7868
PMA Member
3rd Floor, 74 Clerkenwell Road
London EC1M 5QA
F 020 7490 7642
E info@troikatalent.com

TTA T 01245 200555
59 Belvawney Close, Chelmsford, Essex CM1 2HF
E agents@tomorrowstalent.co.uk

**TURNSTONE CASTING &
ENTERTAINMENT** T 0845 5576658
Hilton Hall, Hilton Lane, Essington WV11 2BQ
T 07866 211647
E mark_turner85@hotmail.com

TV MANAGEMENTS T 01425 475544
Brink House, Avon Castle
Ringwood, Hants BH24 2BL
F 01425 480123
E etv@tvmanagements.co.uk

TWINS
See PC THEATRICAL, MODEL & CASTING AGENCY

TWO'S COMPANY T 020 8299 4593
Existing Clients only. Directors. Stage. Writers
244 Upland Road, London SE22 0DN
F 020 8299 3714
E graham@2scompanytheatre.co.uk

UGLY MODELS T 020 7402 5564
Tigris House, 256 Edgware Road, London W2 1DS
F 020 7402 0507
E info@ugly.org
W www.ugly.org

UNITED AGENTS LTD T 020 3214 0800
Personal Manager. PMA Member
12-26 Lexington Street, London W1F 0LE
E info@unitedagents.co.uk
W www.unitedagents.co.uk

UPBEAT MANAGEMENT T 020 8668 3332
Theatre Touring & Events. No Actors
Larg House, Woodcote Grove
Coulsdon, Surrey CR5 2QQ
E info@upbeat.co.uk
W www.upbeat.co.uk

UPSON EDWARDS
See REPRESENTATION UPSON EDWARDS

URBAN HEROES T 020 7043 1072
Lower Ground
124 Boundary Road, London NW8 0RH
F 0870 4792458
E justin@theurbanheroes.com
W www.theurbanheroes.com

URBAN TALENT T 0161 228 6866
Nemesis House, 1 Oxford Court
Bishopsgate, Manchester M2 3WQ
F 0161 228 6727
E liz@nmsmanagement.co.uk
W www.urbantalent.tv

UTOPIA MODEL MANAGEMENT T 07771 884844
348 Moorside Road
Swinton, Manchester M27 9PW
F 0871 2180843
E kya@utopiamodels.co.uk

UVA MANAGEMENT LTD T 01753 652233
*Contact: By e-mail. Commercials. Film. Presenters.
Stage. Television*
Pinewood Film Studios, Pinewood Road
Iver Heath, Buckinghamshire SL0 0NH
E berko@uvamanagement.com
W www.uvamanagement.com

VACCA, Roxane MANAGEMENT T 020 7734 8085
73 Beak Street, London W1F 9SR
F 020 7734 8086

**VALLÉ THEATRICAL
AGENCY THE** T 01992 622861
The Vallé Academy Studios, Wilton House
Delamare Road, Cheshunt, Herts EN8 9SG
F 01992 622868
E agency@valleacademy.co.uk
W www.valleacademy.co.uk

VAMP JAZZ T 020 8992 1571
*Bands. Entertainers. Musicians. Singers
(not Musical Theatre)*
Ealing House
33 Hanger Lane, London W5 3HJ
E vampjazz@aol.com

**VERBECK, Dean
PERSONAL MANAGEMENT** T 01792 701570
c/o 26 Pine Crescent
Morriston, Swansea SA6 6AR
E dean.dvpm@mail.com
W www.deanverbeck.co.uk

VIDAL-HALL, Clare T 020 8741 7647
*PMA Member. Choreographers. Composers. Designers.
Directors. Lighting Designers*
57 Carthew Road, London W6 0DU
F 020 8741 9459
E info@clarevidalhall.com
W www.clarevidalhall.com

VINE, Michael ASSOCIATES T 020 8347 2580
Light Entertainment
1 Stormont Road, London N6 4NS
E stephen@michaelvineassociates.com

VISIONARY TALENT T 07827 466195
56 Ironworks, 58 Dace Road
London E3 2NX
E info@visionarytalent.co.uk
W www.visionarytalent.co.uk

**VM TALENT LTD
(VIC MURRAY TALENT)** T 020 7924 4453
PMA Member
185A/B Latchmere Road
London SW11 2JZ
E info@vmtalent.com
W www.vmtalent.com

Robert Lister HEADSHOTS
Bournemouth 07909 824893
www.robertlister.co.uk

VSA LTD　　　　　　　　T 020 7240 2927
PMA Member. Contact: Andy Charles, Tod Weller
186 Shaftesbury Avenue, London WC2H 8JB
F 020 7240 2930
E info@vsaltd.com
W www.vsaltd.com

W ATHLETIC　　　　　　T 01276 415800
Unit 309, 377-399 London Road
Camberley, Surrey GU15 3HL
E london@wathletic.com
W www.wathletic.com

WADE, Suzann　　　　　T 020 7486 0746
Personal Manager. PMA Member. Contact: By Post only
(No Calls). Accepts Showreels. 2 Agents represent 19
Performers. Film. Musicals. Stage. Television
9 Wimpole Mews, London W1G 8PG
F 020 7486 5664
E info@suzannwade.com
W www.suzannwade.com

WALK TALL MANAGEMENT　　T/F 01474 561200
Contact: By e-mail. Accepts Showreels. 35 Performers
Britannia House, Lower Road
Ebbsfleet, Kent DA11 9BL
E annduke@lineone.net

WARD CASTING　　　　T 020 8886 5676
Studio 5, 155 Commercial Street
London E1 6BJ
E casting@wardcasting.com
W www.wardcasting.com

WARING & McKENNA　　T 020 7629 6444
PMA Member
11-12 Dover Street, Mayfair, London W1S 4LJ
F 020 7629 6466
E dj@waringandmckenna.com
W www.waringandmckenna.com

WELCH, Janet
PERSONAL MANAGEMENT　　T/F 01761 463238
Contact: By Post
Old Orchard, The Street
Ubley, Bristol BS40 6PJ
E info@janetwelchpm.co.uk

WEST CENTRAL
MANAGEMENT　　　　T/F 020 7833 8134
CPMA Member. Co-operative of 21 Performers.
Contact: By Post/e-mail
Room 4, East Block, Panther House
38 Mount Pleasant, London WC1X 0AN
E mail@westcentralmanagement.co.uk
W www.westcentralmanagement.co.uk

WEST END MANAGEMENT　　T 0141 222 2333
Contact: Maureen Cairns, Allan Jones
2nd Floor
34 Argyle Arcade Chambers
Buchanan Street
Glasgow G2 8BD
E info@west-endmgt.com
W www.west-endmgt.com

WHATEVER ARTISTS
MANAGEMENT LTD　　　T 020 7372 4777
F24 Argo House
Kilburn Park Road, London NW6 5LF
F 020 7372 5111
E info@wamshow.biz
W www.wamshow.biz

'the BIG agency for short & tall actors'

actors from 3ft to 5ft & over 7ft
for films, TV, theatre & advertising

tel: +44 (0)1733 240392 • email: office@willowmanagement.co.uk • on-line casting directory: willowmanagement.co.uk

WHITEHALL ARTISTS T 020 8785 3737
10 Lower Common South
London SW15 1BP
F 020 8788 2340
E mwhitehall@msn.com

WILDE MANAGEMENT T 07759 567639
11 Wilton Road, Chorlton
Manchester M21 9GS
T 07759 567640
E wilde.management@gmail.com
W www.wildemanagement.co.uk

**WILKINSON, David
ASSOCIATES** T 020 7371 5188
Existing Clients only
115 Hazlebury Road, London SW6 2LX
F 020 7371 5161
E info@dwassociates.net

**WILLIAMS BULLDOG
MANAGEMENT LTD** T 07766 254877
6 Vicentia Quay
Bridges Wharf, London SW11 3GY
E info@williamsbulldog.co.uk
W www.williamsbulldog.co.uk

WILLIAMSON & HOLMES T 020 7240 0407
51 St Martin's Lane, London WC2N 4EA
E info@williamsonandholmes.co.uk

**WILLOW PERSONAL
MANAGEMENT** T 01733 240392
*Specialist Agency for Short Actors (5 feet & under)
& Tall Actors (7 feet & over)*
151 Main Street, Yaxley
Peterborough, Cambs PE7 3LD
E office@willowmanagement.co.uk
W www.willowmanagement.co.uk

WILLS, Newton MANAGEMENT T 07989 398381
*Personal Manager. Contact: By Post/e-mail. Accepts
Showreels/Voicereels. 3 Agents represent 53 Performers.
Commercials. Dancers. Film. Musicals. Singers. Stage.
Television. Voice Overs*
12 St Johns Road, Isleworth
Middlesex TW7 6NN
F 00 33 4 68218685
E newtoncttg@aol.com
W www.newtonwills.com

WINSLETT, Dave ASSOCIATES T 020 8668 0531
4 Zig Zag Road, Kenley
Surrey CR8 5EL
F 020 8668 9216
E info@davewinslett.com
W www.davewinslett.com

WINTERSONS T 020 7836 7849
59 St Martin's Lane
London WC2N 4JS
E info@nikiwinterson.com
W www.nikiwinterson.com

WIS CELTIC MANAGEMENT T 07966 302812
Welsh, Irish, Scottish Performers
86 Elphinstone Road, Walthamstow
London E17 5EX
F 020 8523 4523

WISE BUDDAH TALENT T 020 7307 1600
Contact: Chris North
74 Great Titchfield Street
London W1W 7QP
F 020 7307 1601
E chris.north@wisebuddah.com
W www.wisebuddah.com

**WMG MANAGEMENT
EUROPE LTD** T 020 7009 6000
Sports Management Company
5th Floor, 33 Soho Square
London W1D 3QU
F 020 3230 1053
W www.wmgllc.com

WYMAN, Edward AGENCY T 029 2075 2351
*Contact: Judith Gay.
By Post/e-mail. Accepts Showreels/Voicereels.
Adults (16+ yrs). English & Welsh Language.
Commercials. Corporate. Television. Voice Overs. Walk-on
& Supporting Artists*
23 White Acre Close
Thornhill, Cardiff CF14 9DG
E wymancasting@yahoo.co.uk
W www.wymancasting.co.uk

XL MANAGEMENT T 01926 810449
Edmund House, Rugby Road
Leamington Spa, Warwickshire CV32 6EL
F 01926 811420
E office@xlmanagement.co.uk
W www.xlmanagement.co.uk

**YAT MANAGEMENT (YOUNG ACTORS THEATRE
MANAGEMENT)** T 020 7278 2101
70-72 Barnsbury Road, London N1 0ES
F 020 7833 9467
E agent@yati.org.uk
W www.yati.org.uk

**YELLOW BALLOON
PRODUCTIONS LTD** T 01483 281500
Contact: Mike Smith
Freshwater House
Outdowns
Effingham, Surrey KT24 5QR
F 01483 281501
E yellowbal@aol.com

**ZWICKLER, Marlene &
ASSOCIATES** T/F 0131 343 3030
1 Belgrave Crescent Lane
Edinburgh EH4 3AG
E info@mza-artists.com
W www.mza-artists.com

Byron's Management

180 Drury Lane, London WC2B 5QF
www.byronsmanagement.co.uk
byronsmanagement@aol.com
T: 020 7242 8096

A & J MANAGEMENT T 020 8342 0542
242A The Ridgeway, Botany Bay, Enfield EN2 8AP
T 020 8367 7139
E info@ajmanagement.co.uk
W www.ajmanagement.co.uk

ABACUS AGENCY T 01306 877144
The Studio, 4 Bailey Road
Westcott, Dorking, Surrey RH4 3QS
F 01306 877813
E admin@abacusagency.co.uk
W www.abacusagency.co.uk

ACADEMY ARTS MANAGEMENT T 01245 422595
6A The Green, Writtle
Chelmsford, Essex CM1 3DU
E info@academyarts.co.uk
W www.academyarts.co.uk

ACT OUT AGENCY T/F 0161 429 7413
Children, Teenagers & New Graduates
22 Greek Street, Stockport
Cheshire SK3 8AB
E ab22actout@aol.com

ALL EXPRESSIONS AGENCY T 020 8898 3321
153 Waverley Avenue, Twickenham TW2 6DJ
E info@allexpressions.co.uk
W www.allexpressions.co.uk

**ALL THE ARTS CHILDREN'S
CASTING AGENCY** T 020 8850 2384
PO Box 61687, London SE9 9BP
T 07908 618083
E jillian@alltheartsagency.co.uk
W www.alltheartsagency.co.uk

ALLSORTS AGENCY T 020 8989 0500
Suite 3 Marlborough Business Centre
96 George Lane, London E18 1AD
F 020 8989 5600
E bookings@allsortsagency.com
W www.allsortsagency.com

**ALLSORTS DRAMA
FOR CHILDREN** T/F 020 8969 3249
In Association with Sasha Leslie Management
34 Crediton Road, London NW10 3DU
E sasha@allsortsdrama.com

ALLSTARS CASTING T 0151 707 2100
66 Hope Street, Liverpool L1 9BZ
T/F 07739 359737
E sylvie@allstarscasting.co.uk
W www.allstarscasting.co.uk

**ALPHABET KIDZ ACTING &
VOICE-OVER AGENCY** T 020 7252 4343
Nice Business Park
19-35 Sylvan Grove
London SE15 1PD
F 020 7252 4341
E contact@alphabetkidz.co.uk
W www.alphabetkidz.co.uk

ANNA'S MANAGEMENT T 020 8958 7636
*Formerly of ALADDIN'S CAVE. Children. Teenagers.
Young Adults*
25 Tintagel Drive, Stanmore
Middlesex HA7 4SR
E annasmanage@aol.com
W www.annasmanagement.com

Children's & Teenagers' Agents

How can my child become an actor?

If your child is interested in becoming an actor, they should try to get as much practical experience as possible. For example, joining the drama club at school, taking theatre studies as an option, reading as many plays as they can, and going to the theatre on a regular basis. They could also attend local youth theatres or drama groups. Some theatres offer evening or Saturday classes.

What are the chances of success?

As any agency or school will tell you, the entertainment industry is highly competitive and for every success story there are many children who will never be hired for paid acting work. Child artists and their parents should think very carefully before getting involved in the industry and be prepared for disappointments along the way.

What is the difference between stage schools and agencies?

Stage schools provide specialised training in acting, singing and dancing for the under 18's. They offer a variety of full and part-time courses. Please see the 'Drama Training, Schools and Coaches' section for listings. Children's and Teenagers' agencies specialise in the representation of child artists, promoting them to casting opportunities and negotiating contracts on their behalf. In return they will take commission, usually ranging from 10-15%. Some larger stage schools also have agencies attached to them. A number of agents are listed in this section.

Why does my child need an agent?

While many parents feel they want to retain control over their child's career, they will not have the contacts and authority a good agent will have in the industry. Casting directors are more likely to look to an agent they know and trust to provide the most suitable children for a job than an independent, unrepresented child. This does not mean to say that a child will never get work without an agent to put them forward for work, but it will certainly be more difficult.

How should these listings be used?

This section lists up-to-date contact details for agencies specialising in the representation of children and teenagers. Every company listed is done so by written request to us. Always research agencies carefully before approaching them to make sure they are suitable for your child. Many have websites you can visit, or ask around for personal recommendations. You should make a short-list of the ones you think are most appropriate rather than sending a standard letter to hundreds of agencies. Please see the main 'Agents and Personal Managers' advice section for further guidance on choosing and approaching agents.

Can Spotlight offer me advice on choosing or changing my child's agent?

Unfortunately Spotlight is not able to advise performers on specific agents, nor is it in a position to handle any financial or contractual queries or complaints. For agent-related queries we suggest you contact The Agents Association www.agents-uk.com or The Personal Managers' Association (PMA) www.thepma.com, or you could try one of the independent advisors on our website www.spotlight.com/artists/advice/independent

Who can I contact for general advice?

Your local education authority should be able to help with most queries regarding your child's education, working hours, chaperones and general welfare if they are aged 16 or under. You could also try contacting an independent advisor for advice, or for legal guidance please see the 'Accountants, Insurance & Law' section for listings.

Should I pay an agent to represent my child? Or sign a contract?

Equity does not recommend that you pay an agent an upfront fee to place your child on their client list. Before signing a contract, you should be very clear about the terms and commitments involved. For advice on both of these issues, or if you experience any problems with a current agent, we recommend that you contact Equity www.equity.org.uk

Why do child actors need licences?

Strict regulations apply to children working in the entertainment industry. These cover areas including the maximum number of performance hours per day/week, rest times, meal times and tutoring requirements. When any child under 16 performs in a professional capacity, the production company must obtain a Child Performance Licence from the child's local education authority.

Who are chaperones?

Child artists must also be accompanied by a chaperone at all times when they are working. Registered chaperones are generally used instead of parents as they have a better understanding of the employment regulations involved, and they have professional experience of dealing with production companies. Registered chaperones will have been police checked and approved by their local education authority to act in loco parentis. Always contact your local education authority if you have any questions or concerns.

What is the Spotlight Children and Young Performers directory?

Children who are currently represented by an agent or attend a stage school can appear in the Spotlight Children and Young Performers directory. This is a casting directory, used by production teams to source child artists for TV, film, stage or commercial work. Each child pays an annual membership fee to have their photo featured in the printed directory along with others represented by the same agency or stage school, as well as receiving their own individual online CV on the Spotlight website, searchable by casting professionals. Please speak to your child's school or agency about joining Spotlight for ongoing promotion to hundreds of casting opportunities. For further information about the directory visit www.spotlight.com/join

... has been ... 0 years. Doreen was a dance a... ...eacher and had her own stage schoo... . lany established actors began their careers with us including Helena Bonham Carter, Simon Le Bon, Nigel Harman and Mark Lester. When Doreen died, Gerry Kinner took over and the agency became Doreen English '95. The agency primarily represents children and young performers but also looks after some selected adults.

The entertainment industry is extremely difficult to get into and much harder for girls than it is for boys as there are so many girls wanting to do it. Parents play a crucial part in helping children achieve a career. 100% commitment is paramount. Castings and auditions are very nearly all held in London and are usually called at very short notice. There is no point in joining an agency if there is nobody to take the child to these. It sometimes takes years to get a child established and there are no guarantees that they will even be called to a casting, let alone be given a part!

Performing in a West End show is extremely hard work and is very poorly paid. If you live outside London it is even harder as rehearsals are usually five days a week in London for approximately eight weeks and during performances you will be in London for two or three days a week. You must be sure that you can be this committed before you audition as it not only wastes the casting team's and agent's time, it is not fair to the child if they are offered a part only for the parents to turn around and tell them that they can't afford to take the time off work.

Another thing worth noting is the school your child attends. Every child under 16 needs an entertainment licence for every job that they are cast for. For that licence, you will be required to produce a copy of their birth certificate, two passport photos, a doctor's letter and a letter from the headteacher giving them permission to have the time off school. It is worth having a chat with the head to ensure that you have the school's support as without it, your child will not be able to work.

If you decide that you can make this kind of commitment then the next step is to find representation. You should NEVER be asked to pay to join an agency. It is a good idea to research the agency that you are looking at. You will be asked to pay the annual subscription to Spotlight and you will need a couple of good quality photographs. There is no point in paying to be in Spotlight and just sending some snapshots of your child in the garden. They need to be clear, head and shoulder shots with no hats/scarves or hands around the face. Remember, it is these photos that the casting agencies look at to choose who they call to a casting so it is worth choosing a good photographer.

Once you have found representation, the agent will put your child forward for castings and auditions that they feel that he or she is most suited to. Your child may be put forward for several parts every day but this does not guarantee a casting for all or indeed any. The agent can only put your child forward and recommend that he or she is seen, but they cannot promise to get work or make your son or daughter 'famous'.

Of course, you may read this and think it all sounds a bit negative but we believe that if we tell you all the pitfalls before you start and you still want to join us, we hope that there will not be disappointments, only success! Good luck to all potential actors and actresses!

For more information about Doreen English '95 contact:
Post: Mrs Gerry Kinner, Doreen English '95, 4 Selsey Avenue, Aldwick, Bognor Regis West Sussex, PO21 2QZ
T 01243 825968

ARAENA/COLLECTIVE   T/F 020 8428 0037
10 Bramshaw Gardens
South Oxhey
Herts WD19 6XP
E info@collectivedance.co.uk

**A.R.K. AGENCY
(ALL ROUND KIDS)**   T 07900 998090
54 Oaklands, Curdworth
Sutton Coldfield B76 9HD
T 07976 755434
E allroundkids@hotmail.co.uk
W www.allroundkids.co.uk

ARNOULD KIDZ   T 020 8942 1879
1 Brook Gardens
Kingston-upon-Thames
Surrey KT2 7ET
T 07720 427828
E info@arnouldkidz.co.uk
W www.arnouldkidz.co.uk

**ASHCROFT ACADEMY OF
DRAMATIC ART & AGENCY**   T 0844 8005328
Malcolm Primary School
Malcolm Road
Penge, London SE20 8RH
T 07799 791586
E info@ashcroftacademy.com
W www.ashcroftacademy.com

**AWA - ANDREA WILDER
AGENCY**   T 07919 202401
23 Cambrian Drive, Colwyn Bay
Conwy LL28 4SL
F 07092 249314
E andreawilder@fastmail.fm
W www.awagency.co.uk

BABYSHAK AGENCY   T 0845 5200400
Bizzy Studios
1st Floor Hall
10-12 Pickford Lane
Bexleyheath, Kent DA7 4QW
F 0845 5200401
E clients@babyshak.com
W www.babyshak.com

BANANAFISH MANAGEMENT   T 0151 708 5509
The Arts Village
20-26 Henry Street
Liverpool L1 5BS
T 07974 206622
E info@bananafish.co.uk
W www.bananafish.co.uk

BELFAST TALENT AGENCY   T 028 9024 3324
The Crescent Arts Centre
Belfast, Antrim BT7 1NH
E info@belfasttalent.com
W www.belfasttalentagency.com

**BIG TALENT SCHOOL &
AGENCY THE**   T 01656 841841
Contact: Shelley Barrett-Norton
Ynyslas Uchaf Farm
Blackmill
Bridgend CF35 6DW
T 07886 020923
E info@thebigtalent.co.uk
W www.thebigtalentschool.co.uk

BIZZYKIDZ   T 0845 5200400
Bizzy Studios, 1st Floor Hall
10-12 Pickford Lane
Bexleyheath
Kent DA7 4QW
F 0845 5200401
E bookings@bizzykidz.com
W www.bizzykidz.com

BODENS AGENCY   T 020 8447 0909
99 East Barnet Road
New Barnet
Herts EN4 8RF
E info@bodens.co
W www.bodens.co

BONNIE & BETTY LTD   T 020 8676 6294
County House
221-241 Beckenham Road
Beckenham, Kent BR3 4UF
E agency@bonnieandbetty.com
W www.bonnieandbetty.com

**BOURNE, Michelle MULTICULTURAL
ACADEMY & AGENCY**   T 07852 932473
Studio 1, 22 Dorman Walk
Garden Way, London NW10 0PF
E info@michellebourneacademy.co.uk
W www.michellebourneacademy.co.uk

BRUCE & BROWN   T 020 7624 7333
17 Lonsdale Road
London NW6 6RA
F 020 7625 4047
E info@bruceandbrown.com
W www.bruceandbrown.com

BRUNO KELLY LTD   T 020 7183 7331
4th Floor, Albany House
324-326 Regent Street
London W1B 3HH
F 020 7183 7332
E info@brunokelly.com
W www.brunokelly.com

BUBBLEGUM   T 01753 642673
Ardreigh
Beaconsfield Road
Farnham Royal, Bucks SL2 3BP
E info@bubblegummodels.com
W www.bubblegummodels.com

All The Arts Casting Agency

www.alltheartsagency.co.uk

PO Box 61687
London SE9 9BP

jillian@alltheartsagency.co.uk

020 8850 2384
07908 618083

BYRON'S MANAGEMENT   T 020 7242 8096
Children & Adults
180 Drury Lane, London WC2B 5QF
E byronsmanagement@aol.com
W www.byronsmanagement.co.uk

**CAPITAL ARTS AGENCY &
CHILDREN'S CHOIR**   T/F 020 8449 2342
Capital Arts Theatre School
Capital Arts Studio, Wyllyotts Centre, Darkes Lane
Potters Bar, Herts EN6 2HN
T 07885 232414
E capitalarts@btconnect.com
W www.capitalarts.org.uk

CARR, Norrie AGENCY   T 020 7253 1771
Babies, Children & Adults
Holborn Studios, 49-50 Eagle Wharf Road
London N1 7ED
F 020 7253 1772
E info@norriecarr.com
W www.norriecarr.com

**CAVAT SCHOOL OF THEATRE ARTS
& AGENCY**   T 020 8651 1099
16A Hook Hill, South Croydon, Surrey CR2 0LA
E enquiries@cavattheatrearts.co.uk
W www.cavattheatrearts.co.uk

**CHADWICK, Jacqueline
ACADEMY THE**   T 07918 685296
Oakdene Studios, Brewery Lane
Leigh WN7 2RJ
E chadwickacademy@yahoo.com
W www.jacquelinechadwickacademy.co.uk

CHILDSPLAY MODELS LLP   T 020 8659 9860
114 Avenue Road, Beckenham, Kent BR3 4SA
F 020 8778 2672
E info@childsplaymodels.co.uk
W www.childsplaymodels.co.uk

CHILLI KIDS   T 0333 666 2468
Talisman House, 47-49 Bath Street
Walsall WS1 3BX
F 0333 666 2469
E info@chillikids.co.uk
W www.chillikids.co.uk

CHRYSTEL ARTS AGENCY   T 01494 773336
6 Eunice Grove, Chesham, Bucks HP5 1RL
T 07799 605489
E chrystelarts@waitrose.com

CONTI, Italia AGENCY LTD   T 020 7608 7500
Italia Conti House, 23 Goswell Road
London EC1M 7AJ
F 020 7253 1430
E agency@italiaconti.co.uk

CORONA MANAGEMENT   T 020 8758 2553
3 Thameside Centre, Kew Bridge Road
Brentford, Middlesex TW8 0HF
E info@coronatheatreschool.com
W www.coronatheatreschool.com

CPA AGENCY   T 01708 766444
The Studios, 219B North Street
Romford, Essex RM1 4QA
F 01708 766077
E info@cpaagency.co.uk
W www.cpastudios.co.uk

CREATIVE KIDZ STAGE SCHOOL   T 07958 377595
9 Weavers Terrace, Fulham, London SW6 1QE
T 07908 144802
E info@creativekidzandco.co.uk

CS MANAGEMENT   T 020 8886 4264
Children & Young Adults
The Croft, 7 Cannon Road
Southgate, London N14 7HE
F 020 8886 7555
E carole@csmanagementuk.com
W www.csmanagementuk.com

**D & B MANAGEMENT &
THEATRE SCHOOL**   T 020 8698 8880
Central Studios, 470 Bromley Road
Bromley, Kent BR1 4PQ
E bonnie@dandbmanagement.com
W www.dandbperformingarts.co.uk

DD'S CHILDREN'S AGENCY   T 020 8502 6866
6 Acle Close, Hainault, Essex IG6 2GQ
T 07957 398501
E ddsagency@yahoo.co.uk
W www.ddtst.com

DEVINE ARTIST MANAGEMENT   T 0844 8844578
145-157 St John Street, London EC1V 4PW
E mail@devinemanagement.co.uk
W www.devinemanagement.co.uk

DRAGON DRAMA   T 020 8617 3141
Improvisational Drama for Children
1B Station Road, Hampton Wick KT1 4HG
E askus@dragondrama.co.uk
W www.dragondrama.co.uk

**DRAMA STUDIO
EDINBURGH THE**   T 0131 453 3284
19 Belmont Road, Edinburgh EH14 5DZ
E info@thedramastudio.com
W www.thedramastudio.com

EARACHE KIDS (VOICE-OVERS)   T 020 7287 2291
177 Wardour Street, London W1F 8WX
F 020 7287 2288
E julie@earachevoices.com
W www.earachevoices.com

**EARNSHAW, Susi
MANAGEMENT**   T 020 8441 5010
The Bull Theatre, 68 High Street
Barnet, Herts EN5 5SJ
F 020 8364 9618
E casting@susiearnshaw.co.uk
W www.susiearnshawmanagement.com

⊜d&b management

is one of the leading Children's / Young Adults agencies in London and continues to place their clients in featured TV, Film and Theatre Productions.

Macauley Keeper
Me & My Monsters

Jacqueline Jossa
Eastenders

Adam Roddie
Johnny English Reborn

Mohammed Mansaray
Law and Order

Ela Warburton
Horrid Henry

Zack Morris
One Night

Odelia Dizel-Cubuca
The Lion King

Lucia Valentino
The Wizard of Oz

Justin Thomas
Dirty Dancing UK Tour

William Price
Priscilla, Queen of the Desert

Kiki Mitchell
Casualty

Nicholas Fagg
Silent Witness

call
020 8698 8880

email
bonnie@dandbmanagement.com

website
www.dandbperformingarts.co.uk

In Association with:

School of Performing Arts
3 Year Full Time Musical Theatre Course

Theatre School
Part-Time training for Children and Young Adults

STOMP! MANAGEMENT *Representing:*
- CHILDREN & TEENAGERS 6-19 yrs
- CONFIDENT, TRAINED, NATURAL. MANY BOY ACTORS.
- COMPLIMENTARY CASTING FACILITIES.
T: 020 8446 9898
www.stompmanagement.com

**EDUCATION IN STAGE & THEATRE ARTS
(E.S.T.A.)** T 020 8741 2843
16 British Grove, Chiswick, London W4 2NL
F 020 8746 3219
E esta@clara.co.uk
W www.estatheatreschool.com

**ELITE ACADEMY OF
PERFORMING ARTS** T 07976 971178
City Studios, 4 Sandford Street
Lichfield, Staffs WS13 6QA
E elitedancing@hotmail.com

ENGLISH, Doreen '95 T/F 01243 825968
Contact: Gerry Kinner
4 Selsey Avenue, Aldwick
Bognor Regis, West Sussex PO21 2QZ

**EUROKIDS CASTING &
MODEL AGENCY** T 01925 761088
The Warehouse Studios, Glaziers Lane
Culcheth, Warrington, Cheshire WA3 4AQ
F 01925 767563
E castings@eka-agency.com
W www.eka-agency.com

**EXPRESSIONS CASTING
AGENCY** T 01623 424334
3 Newgate Lane, Mansfield
Nottingham NG18 2LB
F 01623 647337
E expressions-uk@btconnect.com
W www.expressionsperformingarts.co.uk

FBI AGENCY T 07050 222747
PO Box 250, Leeds LS1 2AZ
T 07515 567309
E casting@fbi-agency.co.uk
W www.fbi-agency.co.uk

**FEA MANAGEMENT
(FERRIS ENTERTAINMENT)** T 0845 4724725
London. Belfast. Cardiff
Number 8, 132 Charing Cross Road
London WC2H 0LA
E info@ferrisentertainment.com
W www.ferrisentertainment.com

FEATHERSTONE, Rosie AGENCY T 07960 351328
21 Kershaw Close, Hornchurch
Essex RM11 1SW
E rosemaryfeatherstone@hotmail.co.uk

FILM CAST CORNWALL & SW T 01326 311419
T 07811 253756
E enquiries@filmcastcornwall.co.uk
W www.filmcastcornwall.co.uk

FIORENTINI, Anna AGENCY T 020 7682 3677
Islington Business Design Centre, Unit 101
52 Upper Street, London N1 0QH
T 07904 962779
E rhiannon@annafiorentini.com
W www.annafiorentini.com

**FOOTSTEPS THEATRE SCHOOL
CASTING AGENCY** T 07584 995309
1st Floor, Morrisons Enterprise 5, 5 Lane Ends
Bradford BD10 8EW
E gwestman500@btinternet.com

**GENESIS THEATRE SCHOOL
& AGENCY** T 01536 460928
88 Hempland Close, Great Oakley
Corby, Northants NN18 8LT
E info@saracharles.com

GLOBAL7 T/F 020 7281 7679
PO Box 56232, London N4 4XP
T 07956 956652
E global7castings@gmail.com
W www.global7casting.com

**GLYNNE, Frances THEATRE STUDENTS
& MANAGEMENT** T 07950 918355
Flat 9, Elmwood, 6 The Avenue
Hatch End, Middlesex HA5 4EP
E franandmo@gmail.com

GO FOR IT CHILDREN'S AGENCY T 020 8943 1120
Children & Teenagers
Green Gables, 47 North Lane
Teddington, Middlesex TW11 0HU
T 07956 646412
E agency@goforitcentre.com
W www.goforitcentre.com

GOBSTOPPERS MANAGEMENT T 01442 269543
37 St Nicholas Mount
Hemel Hempstead, Herts HP1 2BB
T 07961 372319
E chrisgobstoppers@btinternet.com

GOLDMANS MANAGEMENT T 01323 472391
PO Box 23, Shipbourne Road
Tonbridge, Kent TN11 9NY
E casting@goldmansmanagement.co.uk
W www.goldmansmanagement.co.uk

GP ASSOCIATES T 020 8886 2263
4 Gallus Close, Winchmore Hill, London N21 1JR
F 020 8882 9189
E info@gpassociates.co.uk
W www.greasepaintanonymous.co.uk

**HARLEQUIN STUDIOS
AGENCY FOR CHILDREN** T 01273 581742
122A Phyllis Avenue, Peacehaven
East Sussex BN10 7RQ

HARRIS AGENCY LTD T 01923 211644
71 The Avenue, Watford, Herts WD17 4NU
F 01923 211666
E theharrisagency@btconnect.com

HOBSONS KIDS T 020 8995 3628
62 Chiswick High Road, London W4 1SY
F 020 8996 5350
E gaynor@hobsons-international.com
W www.hobsons-international.com

HOXTON STREET MANAGEMENT T 020 7503 5131
Hoxton Hall, 130 Hoxton Street
London N1 6SH
T 07411 479077
E lucy@hoxtonstreetmanagement.co.uk
W www.hoxtonstreetmanagement.co.uk

HSD KIDS AGENCY T 01268 561572
10 Iona Way, Wickford SS12 9QX
T 07858 535860
E hsd.kidsagency@googlemail.com
W www.hsdkidsagency.co.uk

INTER-CITY KIDS T/F 01942 321969
27 Wigan Lane, Wigan
Greater Manchester WN1 1XR
E intercitycasting@btconnect.com

JABBERWOCKY AGENCY T 01580 714306
Children & Teenagers
Glassenbury Hill Farm, Glassenbury Road
Cranbrook, Kent TN17 2QF
F 01580 714346
E info@jabberwockyagency.com
W www.yt93.co.uk

JERMIN, Mark MANAGEMENT T 01792 458855
8 Heathfield, Swansea SA1 6EJ
F 01792 458844
E info@markjermin.co.uk
W www.markjermin.co.uk

JIGSAW ARTS MANAGEMENT T 020 8447 4530
*Representing Children & Young People from Jigsaw
Performing Arts Schools*
64-66 High Street, Barnet, Herts EN5 5SJ
E admin@jigsaw-arts.co.uk
W www.jigsaw-arts.co.uk

**JOHNSTON & MATHERS
ASSOCIATES LTD** T/F 020 8449 4968
PO Box 3167, Barnet
Herts EN5 2WA
E johnstonmathers@aol.com
W www.johnstonandmathers.com

KELLY MANAGEMENT T 020 7402 0444
Studio 13, 22 Brook Mews North
London W2 3BW
E youth@kelly-management.com
W www.kelly-management.com

**KIDS AT JULIE FOX
ASSOCIATES** T 01628 771084
E agent@thekidsatjuliefoxassociates.co.uk
W www.thekidsatjuliefoxassociates.co.uk

KIDS LONDON T 020 7924 9595
67 Dulwich Road, London SE24 0NJ
F 020 8671 5910
E info@kidslondonltd.com
W www.kidslondonltd.com

KIDS PLUS T 01634 263344
Malcolm House, Malcolm Primary School
Malcolm Road, Penge, London SE20 8RH
T 07799 791586
E office@kidsplusagency.co.uk
W www.kidsplusagency.co.uk

KIDZ LTD T 0871 2180884
348 Moorside Road, Swinton, Manchester M27 9PW
F 0871 2180843
E info@kidzltd.com
W www.kidzltd.com

**KIDZ ON THE HILL
PERFORMING ARTS SCHOOL**   T 07881 553480
PO Box 56951, Muswell Hill
London N10 2AS
E kidzonthehill@gmail.com
W www.kidzonthehill.co.uk

**KRACKERS KIDS
THEATRICAL AGENCY**   T/F 01708 502046
6-7 Electric Parade, Seven Kings Road
Ilford, Essex IG3 8BY
E krackerskids@hotmail.com
W www.krackerskids.co.uk

KYT AGENCY   T/F 01227 730177
Mulberry Croft, Mulberry Hill, Chilham CT4 8AJ
T 07967 580213
E richard@kyt.org.uk
W www.kentyouththeatre.co.uk

LAMONT CASTING AGENCY   T 07736 387543
2 Harewood Avenue, Ainsdale
Merseyside PR8 2PH
E diane@lamontcasting.co.uk
W www.lamontcasting.co.uk

**LESLIE, Sasha
MANAGEMENT**   T/F 020 8969 3249
In association with Allsorts Drama for Children
34 Crediton Road, London NW10 3DU
E sasha@allsortsdrama.com

LINTON MANAGEMENT   T 0161 761 2020
3 The Rock, Bury BL9 0JP
F 0161 761 1999
E carol@linton.tv

**LITTLE ADULTS ACADEMY & MODELLING
AGENCY LTD**   T 020 3130 0798
44 Broadway, Stratford, London E15 1XH
E info@littleadults.demon.co.uk
W www.littleadultsagency.co.uk

LIVE & LOUD AGENCY   T 0141 222 2333
Contact: Maureen Cairns, Allan Jones
2nd Floor, 34 Argyle Arcade Chambers
Buchanan Street, Glasgow G2 8BD
E info@liveandloudagency.com

MARMALADE MANAGEMENT   T 07595 177154
21 Beechtree Avenue, Marlow
Buckinghamshire SL7 3NH
E info@marmalademanagement.co.uk
W www.marmalademanagement.co.uk

**McDONAGH, Melanie MANAGEMENT (ACADEMY
OF PERFORMING ARTS
& CASTING AGENCY)**   T 01254 392560
14 Apple Tree Way
Oswaldtwistle
Accrington, Lancashire BB5 0FB
T 07909 831409
E mcdonaghmgt@aol.com
W www.mcdonaghmanagement.co.uk

**MELODY'S THEATRICAL
AGENCY**   T 07583 295898
Melody House, Gillotts Corner
Henley-on-Thames
Oxon RG9 1QU
F 01491 411533
E info@melodysagency.co.uk
W www.jgdance.co.uk

MONDI ASSOCIATES LTD   T 07817 133349
Contact: Michelle Sykes
Unit 3 O, Cooper House
2 Michael Road
London SW6 2AD
E info@mondiassociates.com
W www.mondiassociates.com

MOOSE MANAGEMENT   T 07582 402711
20 Streatham Common South
London SW16 3BU
T 07956 821525
E moosemanagement@rocketmail.com

NFD - THE FILM & TV AGENCY   T/F 01977 681949
PO Box 76, Leeds LS25 9AG
E info@film-tv-agency.com
W www.film-tv-agency.com

**O'FARRELL STAGE &
THEATRE SCHOOL**   T 01268 414409
Babies, Children, Teenagers & Young Adults
36 Shirley Street, Canning Town
London E16 1HU
T 07956 941497
E linda@ofarrells.wanadoo.co.uk

ORR MANAGEMENT AGENCY   T 01204 579842
Children, Teenagers & Adults
1st Floor, 147-149 Market Street
Farnworth, Greater Manchester BL4 8EX
T 07773 227784
E barbara@orrmanagement.co.uk
W www.orrmanagement.co.uk

PALMER, Jackie AGENCY   T 01494 520978
30 Daws Hill Lane, High Wycombe
Bucks HP11 1PW
F 01494 510479
E jackie.palmer@btinternet.com
W www.jackiepalmeragency.co.uk

P'ARTS AGENCY   T 07889 072623
In association with MTPAS
High Street, Stony Stratford
Milton Keynes MK11 1AE
E parts@mtpas.co.uk
W www.parts-agency.co.uk

**PC THEATRICAL, MODEL &
CASTING AGENCY**   T 020 8381 2229
10 Strathmore Gardens, Edgware
Middlesex HA8 5HJ
F 020 8933 3418
E twinagy@aol.com
W www.twinagency.com

PENS PEOPLE   T 01708 457443
75 Victor Walk, Hornchurch
Essex RM12 4XQ
E penny@penspeople.co.uk
W www.penspeople.co.uk

PERFORMERS AGENCY LTD   T 01375 665716
Southend Road, Corringham
Essex SS17 8JT
F 01375 672353
E office@performersagency.biz
W www.performersagency.biz

PHA YOUTH   T 0161 273 4444
Tanzaro House, Ardwick Green North
Manchester M12 6FZ
F 0161 273 4567
E youth@pha-agency.co.uk
W www.pha-agency.co.uk

**PLATFORM TALENT
MANAGEMENT LTD**   T 01276 23256
16 Shalbourne Rise
Camberley
Surrey GU15 2EJ
E casting@kidsagency.tv
W www.kidsagency.tv

**POLLYANNA
MANAGEMENT LTD**   T/F 020 8530 6722
1 Knighten Street, Wapping
London E1W 1PH
E a_sean_toby_duncan@hotmail.com
W www.pollyannatrainingtheatre.org

**POWER MODEL MANAGEMENT
CASTING AGENCY**   T 01603 777190
PO Box 1198, Salhouse
Norwich NR13 6WD
E info@powermodel.co.uk
W www.powermodel.co.uk

PWASSOCIATES   T 01296 733258
7 Catherine Cottages, Calvert Road
Middle Claydon, Bucks MK18 2HA
E emma@pwacademy.com
W www.pwacademy.com

**QUIRKY KIDZ CREATIVE
MANAGEMENT**   T 01494 448107
Custodia House, Queensmead Road
Loudwater, High Wycombe
Buckinghamshire HP10 9XA
E hello@quirkykidz.co.uk
W www.quirkykidz.co.uk

RAMA YOUNG ACTORS   T 07595 023487
Huntingdon House, 278-290 Huntingdon Street
Nottingham NG1 3LY
F 0115 948 3696
E martin@rama-global.co.uk
W www.ramayoungactors.co.uk

RASCALS MODEL AGENCY   T 020 8504 1111
13 Jubilee Parade, Snakes Lane East
Woodford Green, Essex IG8 7QG
F 020 8559 1035
E kids@rascals.co.uk
W www.rascals.co.uk

RAVENSCOURT MANAGEMENT
See CORONA MANAGEMENT

RDDC MANAGEMENT AGENCY   T 01706 211161
52 Bridleway, Waterfoot
Rossendale, Lancashire BB4 9DS
T 07811 239780
E info@rddc.co.uk
W www.rddc.co.uk

**REBEL SCHOOL OF THEATRE ARTS
& CASTING AGENCY LTD**   T 07808 803637
Based in Leeds & Huddersfield
PO Box 169, Huddersfield HD8 1BE
E sue@rebelschool.co.uk
W www.rebelschool.co.uk

**REDROOFS THEATRE
SCHOOL AGENCY**   T 01628 674092
26 Bath Road, Maidenhead
Berks SL6 4JT
T 01628 822982 (Holiday Times)
E sam@redroofs.co.uk
W www.redroofs.co.uk

REFLECTIONS AGENCY   T/F 01322 410003
34 Knowle Avenue, Bexleyheath
Kent DA7 5LX
T 07958 617976
E c.johnson717@ntlworld.com
W www.riverside-reflections.webs.com

RHODES AGENCY   T 01708 747013
5 Dymoke Road, Hornchurch, Essex RM11 1AA
F 01708 730431
E rhodesarts@hotmail.com

RIDGEWAY MANAGEMENT   T 01992 633775
Office: 106 Hawkshead Road
Potters Bar, Hertfordshire EN6 1NG
E info@ridgewaystudios.co.uk
W www.ridgewaystudios.co.uk

**RISING STARS PERFORMANCE
AGENCY**   T 07709 429354
6 Gibsons Place, High Street
Eynsford, Kent DA4 0AA
T 07958 617976
E risingstars_agency@yahoo.co.uk

RISING STARS AGENCY   T 07947 345434
16 Llwyn Yr Eos Grove, Penyard
Merthyr Tydfil, Mid Glamorgan, Wales CF47 0GD
T 07894 164104
E risingstarsagency@yahoo.co.uk
W www.risingstarsagency.co.uk

ROSS, David ACTING LTD   T 07957 862317
8 Farrier Close, Sale
Cheshire M33 2ZL
E info@davidrossacting.com
W www.davidrossacting.com

SCALA KIDS CASTING   T 0113 250 6823
42 Rufford Avenue
Yeadon, Leeds LS19 7QR
F 0113 250 8806
E office@scalakids.com
W www.scalakids.com

SCALLYWAGS AGENCY LTD   T 020 7739 8820
12-18 Hoxton Street, London N1 6NG
F 020 7739 5753
E info@scallywags.co.uk
W www.scallywags.co.uk

SCHOOL CASTING   T 01325 463383
Liddiard Theatre, Polam Hall, Grange Road
Darlington, Durham DL1 5PA
F 01325 383539
E information@polamhall.com
W www.polamhall.com

SCREAM MANAGEMENT   T 0161 850 1996
The Pie Factory, 101 Broadway
Media City, Manchester M50 2EQ
T 0161 850 1994
E info@screammanagement.com
W www.screammanagement.com

SELECT MANAGEMENT   T 07956 131494
PO Box 748, London NW4 1TT
F 020 8203 2007
E mail@selectmanagement.info
W www.selectmanagement.info

SEQUINS CASTING AGENCY   T 020 8360 6601
8 Summerhill Grove, Bush Hill Park
Enfield EN1 2HY
E sequinscastingagency@gmail.com

SEVEN CASTING AGENCY   T 0161 850 1057
Manchester Office: 4th Floor
59 Piccadilly, Manchester M1 2AQ
T 07801 942178
E guy@7casting.co.uk
W www.7casting.co.uk

Mark Jermin
★★★ Management

8 Heathfield, Swansea SA1 6EJ
Phone: 01792 458855
Fax: 01792 458844
Email: info@markjermin.co.uk
www.markjermin.co.uk

★ Children and young adults from all over the UK.

★ Audition workshops and classes in London, Manchester, Bristol and Wales.

★ Children with open performance licences, guaranteed to be licensed for any production and at very short notice.

SEVEN CASTING AGENCY   T 01785 212266
Staffordshire Office: Suite 3
Tudor House, 9 Eastgate Street, Stafford ST16 2NQ
T 07801 942178
E guy@7casting.co.uk
W www.7casting.co.uk

SHINE MANAGEMENT   T 07880 721689
Flat 10, Valentine House, Church Road
Guildford, Surrey GU1 4NG
E enquiries@shinemanagement.net
W www.shinemanagement.net

SINGER, Sandra ASSOCIATES   T 01702 331616
21 Cotswold Road
Westcliff-on-Sea, Essex SS0 8AA
E sandrasingeruk@aol.com
W www.sandrasinger.com

SMARTYPANTS AGENCY   T 01277 633772
San-Marie Studios, Southend Road
Billericay CM11 2PZ
F 01277 633998
E office@smartypantsagency.co.uk
W www.smartypantsagency.co.uk

SMITH, Elisabeth LTD   T 0845 8721331
8 Dawes Lane, Sarratt
Rickmansworth, Herts WD3 6BB
E models@elisabethsmith.co.uk
W www.elisabethsmith.co.uk

SPEAKE, Barbara AGENCY   T 020 8743 6096
East Acton Lane, London W3 7EG
E speakekids2@aol.com
W www.barbaraspeake.com

SRA AGENCY   T 01932 863194
Lockhart Road, Cobham
Surrey KT11 2AX
E agency@susanrobertsacademy.co.uk

**STAGE 84 YORKSHIRE SCHOOL
OF PERFORMING ARTS**   T 01274 569197
Old Bell Chapel, Town Lane
Idle, Bradford
West Yorks BD10 8PR
T 07785 244984
E valeriejackson@stage84.com

STAGE A MANAGEMENT LTD   T 07758 052325
*Represents Centre Stage Academy Theatre School
Students*
6 Oak Tree Court, Meadway
Midhurst, West Sussex GU29 9SE
T 07770 744282
E stageamanagement@gmail.com
W www.csa-theatreschool.co.uk

STAGE KIDS AGENCY   T 01707 328359
Children, Teenagers & Adults
1 Greenfield, Welwyn Garden City
Herts AL8 7HW
E stagekds@aol.com
W www.stagekids.co.uk

**STAGECOACH AGENCY
UK & IRELAND**   T 0845 4082468
PO Box 127, Ross-on-Wye HR9 6WZ
F 0845 4082464
E tarquin@stagecoachagency.co.uk
W www.stagecoachagency.co.uk

**STAGEWORKS PERFORMING
ARTS SCHOOL**   T 07956 176166
The Stablehouse Barn
Remenham Hill
Henley on Thames, Oxon RG9 3HN
E emma_taylor@sky.com
W www.stageworks.org.uk

**STARDOM CASTING AGENCY
& THEATRE SCHOOL**   T/F 01274 818051
16 Pinebury Drive, Queensbury
Bradford BD13 2TA
T 07740 091019
E liz.stardom@btinternet.com

STARMAKER   T 0118 988 7959
17 Kendal Avenue, Shinfield
Reading, Berks RG2 9AR
F 0118 988 8708
E dave@starmakeruk.org
W www.starmakeruk.org

STARSTRUCK MANAGEMENT   T 01522 887894
85 Hewson Road, Lincoln
Lincolnshire LN1 1RZ
E starstruckacademy@hotmail.com

STARSTRUCK TALENT LTD   T 07762 887716
In conjunction with Starstruck Theatre School
22 Knowl Road, Shaw
Nr Oldham, Lancashire OL2 8QQ
E lisa@starstrucktalent.co.uk
W www.starstrucktalent.co.uk

STEP ON STAGE MANAGEMENT   T 07973 900196
5 Poulett Gardens, Twickenham
Middlesex TW1 4QS
E info@steponstageacademy.co.uk
W www.steponstagemanagement.co.uk

STOMP! MANAGEMENT   T 020 8446 9898
c/o Suite 15, Fiboard House
5 Oakleigh Gardens
London N20 9AB
E stompmanagement@aol.com
W www.stompmanagement.com

SWINDON YOUNG ACTORS   T 07588 688681
Contact: Julia Dickinson, Mark Flitton
44 Redcliffe Street, Swindon
Wiltshire SN2 2BZ
T 07825 565161
E sya@gmx.co.uk
W www.swindonyoungactors.com

**TAKE2 CASTING AGENCY &
TALENT MANAGEMENT**   T 00 353 87 2563403
28 Beech Park Road
Foxrock
Dublin 18, Ireland
E pamela@take2.ie
W www.take2.ie

**TALENTED KIDS PERFORMING ARTS
SCHOOL & AGENCY**   T/F 00 353 45 485464
23 Burrow Manor, Calverstown
Kilcullen, Co. Kildare, Ireland
T 00 353 87 2480348
E talentedkids@hotmail.com
W www.talentedkidsireland.com

TANWOOD THEATRICAL AGENCY T 07775 991700
Liberatus Studios, Isis Estate
Stratton Road, Swindon SN1 8PJ
E tanwood@tiscali.co.uk
W www.tanwood.co.uk

TELEVISION WORKSHOP THE   T 0115 845 0764
Nottingham Group
30 Main Street, Calverton
Notts NG14 6FQ
E ian@thetelevisionworkshop.co.uk

**THAMES VALLEY
THEATRICAL AGENCY**   T 07956 256189
PO Box 4794, Henley-on-Thames
Oxon RG9 9FT
T/F 01491 636385
E donna@childactors.tv

THIS IS YOUTH   T 07956 838843
Teenagers & Young Adults
194B Addington Road
Selsdon
Croydon CR2 8LD
E hello@thisisyouth.com
W www.thisisyouth.com

TICKLEDOM AGENCY   T 020 8341 7044
31 Rectory Gardens, London N8 7PJ
T 07947 139414
E agency@tickledomtheatreschool.com
W www.tickledomtheatreschool.com

TK MANAGEMENT   T 07985 510038
Spires Meade, 4 Bridleways
Wendover, Bucks HP22 6DN
F 01296 623696
E tkpamanagement@aol.com

TOMORROW'S TALENT AGENCY   T 01245 200555
Contact: By e-mail only
Based in Chelmsford, Essex
E agents@tomorrowstalent.co.uk
W www.tomorrowstalent.co.uk

TOP TALENT AGENCY LTD   T 01727 855903
Representing Child Actors & Models from Babies to Teenagers
c/o Top Hat Stage & Screen School
PO Box 860
St Albans, Herts AL1 9BR
F 01727 812666
E admin@toptalentagency.co.uk
W www.toptalentagency.co.uk

TRULY SCRUMPTIOUS LTD   T 020 8888 4204
66 Bidwell Gardens
London N11 2AU
F 020 8888 4584
E bookings@trulyscrumptious.co.uk
W www.trulyscrumptious.co.uk

TUESDAYS CHILD   T/F 01625 501765
Children, Teenagers & Adults
Oakfield House
Springwood Way
Macclesfield SK10 2XA
E info@tuesdayschildagency.co.uk
W www.tuesdayschildagency.co.uk

**TURNSTONE CASTING &
ENTERTAINMENT** T 0845 5576658
Hilton Hall, Hilton Lane
Essington WV11 2BQ
T 07866 211647
E mark_turner85@hotmail.com

TWINS
See PC THEATRICAL, MODEL & CASTING AGENCY

URBAN ANGELS T 0845 8387773
PO Box 45453, London SE26 6UZ
F 0845 8387774
E south@urbanangelsagency.com

URBAN ANGELS NORTH T 0845 5191990
Contact: Alysia Lewis
F 0845 8387774
E north@urbanangelsagency.com
W www.urbanangelsagency.com

**VALLÉ THEATRICAL
AGENCY THE** T 01992 622861
The Vallé Academy Studios
Wilton House
Delamare Road
Cheshunt, Herts EN8 9SG
F 01992 622868
E agency@valleacademy.co.uk
W www.valleacademy.co.uk

W-A-P-A AGENCY T 01422 351958
6-8 Akroyd Place, Halifax
West Yorkshire HX1 1YH
F 01422 360958
E enquiries@w-a-p-a.co.uk
W www.w-a-p-a.co.uk

**WILDCATS KIDS
MANAGEMENT** T 07725 915333
PO Box 1198, Stamford
Lincolnshire PE2 2JE
E admin@wildcats-uk.com
W www.wildcatstheatreschool.co.uk

WILLIAMSON & HOLMES T 020 7240 0407
51 St Martin's Lane
London WC2N 4EA
E info@williamsonandholmes.co.uk

WINGS AGENCY T 01483 428998
The Chestnut Suite
Guardian House
Borough
Godalming, Surrey GU7 2AE
F 01483 424522
E admin@wingsagency.co.uk
W www.angelstheatreschool.co.uk

WYSE AGENCY T 01223 832288
Hill House, 1 Hill Farm Road
Whittlesford, Cambs CB22 4NB
E frances.wyse@btinternet.com

**YAT MANAGEMENT
(Young Actors Theatre)** T 020 7278 2101
70-72 Barnsbury Road, London N1 0ES
F 020 7833 9467
E agent@yati.org.uk
W www.yati.org.uk

YOUNG, Sylvia AGENCY T 020 7723 0037
Sylvia Young Theatre School
1 Nutford Place
London W1H 5YZ
T 07779 145732
E info@sylviayoungagency.com

**YOUNG ACTORS COMPANY
LTD THE** T 01223 416474
3 Marshall Road
Cambridge CB1 7TY
T 07836 736352
E info@theyoungactorscompany.com
W www.theyoungactorscompany.com

**YOUNGBLOOD THEATRE
COMPANY** T 020 7240 5299
c/o The BWH Agency Ltd
117 Shaftesbury Avenue
London WC2H 8AD
F 020 7240 2287
E info@thebwhagency.co.uk
W www.thebwhagency.co.uk

**YOUNGSTARS THEATRE
SCHOOL & AGENCY** T 07966 176756
Contact: Coralyn Canfor-Dumas. 4-18 yrs
4 Haydon Dell, Bushey
Herts WD23 1DD
E youngstarsagency@gmail.com

**ZADEK NOWELL
MANAGEMENT** T 020 8883 5805
398 Long Lane
London N2 8JX
E zadeknowell@gmail.com
W www.zadeknowell.com

ACORN ENTERTAINMENTS LTD T 01285 644622
PO Box 64, Cirencester
Glos GL7 5YD
F 01285 642291
E info@acorents.co.uk
W www.acorents.co.uk

**ARTIST PROMOTION
MANAGEMENT** T 020 7224 1992
5th Floor, Langham House
308 Regent Street, London W1B 3AT
F 020 7224 0111
E mail@harveygoldsmith.com
W www.harveygoldsmith.com

ASKONAS HOLT LTD T 020 7400 1700
Classical Music
Lincoln House, 300 High Holborn
London WC1V 7JH
F 020 7400 1799
E info@askonasholt.co.uk
W www.askonasholt.co.uk

AVALON PROMOTIONS LTD T 020 7598 7333
4A Exmoor Street, London W10 6BD
F 020 7598 7300
E enquiries@avalonuk.com
W www.avalonuk.com

**BLOCK, Derek
ARTISTES AGENCY** T 020 7724 2101
70-76 Bell Street
Marylebone, London NW1 6SP
F 020 7724 2102
E dbcp@derekblock.co.uk

FLYING MUSIC T 020 7221 7799
FM House, 110 Clarendon Road
London W11 2HR
F 020 7221 5016
E info@flyingmusic.co.uk
W www.flyingmusic.com

GUBBAY, Raymond LTD T 020 7025 3750
Dickens House, 15 Tooks Court, London EC4A 1LB
F 020 7025 3751
E info@raymondgubbay.co.uk
W www.raymondgubbay.co.uk

HOBBS, Liz GROUP LTD T 0870 0702702
65 London Road, Newark
Nottinghamshire NG24 1RZ
F 01636 703343
E info@lizhobbsgroup.com
W www.lizhobbsgroup.com

HOCHHAUSER, Victor T 020 7794 0987
4 Oak Hill Way, London NW3 7LR
F 020 7431 2531
E admin@victorhochhauser.co.uk
W www.victorhochhauser.co.uk

IMG ARTS & ENTERTAINMENT T 020 8233 5300
McCormack House, Burlington Lane
London W4 2TH
F 020 8233 5301
E concerts@imgworld.com
W www.imgworld.com

**McINTYRE, Phil
ENTERTAINMENT** T 020 7291 9000
85 Newman Street, London W1T 3EU
E info@mcintyre-ents.com
W www.mcintyre-ents.com

MEADOW, Jeremy LTD T 020 7436 2244
73 Great Titchfield Street, London W1W 6RD
F 0870 7627882
E info@jeremymeadow.com
W www.jeremymeadow.com

RBM COMEDY T 020 7630 7733
3rd Floor, 168 Victoria Street, London SW1E 5LB
F 020 7630 6549
E info@rbmcomedy.com
W www.rbmcomedy.com

ACCELERATE LTD T 07782 199181
374 Ley Street, Ilford IG1 4AE
T 07956 104086
E info@accelerate-productions.co.uk
W www.accelerate-productions.co.uk

BODYWORK AGENCY T 07792 851972
25-29 Glisson Road
Cambridge CB1 2HA
F 01223 568231
E agency@bodyworkds.co.uk

CREATIVE KIDZ & CO T 07958 377595
Incorporating NeighbourHood Productions
9 Weavers Terrace
Fulham
London SW6 1QE
T 07908 144802
E info@creativekidzandco.co.uk

DANCERS T 020 7636 1473
1 Charlotte Street, London W1T 1RD
F 020 7636 0328
E info@features.co.uk
W www.features.co.uk

DANCERS@BBA T 020 7395 1405
1st Floor, 23 Tavistock Street
Covent Garden
London WC2E 7NX
F 020 7379 5560
E dancers@buchanan-associates.co.uk
W www.dancersatbba.co.uk

**DANCERS INC
INTERNATIONAL COLLECTIVE** T 020 7557 6650
9-13 Grape Street
Covent Garden
London WC2H 8ED
F 020 7557 6656
E miranda@internationalcollective.com
W www.dancersinc.co.uk

ELLITE MANAGEMENT T 0845 6525361
'The Dancer'
8 Peterson Road
Wakefield WF1 4EB
T 07957 631510
E enquiries@ellitemanagement.co.uk
W www.elliteproductions.co.uk

Ellite **management**

Theatre Dance TV Film Commercials Cruises
Representing
Dancers Singers Choreographers
Full Production Team available for Corporate Events

www.elliteproductions.co.uk
enquiries@ellitemanagement.co.uk

T: 0845 652 5361
M: 07957 631510

EVENT MODEL MANAGEMENT T 07581 223738
Dancers. Models
Studio 230
405 Kings Road
Chelsea, London SW10 0BB
E info@eventmodel.co.uk
W www.eventmodelmanagement.co.uk

FEATURES T 020 7637 1487
1 Charlotte Street
London W1T 1RD
F 020 7636 1657
E info@features.co.uk
W www.features.co.uk

GIELGUD DANCERS T 01444 447020
The Old Cinema
1st Floor
59-61 The Broadway
Haywards Heath
West Sussex RH16 3AS
F 01444 447030
E info@gielgudmanagement.co.uk
W www.gielgudmanagement.co.uk

HEADNOD TALENT AGENCY T/F 020 7502 9478
63 Redchurch Street, London E2 7DJ
E info@headnodagency.com
W www.headnodagency.com

JK DANCE PRODUCTIONS T 0161 432 5222
South Manchester Film & Television Studios
Battersea Road, Stockport SK4 3EA
E info@jkdance.co.uk
W www.jkdance.co.uk

K TALENT T 020 7430 0882
187 Drury Lane, Covent Garden
London WC2B 5QD
E mail@ktalent.co.uk
W www.ktalent.co.uk

**KEW PERSONAL
MANAGEMENT** T 020 8871 3697
PO Box 679, RH1 9BT
E info@kewpersonalmanagement.com
W www.kewpersonalmanagement.com

KMC AGENCIES T 0845 0340772
Garden Studios
11-15 Betterton Street
London WC2H 9BP
E london@kmcagencies.co.uk
W www.kmcagencies.co.uk

KMC AGENCIES T 0161 237 3009
PO Box 122, 48 Great Ancoats Street
Manchester M4 5AB
F 0161 237 9812
E casting@kmcagencies.co.uk
W www.kmcagencies.co.uk

LONGRUN ARTISTES T 020 8316 6662
Contact: Gina Long
Marylebone Dance Studios, 12 Lisson Grove
London NW1 6TS
F 0871 5227926
E gina@longrunartistes.co.uk
W www.longrunartistes.co.uk

Dance Agents

Why do I need a dance agent?

As with any other agent, a dance agent will submit their clients for jobs, negotiate contracts, handle paperwork and offer advice. In return for these services they will charge commission ranging from 10-15%. The agents listed in this section specialise in representing and promoting dancers. They will possess the relevant contacts in the industry that you need to get auditions and jobs.

How should I use these listings?

If you are a dancer getting started in the industry, looking to change your existing agent, or wishing to take on an additional agent that represents you for dance alongside your main acting agent, the following listings will supply you with up-to-date contact details for dance agencies. Every company listed is done so by written request to us. Please see the main 'Agents and Personal Managers' advice section for further guidance on choosing and approaching agents.

Should I pay an agent to join their books? Or sign a contract?

Equity (the actors' trade union) does not recommend that artists pay an agent to join their client list. Before signing a contract, you should be very clear about the terms and commitments involved. For advice on both of these issues, or if you experience any problems with a current agent, we recommend that you contact Equity www.equity.org.uk. They also produce the booklet *You and your Agent* which is free to all Equity members and available from their website's members' area.

What is Spotlight Dancers?

Spotlight Dancers is a specialist casting directory published annually by Spotlight. Members receive a page in the directory containing a headshot and body shot, agency contact details and selected credits as well as an online CV on the Spotlight website. These are used by dance employers throughout the UK to locate dancers and send out casting or audition information. Dancers who attend CDET (Council for Dance Education and Training) accredited schools receive a discount when applying in their graduating year. Dancers wishing to promote themselves for job opportunities in commercial theatre, musicals, opera, film, television, live music and video, corporate events and many other areas of the industry should consider joining: for more information visit www.spotlight.com/artists/dancers

Should I join Spotlight's Actors/ Actresses directory or the Dancers directory?

Depending on your skills, training and experience, you may be eligible for both directories if you are interested in promoting yourself both as an actor and as a dancer. If you join both, you would receive an entry into each directory and two separate online CVs. You would also qualify for a 25% discount off the Dancers membership fee. If you only want to join one or the other, then you will need to consider which area of the industry you want to focus on in your career. Musical theatre experience can qualify you for either directory, depending on whether your training/roles involved mainly dancing or acting. This is something you will need to think about, and something you should discuss with your agent if you sign with one.

Where can I find more information?

Please refer to our dance agent case study in this section and the information and advice articles in the 'Dance Companies' listings for further information about the dance industry.

Dance Agents

CASE STUDY

K Talent was formed in 2004 and was once predominantly an agency for musical theatre performers. Over the past 7 years it has expanded and developed to incorporate all fields of performance.

As with all performers, upon graduation you will have been at the top of your game, but when you enter into the big wide world you will find yourself straight back at the bottom again. Remember that the hard work does not stop as soon as you graduate: this is where it begins. Only a small percentage of graduates get a lucky break straight from college; for the rest there will be a lot of set-backs and a positive mindset is essential to get you through each round of rejection without taking it personally. Finding success at the end of that struggle makes the reward even more enjoyable.

We expect our clients to have an understanding of the industry, particularly in the field they wish to enter. For example, dancers should be aware of current shows and know which would suit them best. It is all very well to be prepared to take part in any show, but you need to be realistic: know your abilities and limits and decide what is right for you and your style. Common sense and a positive attitude are essential in this industry. Dancers also need to be independent and investigate companies and productions so that they can be fully prepared for each casting they attend.

When K Talent takes on new artists we require you to have Spotlight membership and professional photographs taken by a photographer who specialises in dancers' headshots. You would be surprised at the number of people who send in a random holiday snap – this is not a professional headshot! A good 10 x 8 headshot, and not a photocopied piece of paper, is required. Headshots can be done on a budget so look for special offers; you do not need to spend a fortune. Shop around, see whose work you like and make enquiries. What needs to be at the forefront of every performer's mind is that they are a business and like all businesses, investment is crucial. If you do not invest in yourself and promote yourself looking your very best, why should anybody else invest in you?

It is good to have knowledge about self-employment. Filling in tax returns is not something

your agent will do for you, so research all the things a self-employed professional needs to have in place and be knowledgeable about your finances.

Finally, be prepared for interviews. We interview all potential clients, looking for someone who has taken the time and effort to dress appropriately and bringing with them all the information the agent has requested. You need to be articulate and confident, without being arrogant. Remember to ask questions and if it helps to write them down on a pad and take this with you, do so: you don't want to leave without having asked something that is important to you.

What needs to be at the forefront of every performer's mind is that they are a business and like all businesses, investment is crucial.

At K Talent we are fortunate that all of our agents come from an industry background. Having been auditionees and graduates ourselves we can offer first-hand experience of real-life struggles and achievements. We are able to share the excitement of a job offer and feel the pain when castings do not go to plan, and provide a much-needed shoulder to cry on at times! We are there to nurture, guide and advise our artists. It can be an intense relationship and you need to select an agency which will best represent you as an individual. Don't just write to 100 random agents: do your background research on each agency and find out what it is that makes you want to be represented by them. Then write to the most relevant ones, telling them why you would like to be looked after by them over any other agent.

K Talent's aim is to help our clients achieve their goals and we follow your career path every step of the way. Sometimes your career will take an unexpected tangent, but that can be very exciting. Our final piece of advice is to never close the door on any opportunity, as you never know what might happen!

Please visit www.ktalent.co.uk for further information.

MARLOWES DANCERS &
MUSICAL THEATRE AGENCY   T 020 7193 4484
HMS President
Victoria Embankment
Blackfriars, London EC4Y 0HJ
E mitch@marlowes.eu
W www.marlowes.eu

MITCHELL MAAS McLENNAN   T 020 8301 8745
MPA Offices
29 Thomas Street
Woolwich
London SE18 6HU
T 07540 995802
E agency@mmm2000.co.uk
W www.mmm2000.co.uk

PINEAPPLE AGENCY   T 020 7241 6601
Montgomery House
159-161 Balls Pond Road
Islington, London N1 4BG
F 020 7241 3006
E pineapple.agency@btconnect.com
W www.pineappleagency.com

RAZZAMATAZZ
MANAGEMENT   T/F 01342 301617
204 Holtye Road
East Grinstead RH19 3ES
T 07836 268292
E razzamatazzmanagement@btconnect.com

RUDEYE DANCE AGENCY   T 020 7014 3023
73 St John Street
London EC1M 4NJ
E info@rudeye.com
W www.rudeye.com

SCRIMGEOUR, Donald
ARTISTS AGENT   T 020 8444 6248
49 Springcroft Avenue
London N2 9JH
F 020 8883 9751
E vwest@dircon.co.uk

SHOW TEAM
PRODUCTIONS THE   T 0845 4671010
Dancers & Choreographers
36 Vine Street
Brighton BN1 4AG
E info@theshowteam.co.uk
W www.theshowteam.co.uk

SINGER, Sandra
ASSOCIATES   T 01702 331616
Dancers & Choreographers
21 Cotswold Road
Westcliff-on-Sea
Essex SS0 8AA
E sandrasingeruk@aol.com
W www.sandrasinger.com

S.O.S.   T 020 7735 5133
85 Bannerman House
Lawn Lane
London SW8 1UA
T 07740 359770
E info@sportsofseb.com
W www.sportsofseb.com

SUCCESS   T 020 7734 3356
Room 236, 2nd Floor
Linen Hall, 162-168 Regent Street
London W1B 5TB
F 020 7494 3787
E ee@successagency.co.uk
W www.successagency.co.uk

SUMMERS, Mark
MANAGEMENT   T 020 7229 8413
1 Beaumont Avenue
West Kensington
London W14 9LP
E info@marksummers.com
W www.marksummers.com

T W MANAGEMENT AGENCY   T 01253 749332
66-74 The Promenade
Blackpool
Lancashire FY1 1HB
E marie.cavney@twmanagementagency.co.uk
W www.twmanagementagency.co.uk

TASTE OF CAIRO   T 07801 413161
Bellydancers. UK & Europe
22 Gilda Crescent Road
Eccles, Manchester M30 9AG
E hello@tasteofcairo.com
W www.tasteofcairo.com

UNITED PRODUCTIONS   T/F 020 7498 6563
Choreographers, Dancers, Stylists
6 Shaftesbury Mews
Clapham
London SW4 9BP
T 07767 610908
E info@unitedproductions.biz
W www.unitedproductions.biz

W ATHLETIC   T 01276 415800
Unit 310, 377-399 London Road
Camberley, Surrey GU15 3HL
E london@wathletic.com
W www.wathletic.com

WARD CASTING   T 020 8886 5676
Studio 5
155 Commercial Street
London E1 6BJ
E casting@wardcasting.com
W www.wardcasting.com

SPOTLIGHT DANCERS

The UK's only casting directory dedicated to dancers
www.spotlight.com/dancers

A & B PERSONAL MANAGEMENT LTD   **T** 020 7794 3255
PO Box 64671, London NW3 9LH
E billellis@aandb.co.uk

ABNER STEIN   **T** 020 7373 0456
10 Roland Gardens, London SW7 3PH
F 020 7370 6316
E abner@abnerstein.co.uk

AGENCY (LONDON) LTD THE   **T** 020 7727 1346
PMA Member
24 Pottery Lane
Holland Park, London W11 4LZ
F 020 7727 9037
E info@theagency.co.uk
W www.theagency.co.uk

**A R G
(ARTISTS RIGHTS GROUP LTD)**   **T** 020 7436 6400
PMA Member
4 Great Portland Street
London W1W 8PA
F 020 7436 6700
E argall@argtalent.com

**ASPER, Pauline
MANAGEMENT**   **T/F** 01424 870412
PMA Member
Jacobs Cottage
Reservoir Lane
Sedlescombe, East Sussex TN33 0PJ
E pauline.asper@virgin.net

BERLIN ASSOCIATES   **T** 020 7836 1112
PMA Member
7 Tyers Gate, London SE1 3HX
F 020 7632 5296
E agents@berlinassociates.com
W www.berlinassociates.com

BLAKE FRIEDMANN   **T** 020 7284 0408
Novels, Non-Fiction & TV/Film Scripts
122 Arlington Road
London NW1 7HP
F 020 7284 0442
E info@blakefriedmann.co.uk
W www.blakefriedmann.co.uk

BRITTEN, Nigel MANAGEMENT   **T** 01243 850032
55 West Street, Chichester
West Sussex PO19 1RU
E office@nbmanagement.com

**BRODIE, Alan
REPRESENTATION LTD**   **T** 020 7253 6226
PMA Member
Paddock Suite, The Courtyard
55 Charterhouse Street
London EC1M 6HA
F 020 7079 7990
E info@alanbrodie.com
W www.alanbrodie.com

**CANN, Alexandra
REPRESENTATION**   **T** 020 7584 9047
PMA Member
Box 116, 4 Montpelier Street
London SW7 1EE
E alex@alexandracann.co.uk

**CASAROTTO RAMSAY &
ASSOCIATES LTD**   **T** 020 7287 4450
PMA Member
Waverley House, 7-12 Noel Street, London W1F 8GQ
F 020 7287 9128
E info@casarotto.co.uk
W www.casarotto.co.uk

CLOWES, Jonathan LTD   **T** 020 7722 7674
PMA/Association of Authors' Agents Member
10 Iron Bridge House, Bridge Approach
London NW1 8BD
F 020 7722 7677
E admin@jonathanclowes.co.uk

COCHRANE, Elspeth PERSONAL MANAGEMENT
Existing Clients only. No New Applicants. See ASQUITH & HORNER in Agents & Personal Managers section

CURTIS BROWN GROUP LTD   **T** 020 7393 4400
PMA Member
5th Floor, Haymarket House
28-29 Haymarket, London SW1Y 4SP
F 020 7393 4401
E cb@curtisbrown.co.uk
W www.curtisbrown.co.uk

DAISH, Judy ASSOCIATES LTD   **T** 020 8964 8811
PMA Member
2 St Charles Place, London W10 6EG
F 020 8964 8966
E judy@judydaish.com
W www.judydaish.com

DENCH ARNOLD AGENCY THE   **T** 020 7437 4551
PMA Member
10 Newburgh Street, London W1F 7RN
F 020 7439 1355
E contact@dencharnold.com
W www.dencharnold.com

de WOLFE, Felix   **T** 020 7242 5066
PMA Member
Kingsway House, 103 Kingsway, London WC2B 6QX
F 020 7242 8119
E info@felixdewolfe.com
W www.felixdewolfe.com

DREW, Bryan LTD   **T** 020 7823 2346
31 Oakley House, 103 Sloane Street
London SW1X 9PP
E bryan@bryandrewltd.com

**FARNES, Norma
MANAGEMENT**   **T** 020 7727 1544
9 Orme Court, London W2 4RL
F 020 7792 2110

**FILLINGHAM, Janet
ASSOCIATES**   **T** 020 8748 5594
PMA Member
52 Lowther Road, London SW13 9NU
F 020 8748 7374
E info@janetfillingham.com
W www.janetfillingham.com

FILM RIGHTS LTD   **T** 020 7316 1837
Suite 306, Belsize Business Centre
258 Belsize Road, London NW6 4BT
F 020 7624 3629
E information@filmrights.ltd.uk
W www.filmrights.ltd.uk

SAMUEL FRENCH LTD

Publishers of Plays • Agents for the Collection of Royalties
Specialist Booksellers
52 Fitzroy Street London W1T 5JR
Tel 020 7255 4300 (Bookshop) 020 7387 9373 (Enquiries)
Fax 020 7387 2161 www.samuelfrench-london.co.uk
e-mail: theatre@samuelfrench-london.co.uk

FITCH, Laurence LTD   T 020 7316 1837
Suite 306, Belsize Business Centre
258 Belsize Road, London NW6 4BT
F 020 7624 3629

FRENCH, Samuel LTD   T 020 7387 9373
PMA Member
52 Fitzroy Street, Fitzrovia
London W1T 5JR
F 020 7387 2161
E theatre@samuelfrench-london.co.uk
W www.samuelfrench-london.co.uk

FUTERMAN, ROSE &
ASSOCIATES   T 020 8255 7755
PMA Member. TV/Film, Showbiz & Music Biographies
91 St Leonards Road, London SW14 7BL
F 020 8286 4860
E guy@futermanrose.co.uk
W www.futermanrose.co.uk

GILLIS, Pamela
MANAGEMENT   T 020 8340 7868
46 Sheldon Avenue, London N6 4JR
F 020 8341 5564

GLASS, Eric LTD   T 020 7229 9500
25 Ladbroke Crescent, Notting Hill
London W11 1PS
F 020 7229 6220
E eglassltd@aol.com

HANCOCK, Roger LTD   T 020 8341 7243
PMA Member
7 Broadbent Close, Highgate Village
London N6 5JW
E tim@rogerhancock.com

HIGHAM, David
ASSOCIATES LTD   T 020 7434 5900
PMA Member
5-8 Lower John Street, Golden Square
London W1F 9HA
F 020 7437 1072
E dha@davidhigham.co.uk
W www.davidhigham.co.uk

HOSKINS, Valerie
ASSOCIATES LTD   T 020 7637 4490
PMA Member
20 Charlotte Street, London W1T 2NA
F 020 7637 4493
E vha@vhassociates.co.uk

INDEPENDENT TALENT
GROUP LTD   T 020 7636 6565
PMA Member. Formerly ICM, London
Oxford House, 76 Oxford Street
London W1D 1BS
F 020 7323 0101
W www.independenttalent.com

JFL AGENCY LTD   T 020 3137 8182
PMA Member
48 Charlotte Street
London W1T 2NS
E agents@jflagency.com
W www.jflagency.com

KASS, Michelle ASSOCIATES   T 020 7439 1624
PMA Member
85 Charing Cross Road
London WC2H 0AA
F 020 7734 3394
E office@michellekass.co.uk

KENIS, Steve & Co   T 020 7434 9055
PMA Member
Royalty House, 72-74 Dean Street
London W1D 3SG
F 020 7287 6328
E sk@sknco.com

MACFARLANE CHARD
ASSOCIATES LTD   T 020 7636 7750
PMA Member
33 Percy Street
London W1T 2DF
F 020 7636 7751
E enquiries@macfarlane-chard.co.uk
W www.macfarlane-chard.co.uk

MACNAUGHTON
LORD REPRESENTATION   T 020 7499 1411
PMA Member
44 South Molton Street
London W1K 5RT
F 020 7493 2444
E info@mlrep.com
W www.mlrep.com

MANN, Andrew LTD   T 020 7609 6218
PMA Member
39-41 North Road
London N7 9DP
E info@andrewmann.co.uk
W www.andrewmann.co.uk

MANS, Johnny PRODUCTIONS   T 01992 470907
Incorporating Encore Magazine
PO Box 196
Hoddesdon
Herts EN10 7WG
E johnnymansagent@aol.com
W www.johnnymansproductions.co.uk

MARJACQ SCRIPTS LTD   T 020 7935 9499
Prose. Screenplays. No Stage Plays or Musicals
34 Devonshire Place
London W1G 6JW
F 020 7935 9115
E enquiries@marjacq.com
W www.marjacq.com

Agents: Literary & Play

MARVIN, Blanche MBE T/F 020 7722 2313
Drama Critic for LTR
21A St Johns Wood High Street
London NW8 7NG
E blanchemarvin17@hotmail.com

M.B.A. LITERARY AGENTS LTD T 020 7387 2076
PMA Member
62 Grafton Way, London W1T 5DW
F 020 7387 2042
E fiona@mbalit.co.uk
W www.mbalit.co.uk

McLEAN, Bill PERSONAL MANAGEMENT T 020 8789 8191
23B Deodar Road
London SW15 2NP

MLR
See MACNAUGHTON LORD REPRESENTATION

MORRIS, William ENDEAVOR ENTERTAINMENT T 020 7534 6800
PMA Member
Centre Point
103 New Oxford Street
London WC1A 1DD
F 020 7534 6900
W www.wme.com

NARROW ROAD COMPANY THE T 020 8763 9895
PMA Member
182 Brighton Road, Coulsdon
Surrey CR5 2NF
F 020 8763 2558
E richardireson@narrowroad.co.uk

PFD T 020 7344 1000
PMA Member
Drury House, 34-43 Russell Street
London WC2B 5HA
F 020 7836 9539
E info@pfd.co.uk
W www.pfd.co.uk

POLLINGER LTD T 020 7404 0342
9 Staple Inn, Holborn
London WC1V 7QH
F 020 7242 5737
E info@pollingerltd.com
W www.pollingerltd.com

ROSICA COLIN LTD T 020 7370 1080
1 Clareville Grove Mews
London SW7 5AH
F 020 7244 6441

SAYLE SCREEN LTD T 020 7823 3883
PMA Member. Screenwriters & Directors for Film,
Stage & Television
11 Jubilee Place, London SW3 3TD
F 020 7823 3363

SEIFERT, Linda MANAGEMENT LTD T 020 7292 7390
PMA Member
91 Berwick Street, London W1F 0NE
F 020 7292 7391
E contact@lindaseifert.com
W www.lindaseifert.com

SHARLAND ORGANISATION LTD T 01933 626600
PMA Member
The Manor House, Manor Street
Raunds, Northants NN9 6JW
E tso@btconnect.com

SHEIL LAND ASSOCIATES LTD T 020 7405 9351
PMA Member. Literary, Film & Stage
52 Doughty Street, London WC1N 2LS
F 020 7831 2127
E info@sheilland.co.uk

STEEL, Elaine T 01273 739022
PMA Member. Writers' Agent
110 Gloucester Avenue, London NW1 8HX
F 01273 772400
E es@elainesteel.com

STEINBERG, Micheline ASSOCIATES T 020 7631 1310
PMA Member
104 Great Portland Street, London W1W 6PE
E info@steinplays.com
W www.steinplays.com

STEVENS, Rochelle & Co T 020 7359 3900
PMA Member
2 Terretts Place, Upper Street
London N1 1QZ
F 020 7354 5729
E info@rochellestevens.com

SWA (S W AGENCY) T 020 7281 1449
Writers' Agent
155 Stroud Green Road, London N4 3PZ
E info@swagency.co.uk
W www.swagency.co.uk

TENNYSON AGENCY THE T 020 8543 5939
10 Cleveland Avenue, Merton Park
London SW20 9EW
E submissions@tenagy.co.uk

TYRRELL, Julia MANAGEMENT T 020 8374 0575
PMA Member
57 Greenham Road
London N10 1LN
F 020 8374 5580
E julia@jtmanagement.co.uk
W www.jtmanagement.co.uk

WARE, Cecily LITERARY AGENTS T 020 7359 3787
PMA Member
19C John Spencer Square, London N1 2LZ
F 020 7226 9828
E info@cecilyware.com
W www.cecilyware.com

WEINBERGER, Josef LTD T 020 7580 2827
PMA Member
12-14 Mortimer Street, London W1T 3JJ
F 020 7436 9616
E general.info@jwmail.co.uk
W www.josef-weinberger.com

WESSON, Penny T 020 7722 6607
PMA Member
26 King Henry's Road, London NW3 3RP
F 020 7483 2890
E penny@pennywesson.demon.co.uk

APM ASSOCIATES   T 01753 639204
Contact: Linda French
Pinewood Studios, Pinewood Road
Iver Heath, Bucks SL0 0NH
F 01753 639205
E apm@apmassociates.net
W www.apmassociates.net

**ARLINGTON
ENTERPRISES LTD**   T 020 7580 0702
1-3 Charlotte Street, London W1T 1RD
F 020 7580 4994
E info@arlington-enterprises.co.uk
W www.arlingtonenterprises.co.uk

BARR, Becca MANAGEMENT   T 020 3137 2980
Dorland House, 5th Floor
14-16 Regent Street, London SW1Y 4PH
E becca@beccabarrmanagement.co.uk
W www.beccabarrmanagement.co.uk

**BLACKBURN SACHS
ASSOCIATES**   T 020 7292 7555
Argyll House, All Saints Passage, London SW18 1EP
E presenters@blackburnsachsassociates.com
W www.blackburnsachsassociates.com

CAMERON, Sara MANAGEMENT
See TAKE THREE MANAGEMENT

**CHASE PERSONAL
MANAGEMENT**   T 020 8940 7198
2nd Floor, 3 Kew Road, Richmond, Surrey TW9 2NQ
T 07775 683955
E sue@chasemanagement.co.uk
W www.chasepersonalmanagement.co.uk

CHP ARTIST MANAGEMENT   T 01844 345630
Meadowcroft Barn, Crowbrook Road, Askett
Princes Risborough, Buckinghamshire HP27 9LS
E contact@chproductions.org.uk
W www.chproductions.org.uk

CINEL GABRAN MANAGEMENT   T 029 2066 6600
PO Box 5163, Cardiff CF5 9BJ
F 0845 0666601
E info@cinelgabran.co.uk
W www.cinelgabran.co.uk

CINEL GABRAN MANAGEMENT   T 0845 0666605
PO Box 101, Whitby, North Yorkshire YO21 3WT
F 0845 0666601
E mail@cinelgabran.co.uk
W www.cinelgabran.co.uk

CRAWFORDS   T 020 8947 9999
PO Box 56662, London W13 3BH
E cr@wfords.com
W www.crawfords.tv

CURTIS BROWN GROUP LTD   T 020 7393 4460
Haymarket House, 28-29 Haymarket, London SW1Y 4SP
F 020 7393 4401
E presenters@curtisbrown.co.uk
W www.curtisbrown.co.uk

DAA (DEBI ALLEN ASSOCIATES)   T 020 7255 6123
The Heals Building
22 Torrington Place, London WC1E 7HP
F 020 7255 6128
E info@debiallenassociates.com
W www.debiallenassociates.com

DAVID ANTHONY PROMOTIONS   T 01925 632496
PO Box 286, Warrington, Cheshire WA2 8GA
T 07836 752195
E dave@davewarwick.co.uk
W www.davewarwick.co.uk

**DOWNES PRESENTERS
AGENCY**   T 020 8304 0541
96 Broadway, Bexleyheath, Kent DA6 7DE
E downes@presentersagency.com
W www.presentersagency.com

**EVANS, Jacque
MANAGEMENT LTD**   T 020 8699 1202
Top Floor Suite, 14 Holmesley Road, London SE23 1PJ
F 020 8699 5192
E jacque@jemltd.demon.co.uk

**EXCELLENT TALENT
COMPANY THE**   T 0845 2100111
118-120 Great Titchfield Street, London W1W 6SS
F 020 7637 4091
E marie-claire@excellenttalent.com
W www.excellenttalent.com

**EXPERTS MANAGEMENT
SERVICES LTD**   T 01625 858556
T/A Jane Hughes Management
PO Box 200, Stockport, Cheshire SK12 1GW
T 07766 130604
E gill@jhm.co.uk

FBI AGENCY   T 07050 222747
PO Box 250, Leeds LS1 2AZ
T 07515 567309
E casting@fbi-agency.co.uk
W www.fbi-agency.co.uk

FLETCHER ASSOCIATES   T 020 8361 8061
Broadcasting Experts & Journalists
25 Parkway, London N20 0XN
F 020 8361 8866
W www.fletcherassociates.net

**FORD-CRUSH, June
PERSONAL MANAGEMENT
& REPRESENTATION**   T 020 8742 7724
PO Box 57948, London W4 2UJ
T 07711 764160
E june@junefordcrush.com
W www.junefordcrush.com

GAY, Noel   T 020 7836 3941
19 Denmark Street, London WC2H 8NA
F 020 7287 1816
E info@noelgay.com
W www.noelgay.com

GLOBAL7 T/F 020 7281 7679
PO Box 56232, London N4 4XP
T 07956 956652
E global7castings@gmail.com
W www.global7casting.com

GLORIOUS MANAGEMENT T 020 7704 6555
Lower Ground Floor, 79 Noel Road
London N1 8HE
E lisa@glorioustalent.co.uk
W www.gloriousmanagement.com

GRANT, James MEDIA T 020 8742 4950
94 Strand On The Green, Chiswick, London W4 3NN
F 020 8742 4951
E enquiries@jamesgrant.co.uk
W www.jamesgrant.co.uk

**GURNETT, J. PERSONAL
MANAGEMENT LTD** T 020 7440 1850
12 Newburgh Street, London W1F 7RP
F 020 7287 9642
E info@jgpm.co.uk
W www.jgpm.co.uk

**HICKS, Jeremy
ASSOCIATES LTD** T 020 7734 7957
3 Richmond Buildings, London W1D 3HE
F 020 7734 6302
E info@jeremyhicks.com
W www.jeremyhicks.com

INTERNATIONAL ARTISTES LTD T 020 7025 0600
4th Floor, Holborn Hall
193-197 High Holborn, London WC1V 7BD
F 020 7404 9865
E reception@internationalartistes.com
W www.internationalartistes.com

**JLA
(JEREMY LEE ASSOCIATES LTD)** T 020 7907 2800
Supplies celebrities and after dinner speakers
80 Great Portland Street
London W1W 7NW
F 020 7907 2801
E talk@jla.co.uk
W www.jla.co.uk

JOYCE, Michael MANAGEMENT T 020 3178 7190
3rd Floor, 33 Glasshouse Street, London W1B 5DG
T 07854 251372
E info@michaeljoyce.tv
W www.michaeljoycemanagement.com

KBJ MANAGEMENT LTD T 020 7434 6767
TV Presenters
5 Soho Square, London W1D 3QA
F 020 7287 1191
E general@kbjmgt.co.uk
W www.kbjmgt.co.uk

KNIGHT AYTON MANAGEMENT T 020 7831 4400
35 Great James Street, London WC1N 3HB
F 020 7831 4455
E info@knightayton.co.uk
W www.knightayton.co.uk

**KNIGHT, Hilary
MANAGEMENT LTD** T 01604 781818
Grange Farm, Church Lane
Old, Northamptonshire NN6 9QZ
E hilary@hkmanagement.co.uk
W www.hkmanagement.co.uk

LEIGH, Mike ASSOCIATES T 020 7935 5500
37 Marylebone Lane, London W1U 2NW
F 020 7486 5886
W www.mikeleighassoc.com

**LYTE, Seamus
MANAGEMENT LTD** T 07930 391401
Contact: By e-mail
E seamus@seamuslyte.com

**MACFARLANE CHARD
ASSOCIATES LTD** T 020 7636 7750
33 Percy Street, London W1T 2DF
F 020 7636 7751
E enquiries@macfarlane-chard.co.uk
W www.macfarlane-chard.co.uk

MARKS PRODUCTIONS LTD T 020 7486 2001
2 Gloucester Gate Mews, London NW1 4AD

MARSH, Billy ASSOCIATES LTD T 020 7449 6930
76A Grove End Road, St John's Wood
London NW8 9ND
F 020 7449 6933
E talent@billymarsh.co.uk
W www.billymarsh.co.uk

McKENNA, Deborah LTD T 020 8846 0966
Celebrity Chefs & Lifestyle Presenters only
64-66 Glentham Road, London SW13 9JJ
F 020 8846 0967
E info@deborahmckenna.com
W www.deborahmckenna.com

**MEDIA PEOPLE
(THE CELEBRITY GROUP)** T 0871 2501234
12 Archery Close, Connaught Square
London W2 2BE
E info@celebrity.co.uk
W www.celebrity.co.uk

MILES, John ORGANISATION T 01275 854675
Cadbury Camp Lane
Clapton-in-Gordano
Bristol BS20 7SB
F 01275 810186
E john@johnmiles.org.uk
W www.johnmilesorganisation.org.uk

MONDI ASSOCIATES LTD T 07817 133349
Contact: Michelle Sykes
Unit 3 O, Cooper House, 2 Michael Road
London SW6 2AD
E info@mondiassociates.com
W www.mondiassociates.com

MPC ENTERTAINMENT T 020 7624 1184
MPC House, 15-16 Maple Mews, London NW6 5UZ
F 020 7624 4220
E info@mpce.com
W www.mpce.com

MTC (UK) LTD T 020 7935 8000
71 Gloucester Place, London W1U 8JW
F 020 7935 8066
E nicki@mtc-uk.com
W www.mtc-uk.com

NOEL, John MANAGEMENT T 020 7428 8400
Block B, Imperial Works
Perren Street, London NW5 3ED
F 020 7428 8401
E john@johnnoel.com
W www.johnnoel.com

Presenters Agents

How do I become a presenter?

There is no easy answer to this question. Some presenters start out as actors and move into presenting work, others may be 'experts' such as chefs, designers or sports people who are taken on in a presenting capacity. Others may have a background in stand-up comedy. All newsreaders are professional journalists with specialist training and experience. Often presenters work their way up through the production side of broadcasting, starting by working as a runner or researcher and then moving to appear in front of the camera. To get this kind of production work you could contact film and TV production companies, many of whom are listed in Contacts. A number of performing arts schools, colleges and academies also offer useful part-time training courses for presenters. See the 'Drama Training, Schools and Coaches' section for college/school listings.

Why do I need a presenting agent?

As with any other agent, a presenting agent will promote their clients to job opportunities, negotiate contracts on their behalf, handle paperwork and offer advice. In return for these services they take commission ranging from 10-15%. The following pages contain contact details for the UK's leading presenter agencies. They will possess the relevant contacts in the industry that you need to get auditions and jobs.

How should I use these listings?

Before you approach any agency looking for representation, do some research into their current client list and the areas in which they specialise. Many have websites you can visit. Once you have made a short-list of the ones you think are most appropriate, you should send them your CV with a covering letter and a good quality, recent photograph which is a genuine likeness of you. Showreels can also be a good way of showcasing your talents, but only send these if you have checked with the agency first. Enclosing a stamped-addressed envelope with sufficient postage (SAE) will also give you a better chance of a reply. Please see the main 'Agents and Personal Managers' advice section for further guidance on choosing and approaching agents.

Should I pay a presenter's agent to join their books? Or sign a contract?

As with other types of agencies, Equity (the actors' trade union) does not recommend that artists pay an agent to join their client list. Before signing any contract, you should be very clear about the terms and commitments involved. For advice on both of these issues, or if you experience any problems with a current agent, we recommend that you contact Equity www.equity.org.uk. They also produce the booklet *You and your Agent* which is free to all Equity members and available from their website's members' area.

What is Spotlight Presenters?

Spotlight Presenters is a specialist casting directory published annually. It contains photographs and contact details for over seven hundred professional TV and radio presenters and is a great way of promoting yourself for work. It is used by production companies, casting directors, TV and radio stations, advertising agencies and publicists to browse and locate talent for future productions. Membership is available to any presenter with proven professional broadcast experience. Just starting out in your presenting career? New presenters with limited broadcast experience or training can join the Spotlight Presenters directory in the 'Emerging Talent' pages. Please see www.spotlight.com/artists/presenters to join or for more information.

Should I join the Spotlight Actors/ Actresses directory or the Presenters directory?

Depending on your skills, training and experience, you may be eligible for both directories if you are interested in promoting yourself as an actor and as a presenter. You would receive an entry into each directory and two separate online CVs. You would also qualify for a 25% discount off the Presenters membership fee. You will however have to prove that you already have professional experience and/ or relevant training.

Presenters Agents

CASE STUDY

Peoplematter.TV represents and partners in business with specialist journalists and presenters. The company works to build on their client's broadcast exposure through commercial and business relationships. Tony Fitzpatrick, founder of the agency, has plenty of advice for anyone thinking of becoming a presenter...

Each year the 'marketplace' for presenters becomes ever more crowded. New and hopeful raw recruits enter the market at one end of the 'presenting spectrum' whilst older and well-established broadcasters and presenters are being squeezed out of their prime time roles by 'younger models'. So, every year the 'buyer's market' becomes more crowded, and the law of 'supply and demand' dictates that presenters can be asked to do more for less! And if that wasn't bad enough, the 'reality show' format has created unrealistic expectations amongst the public – suddenly anyone can become a broadcaster. It is unfortunate that many of these 'reality stars' have skewed our understanding of what it takes to be a 'Presenter'. They may be famous for their appearance on our screens for weeks on end – they may even get a temporary column in a magazine for a while. But that fame is fleeting and they in turn are replaced by a new reality star next season. There are so many 'ex-Big Brother' stars that you couldn't even get them together in one studio – let alone find TV jobs for them!

So – if you're still keen to join the 'broadcast jungle' read on!

The very best broadcasters know how they make a difference in the world. They can help change views and opinions. They can impart knowledge which can change the lives of viewers and readers. Imagine if your news item explained how somebody could save a life?

A broadcasting career should be just that – a career! A career where you learn your craft from others more qualified and in which you strive to be the best you can be. A career isn't part-time. It isn't something that will come easily and it will have a catalogue of setbacks that will make you wonder why you didn't take the accountancy course that your mum always wanted you to! But the rewards are great if you succeed.

The very best broadcasters know how they make a difference in the world. They can help change views and opinions. They can impart knowledge which can change the lives of viewers and readers. Imagine if your news item explained how somebody could save a life? Anne Diamond – the seasoned broadcaster and health campaigner – did just that when she used her journalist skills to launch a broadcast campaign to stop Cot Death, or SIDS (Sudden Infant Death Syndrome), in 1991. Since then there has been a dramatic reduction in the annual death rate of SIDS in Britain, measured in thousands of babies' lives, largely attributed to this campaign. When Michael Buerk and cameraman Mohammed Amin first brought the plight of millions of starving Ethiopians to British screens in 1984, the reports were watched in horror by singer Bob Geldof. He bullied and cajoled a host of pop stars into gathering to form Live Aid, and persuaded millions of people to part with their money to help the starving.

Without their broadcasts lives might never have changed for the better. That's why we called our company Peoplematter. There are many broadcasters – but very few who make a difference in people's lives! If you want to be one of the 'people who make a difference' here are our suggestions.

Remember – it will take more than good looks and an engaging smile to get you on that first rung of the ladder!

Be interested

If you're not, why should anybody else be? Unfortunately all agents receive a lot of unsolicited requests from aspiring presenters. As a specialist agency we only represent those specialists whose experience and journalistic talents truly make them 'people who matter'. But so often we receive requests from generalist presenters with no experience and no specialist talent. If they aren't interested in researching their own future agent – what hope do they think they will have in finding the right one? If you have a broadcast company in mind, research them and find out everything there is to know about them. Watch their channel. Read about them. Research the contacts you're hoping to pitch to. Know them well – and know why they should want you on their team. And, here's a word to the wise, in every letter received by an agent will include the words 'willing', 'keen', 'vibrant personality' and 'dedicated'! So you need to make yours stand out by using language that communicates your enthusiasm and commitment – by saying something real!

Be specialised!

Presenting to camera can be faked. Being passionate about your subject can't be! You may want to go on to be a generalist news reporter but unless you have perfected a specialist area, you'll never be able to learn a new one quickly. Having a specialism provides you with a way of learning and provides you with a passion! It is the passion that separates out presenters from auto cue readers. You can't fake passion! And interest and passion are nothing without the ability to…

Communicate your subject

You need to be able to make the most complex of subjects or issues understandable to your viewer. The best broadcasters are great journalists. Your goal is to distil a mass of information and find a simple way of telling your story which engages your audience and enriches their lives forever. Today's best broadcasters all started their careers in journalism. They learned their craft and honed it to be the best in their field.

Regard your agent as your business partner

If you aren't working, they aren't earning! As a business partner you should both be working to achieve the same ends, sharing your talents for each other's best benefit. Therefore, you should both communicate. You must jointly agree realistic expectations. How will either of you know if you've been successful if you haven't both agreed on joint objectives?

Be proactive

Your agent shouldn't be the only one in your business partnership who is working to make contacts. You must as well. Your agent should be using their industry contacts to ensure that your name is being promoted and you are being put up for suitable jobs, but you need to put yourself out there as well. Make sure you are looking out for work experience or industry opportunities. Every social occasion is a chance to meet people who will be contacts for the future. And any good journalist makes sure they keep their contacts organised. Every email address and telephone number logged now is a future opportunity for you. Also let your agent know of things that you hear about. They can't be everywhere, but you might be able to!

Be grown up if there are problems

And, if there are problems between you and your agent, then discuss your issues together. You should jointly decide whether to move forward together – or apart! If you're going to be in the industry for a long time (and hopefully you are) then you will find that it's a small world! Whatever you do today will definitely be remembered in ten years' time. Remembering that golden rule can save a great deal of embarrassment in years to come. So what are the secrets of success as a presenter or broadcaster? Work hard to be the best at what you do. Treat everyone with respect. Take responsibility for your own career. And above all have fun. If you have the opportunity to change one person's life through your broadcasting career it will all have been worth it.

Please visit www.peoplematter.tv for further information.

OFF THE KERB PRODUCTIONS   T 020 7437 0607
Comedy Presenters & Comedians
3rd Floor, Hammer House
113-117 Wardour Street, London W1F 0UN
F 020 7437 0647
E westend@offthekerb.co.uk
W www.offthekerb.co.uk

PANMEDIA UK LTD   T 020 8446 9662
18 Montrose Crescent, London N12 0ED
E enquiries@panmediauk.co.uk
W www.panmediauk.co.uk

PEOPLEMATTER.TV   T 020 7415 7070
Contact: Tony Fitzpatrick
40 Bowling Green Lane, Clerkenwell
London EC1R 0NE
F 020 7415 7074
E tony@peoplematter.tv
W www.peoplematter.tv

PFD   T 020 7344 1000
Presenters. Public Speakers
Drury House, 34-43 Russell Street, London WC2B 5HA
F 020 7836 9539
E info@pfd.co.uk
W www.pfd.co.uk

PVA MANAGEMENT LTD   T 01905 616100
County House, St Mary's Street, Worcester WR1 1HB
F 01905 610709
E post@pva.co.uk
W www.pva.co.uk

**RARE TALENT ACTORS
MANAGEMENT**   T 0161 273 4444
Tanzaro House, Ardwick Green North
Manchester M12 6FZ
F 0161 273 4567
E info@raretalentactors.com
W www.raretalentactors.com

**RAZZAMATAZZ
MANAGEMENT**   T/F 01342 301617
204 Holtye Road, East Grinstead
West Sussex RH19 3ES
T 07836 268292
E razzamatazzmanagement@btconnect.com

RED 24 MANAGEMENT   T 020 7559 3611
The Hospital Club, 3rd Floor,
24 Endell Street, London WC2H 9HQ
E info@red24management.com
W www.red24management.com

RED CANYON MANAGEMENT   T 07931 381696
T 07939 365578
E info@redcanyon.co.uk
W www.redcanyon.co.uk

RPM2   T 0845 3625456
Studio House, Delamare Road
Cheshunt, Hertfordshire EN8 9SH
E rhino-rpm2@hotmail.com
W www.rhino2-rpm.com

SINGER, Sandra ASSOCIATES   T 01702 331616
21 Cotswold Road, Westcliff-on-Sea
Essex SS0 8AA
E sandrasingeruk@aol.com
W www.sandrasinger.com

SOMETHIN' ELSE   T 020 7250 5500
20-26 Brunswick Place
London N1 6DZ
F 020 7250 0937
E info@somethinelse.com
W www.somethinelse.com

SPEAK-EASY LTD   T 01604 686100
Kate Moon Management, PO Box 648
Draughton, Northampton NN6 9XT
E kate@katemoonmanagement.co.uk
W www.katemoonmanagement.co.uk

TAKE THREE MANAGEMENT   T 020 7209 3777
110 Gloucester Avenue, Primrose Hill
London NW1 8HX
F 020 7209 3770
E info@take3management.com
W www.take3management.co.uk

TALENT4 MEDIA LTD   T 020 7183 4330
Studio LG16, Shepherds Building Central
Charecroft Way, London W14 0EH
F 020 7183 4331
E enquiries@talent4media.com
W www.talent4media.com

TRIPLE A MEDIA   T/F 020 3370 4988
30 Great Portland Street
London W1W 8QU
E andy@tripleamedia.com
W www.tripleamedia.com

TROIKA   T 020 7336 7868
3rd Floor, 74 Clerkenwell Road
London EC1M 5QA
F 020 7490 7642
E info@troikatalent.com
W www.troikatalent.com

WANDER, Jo MANAGEMENT   T 020 7209 3777
110 Gloucester Avenue, Primrose Hill
London NW1 8HX
E jo@jowandermanagement.com
W www.jowandermanagement.com

WISE BUDDAH TALENT   T 020 7307 1600
74 Great Titchfield Street, London W1W 7QP
F 020 7307 1601
E talent@wisebuddah.com
W www.wisebuddah.com

**ZWICKLER, Marlene
& ASSOCIATES**   T/F 0131 343 3030
1 Belgrave Crescent Lane
Edinburgh EH4 3AG
E info@mza-artists.com
W www.mza-artists.com

ACCENT BANK   T 020 7223 5160
420 Falcon Wharf, 34 Lombard Road
London SW11 3RF
E info@accentbank.co.uk
W www.accentbank.co.uk

AD VOICE   T 020 7323 2345
Oxford House, 76 Oxford Street, London W1D 1BS
F 020 7323 0101
E info@advoice.co.uk
W www.advoice.co.uk

ALPHABET KIDZ   T 020 7252 4343
Acting & Voice-Over Agency
Nice Business Park, 19-35 Sylvan Grove
London SE15 1PD
F 020 7252 4341
E contact@alphabetkidz.co.uk
W www.alphabetkidz.co.uk

AMERICAN AGENCY
VOICES THE   T 020 7485 8883
14 Bonny Street, London NW1 9PG
E americanagency@btconnect.com
W www.americanagency.tv

ANOTHER TONGUE VOICES LTD   T 020 7494 0300
The Basement, 10-11 D'Arblay Street
London W1F 8DS
F 020 7494 7080
E john@anothertongue.com
W www.anothertongue.com

ASQUITH & HORNER   T 020 8466 5580
Contact: By Telephone/Post (SAE)
The Studio, 14 College Road
Bromley, Kent BR1 3NS
T 07770 482144
E asquith@dircon.co.uk

BRAIDMAN, Michelle
ASSOCIATES LTD   T 020 7237 3523
2 Futura House, 169 Grange Road
London SE1 3BN
F 020 7231 4634
E info@braidman.com

CALYPSO VOICES   T 020 7734 6415
25-26 Poland Street, London W1F 8QN
F 020 7437 0410
E jane@calypsovoices.com
W www.calypsovoices.com

CASTAWAY   T 020 7240 2345
Suite 3, 15 Broad Court
London WC2B 5QN
F 020 7240 2772
E info@castaway.org.uk
W www.castaway.org.uk

CINEL GABRAN MANAGEMENT   T 029 2066 6600
PO Box 5163, Cardiff CF5 9BJ
F 0845 0666601
E info@cinelgabran.co.uk
W www.cinelgabran.co.uk

CINEL GABRAN MANAGEMENT   T 0845 0666605
PO Box 101, Newholm
Whitby, North Yorkshire YO21 3WT
F 0845 0666601
E mail@cinelgabran.co.uk
W www.cinelgabran.co.uk

CONWAY VAN GELDER
GRANT LTD   T 020 7287 1070
3rd Floor, 8-12 Broadwick Street, London W1F 8HW
F 020 7287 1940
E kate@conwayvg.co.uk
W www.conwayvangeldergrant.com

International Centre for Voice
Based at the Central School of Speech & Drama   Patrons: Cicely Berry CBE and Barbara Houseman
The ICV exists to serve the needs of professional users of voice and speech, including actors, singers, directors, voice coaches, musicians and teachers. We host workshops with world-renowned practitioners and enable members to develop their practice and research as part of a supportive network of people who are passionate about voice.
For further details please visit www.icvoice.co.uk or email icv@cssd.ac.uk

CREATIVE KIDZ STAGE SCHOOL   T 07958 377595
Incorporating NeighbourHood Productions
9 Weavers Terrace, Fulham, London SW6 1QE
T 07908 144802
E info@creativekidzandco.co.uk

CUT GLASS VOICES   T 020 7267 2339
169-175 Queens Crescent, Camden, London NW5 4DS
E info@cutglassproductions.com
W www.cutglassproductions.com

DAMN GOOD VOICES   T 07702 228185
25B Eastlake Road, London SE5 9QJ
T 07809 549887
E damngoodvoices@me.com
W www.damngoodvoices.com

DIAMOND MANAGEMENT   T 020 7631 0400
31 Percy Street, London W1T 2DD
F 020 7631 0500
E cc@diman.co.uk

DREW, Bryan LTD   T 020 7823 2346
31 Oakley House
103 Sloane Street, London SW1X 9PP
E bryan@bryandrewltd.com

EARACHE VOICES   T 020 7287 2291
177 Wardour Street, London W1F 8WX
F 020 7287 2288
E alex@earachevoices.com
W www.earachevoices.com

EVANS O'BRIEN   T 020 8318 9058
2 Lampmead Road, London SE12 8QL
E info@evansobrien.co.uk
W www.evansobrien.co.uk

EXCELLENT TALENT COMPANY THE   T 0845 2100111
118-120 Great Titchfield Street
London W1W 6SS
F 020 7637 4091
E info@excellenttalent.com
W www.excellenttalent.com

FERRIS ENTERTAINMENT VOICES   T 0845 4724725
London. Belfast. Cardiff
Number 8, 132 Charing Cross Road
London WC2H 0LA
E info@ferrisentertainment.com
W www.ferrisentertainment.com

FIRST VOICE AGENCY   T 01494 678277
Foxgrove House, School Lane
Seer Green HP9 2QJ
F 01494 730166
E jenny@firstvoiceagency.com
W www.firstvoiceagency.com

FOREIGN LEGION   T 020 8450 4451
1 Kendal Road, London NW10 1JH
E voices@foreignlegion.co.uk
W www.foreignlegion.co.uk

FOREIGN VERSIONS LTD   T 0333 123 2001
Translation
E info@foreignversions.co.uk
W www.foreignversions.com

GAY, Noel VOICES   T 020 7836 3941
19 Denmark Street, London WC2H 8NA
F 020 7287 1816
E info@noelgay.com
W www.noelgay.com

GLOBAL7   T/F 020 7281 7679
PO Box 56232, London N4 4XP
T 07956 956652
E global7castings@gmail.com
W www.global7casting.com

GORDON & FRENCH   T 020 7734 4818
Contact: By Post
12-13 Poland Street, London W1F 8QB
F 020 7734 4832
E voices@gordonandfrench.net
W www.gordonandfrench.co.uk

GREAT BRITISH VOICE COMPANY THE   T 0845 8622202
339 Norristhorpe Lane, Liversedge
West Yorkshire WF15 7AZ
E info@greatbritishvoice.co.uk
W www.greatbritishvoice.co.uk

HAMILTON HODELL LTD   T 020 7636 1221
Contact: Louise Donald
5th Floor, 66-68 Margaret Street, London W1W 8SR
F 020 7636 1226
E louise@hamiltonhodell.co.uk
W www.hamiltonhodell.co.uk

HARVEY VOICES   T 020 7952 4361
No unsolicited correspondence
58 Woodlands Road, London N9 8RT
E info@harveyvoices.co.uk
W www.harveyvoices.co.uk

HOBSONS SINGERS   T 020 8995 3628
62 Chiswick High Road, London W4 1SY
F 020 8996 5350
E singers@hobsons-international.com
W www.hobsons-international.com

HOBSONS VOICES   T 020 8995 3628
62 Chiswick High Road, London W4 1SY
F 020 8996 5350
E voices@hobsons-international.com
W www.hobsons-international.com

Voice-Over Agents

How do I become a voice-over artist?

The voice-over business has opened up a lot more to newcomers in recent years; you don't have to be a celebrity already to be booked for a job. However, it is a competitive industry, and it is important to bear in mind that only a select few are able to earn a living from voice-over work. It is more likely that voice-over work could become a supplement to your regular income.

In order to get work you must have a great voice and be able to put it to good use. Being able to act does not necessarily mean that you will also be able to do voice-overs. Whether your particular voice will get you the job or not will ultimately depend on the client's personal choice, so your technical ability to do voice-over work initially comes second in this industry. Once the client has chosen you, however, then you must be able to consistently demonstrate that you can take direction well, you don't need numerous takes to get the job finished, you have a positive attitude and you don't complain if recording goes a little over schedule.

Before you get to this stage, however, you will need a professional-sounding voicereel and, in the majority of cases, an agent.

How do I produce a voicereel?

Please see the 'Promotional Services' section for advice on creating your voicereel.

Why do I need a voice-over agent?

As with any other agent, a voice-over agent will promote their clients to job opportunities, negotiate contracts on their behalf, handle paperwork and offer advice. In return for these services they take commission ranging from 10-15%. The agents listed in this section specialise in representing and promoting voice-over artists, mostly in the commercial and corporate sectors, but also areas such as radio and animation. They will possess the relevant contacts in the industry that you need to get auditions and jobs. In this industry in particular, time is money, and clients are often more likely to trust that an agent can provide someone who can get the job done in the least amount of takes but still sounds good in every project, rather than taking on an unknown newcomer.

How do I find work in radio?

Please see the 'Radio' section of Contacts for further information on this specific area of voice work.

How should I use these listings?

Whether you are completely new to the industry, looking to change your existing agent, or wishing to take on an additional agent to represent you for voice-overs alongside your main acting or presenting agent, the following listings will supply you with up-to-date contact details for voice-over agencies. Every company listed is done so by written request to us. Please see the main 'Agents and Personal Managers' advice section for further guidance on choosing and approaching agents.

Should I pay an agent to join their books? Or sign a contract?

Equity (the actors' trade union) does not recommend that artists pay an agent to join their client list. Before signing a contract, you should be very clear about the terms and commitments involved. For advice on both of these issues, or if you experience any problems with a current agent, we recommend that you contact Equity www.equity.org.uk. They also produce the booklet *You and your Agent* which is free to all Equity members and available from their website's members' area.

Voice-Over Agents

CASE STUDY

Laura Milne has been managing The Joneses for a year and a half; prior to this she had been working at Earache Voices. The agency has been running for fifteen years and was re-branded as The Joneses five years ago by the talent agency Amanda Howard Associates. The Joneses was created as a personality-based voice agency, specialising in actors with extraordinary talent who offer a unique and fresh approach to voice-overs.

The voice-over industry is booming. We are seeing more voice agencies popping up on a yearly basis, and increasingly theatrical agencies are using this side to find work for their clients. As a result we are hearing a surge of recognisable voices on the air waves, which makes it tougher for lesser-known voices to break into the industry and secure representation. As is the case advertisers and their clients often choose these well-known familiar faces with their distinctive voices instead of some very talented and individual alternatives. With this in mind how do you decide which agency will be the best at promoting you as a voice-over artist and how do you get them to notice you? Do your homework!

Voice-over agencies are steadily becoming more specialised to stand out from each other, so where do you fit in? Do you have a comedy edge? Are you a presenter or a straight actor? Taking this into account, make sure you tailor your voicereel to your talents. Don't feel pressured to include every genre of voice-over, just ensure that you include commercials and narration in a style in which you excel in. Consider where you fit in and target agencies that lean towards this field.

Make sure your voicereel is of an excellent professional quality and when recording with a studio take control and ensure you have an active part in choosing the scripts. Consider the style of the piece and whether it suits you. Make certain it isn't a readily recycled read as so often voice-over agents hear the same voicereels doing the rounds and this won't make you stand out. Do some research and gather your own scripts to make

your reel more individual. It is better to stick to your natural voice unless you have a talent for different accents or improvisations; there are so many voices to pick from now that there isn't a need to move away from what you do best.

Take time over your application and make sure you find out who runs each voice-over agency so that you can address them personally. Check to see if you can offer something different to the current client list and be explicit with the reasons as to why you would be an asset.

How do you decide which agency will be the best at promoting you as a voice-over artist and how do you get them to notice you? Do your homework!

All agents love to know what projects you're currently involved in so be certain to mention any recent TV, film or theatre credits and the more high profile the better.

When following up your application be aware that we receive hundreds of submissions so it does take a while to get back to you personally. If you feel that your reel has been with an agency for too long then a gentle nudge by email is the best way to get us to respond.

And finally, if you have a theatrical agent, approach them about your interest in voice-over management. Your agent may have good relations with certain voice-over agencies or may have a voice side in-house, in which case they can help push you in the right direction.

Good luck to you!

Please visit www.meetthejoneses.co.uk for further information.

The Voiceover Handbook
The paperback guide to being a UK voiceover artist

Available now from Amazon and
online at www.voiceovers.co.uk.
ISBN 978-0-9567438-0-0

Voiceovers.co.uk
official book

HOPE, Sally ASSOCIATES   T 020 7613 5353
108 Leonard Street, London EC2A 4XS
F 020 7613 4848
E casting@sallyhope.biz
W www.sallyhope.biz

HOWARD, Amanda ASSOCIATES
See JONESES THE

ICAN TALK LTD   T 01858 466749
Palm Tree Mews, 39 Tymecrosse Gardens
Market Harborough, Leicestershire LE16 7US
F 01858 455445
E hello@icantalk.co.uk
W www.icantalk.co.uk

J H A VOICE   T 020 7734 7597
3 Richmond Buildings, London W1D 3HE
F 020 7734 6302
E info@jeremyhicks.com
W www.jeremyhicks.com

JONESES THE   T 020 7287 9666
21 Berwick Street, London W1F 0PZ
F 020 7287 7785
E mail@meetthejoneses.co.uk
W www.meetthejoneses.co.uk

JUST VOICES AGENCY THE   T 020 7881 2567
140 Buckingham Palace Road, London SW1W 9SA
F 020 7881 2569
E info@justvoicesagency.com
W www.justvoicesagency.com

KIDZTALK LTD   T 01737 350808
Young Voices, Children, Teenagers, Twenties
F 01737 352456
E studio@kidztalk.com
W www.kidztalk.com

KMA VOICES   T 020 7439 1456
11 Connaught Place, London W2 2ET
F 020 7734 6530
E email@kenmcreddie.com
W www.kenmcreddie.com/voices

LEHRER, Jane VOICES   T 020 7435 9118
PO Box 66334, London NW6 9QT
F 020 7435 9117
E voices@janelehrer.co.uk
W www.janelehrer.co.uk/voices.html

LIP SERVICE CASTING LTD   T 020 7734 3393
60-66 Wardour Street, London W1F 0TA
F 020 7734 3373
E bookings@lipservice.co.uk
W www.lipservice.co.uk

MARKHAM, FROGGATT & IRWIN   T 020 7636 4412
4 Windmill Street, London W1T 2HZ
F 020 7637 5233
E tig@markhamfroggattirwin.co.uk
W www.markhamfroggattirwin.com

PEMBERTON VOICES   T 020 7734 4144
51 Upper Berkeley Street, London W1H 7QW
E rosemary@pembertonassociates.com
W www.pembertonvoices.com

PEMBERTON VOICES   T 0161 235 8440
Express Networks
1 George Leigh Street, Manchester M4 5DL
F 0161 235 8442
E rosemary@pembertonassociates.com
W www.pembertonvoices.com

QVOICE   T 020 7025 0660
4th Floor, Holborn Hall
193-197 High Holborn, London WC1V 7BD
F 020 7025 0659
E info@qvoice.co.uk
W www.qvoice.co.uk

RABBIT VOCAL
MANAGEMENT LTD   T 020 7287 6466
3rd Floor, 27 Poland Street, London W1F 8QW
F 020 7287 6566
E info@rabbitvocalmanagement.co.uk
W www.rabbitvocalmanagement.co.uk

RED 24 VOICES   T 020 7559 3611
The Hospital Club, 3rd Floor
24 Endell Street, London WC2H 9HQ
E paul@red24voices.com
W www.red24voices.com

RHUBARB VOICES   T 020 8742 8683
1st Floor, 1A Devonshire Road, London W4 2EU
F 020 8742 8693
E enquiries@rhubarbvoices.co.uk
W www.rhubarbvoices.co.uk

RONAN, Lynda PERSONAL
MANAGEMENT   T 020 7183 0017
Hunters House, 1 Redcliffe Road, London SW10 9NR
F 020 7183 0547
E info@lyndaronan.com
W www.lyndaronan.com

RPM2   T/F 0845 2415585
Studio House, Delamare Road
Cheshunt, Hertfordshire EN8 9SH
T 0845 3625456
E rhino-rpm2@hotmail.com   W www.rhino2-rpm.com

voiceover agency
www.damngoodvoices.com
+44 (0)7702 228185

THE UK'S NUMBER 1

CRYING OUT LOUD
PRODUCTIONS

voiceover demo production company
www.cryingoutloud.co.uk
+44 (0)7809 549887

SHINING MANAGEMENT LTD T 020 7734 1981
81 Oxford Street, London W1D 2EU
E info@shiningvoices.com
W www.shiningvoices.com

SPEAK-EASY LTD T 01604 686100
PO Box 648, Draughton, Northampton NN6 9XT
E enquiries@speak-easy.co.uk
W www.speak-easy.co.uk

SVMK LTD T 020 7434 0002
47 Dean Street, London W1D 5BE
E info@svmk.co.uk
W www.svmk.co.uk

TALKING HEADS T 020 7292 7575
Argyll House, All Saints Passage, London SW18 1EP
E voices@talkingheadsvoices.com
W www.talkingheadsvoices.com

TERRY, Sue VOICES LTD T 020 7434 2040
3rd Floor, 18 Broadwick Street, London W1F 8HS
F 020 7434 2042
E sue@sueterryvoices.co.uk
W www.sueterryvoices.co.uk

TONGUE & GROOVE T 0161 228 2469
PO Box 173, Manchester M19 0AR
F 0161 249 3666
E info@tongueandgroove.co.uk
W www.tongueandgroove.co.uk

UNITED VOICES T 020 3214 0937
12-26 Lexington Street, London W1F 0LE
E voices@unitedagents.co.uk
W www.unitedvoices.tv

VOCAL POINT T 020 7419 0700
131 Great Titchfield Street, London W1W 5BB
E enquiries@vocalpoint.net
W www.vocalpoint.net

VOICE BANK LTD T 0161 973 8879
PO Box 825, Altrincham, Cheshire WA15 5HH
T 07931 792670
E elinors@voicebankltd.co.uk
W www.voicebankltd.co.uk

VOICE SHOP T 020 8742 7077
1st Floor, Thomas Place
1A Devonshire Road, London W4 2EU
F 020 8742 7011
E info@voice-shop.co.uk
W www.voice-shop.co.uk

VOICE SQUAD T 020 8450 4451
1 Kendal Road, London NW10 1JH
E voices@voicesquad.com
W www.voicesquad.com

**VOICEBANK, THE IRISH
VOICE-OVER AGENCY** T 00 353 1 6789800
62 Lower Baggot Street, Dublin 2, Ireland
E voicebank@voicebank.ie
W www.voicebank.ie

VOICECALL T 020 7209 1064
67A Gondar Gardens, London NW6 1EP
E voices@voicecall-online.co.uk
W www.voicecall-online.co.uk

**VOICEOVER GALLERY
(LONDON) THE** T 020 7987 0951
12 Cock Lane, London EC1A 9BU
E london@thevoiceovergallery.co.uk
W www.thevoiceovergallery.co.uk

**VOICEOVER GALLERY
(MANCHESTER) THE** T 0161 881 8844
1st Floor, 1 Ridgefield
King Street, Manchester M2 6EG
E manchester@thevoiceovergallery.co.uk
W www.thevoiceovergallery.co.uk

VOICEOVERS.CO.UK T 020 7099 2264
PO Box 326, Plymouth, Devon PL4 9YQ
F 020 3411 2699
E info@voiceovers.co.uk
W www.voiceovers.co.uk

**VSI - VOICE &
SCRIPT INTERNATIONAL** T 020 7692 7700
Foreign Language Specialists
132 Cleveland Street, London W1T 6AB
F 020 7692 7711
E info@vsi.tv
W www.vsi.tv

WAM VOICES T 020 7495 6665
The Voice Agency of Waring & McKenna
11-12 Dover Street
Mayfair, London W1S 4LJ
F 020 7629 6466
E info@wamvoices.com
W www.wamvoices.com

WOOTTON, Suzy VOICES T 01604 765872
72 Towcester Road, Far Cotton
Northampton NN4 8LQ
E suzy@suzywoottonvoices.com
W www.suzywoottonvoices.com

YAKETY YAK T 020 7430 2600
7A Bloomsbury Square, London WC1A 2LP
F 020 7404 6109
E info@yaketyyak.co.uk
W www.yaketyyak.co.uk

iCan talk

Voice Over Agency

t: 01858 466749
e: hello@icantalk.co.uk
w: www.icantalk.co.uk

AVENUE ARTISTES LTD *The South's most efficient casting service*

ACTORS, SUPPORTING ARTISTES, EXTRAS & WALK ONS AVAILABLE
FOR TELEVISION, FILMS, COMMERCIALS, ADVERTISING etc

PO Box 1573, Southampton SO16 3XS   TEL: 02380 760930
EMAIL: info@avenueartistes.com WEBSITE: www.avenueartistes.com

---

2020 CASTING LTD　　　**T** 020 8746 2020
2020 Hopgood Street, London W12 7JU
F 020 8735 2727
E info@2020casting.com
W www.2020casting.com

AGENCY OAKROYD　　　**T** 07840 784337
Oakroyd, 89 Wheatley Lane
Ben Rhydding, Ilkley, Yorkshire LS29 8PP
F 01943 600820
E paula@agencyoakroyd.com
W www.agencyoakroyd.com

ALLSORTS AGENCY　　　**T** 020 8989 0500
Modelling
Suite 3, Marlborough Business Centre
96 George Lane, London E18 1AD
F 020 8989 5600
E bookings@allsortsagency.com
W www.allsortsagency.com

ARTIST MANAGEMENT UK LTD　**T** 0151 523 6222
PO Box 96, Liverpool L9 8WY
E chris@artistmanagementuk.com
W www.artistmanagementuk.com

AVENUE ARTISTES LTD　　**T** 023 8076 0930
PO Box 1573, Southampton SO16 3XS
E info@avenueartistes.com
W www.avenueartistes.com

AWA - ANDREA WILDER AGENCY T 07919 202401
23 Cambrian Drive, Colwyn Bay
Conwy LL28 4SL
F 07092 249314
E casting@awagency.co.uk
W www.awagency.co.uk

BENNETTON - CMP　　　**T** 01924 882414
Raines Business Centre
Raines House
Denby Dale Road, Wakefield, West Yorkshire WF1 1HR
T 07540 693657
E enquiries@bennetton-cmp.co.uk
W www.bennetton-cmp.co.uk

Bennetton-cmp

Bennetton casting, modelling and promotions (cmp) has been involved in the media for 2 decades providing hands on experience, to both clients and associates, which is second to none.

Our assignments are many fold with television work, film & cinema, advertising, modelling and promotions. Our work also extends into magazine & editorial assignments, exhibition and events.

Bennetton is renowned for building an excellent rapport with each individual on our books. We pride ourselves on first class dedication to our client's specification, to ensure we make the right choice for all assignments delivering high quality services.

Contact us at:
Bennetton-cmp, Raines Business Centre, Raines House, Denby Dale Road, WAKEFIELD, West Yorkshire, WF1 1HR.
T: 01924 882414　**T:** 07540 693657　**Fax:** 01924 291008
E: enquiries@bennetton-cmp.co.uk www.bennetton-cmp.co.uk

BONNIE & BETTY LTD　　**T** 020 8676 6294
County House, 221-241 Beckenham Road
Beckenham, Kent BR3 4UF
E agency@bonnieandbetty.com
W www.bonnieandbetty.com

BOSS CASTING　　　　**T** 0161 237 0101
Fourways House, 57 Hilton Street
Manchester M1 2EJ
F 0161 236 1237
E cath@bosscasting.co.uk
W www.bosscasting.co.uk

BROADCASTING AGENCY　　**T** 020 7490 4225
3rd Floor, Block A, Morelands
5-23 Old Street, London EC1V 9HL
E info@broadcastingagency.co.uk
W www.broadcastingagency.co.uk

BROOK, Dolly CASTING AGENCY T 01371 875767
PO Box 5436, Dunmow CM6 1WW
F 01371 875996
E dollybrookcasting@btinternet.com

CAIRNS AGENCY THE　　**T** 0141 222 2333
Contact: Maureen Cairns, Allan Jones
2nd Floor, 34 Argyle Arcade Chambers
Buchanan Street, Glasgow G2 8BD
E info@thecairnsagency.com

CASTING COLLECTIVE LTD THE **T** 020 8962 0099
Olympic House, 317-321 Latimer Road
London W10 6RA
F 020 8962 0333
E casting@castingcollective.co.uk
W www.castingcollective.co.uk

CASTING NETWORK LTD THE　**T** 020 8391 2979
4 Vidler Close, Chessington, Surrey KT9 2GL
F 020 8391 5119
E info@thecastingnetwork.co.uk
W www.thecastingnetwork.co.uk

CELEX CASTING LTD　　**T** 01332 232445
Adults & Children available
PO Box 7317, Derby DE1 0GS
T 07932 066021
E anne@celex.co.uk

CENTRAL CASTING LTD　　**T** 020 7722 1551
See also KNIGHT Ray CASTING
21A Lambolle Place, Belsize Park
London NW3 4PG
E casting@rayknight.co.uk
W www.rayknight.co.uk

CREATIVE KIDZ & CO　　**T** 07958 377595
9 Weavers Terrace, Fulham, London SW6 1QE
T 07908 144802
E info@creativekidzandco.co.uk

DAVID AGENCY THE　　**T** 020 8834 1615
26-28 Hammersmith Grove, London W6 7BA
E casting@davidagency.co.uk
W www.davidagency.co.uk

Walk-On & Supporting Artists Agents

Who are Walk-on and Supporting Artists?

Sometimes known as 'Extras', walk-on and supporting artists appear in the background of TV and film scenes in order to add a sense of realism, character or atmosphere. They do not have individual speaking roles, unless required to make background/ambient noise. Working as a walk-on or supporting artist does not require any specific 'look', training or experience as such; however it does involve more effort than people think. Artists are often required to start very early in the morning (6am is not uncommon), and days can be long with lots of waiting around, sometimes in tough conditions on location. It is certainly not glamorous, nor is it a way to become a TV or film star! Artists must be reliable and available at very short notice, which can make it difficult to juggle with other work or family commitments. Requirements vary from production to production and, as with mainstream acting work, there are no guarantees that you will get regular work, let alone be able to earn a living as a walk-on.

How should I use these listings?

If you are serious about working as a walk-on artist, you will need to register with an agency in order to be put forward for jobs. In return for finding you work, you can expect an agency to take between 10-15% in commission. The listings in this section contain contact details of many walk-on and supporting artist agencies. Some will specialise in certain areas, so make sure you research the different companies carefully to see if they are appropriate for you. Many have websites you can visit. It is also worth asking questions about how long an agency has existed, and about their recent production credits. When approaching an agency for representation, you should send them your CV with a covering letter and a recent photograph which is a genuine, natural likeness of you. Enclosing a stamped-addressed envelope with sufficient postage (SAE) will give you a better chance of a reply.

Should I pay a Walk-on agent to join their books? Or sign a contract?

As with other types of agencies, Equity does not generally recommend that artists pay an agent to join their client list. Before signing any contract, you should be clear about the terms and commitments involved. Always speak to Equity www.equity.org.uk or BECTU www.bectu.org.uk if you have any concerns or queries. Equity also produces the booklet *You and your Agent* which is free to all Equity members and available from their website's members' area.

Where can I find more information?

You may find it useful to contact the Film Artists Association, a subdivision of BECTU, who provide union representation for walk-on and supporting artists. You can read their case study in this section or for further details visit www.bectu.org.uk/get-involved/background-artistes

Walk-On & Supporting Artists Agents

CASE STUDY

If you are working, or intend to work, as a background artiste, stand-in or a double you could consider becoming a member of the Film Artistes Association. The FAA is a subdivision of BECTU, the independent trade union for those working in broadcasting, film, theatre, entertainment, leisure, interactive media and allied areas.

Central to BECTU's role in this dynamic and expanding sector is to give freelance members advice on agreed rates of pay and assist them when they need us. Some of our members are household names, and many more have won awards for their professional excellence — including Oscars, BAFTA awards and Royal Society awards. The FAA, which was formed in 1927, is a growing part of the union and represents background artistes, stand-ins and doubles who render such performances or services to set the atmosphere of scenes both on and off the camera.

Productions of course can be set in any period, country, or indeed planet and consequently background artistes are also expected to work with such clothing, make-up, wigs and hairstyles as the production dictates. This work is critical to the atmosphere of a scene and to the audience's suspension of disbelief. In a battle scene or horror film, for example, an artiste who does not die convincingly could completely change the audience's response from shock and revulsion to mirth, thus destroying the whole scene. This is why experienced background artistes provide an essential service to film-makers and independent producers. Whilst these workers may not be in the foreground of a particular shot, their skills are vital to the quality of the final work.

The FAA is not an agency and therefore doesn't find work for members. The current unlicensed agency market has led to the emergence, and sudden disappearance, of rogue agents who have cheated a number of background artistes in the past. So bear in mind that no reputable agency will put you or anyone else on their books

without seeing you. After all you could be tall, dark and handsome according to your CV (and even your photo), but a good agency will ask to see you to confirm this before accepting you on their books — and you can check them out too. Also beware of agencies trying to hide their location using PO Box numbers and premium rate telephone lines. Having acting experience and being confident, determined, reliable and punctual are all qualities a good agent will seek out.

If you work as a background artiste or you still think this is for you (and it's definitely not for everyone), you should join the FAA subdivision of BECTU. We negotiate and police the rates of pay within the film and TV sector. We offer individual legal assistance and help keep you out of trouble, or get you out when you're in it. BECTU is here to help you get the most out of the industry and avoid the worst: the latest pay increase we won for FAA members, at this time of national recession, is a whopping 5.2%.

If you're already a member, take a moment to check out our range of benefits and services on our website.

Having acting experience and being confident, determined, reliable and punctual are all qualities a good agent will seek out.

Finally, the entertainment industry is perceived as attractive because of the explosion of reality TV and the message that anyone can be a star. This is a very competitive industry, so don't believe that if an agent takes you on it will lead to instant success, fame and fortune. However, if it is a job you like and you are treated fairly it could be a most enjoyable way of earning money.

Please visit www.bectu.org.uk or call 020 7346 0900 for further information.

DK MODEL MANAGEMENT   T 0114 257 3480
4 Park Square, Thorncliffe Park
Chapeltown, Sheffield
South Yorkshire S35 2PH
F 0114 257 3482
E mail@dkmodels.net
W www.dkmodels.net

DOE, John ASSOCIATES   T 01543 300689
262 Beacon Street, Lichfield WS13 7BH
T 07957 114175
E casting@johndoemgt.com
W www.johndoemgt.com

ELLIOTT AGENCY LTD THE   T 01273 454111
10 High Street
Shoreham-by-Sea BN43 5DA
E elliottagency@btconnect.com
W www.elliottagency.co.uk

ETHNIKA CASTING   T 0845 6031266
14 Bowmont Gardens, Glasgow G12 9LR
T 07778 296002
E ethnikacasting@yahoo.co.uk
W www.ethnikacasting.co.uk

**EUROKIDS & EKA
CASTING AGENCIES**   T 01925 761088
The Warehouse Studios, Glaziers Lane
Culcheth, Warrington, Cheshire WA3 4AQ
F 01925 767563
E castings@eka-agency.com
W www.eka-agency.com

EXTRA-PEOPLE LTD   T 020 7734 7606
42 Old Compton Street, Soho
London W1D 4TX
F 020 7287 2855
E contact@extra-people.com
W www.extra-people.com

EXTRASPECIAL LTD   T 020 7240 9240
The Price Building, 110 York Road
Battersea, London SW11 3RD
F 020 7240 4879
E info@extraspecialartists.com

FACE MUSIC   T 01209 820796
Musician's Agency
Lambourne Farm, TR16 5HA
E facemusic@btinternet.com

SÉVA DHALIVAAL
07956 553879

FBI AGENCY   T 07050 222747
PO Box 250, Leeds LS1 2AZ
T 07515 567309
E casting@fbi-agency.co.uk
W www.fbi-agency.co.uk

FEATURED & BACKGROUND
CASTING LTD   T 01628 522688
Contact: Lois Ward, Suzanne Johns
13A Waldeck House, Waldeck Road
Maidenhead, Berkshire SL6 8BR
T 07808 781167
E info@fabcastingagency.com
W www.fabcastingagency.com

FILM CAST CORNWALL & SW   T 01326 311419
T 07811 253756
E enquiries@filmcastcornwall.co.uk
W www.filmcastcornwall.co.uk

FRESH AGENTS LTD   T 01273 711777
Actors. Extras. Modelling. Promotional
Suite 5, Saks House
19 Ship Street
Brighton BN1 1AD
T 0845 4080998
E info@freshagents.co.uk
W www.freshagents.co.uk

GOLD-CAST AGENCY   T 07970 187801
PO Box 30, Treharris
Mid Glamorgan CF46 9AN
E enquiries@gold-castagency.co.uk
W www.gold-castagency.co.uk

GUYS & DOLLS CASTING   T 020 8906 4144
Trafalgar House, Grenville Place
Mill Hill, London NW7 3SA
T 07890 774454
E info@guysanddollscasting.com
W www.guysanddollscasting.com

HERRON, Alana
PERSONAL MANAGEMENT   T 07877 984636
51 Medrox Gardens
Glasgow G67 4AL
E alana@alanaherron.com
W www.alanaherron.com

INDUSTRY CASTING   T 0161 839 1551
332 Royal Exchange, Manchester M2 7BR
F 0161 839 1661
E lois@industrypeople.co.uk
W www.industrycasting.co.uk

IPM TALENT   T 0113 244 3222
Contact: Stewart Ross
The Studio, 102 Kirkstall Road
Leeds, West Yorkshire LS3 1JA
E stewart@ipmcasting.com
W www.ipmcasting.com

JACLYN AGENCY   T 01603 622027
52 Bessemer Road, Norwich
Norfolk NR4 6DQ
E info@jaclynagency.co.uk
W www.jaclynagency.co.uk

JPM EXTRAS   T 0191 221 2491
A Division of Janet Plater Management Ltd
D Floor, Milburn House
Dean Street, Newcastle upon Tyne NE1 1LF
E extras@tynebridge.demon.co.uk
W www.janetplatermanagement.co.uk

KNIGHT, Ray CASTING   T 020 7722 4111
21A Lambolle Place, Belsize Park
London NW3 4PG
E casting@rayknight.co.uk
W www.rayknight.co.uk

KREATE PROMOTIONS   T 020 7401 9007
Unit 232
Great Guildford Business Square
30 Great Guildford Street
London SE1 0HS
F 020 7401 9008
E hello@kreate.co.uk
W www.kreate.co.uk

LEMON CASTING LTD   T 0161 205 2096
The Sharp Project
Thorpe Road
Newton Heath, Manchester M40 5BJ
T 07723 317489
E info@lemoncasting.co.uk

LINTON MANAGEMENT   T 0161 761 2020
3 The Rock, Bury BL9 0JP
F 0161 761 1999
E mail@linton.tv
W www.lintonmanagement.co.uk

MAD DOG CASTING LTD   T 020 7269 7910
2nd Floor, Holborn Hall
193-197 High Holborn
London WC1V 7BD
F 020 7831 7267
E info@maddogcasting.com
W www.maddogcasting.com

McDONAGH, Melanie
MANAGEMENT (ACADEMY OF PERFORMING
ARTS & CASTING AGENCY)   T 01254 392560
14 Apple Tree Way
Oswaldtwistle
Accrington, Lancashire BB5 0FB
T 07909 831409
E mcdonaghmgt@aol.com
W www.mcdonaghmanagement.co.uk

NEMESIS AGENCY LTD   T 0161 228 6404
Nemesis House, 1 Oxford Court
Bishopsgate, Manchester M2 3WQ
F 0161 228 6727
E julie@nmsmanagement.co.uk
W www.nemesiscasting.co.uk

NIDGES CASTING AGENCY
See BOSS CASTING

NORTHERN PROFESSIONALS CASTING COMPANY   T 0191 257 8635
21 Cresswell Avenue, North Shields
Tyne & Wear NE29 9BQ
E bill@northernprocasting.co.uk
W www.northernprocasting.co.uk

ORIENTAL CASTING AGENCY LTD   T 020 8660 0101
Contact: Billie James
22 Wontford Road, Purley
Surrey CR8 4BL
F 020 8674 9303
E billiejames@btconnect.com
W www.orientalcasting.com

PAN ARTISTS AGENCY LTD   T 0800 6349147
Cornerways
34 Woodhouse Lane
Sale, Cheshire M33 4JX
T 07890 715115
E panartists@btconnect.com
W www.panartists.co.uk

PC THEATRICAL MODEL & CASTING AGENCY   T 020 8381 2229
10 Strathmore Gardens, Edgware
Middlesex HA8 5HJ
F 020 8933 3418
E twinagy@aol.com
W www.twinagency.com

PERFORMERS LEAGUE AGENCY LTD THE   T 07538 800083
Studio 55, 55 Openshaw Road
Abbeywood, London SE2 0TB
T 07946 781116
E johnson@tpla.co.uk
W www.tpla.co.uk

PHA CASTING   T 0161 273 4444
Tanzaro House
Ardwick Green North
Manchester M12 6FZ
F 0161 273 4567
E info@pha-agency.co.uk
W www.pha-agency.co.uk

PHOENIX CASTING AGENCY   T 0117 973 1100
PO Box 387, Bristol BS99 3JZ
F 0117 973 4160
E info@phoenixagency.biz
W www.phoenixagency.biz

POLEASE   T 05600 650524
Specialist in Police & Military
1 Noake Road, Hucclecote
Gloucester GL3 3PE
T 07811 504079
E info@polease.co.uk
W www.polease.co.uk

POWER MODEL MANAGEMENT CASTING AGENCY   T 01603 777190
PO Box 1198, Salhouse
Norwich NR13 6WD
E info@powermodel.co.uk
W www.powermodel.co.uk

RAPID TALENT MANAGEMENT   T 020 7734 5775
5 Vancouver Road, Sovereign Harbour
Eastbourne, East Sussex BN23 5BF
T 07980 899156
E enquiries@rapidtalent.co.uk
W www.rapidtalent.co.uk

RAY'S NORTHERN CASTING AGENCY   T/F 0161 643 6745
7 Wince Close, Alkrington
Middleton, Manchester M24 1UJ
E rayscasting@yahoo.co.uk

REGENCY AGENCY   T 0113 255 8980
25 Carr Road, Calverley
Leeds LS28 5NE

REVOLUTION TALENT MANAGEMENT   T 0141 221 2258
Central Chambers, 93 Hope Street
Glasgow G2 6LD
F 0141 221 8622
E enquiries@revolutiontalentmanagement.com
W www.revolutiontalentmanagement.com

REYNOLDS, Sandra AGENCY   T 020 7387 5858
Amadeus House, 27B Floral Street
London WC2E 9DP
F 020 7387 5848
E info@sandrareynolds.co.uk
W www.sandrareynolds.co.uk

REYNOLDS, Sandra AGENCY (EAST ANGLIA)   T 01603 623842
Bacon House, 35 St Georges Street
Norwich NR3 1DA
F 01603 219825
E info@sandrareynolds.co.uk
W www.sandrareynolds.co.uk

RHODES AGENCY　　T 01708 747013
5 Dymoke Road, Hornchurch
Essex RM11 1AA
F 01708 730431
E rhodesarts@hotmail.com

**SA19 - THE UNIFORMED
ARTISTE AGENCY**　　T 020 8746 2523
2020 Hopgood Street
Shepherds Bush
London W12 7JU
F 020 8735 2727
E info@sa19.co.uk
W www.sa19.co.uk

**SAPPHIRES MODEL
MANAGEMENT**　　T 0844 8845404
51-53 Rupert Street
London W10 7PH
F 0870 9127563
E contact@sapphiresmodel.com
W www.sapphiresmodel.com

SCREAM MANAGEMENT　　T 0161 850 1996
The Pie Factory
101 Broadway
Media City, Manchester M50 2EQ
T 0161 850 1995
E info@screammanagement.com
W www.screammanagement.com

SCREENLITE AGENCY　　T 01932 561388
Shepperton Studios
Studios Road
Shepperton, Middlesex TW17 0QD
T 01932 592271
E enquiries@screenliteagency.co.uk
W www.screenliteagency.co.uk

SEVEN CASTING AGENCY　　T 0161 850 1057
Manchester Office: 4th Floor
59 Piccadilly, Manchester M1 2AQ
T 07801 942178
E guy@7casting.co.uk
W www.7casting.co.uk

SEVEN CASTING AGENCY　　T 01785 212266
Staffordshire Office: Suite 3
Tudor House
9 Eastgate Street, Stafford ST16 2NQ
T 07801 942178
E guy@7casting.co.uk
W www.7casting.co.uk

SHARMAN, Alan AGENCY　　T 0121 212 0090
Office 9 Fournier House
8 Tenby Street, Jewellery Quarter
Birmingham B1 3AJ
E info@alansharmanagency.com
W www.alansharmanagency.com

SLICK CASTING LTD　　T/F 020 8531 5061
Unit 23, Oaklands Avenue, London N9 7LN
T 07944 939462
E info@slickcasting.com
W www.slickcasting.com

**SNODE, Chris
PROMOTIONS LTD**　　T 020 8771 4700
56 Church Road, Crystal Palace
London SE19 2EZ
F 020 8771 4704
E agent@sportspromotions.co.uk
W www.sportspromotions.co.uk

SOLOMON ARTISTES　　T 020 7748 4409
30 Clarence Street, Southend-on-Sea
Essex SS1 1BD
T 01702 437118
E info@solomon-artistes.co.uk
W www.solomon-artistes.co.uk

SPIRIT MODEL MANAGEMENT　　T 01952 510145
Alternative & Character Agency
91 Stocking Park Road, Lightmoor Village
Telford, Shropshire TF4 3QZ
T 07896 978972
E info@spiritmodels.co.uk
W www.spiritmodels.co.uk

STAV'S CASTING AGENCY　　T 07538 931648
82 Station Crescent, Tottenham
Haringey, London N15 5BD
E stavros.louca@btinternet.com
W www.stavscastingagency.com

**SUMMERS, Mark
MANAGEMENT**　　T 020 7229 8413
1 Beaumont Avenue, West Kensington
London W14 9LP
E louise@marksummers.com
W www.marksummers.com

TUESDAYS CHILD LTD　　T/F 01625 501765
Children & Adults
Oakfield House, Springwood Way
Macclesfield SK10 2XA
E info@tuesdayschildagency.co.uk
W www.tuesdayschildagency.co.uk

TURNSTONE CASTING AGENCY　　T 0845 5576658
Hilton Hall, Hilton Lane
Essington WV11 2BQ
T 07866 211647
E mark_turner85@hotmail.com

UNI-VERSAL EXTRAS　　T 0845 0090344
Pinewood Studios, Pinewood Road
Iver Heath, Buckinghamshire SL0 0NH
E info@universalextras.co.uk
W www.universalextrascasting.co.uk

WARD CASTING　　T 020 8886 5676
Studio 5, 155 Commercial Street
London E1 6BJ
E casting@wardcasting.com
W www.wardcasting.com

THE KNIGHTS OF MIDDLE ENGLAND

The Knights of Middle England are a professional Jousting Stunt Team providing a range of services for the Theatre, Film & TV industry and are the UK's leading Jousting School.
We offer: • Trained Horses & Riders for the TV & Film Industry • Medieval Knights Sword fighting
• Hire of Medieval equipment, props & costumes • Jousting Shows & Demonstrations
• Learn to Joust with our tailor-made courses/lessons or experience days.
**Based in the heart of the Midlands in Warwick, Warwickshire. Direct Trains – Euston to Coventry – 1hr only / London Marylebone to Warwick –
1hr 30 mins – pick up available   e:** info@knightsofmiddleengland.co.uk   **t:** 00 44 (0)1926 400401   **www.knightsofmiddleengland.co.uk**

A1 ANIMALS   T/F 01608 683954
Farm, Domestic & Exotic Animals
Wattel Hill Farm, Dunstew
Ledwell, Oxon OX7 7AN
E a1animals@btinternet.com
W www.a1animals.co.uk

A-Z ANIMALS LTD   T 01372 377111
The Bell House, Bell Lane
Fetcham, Surrey KT22 9ND
E info@a-zanimals.co.uk
W www.a-zanimals.co.uk

**ACTION STUNT DOGS
& ANIMALS**   T/F 01869 338546
3 The Chestnuts, Clifton
Deddington, Oxon OX15 0PE
E gill@stuntdogs.net

ALTERNATIVE ANIMALS   T 07956 564715
Contact: Trevor Smith. Animatronics. Taxidermy
28 Greaves Road, High Wycombe, Bucks HP13 7JU
F 01494 441385
E animalswork1@yahoo.co.uk
W www.animalswork.co.uk

ANIMAL ACTING   T 0161 655 3700
Animals. Horse-drawn Vehicles. Props. Stunts
7 Dovedale Court, Windermere Road
Middleton, Manchester M24 5QT
T 07831 800567
E information@animalacting.com
W www.animalacting.com

ANIMAL ACTORS   T 07710 348777
Animals. Birds. Reptiles
95 Ditchling Road, Brighton
Sussex BN1 4ST

ANIMAL AMBASSADORS   T/F 01635 200900
Old Forest, Hampstead Norreys Road
Hermitage, Berks RG18 9SA
T 07831 558594
E kayweston@tiscali.co.uk
W www.animalambassadors.co.uk

**ANIMAL WELFARE
FILMING FEDERATION**   T 07770 666088
Free Consultancy Service
28 Greaves Road, High Wycombe, Bucks HP13 7JU
F 01494 441385
E animalswork1@yahoo.co.uk
W www.animalworld.org.uk

ANIMALS GALORE LTD   T 01342 842400
208 Smallfield Road, Horley
Surrey RH6 9LS
W www.animals-galore.co.uk

ANIMALS O KAY   T 01923 291277
16 Queen Street, Chipperfield
Kings Langley, Herts WD4 9BT
E kayraven@btinternet.com
W www.animalsokay.com

**ANIMALS WORK WITH
TREVOR SMITH**   T 07956 564715
Contact: Trevor Smith
28 Greaves Road, High Wycombe, Bucks HP13 7JU
T 07770 666088
E animalswork1@yahoo.co.uk
W www.animalswork.co.uk

CELEBRITY REPTILES   T/F 020 8659 0877
11 Tramway Close, London SE20 7DF
E info@celebrityreptiles.co.uk
W www.celebrityreptiles.co.uk

CHEESEMAN, Virginia   T 01628 522632
21 Willow Close, Flackwell Heath
High Wycombe, Bucks HP10 9LH
T 07971 838724
E virginia@virginiacheeseman.co.uk
W www.virginiacheeseman.co.uk

COTSWOLD FARM PARK   T 01451 850307
Rare Breed Farm Animals
Guiting Power, Cheltenham, Gloucestershire GL54 5UG
F 01451 850423
E info@cotswoldfarmpark.co.uk

CREATURE FEATURE   T/F 01387 860648
Animal Agent
Gubhill Farm, Ae, Dumfries
Scotland DG1 1RL
T 07770 774866
E david@creaturefeature.co.uk
W www.creaturefeature.co.uk

DOG EXTRAS   T 01476 862028
11 Colster Way, Colsterworth
Grantham, Lincs NG33 5JT
T 07956 369890
E info@dog-extras.co.uk
W www.dog-extras.co.uk

DOLBADARN FILM HORSES   T/F 01286 870277
Dolbadarn Hotel, High Street, Llanberis
Gwynedd, North Wales LL55 4SU
T 07710 461341
E info@filmhorses.co.uk
W www.filmhorses.co.uk

DUDLEY, Yvonne
LRPS ARAD FISTD   T 020 8989 1528
Glamour Dogs & Stories for Films
55 Cambridge Park, Wanstead
London E11 2PR
T 07528 519591

FILM & TV HORSES   T/F 01753 864464
Crown Farm, Eton Wick Road
Eton, Windsor SL4 6PG
T 07831 629662
E filmhorses@yahoo.co.uk
W www.filmhorses.com

GET STUFFED   T 020 7226 1364
Taxidermy
105 Essex Road, London N1 2SL
T 07831 260062
E taxidermy@thegetstuffed.co.uk
W www.thegetstuffed.co.uk

GRAY, Robin COMMENTARIES   T 01420 23347
Equestrian Equipment. Horse Race Commentaries.
Voice Overs
Comptons, Isington, Alton, Hants GU34 4PL
T 07831 828424
E gray@isington.fsnet.co.uk

HILTON HORSES   T 07958 292222
Contact: Samantha Jones
478 London Road, Ashford, Middlesex TW15 3AD
E samantha@hilton-horses.com
W www.hilton-horses.com

KNIGHTS OF ARKLEY THE   T/F 01269 861001
Glyn Sylen Farm, Five Roads, Llanelli SA15 5BJ
E penny@knightsofarkley.fsnet.co.uk
W www.knightsofarkley.com

KNIGHTS OF MIDDLE
ENGLAND THE   T 01926 400401
Horses & Riders for Film, Opera & Television
Warwick International School of Riding, Guys Cliffe
Coventry Road, Warwick CV34 5YD
E info@knightsofmiddleengland.co.uk
W www.knightsofmiddleengland.co.uk

MILLENNIUM BUGS   T 01494 442750
Live Insects
28 Greaves Road, High Wycombe, Bucks HP13 7JU
F 01494 441385
E animalswork1@yahoo.co.uk
W www.animalworld.org.uk

MINI PONY HIRE   T 07777 678687
18 South View
Cambois, Blyth
Northumberland NE24 1RX
E miniponyhire@hotmail.co.uk
W www.miniponyhire.com

MORTON, Geoff   T 01430 860185
Shire Horse & Equipment
Hasholme Carr Farm
Holme on Spalding Moor
York YO43 4BD
T 01430 860393

NOLTON STABLES   T 01437 710360
Nolton, Nr Newgale
Haverfordwest
Pembrokeshire SA62 3NW
F 01437 710967
E noltonstables@aol.com
W www.noltonstables.com

OTTERS   T 01285 760234
Contact: Daphne & Martin Neville
Tame Otters
Baker's Mill, Frampton Mansell
Stroud, Glos GL6 8JH
E martin_neville_bakers_mill@yahoo.co.uk

PROP FARM LTD   T 01909 723100
Contact: Pat Ward
Grange Farm, Elmton
Nr Creswell, North Derbyshire S80 4LX
F 01909 721465
E les@propfarm.co.uk

ROCKWOOD ANIMALS
ON FILM   T 029 2088 5420
Lewis Terrace, Llanbradach
Caerphilly CF83 3JZ
T 07973 930983
E martin@rockwoodanimals.com
W www.rockwoodanimals.com

SCHOOL OF NATIONAL
EQUITATION LTD   T 01509 852366
Contact: Sam Humphrey
Bunny Hill Top, Costock
Loughborough
Leicestershire LE12 6XN
T 07977 930083
E sam@bunnyhill.co.uk
W www.bunnyhill.co.uk

WHITE DOVES
COMPANY LTD THE   T 020 8508 1414
Provision of up to 150 Doves for Release
Suite 210 Sterling House, Langston Road
Loughton, Essex IG10 3TS
F 020 8502 2461
E thewhitedovecompany@yahoo.co.uk
W www.thewhitedovecompany.co.uk

WOLF SPECIALISTS THE   T 0118 971 3330
The UK Wolf Conservation Trust
UK Wolf Centre, Butlers Farm
Beenham, Berks RG7 5NT
E ukwct@ukwolf.org
W www.ukwolf.org

YORKSHIRE TERRIER   T 07963 818845
Based in Central London
17 Gardnor Road, London NW3 1HA
E woodlandcreature10@hotmail.com

ALDERSHOT: West End Centre   T 01252 408040
Queens Road, Aldershot
Hants GU11 3JD
BO 01252 330040
E westendcentre@hants.gov.uk
W www.westendcentre.co.uk

BILLERICAY: Billericay
Arts Association   T 01277 659286
The Fold, 72 Laindon Road, Billericay
Essex CM12 9LD
E baathefold@yahoo.co.uk
W www.baathefold.org.uk

BINGLEY: Bingley Arts Centre   T 01274 431576
Main Street, Bingley
West Yorkshire BD16 2LZ
E community-halls@bradford.gov.uk

BIRMINGHAM:
The Custard Factory   T 0121 224 7777
Gibb Street, Digbeth
Birmingham B9 4AA
F 0121 604 8888
E info@custardfactory.co.uk
W www.custardfactory.co.uk

BOSTON: Blackfriars
Theatre & Arts Centre   T 01205 363108
Contact: Mike Raymond
Spain Lane, Boston
Lincolnshire PE21 6HP
F 01205 358855
E director@blackfriarsartscentre.co.uk
W www.blackfriarsartscentre.co.uk

BRACKNELL: South Hill
Park Arts Centre   T 01344 484858
Contact: Ron McAllister (Chief Executive)
Ringmead, Bracknell
Berkshire RG12 7PA
BO 01344 484123
E admin@southhillpark.org.uk
W www.southhillpark.org.uk

BRADFORD: Theatre in The Mill   T 01274 233185
University of Bradford, Shearbridge Road
Bradford, West Yorkshire BD7 1DP
BO 01274 233200
E theatre@bradford.ac.uk
W www.bradford.ac.uk/theatre

BRENTFORD:
Watermans Arts Centre   T 020 8232 1019
40 High Street, Brentford TW8 0DS
BO 020 8232 1010
E info@watermans.org.uk
W www.watermans.org.uk

BRIDGWATER:
Bridgwater Arts Centre   T 01278 422700
11-13 Castle Street, Bridgwater
Somerset TA6 3DD
E info@bridgwaterartscentre.co.uk
W www.bridgwaterartscentre.co.uk

BRISTOL: Arnolfini   T 0117 917 2300
16 Narrow Quay, Bristol BS1 4QA
F 0117 917 2303
E boxoffice@arnolfini.org.uk

BUILTH WELLS:
Wyeside Arts Centre   T 01982 553668
Castle Street, Builth Wells
Powys LD2 3BN
BO 01982 552555
E house@wyeside.co.uk
W www.wyeside.co.uk

BURY: The Met   T 0161 761 7107
Contact: David Agnew (Director)
Market Street, Bury
Lancs BL9 0BW
BO 0161 761 2216
E post@themet.biz
W www.themet.biz

CANNOCK: Prince of
Wales Centre   T 01543 466453
Contact: Richard Kay (General Manager)
Church Sreet, Cannock, Staffs WS11 1DE
BO 01543 578762
E princeofwales@cannockchasedc.gov.uk

CARDIFF: Chapter Arts Centre   T 029 2031 1050
Market Road, Canton, Cardiff CF5 1QE
BO 029 2030 4400
W www.chapter.org

CHIPPING NORTON:
The Theatre   T 01608 642349
Contact: John Terry (Director), Ambereene Hitchcox
(Head of Operations)
2 Spring Street, Chipping Norton, Oxon OX7 5NL
BO 01608 642350
E admin@chippingnortontheatre.com
W www.chippingnortontheatre.com

CHRISTCHURCH:
The Regent Centre   BO 01202 499199
Contact: Eliot Walker (Manager)
51 High Street, Christchurch, Dorset BH23 1AS
E info@regentcentre.co.uk
W www.regentcentre.co.uk

CIRENCESTER:
New Brewery Arts   T 01285 657181
Brewery Court, Cirencester, Glos GL7 1JH
F 01285 644060
E admin@newbreweryarts.org.uk
W www.newbreweryarts.org.uk

COLCHESTER:
Colchester Arts Centre   T 01206 500900
Contact: Anthony Roberts (Director)
Church Street, Colchester
Essex CO1 1NF
E info@colchesterartscentre.com
W www.colchesterartscentre.com

COVENTRY:
Warwick Arts Centre   T 024 7652 3734
Contact: Alan Rivett (Director)
University of Warwick, Coventry CV4 7AL
BO 024 7652 4524
E arts.centre@warwick.ac.uk
W www.warwickartscentre.co.uk

CUMBERNAULD:
Cumbernauld Theatre   T 01236 737235
Kildrum, Cumbernauld G67 2BN
BO 01236 732887
E info@cumbernauldtheatre.co.uk
W www.cumbernauldtheatre.co.uk

DARLINGTON:
Darlington Arts Centre   T 01325 348843
Vane Terrace, Darlington, County Durham DL3 7AX
BO 01325 486555
W www.darlingtonarts.co.uk

EDINBURGH:
Scottish Storytelling Centre   T 0131 556 9579
Contact: Dr Donald Smith (Director)
43-45 High Street, Edinburgh EH1 1SR
E reception@scottishstorytellingcentre.com
W www.scottishstorytellingcentre.co.uk

Arts Centres

EPSOM: Playhouse   T 01372 742226
Contact: Elaine Teague
Ashley Avenue, Epsom
Surrey KT18 5AL
BO 01372 742555
E eteague@epsom-ewell.gov.uk
W www.epsomplayhouse.co.uk

EXETER: Exeter Phoenix   T 01392 667060
Contact: Patrick Cunningham (Director)
Bradninch Place, Gandy Street
Exeter, Devon EX4 3LS
BO 01392 667080
E admin@exeterphoenix.org.uk
W www.exeterphoenix.org.uk

FAREHAM: Ashcroft Arts Centre   T 01329 235161
Contact: Annabel Cook (Director/Programmer)
Osborn Road, Fareham
Hants PO16 7DX
BO 01329 223100
E info@ashcroft.org.uk
W www.ashcroft.org.uk

FROME: Merlin Theatre   T 01373 461360
Bath Road, Frome
Somerset BA11 2HG
BO 01373 465949
E admin@merlintheatre.co.uk
W www.merlintheatre.co.uk

GAINSBOROUGH:
Trinity Arts Centre   T 01427 676655
Trinity Street, Gainsborough
Lincolnshire DN21 2AL
W www.trinityarts.co.uk

GREAT TORRINGTON:
The Plough Arts Centre   T 01805 622552
9-11 Fore Street, Great Torrington
Devon EX38 8HQ
BO 01805 624624
E mail@theploughartscentre.org.uk
W www.theploughartscentre.org.uk

HAVANT: Spring Arts
& Heritage Centre   BO 023 9247 2700
Contact: Amanda O'Reilly (Director)
East Street, Havant
Hants PO9 1BS
E info@thespring.co.uk
W www.thespring.co.uk

HELMSLEY:
Helmsley Arts Centre   T 01439 772112
Contact: Umay Jones (Marketing Manager)
Meeting House Court, Helmsley
York YO62 5DW
BO 01439 771700
E marketinghelmsleyarts@yahoo.co.uk
W www.helmsleyarts.co.uk

HEMEL HEMPSTEAD:
Old Town Hall Theatre   T 01442 228095
Contact: Sara Railson (Art & Entertainment Manager)
High Street, Hemel Hempstead, Herts HP1 3AE
BO 01442 228091
E othadmin@dacorum.gov.uk
W www.oldtownhall.co.uk

HEXHAM: Queens Hall Arts   T 01434 652476
Contact: Geof Keys (Artistic Director)
Beaumont Street, Hexham
Northumberland NE46 3LS
BO 01434 652477
E boxoffice@queenshall.co.uk
W www.queenshall.co.uk

HORSHAM: The Capitol   T 01403 756080
North Street, Horsham, West Sussex RH12 1RG
F 01403 756092
W www.thecapitolhorsham.com

HUDDERSFIELD: Kirklees
Communities & Leisure Services   T 01484 222087
The Stadium Business & Leisure Complex, Stadium Way
Huddersfield HD1 6PG
E arts.creativity@kirklees.gov.uk
W www.kirklees.gov.uk

INVERNESS: Eden Court   T 01463 239841
Contact: Colin Marr (Director)
Bishop's Road, Inverness IV3 5SA
BO 01463 234234
E admin@eden-court.co.uk
W www.eden-court.co.uk

ISLE OF WIGHT: Quay Arts   T 01983 822490
Sea Street, Newport Harbour, Isle of Wight PO30 5BD
F 01983 526606
E info@quayarts.org
W www.quayarts.org

JERSEY: Jersey Arts Centre   T 01534 700400
Contact: Daniel Austin (Director)
Phillips Street, St Helier, Jersey JE2 4SW
BO 01534 700444
E enquiries@artscentre.je
W www.artscentre.je

KENDAL: Brewery Arts Centre   T 01539 722833
Contact: Richard Foster (Chief Executive)
Highgate, Kendal, Cumbria LA9 4HE
BO 01539 725133
E admin@breweryarts.co.uk
W www.breweryarts.co.uk

KING'S LYNN:
King's Lynn Arts Centre   T 01553 779095
29 King Street, King's Lynn, Norfolk PE30 1HA
BO 01553 764864
W www.kingslynnarts.co.uk

LEICESTER: Phoenix Square   T 0116 242 2803
Midland Street, Leicester LE1 1TG
BO 0116 242 2800
W www.phoenix.org.uk

LICHFIELD: Lichfield District
Arts Association   T 01543 262223
Contact: Brian Pretty (Director)
Donegal House, Bore Street, Lichfield WS13 6LU
E info@lichfieldarts.org.uk
W www.lichfieldarts.org.uk

LISKEARD:
Sterts Theatre & Arts Centre   T 01579 362962
Upton Cross, Liskeard, Cornwall PL14 5AZ
T 01579 362382
W www.sterts.co.uk

LONDON: The Albany   T 020 8692 4446
Douglas Way, Deptford, London SE8 4AG
F 020 8469 2253
E albany@thealbany.org.uk
W www.thealbany.org.uk

LONDON: The Amadeus   T 020 7286 1686
50 Shirland Road, Little Venice, London W9 2JA
E info@theamadeus.co.uk
W www.theamadeus.co.uk

LONDON: Artsdepot   BO 020 8369 5454
5 Nether Street, Tally Ho Corner
North Finchley, London N12 0GA
E info@artsdepot.co.uk
W www.artsdepot.co.uk

LONDON: BAC T 020 7223 6557
Lavender Hill, Battersea, London SW11 5TN
BO 020 7223 2223
E mailbox@bac.org.uk
W www.bac.org.uk

LONDON: Beyond T 020 8809 6946
21 Stonehouse, 199 Eade Road, London N4 1DN
T 07886 984526
E amy@beyond-centre.com
W www.beyond-centre.com

LONDON: Chats Palace T 020 8533 0227
Contact: Sarah Wickens (Centre Director)
42-44 Brooksby's Walk
Hackney, London E9 6DF
E info@chatspalace.com
W www.chatspalace.com

LONDON: The Cockpit T 020 7258 2920
Gateforth Street, London NW8 8EH
BO 020 7258 2925
E mail@thecockpit.org.uk
W www.thecockpit.org.uk

LONDON: The Drill Hall T 020 7307 5061
16 Chenies Street, London WC1E 7EX
BO 020 7307 5060
E box.office@drillhall.co.uk
W www.drillhall.co.uk

LONDON: The Hangar Arts Trust T 020 8317 8401
Contact: Alex Frith (Space Manager/Trust Chairman)
7A Melish House, Harrington Way
London SE18 5NR
E alex@aircraftcircus.com
W www.hangarartstrust.org

**LONDON:
Hoxton Hall Arts Centre** T 020 7684 0060
Contact: Cat Gray (Administrator)
130 Hoxton Street, London N1 6SH
E info@hoxtonhall.co.uk
W www.hoxtonhall.co.uk

**LONDON: Institute of
Contemporary Arts** T 020 7930 0493
*Contact: Jamie Eastman (Head of Live Performance).
No in-house productions or castings*
The Mall, London SW1Y 5AH
BO 020 7930 3647
W www.ica.org.uk

LONDON: Islington Arts Factory T 020 7607 0561
2 Parkhurst Road, London N7 0SF
F 020 7700 7229
E info@islingtonartsfactory.org
W www.islingtonartsfactory.org

LONDON: Jacksons Lane T 020 8340 5226
269A Archway Road, London N6 5AA
BO 020 8341 4421
E reception@jacksonslane.org.uk
W www.jacksonslane.org.uk

**LONDON: Menier
Chocolate Factory** T 020 7378 1712
Contact: David Babani (Artistic Director)
53 Southwark Street, London SE1 1RU
BO 020 7378 1713
E office@menierchocolatefactory.com
W www.menierchocolatefactory.com

LONDON: The Nettlefold T 020 7926 8070
*Contact: Joanne Johnson, Mark Sheehan (Centre
Development Officers)*
West Norwood Library Centre
1 Norwood High Street, London SE27 9JX

LONDON: October Gallery T 020 7831 1618
Contact: Jo Walsh
24 Old Gloucester Street, London WC1N 3AL
F 020 7405 1851
E rentals@octobergallery.co.uk
W www.octobergallery.co.uk

LONDON: Oval House Theatre T 020 7582 0080
*Contact: Rachel Briscoe & Rebecca Atkinson-Lord (Directors
of Theatre), Deborah Bestwick (Director)*
52-54 Kennington Oval, London SE11 5SW
E info@ovalhouse.com
W www.ovalhouse.com

**LONDON: Polish Social
& Cultural Association** T 020 8741 1940
238-246 King Street, London W6 0RF

LONDON: Riverside Studios T 020 8237 1000
Crisp Road, Hammersmith, London W6 9RL
BO 020 8237 1111
E reception@riversidestudios.co.uk
W www.riversidestudios.co.uk

**LONDON: The Stables Gallery
& Arts Centre** T 020 8452 8655
Gladstone Park, Dollis Hill Lane, London NW2 6HT
E stablesgallery@msn.com
W www.brentarts.org.uk

**MAIDENHEAD: Norden Farm
Centre For The Arts** T 01628 682555
Contact: Jane Corry (Director)
Altwood Road, Maidenhead SL6 4PF
BO 01628 788997
E admin@nordenfarm.org
W www.nordenfarm.org

MAIDSTONE: Hazlitt Arts Centre T 01622 753922
Contact: Mandy Hare (Theatre & Events Manager)
Earl Street, Maidstone, Kent ME14 1PL
BO 01622 758611
E theatreandevents@maidstone.gov.uk

MANCHESTER: The Lowry BO 0843 2086000
Contact: Steve Cowton (Senior Theatre Programmer)
Pier 8, Salford Quays M50 3AZ
F 0161 876 2021
E boxofficeadmin@thelowry.com
W www.thelowry.com

MILFORD HAVEN: Torch Theatre T 01646 694192
Contact: Peter Doran (Artistic Director)
St Peter's Road, Milford Haven
Pembrokeshire SA73 2BU
BO 01646 695267
E info@torchtheatre.co.uk
W www.torchtheatre.co.uk

**NORTH SHIELDS:
North Tyneside Arts** T 0191 643 7093
Saville Exchange, Howard Street
North Shields NE30 1SE
E saville-arts@northtyneside.gov.uk

NORWICH: Norwich Arts Centre T 01603 660387
St Benedicts Street, Norwich, Norfolk NR2 4PG
BO 01603 660352
E stuart@norwichartscentre.co.uk
W www.norwichartscentre.co.uk

**NUNEATON: Abbey Theatre
& Arts Centre** T 024 7632 7359
Contact: Tony Deeming (Chairman)
Pool Bank Street, Nuneaton, Warks CV11 5DB
BO 024 7635 4090
E admin@abbeytheatre.co.uk
W www.abbeytheatre.co.uk

PLYMOUTH:
Plymouth Arts Centre   T 01752 206114
Contact: Kate Sparshatt (Chief Executive Officer)
38 Looe Street, Plymouth, Devon PL4 0EB
F 01752 206118
E info@plymouthartscentre.org
W www.plymouthartscentre.org

POOLE: Lighthouse Poole
Centre for The Arts   T 0844 4068666
Kingland Road, Poole, Dorset BH15 1UG
W www.lighthousepoole.co.uk

RADLETT: The Radlett Centre   T 01923 857546
1 Aldenham Avenue, Radlett, Herts WD7 8HL
F 01923 857592
E admin@radlettcentre.com
W www.radlettcentre.co.uk

ROTHERHAM: Rotherham
Civic Theatre   T 01709 823641
Contact: Mark Scott (Theatre Manager)
Catherine Street, Rotherham
South Yorkshire S65 1EB
BO 01709 823621
W www.rotherham.gov.uk/theatres

SALISBURY:
Salisbury Arts Centre   T 01722 343020
Bedwin Street, Salisbury, Wiltshire SP1 3UT
BO 01722 321744
E info@salisburyarts.co.uk
W www.salisburyartscentre.co.uk

SHREWSBURY: The Gateway
Education & Arts Centre   T 01743 355159
The Gateway, Chester Street
Shrewsbury, Shropshire SY1 1NB
E gateway.centre@shropshire-cc.gov.uk
W www.shropshire.gov.uk

SOUTHPORT:
Southport Arts Centre   T 0151 934 2131
Lord Street, Southport, Merseyside PR8 1DB
BO 01704 540011
E artsops@seftonarts.co.uk
W www.seftonarts.co.uk

STAMFORD:
Stamford Arts Centre   T 01780 480846
Contact: Graham Burley (General Manager)
27 St Mary's Street, Stamford
Lincolnshire PE9 2DL
BO 01780 763203
E boxoffice@stamfordartscentre.com
W www.stamfordartscentre.co.uk

STIRLING:
MacRobert Arts Centre   T 01786 467155
University of Stirling, Stirling FK9 4LA
BO 01786 466666
E info@macrobert.org
W www.macrobert.org

SWANSEA: Taliesin Arts Centre   T 01792 295238
Contact: Sybil Crouch (Head of Cultural Services)
Swansea University, Singleton Park
Swansea SA2 8PZ
E s.e.crouch@swansea.ac.uk
W www.taliesinartscentre.co.uk

TAUNTON: Brewhouse Theatre
& Arts Centre   T 01823 274608
Contact: Robert Miles (Director)
Coal Orchard, Taunton, Somerset TA1 1JL
BO 01823 283244
E info@thebrewhouse.net
W www.thebrewhouse.net

TOTNES: The Arts at Dartington   T 01803 847074
Dartington Space, Dartington Hall
Totnes, Devon TQ9 6EN
BO 01803 847070
E arts@dartington.org
W www.dartington.org/arts

TUNBRIDGE WELLS:
Trinity Theatre   T 01892 678670
Church Road, Tunbridge Wells, Kent TN1 1JP
BO 01892 678678
E enquiries@trinitytheatre.net

ULEY: Prema   T 01453 860703
Contact: Gordon Scott (Director)
South Street, Uley
Nr Dursley, Glos GL11 5SS
E info@prema.demon.co.uk
W www.prema.demon.co.uk

VALE OF GLAMORGAN:
St Donats Arts Centre   T 01446 799095
Contact: Sharon Stone (General Manager)
St Donats Castle
The Vale of Glamorgan CF61 1WF
BO 01446 799100
E admin@stdonats.com

WAKEFIELD:
Wakefield Arts Centre   T 01924 789815
Wakefield College, Thornes Park Centre
Thornes Park, Horbury Road
Wakefield WF2 8QZ
BO 01924 211311
W www.theatreroyalwakefield.co.uk

WASHINGTON:
The Arts Centre Washington   T 0191 219 3455
Biddick Lane, Fatfield
Washington, Tyne & Wear NE38 8AB
F 0191 219 3458
E matthew.blyth@sunderland.gov.uk

WELLINGBOROUGH: The Castle   T 01933 229022
Contact: Gail Arnott (Executive Director), Nik Ashton
(Artistic Director)
Castle Way, Wellingborough
Northants NN8 1XA
BO 01933 270007
E info@thecastle.org.uk
W www.thecastle.org.uk

WIMBORNE: Layard Theatre   T 01202 847529
Contact: Chris Thomas (Director of Drama), Christine Haynes
(Administrator)
Canford School, Canford Magna
Wimborne, Dorset BH21 3AD
BO 01202 847525
E layardtheatre@canford.com

WINCHESTER:
The Tower @ Kings   T 01962 867986
Contact: Ben Ward (Tower Co-ordinator)
Romsey Road, Winchester, Hampshire SO22 5PW
W www.towerarts.co.uk

WINDSOR: The Firestation
Centre for Arts & Culture   T 01753 866865
The Old Court, St Leonards Road
Windsor, Berks SL4 3BL
E info@firestationartscentre.com
W www.firestationartscentre.com

WREXHAM: Oriel Wrecsam/
Wrexham Arts Centre   T 01978 292093
Rhosddu Road, Wrexham LL11 1AU
E oriel.wrecsam@wrexham.gov.uk

C →

Casting Directors
Consultants
Costumes, Wigs & Make-Up
Critics

CDG
For information regarding membership of
the Casting Directors' Guild please see:

W www.thecdg.co.uk

Casting Directors

Who are casting directors?

Casting directors are employed by directors/ production companies to source the best available actors for roles across TV, film, radio, theatre and commercials. They do the groundwork and present a shortlist of artists to the director, who often makes the final selection. Many casting directors work on a freelance basis, others are employed permanently by larger organisations such as the BBC or the National Theatre. Discovering new and emerging talent also plays an important part in their job.

Why should I approach them?

If you are an actor looking for work, you can promote yourself directly to casting directors by sending them your photo and CV. They keep actors' details on file and may consider you for future productions. Bear in mind that you will not be guaranteed a response as casting directors are physically unable to reply to every one of the vast numbers of letters they receive from actors, but it is worth your while to explore this opportunity to find work.

How should I approach them?

Many of the following casting directors have indicated the method in which they prefer actors to contact them for the first time. This tends to be by post but some accept or prefer e-mails. Some are happy to receive telephone calls, but be aware that casting directors are very busy and you should not continually call them with questions or updates once you have sent your CV. If they have not specified whether they prefer postal or e-mail contact, you should send them your CV, a headshot and a covering letter by post only, as this is the traditional method of contacting casting professionals. You should **always** include a stamped-addressed envelope (SAE) big enough to contain your 10 x 8 photo and with sufficient postage. This will increase your chances of getting a reply. Write your name and telephone number on the back of your headshot in case it gets separated from your CV.

Should I send a casting director my showreel and/or voicereel?

Some casting directors have also indicated that they are happy for actors to send showreels and/ or voicereels along with their CVs and headshots, but if this is not indicated, we would recommend that you leave these out of your correspondence but indicate in your covering letter that they are available. If a casting director is interested in you, they can contact you later for these items, but they usually prefer not to sift through hundreds of unsolicited showreels until they have first established an interest in an actor.

How do I target my search?

It is not advisable to send a generic CV to every casting director listed in this section. Research the names and companies and then target your letters accordingly. Find out what areas of the industry each one usually casts for (some specify this in their listing) and what productions they have previously cast. Keep an eye on TV, film and theatre credits so you become familiar with the casting directors used for different productions. Some of these casting directors have their own websites. If a casting director has 'CDG Member' after their name, it means they are a member of the Casting Directors' Guild, the professional organisation of casting directors working in the UK (see www.thecdg.co.uk for more information and their case study in this section).

How do I write an effective CV and covering letter?

Once you have made a short-list of suitable casting directors you should send them your CV, your headshot, and an individually tailored covering letter. The covering letter should demonstrate that you have researched the casting director, and ideally you will have a particular reason for contacting them at this time: perhaps you can tell them about your next showcase, or where they can see you currently appearing on stage. Your CV should be no longer than one page, up-to-date and spell-checked. Please see the 'Promotional Services' section of Contacts for further advice on writing CVs and covering letters.

How do I prepare for a casting/audition?

Make sure you are fully prepared with accurate information about the audition time, venue, format and the people you will be meeting. Unless it's a last minute casting, you should always read the script in advance and try to have some opinions on it. If you are asked in advance to prepare a piece, always stick to the brief with something suitable and relevant. On the day, allow plenty of time to get there so you are not flustered when you arrive. Try to be positive and enjoy yourself. Remember, the casting director doesn't want to spend several days auditioning - they want you to get the job! Never criticise previous productions you have worked on. And at the end of the casting, remember to take your script away unless you are asked to leave it, otherwise it can look as if you're not interested. Please see 'Rehearsal Rooms and Casting Suites' for more detailed advice on preparing for and attending auditions.

Should I attend a casting in a house or flat?

Professional auditions are rarely held anywhere other than an official casting studio or venue. Be very wary if you are asked to go elsewhere. Trust your instincts. If something doesn't seem right to you, it probably isn't. Always take someone with you if you are in any doubt.

How do I become a casting director?

The best way to gain experience in this field is to work as a casting assistant. Vacancies are sometimes advertised in The Stage www.thestage.co.uk or PCR www.pcrnewsletter.com. Alternatively you could try sending your CV to casting directors asking for an internship or work experience. Just as we advise actors, remember to research any casting director you are considering approaching to make sure they actually work in the area you are interested in. Work experience is likely to be unpaid, but the experience and contacts you gain will be invaluable. You may find it helpful to refer to Equity's advice leaflet *Low Pay/No Pay* which is available to all Equity members from their website's members' area.

Casting Directors

When you read CDG after a Casting Director's name, you know he/she is a member of The Casting Directors' Guild and will therefore have a minimum of five years' experience. The current CDG Committee has prepared the following advice for actors.

Casting directors are there to help actors and not to hinder them. We want you to do your best as that reflects back on us, and you should realise that we are only as good as the actors we submit for each role.

Much of our work consists of creating a shortlist of potential actors and reducing it to a suitably sized group to present for audition. We also spend a great deal of time watching you work. Members of the CDG endeavour to cover as many performances as possible on film, television and in the theatre. There is no substitute to seeing you act.

When asked to attend an interview or audition, an actor should feel confident in asking his/her agent any relevant questions about the role and the project. If this is not forthcoming, arrive early and seek information from the casting director or, better still, contact him/her the day before. If it is only possible to speak to the casting director on the day, preferably do so before entering the audition room, rather than in front of the director or producer. The casting director will be happy to help.

Sometimes you will only receive pages for a role, but a casting director will always endeavour to give you as much information about a character as is available. When possible, read the entire play/screenplay rather than just the scenes your 'character' appears in, and ideally be able to talk about the script as a whole during the interview. Take your time when reading; preparation is worth a lot but don't be fazed if you get lost over their script. If you feel that a scene is going terribly it's ok to start again.

For most non-theatre jobs these days you will find that your meeting will be recorded on video tape. These tapes are then shown to the various producers involved, and this is when the process can slow down. It takes time to build a company and for final casting choices to be made.

Casting is a matter of interpretation. As well as character information derived from the script, the vision of the producer, director, casting director and indeed the actor all come into play.

There are many reasons why one actor will be chosen over another, and even the best audition might not necessarily secure a part. Every aspect of the actor comes into play. Is he/she too young or too mature? Do they work as a family? Could they be mother and son? Does the chemistry work? There is also the frustrating problem of scripts, and parts, being re-written. A character may have an entirely different physical description in a later draft. Sadly we do not have control over this.

When it comes to contacting casting directors, most are happy to receive letters, updated photos and CVs. The best correspondence for casting directors to receive is performance information. Letters should be brief and to the point, with the production name, director, venue and/or TV channel clearly stated. If you are enquiring about work be as specific as possible, e.g. "I would like to be seen for the part of … in … because …" or something similar. Dear Sir or Madam letters just don't work.

CVs should be well laid out. List most recent work first and use your spell checker. 6x4 photos are fine to send but include an SAE if you want them returned. Casting directors rarely like unsolicited DVDs and showreels: you must be aware that we do get inundated. Also bear in mind that not receiving a response to your letter does not mean it hasn't been read and filed: it is virtually impossible to reply to the volume of mail received from actors.

In our greener world it's great that Spotlight and other web media now have the facility for us to view CVs, photos and showreels online. Use the technology: it's very easy to keep your CV up-to-date online and you can change your photo at any time of year without having to do a huge mail out to let people know.

Actors are a fundamental tool of this industry: CDG members are aware of this and aim to put actors at their ease. Audition nerves are a given but you should feel secure that the reason you are in the room is because someone wants you to get that role and not because they want to see you fail.

Please visit www.thecdg.co.uk for further information.

1066 PRODUCTIONS T 020 7193 6156
8 Blackstone House
Off Bowen Drive
West Dulwich
London SE21 8NY
E loischada@1066productions.com
W www.1066productions.com

A C A CASTING T/F 020 7384 2635
Contact: Catherine Arton
32A Edenvale Street, London SW6 2SF
E catherine@acacasting.com

ADAMSON-PARKER, Jo T 0113 219 2896
Northern Spirit Creative (Casting)
Studio 81
Kirkstall Road, Leeds LS3 1LH
T 07787 311270
E jo@northernspiritcreative.co.uk
W www.northernspiritcreative.co.uk

AILION, Pippa T/F 020 8670 4816
CDG Member
3 Towton Road, London SE27 9EE
E enquiries@pippaailioncasting.co.uk

ALL DIRECTIONS OF LONDON
Contact: By Post only
7 Rupert Court, Off Wardour Street
London W1D 6EB

ANDERSON, Jane
CDG Member. Contact: By e-mail. Accepts Showreels.
Film. Television
E casting@janeandersononline.com
W www.janeandersononline.com

ANDREW, Dorothy CASTING T 0161 339 5636
CDG Member
E dorothyandrewcasting@gmail.com

ARNOLD, Jim CASTING T 07973 942220
Contact: By Post/email only.
Accepts Showreels/Voicereels
51 St Martin's Lane, London WC2N 4EA
E jim@jacasting.co.uk
W www.jacasting.co.uk

ASHTON HINKINSON CASTING T 020 7580 6101
1 Charlotte Street, London W1T 1RD
F 020 7637 0328
E casting@ahcasting.com
W www.ashtonhinkinson.com

BAIG, Shaheen CASTING T 020 7631 5258
PO Box 7006, London W1A 1US
E info@shaheenbaigcasting.com
W www.shaheenbaigcasting.com

BARNES, Derek T 020 8228 7096
CDG Member
BBC DRAMA SERIES CASTING
BBC Elstree, Room N221
Neptune House, Clarendon Road
Borehamwood, Herts WD6 1JF
F 020 8228 8311

BEACH CASTING LTD T 0844 5679595
Contact: Brendan McNamara
1st Floor, 21 Whiston Road, London E2 8EX
T 07903 630964
E brendan@beach-casting.com
W www.beach-casting.com

THE CASTING
DIRECTORS' GUILD
OF GREAT BRITAIN
& IRELAND

The professional organisation for
Casting Directors of film, television,
theatre and commercials in the UK.

Setting the benchmark of professionalism
in the industry since 1995. Visit our site to
find over 100 affiliated Casting Directors.

www.thecdg.co.uk
Email: info@thecdg.co.uk

BEASTALL, Lesley CASTING   T 020 7727 6496
Contact: Lesley Beastall
41E Elgin Crescent, London W11 2JD
T 07956 516603
E lesley@lbcasting.co.uk

BEATTIE, Victoria
Contact: By e-mail. Film
E victoria@justcasting.net

BEAUCHAMP, Lauren CASTING   T 07961 982198
34A Brightside, Billericay CM12 0LJ
F 01277 656147
E laurenbeauchamp@talktalk.net

BECKLEY, Rowland
BBC DRAMA SERIES CASTING
BBC Elstree, Room N222
Neptune House, Clarendon Road
Borehamwood, Herts WD6 1JF
F 020 8228 7130

BERTRAND, Leila CASTING   T/F 020 8964 0683
53 Hormead Road, London W9 3NQ
E leilabcasting@gmail.com

BEVAN, Lucy   T 020 8567 6655
CDG Member
Ealing Studios, Ealing Green, London W5 5EP

BEWICK, Maureen CASTING   T 020 8450 1604
104A Dartmouth Road, London NW2 4HB

BIRD, Sarah   T 020 7371 3248
CDG Member
PO Box 32658, London W14 0XA

BIRKETT, Hannah CASTING   T 01543 300689
262 Beacon Street, Lichfield
Staffordshire WS13 7BH
T 07957 114175
E hannah@hbcasting.com

BLIGH, Nicky
CDG Member
E nicky@nickyblighcasting.com

BRACKE, Siobhan   T 020 8891 5686
CDG Member. Contact: By Post
Basement Flat, 22A The Barons
St Margaret's TW1 2AP

BUCKINGHAM, Jo   T 07753 605491
CDG Member
E jo@jobuckinghamcasting.co.uk

CANDID CASTING   T 020 7490 8882
1st Floor, 32 Great Sutton Street, London EC1V 0NB
F 020 7490 8966
E mail@candidcasting.co.uk
W www.candidcasting.co.uk

CANNON, John   T 020 8228 7322
CDG Member
BBC DRAMA SERIES CASTING, BBC Elstree
Room N223, Neptune House
Clarendon Road, Borehamwood, Herts WD6 1JF
F 020 8228 8311
E john.cannon@bbc.co.uk

CANNON DUDLEY &
ASSOCIATES   T 020 7433 3393
Contact: Carol Dudley (CDG Member). By Post. Film.
Stage. Television
43A Belsize Square, London NW3 4HN
F 020 7813 2048
E cdacasting@blueyonder.co.uk

CARLING, Di CASTING   T 020 7287 6446
CDG Member
1st Floor, 49 Frith Street
London W1D 4SG
F 020 7287 6844

CARROLL, Anji   T 01630 647242
CDG Member. Contact: By e-mail (Small Attachments only).
Film. Stage. Television
T 07957 253769
E anji@anjicarroll.tv

CASTING COMPANY (UK) THE
Contact: Michelle Guish
PO Box 66013, London W3 3BX
E casting@michguish.com

CASTING CONNECTION THE   T 0161 432 4122
Contact: Michael Syers
Dalrossie House, 16 Victoria Grove
Stockport, Cheshire SK4 5BU

CASTING COUCH THE   T 07932 785807
Contact: Moira Townsend. No CVs/Photos by Post
213 Trowbridge Road
Bradford on Avon
Wiltshire BA15 1EU
E moira@everymansland.com

CATLIFF, Suzy   T 020 8442 0749
CDG Member
PO Box 39492, London N10 3YX
E soosecat@mac.com
W www.suzycatliff.co.uk

CHAND, Urvashi   T 020 8208 3861
CDG Member
Cinecraft, 69 Teignmouth Road
London NW2 4EA
E urvashi@cinecraft.biz

CHARD, Alison   T 020 7223 9125
CDG Member
23 Groveside Court
4 Lombard Road
Battersea, London SW11 3RQ
E chardcasting@btinternet.com

CHARKHAM CASTING   T 07956 456630
Contact: Beth Charkham
Suite 361, 14 Tottenham Court Road
London W1T 1JY
E charkhamcasting@btconnect.com

CLARK, Andrea   T 020 8876 6869
Children & Adults. Commercials. Film. Stage. Television
E andrea@aclarkcasting.com
W www.aclarkcasting.com

CLAYPOLE, Sam CASTING
PO Box 123, Darlington
Durham DL3 7WA
E contact@samclaypolecasting.com
W www.samclaypolecasting.com

CLAYTON, Rosalie   T/F 020 7242 8109
CDG Member
E rosalie@rosalieclayton.com

COGAN, Ben   T 020 8228 7516
BBC DRAMA SERIES CASTING
BBC Elstree, Room N221
Neptune House
Clarendon Road
Borehamwood, Herts WD6 1JF
F 020 8228 8311

SHEILA BURNETT
PHOTOGRAPHY
Studio or Location : Student Rates

Helen Lederer

Philip Langhorne

Mathew Horne

Jeff Stewart

Sara Crowe

Ewan Mcgregor

Matthew Lewis

Imelda Staunton

John Altman

020 7289 3058
www.sheilaburnett-headshots.com

COLLINS, Jayne CASTING T 020 7223 0471
CDG Member
The Price Building, 110 York Road
London SW11 3RD
E info@jaynecollinscasting.com
W www.jaynecollinscasting.com

COLLYER-BRISTOW, Ellie T 07986 607075
35 Blackheath Park, London SE3 9RW
E elliecollyerbristow@yahoo.co.uk

CORDORAY, Lin
66 Cardross Street, London W6 0DR

COTTON, Irene T 020 8299 1595
CDG Member
25 Druce Road, Dulwich Village
London SE21 7DW
T/F 020 8299 2787
E irenecotton@btinternet.com

CRAMPSIE, Julia T 020 8228 7170
Casting Executive
BBC DRAMA SERIES CASTING
BBC Elstree, Room N224, Neptune House
Clarendon Road, Borehamwood, Herts WD6 1JF
F 020 8228 8311

CRANE, Carole CASTING T 07976 869442
E crane.shot@virgin.net

CRAWFORD, Kahleen CASTING T 0141 425 1725
Film City Glasgow, Govan Town Hall
401 Govan Road, Glasgow G51 2QJ
T 07950 414164
E casting@kahleencrawford.com
W www.kahleencrawford.com

**CROCODILE CASTING
COMPANY THE** T 020 8203 7009
Contact: Claire Toeman, Tracie Saban. By e-mail only
E croccast@aol.com
W www.crocodilecasting.com

CROSS, Louise T 020 8341 2200
CDG Member
128A North View Road, London N8 7LP

CROWE, Sarah CASTING T 020 7286 5080
75 Amberley Road, London W9 2JL
F 020 7286 5030
E sarah@sarahcrowecasting.co.uk

CROWLEY, Suzanne
CDG Member. See CROWLEY POOLE CASTING

CROWLEY POOLE CASTING T 020 7379 5965
*Contact: Suzanne Crowley (CDG Member), Gilly Poole
(CDG Member)*
11 Goodwins Court, London WC2N 4LL
F 020 7379 5971

DAVIES, Jane CASTING T 020 8715 1036
*Contact: Jane Davies (CDG Member),
John Connor (CDG Member)*
PO Box 680, Sutton
Surrey SM1 3ZG
F 020 8644 9746
E info@janedaviescasting.co.uk

DAVIS, Leo (Miss) T 020 7229 3471
Just Casting
20th Century Theatre
291 Westbourne Grove
London W11 2QA
F 020 7792 2143

DAVY, Gary T 020 7713 0888
CDG Member. Film. Television
Top Floor, 15 Crinan Street
York Way, Kings Cross, London N1 9SQ
E casting@garydavy.com

DAWES, Gabrielle T 020 7435 3645
CDG Member
PO Box 52493, London NW3 9DZ
E gdawescasting@tiscali.co.uk

DAWES, Stephanie T 07802 566642
CDG Member
13 Nevern Square, London SW5 9NW
E stephaniedawes5@gmail.com

DAY, Kate T/F 01865 858709
CDG Member
Pound Cottage, 27 The Green South
Warborough, Oxon OX10 7DR

DE FREITAS, Paul
CDG Member
E info@pauldefreitas.com

DEITCH, Jane ASSOCIATES T 020 7395 7525
80-81 St Martin's Lane, London WC2N 4AA
E casting@janedeitch.co.uk

DICKENS, Laura T 07958 665468
CDG Member
197 Malpas Road, London SE4 1BH
E dickenscasting@aol.com

DONNELLY, Laura CASTING T 07917 414014
Animation. Commercials. Film. Stage. Television
91 Mitre Road, Jordanhill, Glasgow G14 9PH
E laura@lauradonnellycasting.com
W www.lauradonnellycasting.com

DOWD, Kate T 020 7580 8866
74 Wells Street, London W1T 3QG
F 020 7580 6688

DOWLING ERDELY CASTING T 07958 391198
2 Eleanor Road, London N11 2QS
T 07970 071605
E info@dowlingerdely.com
W www.dowlingerdely.com

DRURY, Malcolm T 020 8748 9232
CDG Member
34 Tabor Road, London W6 0BW

DUDLEY, Carol
CDG Member. See CANNON DUDLEY & ASSOCIATES

DUFF, Julia T 020 7836 5557
CDG Member
PO Box 67506, London EC1P 1PH
E info@juliaduff.co.uk

DUFF, Maureen T 020 7586 0532
CDG Member
PO Box 47340, London NW3 4TY
E belgrove@dircon.co.uk

EARNSHAW, Rob T 07707 083674
35 Bishops Hill, Hexham
Northumberland NE46 4NH
E robertearnshaw@btinternet.com
W www.robertearnshawcasting.co.uk

EARNSHAW, Rob T 07707 083674
117 Park Lane, London W1K 7AH
E robertearnshaw@btinternet.com
W www.robertearnshawcasting.co.uk

Sean Gleeson

STUARTALLEN
P H O T O G R A P H E R

07776 258829

www.stuartallenphotos.com

Production, Publicity, Portraits

STUDENT DISCOUNTS

Natalie Barrett

EAST, Irene CASTING   T 020 8876 5686
CDG Member. Contact: By Post. Film. Stage
40 Brookwood Avenue, Barnes
London SW13 0LR
E irneast@aol.com

EH7 CASTING   T 0131 556 9339
9 Claremont Bank, Edinburgh EH7 4DR
E contact@eh7casting.com
W www.eh7casting.com

EJ CASTING   T 020 7564 2688
PO Box 63617, London SW9 1AN
T 07891 632946
E info@ejcasting.com

EMMERSON, Chloe   T 020 8740 0982
46 Bassein Park Road, London W12 9RZ
E c@chloeemmerson.com

EVANS, Camilla CASTING   T 07768 977050
CDG Member
c/o HG14, The Aberdeen Centre
22-24 Highbury Grove, London N5 2EA
E camilla@camillaevans.com
W www.thecdg.co.uk

EVANS, Richard   T 020 8994 6304
CDG Member
10 Shirley Road, London W4 1DD
E contact@evanscasting.co.uk
W www.evanscasting.co.uk

EYE CASTING THE LTD   T 020 7377 2700
1st Floor, 92 Commercial Street (Entrance Puma Court)
London E1 6LZ
F 05602 059199
E jody@theeyecasting.com
W www.theeyecasting.com

FEARNLEY, Ali CASTING   T 020 7613 7320
3rd Floor, 58-60 Rivington Street
London EC2A 3AU
T 07764 945614
E cast@alifearnley.com

FIGGIS, Susie   T 020 7482 2200
19 Spencer Rise, London NW5 1AR

FILDES, Bunny CASTING   T 020 7935 1254
CDG Member
56 Wigmore Street, London W1

FOX, Celestia   T 020 7720 6143
23 Leppoc Road, London SW4 9LS
E celestiafox@me.com

FOX CASTING   T 01628 771084
Contact: By e-mail only
E casting@foxcasting.co.uk

FRAZER, Janie
CDG Member
E janiefrazercasting@gmail.com

FRECK, Rachel   T/F 020 8673 2455
CDG Member
E casting@rachelfreck.com

FREE RANGE CASTING   T 07854 794007
Contact: Sandy Tedford
Highbury Barn Studio
23A Highbury Park
London N5 1TH
E sandy@freerangecasting.com
W www.freerangecasting.com

FREND, Amanda
87 Swindon Road, Horsham
West Sussex RH12 2HF
E amandafrendcasting@hotmail.co.uk

FRISBY, Jane CASTING   T 020 8341 4747
Contact: By Post. Accepts Showreels/Voicereels only on request. Commercials. Film. Stage
51 Ridge Road, London N8 9LJ
E janefrisby@hotmail.co.uk

FUNNELL, Caroline   T 020 7326 4417
CDG Member
25 Rattray Road, London SW2 1AZ

GALLAGHER, Juliet CASTING
E julietgallagher@hotmail.com
W www.julietgallagher.com

GANE CASTING   T 020 8446 2551
Contact: Natasha Gane
52 Woodhouse Road
London N12 0RJ
T 07970 535911
E natasha@ganecasting.com

GILLHAM, Tracey CASTING   T 020 8570 2851
CDG Member
E tracey@traceygillhamcasting.co.uk

GILLON, Tamara CASTING   T 020 8766 0099
26 Carson Road, London SE21 8HU
F 020 8265 6330
E tamara@tamaragillon.com
W www.tamaragillon.com

Casting Directors

GLOBAL7 T/F 020 7281 7679
PO Box 56232, London N4 4XP
T 07956 956652
E global7castings@gmail.com
W www.global7casting.com

GOLD, Nina T 020 8960 6099
CDG Member
117 Chevening Road, London NW6 6DU
F 020 8968 6777
E info@ninagold.co.uk

GOOCH, Miranda CASTING T 020 8962 9578
Contact: By Post/e-mail. Accepts Showreels/Voicereels.
Film. Stage. Television
102 Leighton Gardens, London NW10 3PR
F 020 8962 9579
E mirandagooch@gmail.com

GREEN, Jill CASTING T 020 8815 1825
CDG Member
PO Box 56927, London N10 3UR

GREENE, Francesca CASTING T 020 8450 5577
37 Keyes Road, London NW2 3XB
E francesca@francescagreene.co.uk
W www.francescagreenecasting.com

GROSVENOR, Angela T 020 8244 5665
CDG Member
66 Woodland Road, London SE19 1PA
E angela.grosvenor@virgin.net

GUISH, Michelle
See CASTING COMPANY (UK) THE

HALL, Janet T 01706 377900
3 Shore Road, Littleborough
Lances OL15 9LG
T 07956 822773
E janethall1@yahoo.co.uk

HALL, Pippa
Children. Teenagers
E pippa@pippahallcasting.com

HAMMOND, Louis T 020 7927 8392
97 Mortimer Street, London W1W 7SU
E louis.hammond@virgin.net

HAMMOND COX CASTING T 07779 084425
Contact: Thom Hammond
E office@hammondcoxcasting.com
W www.hammondcoxcasting.com

HAMPSON, Janet CASTING T 0161 408 2037
32 Queens Drive
Heaton Mersey SK4 3JW
T 07931 513223
E janet@janethampson.co.uk
W www.janethampson.co.uk

HANCOCK, Gemma
CDG Member. Contact: By e-mail
E gemma@hancockstevenson.com

HARKIN, Julie CASTING T 020 7998 5975
CDG Member
5 Albermarle Way, London EC1V 4JB
E julie@julieharkincasting.com

HAWES, Jo T 01628 773048
Children's Casting & Administration for Theatre
21 Westfield Road, Maidenhead
Berkshire SL6 5AU
T 07824 337222
E jo.hawes@virgin.net

HAWSER, Gillian CASTING T 020 7731 5988
CDG & CSA Member. Contact: Gillian Hawser
24 Cloncurry Street, London SW6 6DS
F 020 7731 0738
E gillianhawser@btinternet.com

HILL, Serena T 00 61 2 92501727
Sydney Theatre Company
Pier 4, Hickson Road
Walsh Bay, NSW 2000, Australia
E shill@sydneytheatre.com.au

HOOTKINS, Polly T 020 7692 1184
CDG Member. Contact: By e-mail
6 Howitt Close, London NW3 4LX
T 07545 784294
E phootkins@clara.net

HORAN, Julia T 020 7267 5261
CDG Member
26 Falkland Road, London NW5 2PX

HUBBARD CASTING T 020 7631 4944
Contact: Dan Hubbard (CDG Member), Amy Hubbard,
Ros Hubbard, John Hubbard. No Showreels
14 Rathbone Place, London W1T 1HT
F 020 7636 7117
E info@hubbardcasting.com

HUGHES, Sarah T 020 8291 0304
CDG Member
E sarahhughescasting@gmail.com
W www.sarahhughescasting.co.uk

HUGHES, Sylvia T/F 01625 560000
Casting Suite, The Deanwater
Wilmslow Road, Woodford
Cheshire SK7 1RJ
T 07770 520007
E sylviahughes@hotmail.co.uk

JAFFA, Janis CASTING T 020 8743 9561
CDG Member. Contact: By Post. Accepts Showreels
67 Starfield Road
London W12 9SN
E janis@janisjaffacasting.co.uk

JAFFREY, Jennifer T 01753 785162
Contact: By Post
Room 11, Heath Farm, Pinewood Studios
Pinewood Road, Iver Heath, Bucks SL0 0NH
F 01753 785163
E jaffreyproductions@btconnect.com

JAY, Jina CASTING T 020 8607 8888
CDG Member
Office 2, Sound Centre
Twickenham Film Studios
The Barons, St Margarets
Twickenham, Middlesex TW1 2AW
F 020 8607 8982

JELOWICKI, Ilenka T 020 7269 7910
Mad Dog Casting Ltd. Contact: By Post/e-mail. Accepts
Showreels/Voicereels. Real People. Street Casting
2nd Floor, Holborn Hall
193-197 High Holborn
London WC1V 7BD
F 020 7831 7267
E info@maddogcasting.com

JENKINS, Lucy
CDG Member. See JENKINS McSHANE CASTING

JENKINS, Victor
CDG Member. See VALENTINE HENDRY & JENKINS

Valerie Colgan

- For professional actors who need a voice production "MOT"
- Private individual classes
- Valerie Colgan and a consortium of tutors as appropriate on audition technique

Ex Head of Drama at the City Lit • 5 Drama Schools • The Actors Centre

Tel: 020 7267 2153 The Green, 17 Herbert Street, London NW5 4HA

JENKINS McSHANE CASTING T 020 8943 5328
Contact: Lucy Jenkins (CDG Member)
74 High Street, Hampton Wick
Kingston on Thames KT1 4DQ
E lucy@jenkinsmcshanecasting.com

JENKINS McSHANE CASTING T 020 8693 7411
Contact: Sooki McShane (CDG Member)
8A Piermont Road, East Dulwich
London SE22 0LN
E sooki@jenkinsmcshanecasting.com

JN PRODUCTION T 020 7278 8800
27 Cowper Street, London EC2A 4AP
F 020 7780 7470
E james@jnproduction.com

JOHN, Priscilla T 020 8741 4212
CDG Member
PO Box 22477, London W6 0GT
F 020 8741 4005

JOHNSON, Alex CASTING T 020 7229 8779
15 McGregor Road, London W11 1DE
E alex@alexjohnsoncasting.com

JOHNSON, Marilyn T 020 7497 5552
CDG Member
1st Floor, 11 Goodwins Court, London WC2N 4LL
E casting@marilynjohnsoncasting.com

JONES, Doreen T 020 8746 3782
CDG Member
PO Box 22478, London W6 0WJ
F 020 8748 8533
E artists@dorcast.demon.co.uk

JONES, Lenka T 07921 182055
Coach House, Pinewood Road
Iver Heath, Buckinghamshire SL0 0NH
E lenki13@yahoo.co.uk

JONES, Sue
CDG Member
E info@suejones.net

KATE & LOU CASTING T 07885 763429
The Basement, Museum House
25 Museum Street, London WC1A 1JT
T 07976 252531
E cast@kateandloucasting.com
W www.kateandloucasting.com

KENNEDY, Anna CASTING T 020 8677 6710
8 Rydal Road, London SW16 1QN
E anna@kennedycasting.com

KEOGH, Beverley CASTING LTD T 0161 273 4400
29 Ardwick Green North, Ardwick Green
Manchester M12 6DL
F 0161 273 4401
E drama@beverleykeogh.tv

KESTER, Gaby T 020 8324 2571
Room B1.14, Ancillary Block, Elstree Film Studios
Shenley Road, Borehamwood, Herts WD6 1JG
E casting@gabykester.com

KIBBEY, Leoni CASTING T 01727 375166
T 07855 313552
E casting@leonikibbey.com
W www.leonikibbey.com

KING, Cassandra CASTING T 020 8977 2345
73 Victor Road, Teddington TW11 8SP
T 07813 320673
E cassyking@yahoo.co.uk

KLIMEK, Nana CASTING T 020 7502 9478
63 Redchurch Street, London E2 7DJ
E casting@nanaklimek.com
W www.nanaklimek.com

KNIGHT-SMITH, Jerry T 0161 615 6761
CDG Member
Royal Exchange Theatre Company, St Ann's Square
Manchester M2 7DH
F 0161 615 6691

KOREL, Suzy T 020 7586 9611
CDG Member
E suzy@korel.org

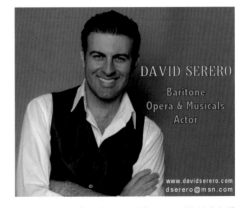

DAVID SERERO
Baritone
Opera & Musicals
Actor

www.davidserero.com
dserero@msn.com

KRUGER, Beatrice   T 00 39 06 58332747
FBI Casting S.r.l.
46 via della Pelliccia, 00153 Roma, Italy
F 00 39 06 23328203
E beatrice.kruger@fbicasting.it
W www.fbicasting.com

KYLE, Greg   T 020 8876 6763
71B North Worple Way, Mortlake
London SW14 8PR
E kylecasting@btinternet.com

LADIDA   T 020 7379 6199
19 Percy Street, London W1T 1DU
F 020 7379 6198
E casting@ladidagroup.com
W www.ladidagroup.com

LARCA LTD   T 07779 321954
Welsh Language/English. Commercials.
Film. Stage. Television
Ynyslas Uchaf Farm, Blackmill
Bridgend CF35 6DW
F 01656 841815
W www.leigh-annregancasting.co.uk

LEVENE, Jon   T 020 7792 8501
T 07977 570899
E jonlevene@mac.com
W www.jonlevenecasting.co.uk

LIHUK CASTING   T 00 972 777675006
28 Meir Yaari, Tel Aviv 69371
Israel
E info@lihuk.co.il
W www.lihuk.co.il

LINDSAY-STEWART, Karen   T 020 7439 0544
CDG Member
PO Box 2301, London W1A 1PT

LIP SERVICE CASTING LTD   T 020 7734 3393
Contact: By Post. Accepts Voicereels. Voice Overs only
60-66 Wardour Street
London W1F 0TA
F 020 7734 3373
E bookings@lipservice.co.uk
W www.lipservice.co.uk

LITTLE NARRATIVES CASTING   T 01509 828365
Contact: Clair Haynes
20 Hawcliffe Road, Mountsorrel
Leicester LE12 7AA
E info@littlenarratives.com
W www.littlenarratives.com/casting

LUNN, Maggie   T 020 7226 7502
CDG Member
Unit HG14, Aberdeen Centre
22-24 Highbury Grove
London N5 2EA
E maggie@maggielunn.co.uk

MAGSON, Kay   T 0113 236 0251
CDG Member. Contact: By e-mail. Stage
PO Box 175, Pudsey
Leeds LS28 7WY
E kay.magson@btinternet.com

MANN, Andrew   T 020 7993 6042
Studio 125, 77 Beak Street
London W1F 9DB
T 020 7993 5165
E andrew.mann@castinguk.com
W www.andrewmanncasting.co.uk

MARCH, Heather CASTING   T 020 8981 4184
Contact: By e-mail. Commercials. Idents.
Photographic. Pop Promos
14 Albany Works
Gunmakers Lane, London E3 5SB
E hm@heathermarchcasting.com
W www.heathermarchcasting.com

McCANN, Joan   T 020 8993 1747
CDG Member
26 Hereford Road, London W3 9JW
F 020 8992 8715

McLEOD, Carolyn CASTING   T 07946 476425
Contact: By e-mail only. Film. Television
2nd Floor, 189 Wardour Street
London W1F 8ZD
E info@cmcasting.co.uk
W www.cmcasting.co.uk

McLEOD, Thea   T 07941 541314
E mcleodcasting@hotmail.com

McMURRICH, Chrissie   T 020 8568 0137
Contact: By Post. Accepts Showreels
16 Spring Vale Avenue, Brentford
Middlesex TW8 9QH

McSHANE, Sooki
CDG Member. See JENKINS McSHANE CASTING

McWILLIAMS, Debbie   T 020 7564 8860
T 07785 575805
E debbie@debbiemcwilliamscasting.com

MEULENBERG, Thea   T 00 31 20 6265846
Keizersgracht 116, 1015 CW
Amsterdam, The Netherlands
F 00 31 20 6229894
E info@theameulenberg.com
W www.theameulenberg.com

MILLER, Hannah
CDG Member. See ROYAL SHAKESPEARE COMPANY

MOISELLE, Frank   T 00 353 1 2802857
7 Corrig Avenue, Dun Laoghaire
Co. Dublin, Ireland
F 00 353 1 2803277

MOISELLE, Nuala   T 00 353 1 2802857
7 Corrig Avenue, Dun Laoghaire
Co. Dublin, Ireland
F 00 353 1 2803277

MOORE, Stephen   T 020 8228 7109
BBC DRAMA SERIES CASTING
BBC Elstree, Room N222
Neptune House, Clarendon Road
Borehamwood, Herts WD6 1JF
F 020 8228 8311

MORGAN, Andy CASTING   T 020 8674 5375
CDG Member
Coach House, 114 Palace Road, London SW2 3JZ

MORLEY, Adam   T 07855 133836
The Lodge, Wentworth Hall, The Ridgeway
Mill Hill, London NW7 1RJ
E adam.e.morley@gmail.com

MORRISON, Melika   T/F 020 7381 1571
Contact: By Post. Accepts Showreels. Film.
Radio. Television
12A Rosebank, Holyport Road
London SW6 6LG

MOUNTJOY, Lee CASTING   T 0161 850 1656
21 St Marys Street
Manchester M15 5WB
T 020 7112 8353
E info@leemountjoy.com
W www.leemountjoy.com

MUGHAL, Naila
ARTISTES AGENCY   T 07983 534113
Actors. Dancers. Extras. Hair Stylists.
Make-up Artistes. Singers
E naila@nailamughal.com
W www.nailamughalartistes.com

MUGSHOTS   T 07880 896911
Contact: Becky Kidd
E becky@mugshots.co.uk

MURDER MY DARLINGS   T 020 7386 0560
Contact: Sue Pocklington
Based in London
E office@murdermydarlings.com

MURPHY CHARPENTIER
CASTING   T 07976 931264
Contact: Sabrina Murphy, Alix Charpentier
22 Gledhow Gardens
London SW5 0AZ
T 07956 450755
E casting@murphycharpentiercasting.com
W www.murphycharpentier.co.uk

NAPIER-BELL CASTING   T 07702 748078
179 Wardour Street, London W1F 8WY
E fiona@napier-bell.tv
W www.napier-bell.tv

NATIONAL THEATRE
CASTING DEPARTMENT   T 020 7452 3336
Contact: Wendy Spon, Head of Casting (CDG Member),
Alastair Coomer, Deputy Head of Casting (CDG Member),
Juliet Horsley, Casting Associate, Charlotte Sutton, Casting
Assistant. By Post
Upper Ground, South Bank
London SE1 9PX
F 020 7452 3340
W www.nationaltheatre.org.uk

NEEDLEMAN, Sue   T 020 8959 1550
CDG Member
19 Stanhope Gardens, London NW7 2JD

NORCLIFFE, Belinda   T 020 8992 1333
Contact: Belinda Norcliffe, Matt Selby
23 Brougham Road, London W3 6JD
F 020 8992 8643
E belinda@bncasting.co.uk
W www.belindanorcliffe.com

NORTH, Sophie   T 020 8450 6474
59A Teignmouth Road, London NW2 4EB
T 07956 516606
E sophie@sophienorthcasting.com

O'BRIEN, Debbie   T 01462 742919
72 High Street, Ashwell
Nr Baldock, Herts SG7 5NS
F 01462 743110

O'CONNOR, Orla   T 0131 553 0559
The Out of The Blue Drill Hall, 36 Dalmeny Street
Edinburgh EH6 8RG
E info@orlaoconnorcasting.co.uk

O'DONNELL, Rory　　T 07940 073165
178A Adelaide Avenue, London SE4 1JN
F 020 8690 8005
E tyrconnellpictures@hotmail.com

PALMER, Helena
CDG Member. See ROYAL SHAKESPEARE COMPANY

PARLOUR CASTING　　T 020 3318 3010
Contact: Rose Wicksteed, Amelia Hashemi
Based in London
F 020 3318 3090
E info@parlourcasting.com
W www.parlourcasting.com

PARRISS, Susie CASTING　　T 020 8543 3326
CDG Member
PO Box 40, Morden SM4 4WJ
F 020 8543 3327

PETTS, Tree CASTING　　T 020 8458 8898
125 Hendon Way, London NW2 2NA
T 07966 283252
E casting@treepetts.co.uk

PLANTIN, Kate　　T 01932 782350
4 Riverside, Lower Hampton Road
Sunbury on Thames TW16 5PW
F 01932 783235
E kateplantin@hotmail.com

POLENTARUTTI, Tania CASTING　　T 020 8555 3163
CDG Member. Contact: By e-mail
T 07720 299635
E tania@filmtvcasting.com

POOLE, Gilly
CDG Member. See CROWLEY POOLE CASTING

POWELLCASTING
Contact: Annelie Powell
E mail@powellcasting.com
W www.powellcasting.com

PROCTOR, Carl　　T 020 7681 0034
CDG Member
15B Bury Place, London WC1A 2JB
T 07956 283340
E carlproctor@btconnect.com
W www.carlproctor.com

PRYOR, Andy　　T 020 7851 8535
CDG Member
79 Wardour Street, London W1D 6QB
F 020 7836 8299

PURO CASTING　　T 020 7193 8799
F 07006 056678
E office@purocasting.com
W www.purocasting.com

RADCLIFFE, Gennie　　T 0161 952 1000
CDG Member
Granada Television, Quay Street
Manchester M60 9EA
F 0161 952 0573

RANCH CASTING
COMPANY THE　　T 020 8374 6072
Contact: By e-mail/Telephone. Commercials. Corporate.
Idents. Photographic Campaigns. Pop Promos
Manor Court, Aylmer Road
London N2 0PJ
F 020 8442 9190
E info@theranchcasting.co.uk
W www.theranchcasting.co.uk

REICH, Liora　　T 020 8444 1686
25 Manor Park Road, London N2 0SN
E casting@liorareich.fsnet.co.uk

REYNOLDS, Gillian
CASTING　　T 00 353 87 2619718
E gillianreynoldscasting@gmail.com
W www.gillianreynoldscasting.com

REYNOLDS, Simone　　T 020 8672 5443
CDG Member
60 Hebdon Road, London SW17 7NN

RHODES JAMES, Kate　　T 020 8977 3252
CDG Member
KRJ Casting, Teddington Studios
Broom Road, Teddington TW11 9NT
E office@krjcasting.com

RICHTER, Ilisa　　T 020 7490 4225
3rd Floor, Block A, Morelands
5-23 Old Street, London EC1V 9HL
E ilisa@broadcastingagency.co.uk

RIPLEY, Jane　　T 020 8340 5123
E jane@janeripleycasting.co.uk

ROBERTSON, Sasha CASTING　　T 020 8993 8118
Contact: Sasha Robertson (CDG Member), Maddy Hinton
(Associate)
5 Cumberland Road, London W3 6EX
E casting@sasharobertson.com
W www.sasharobertsoncasting.com

RONANE, Jessica CASTING　　T 020 7534 9750
CDG Member
26 Aybrook Street, London W1U 4AN
E jessica@jessicaronane.com

ROSE, Dionne
78 York Street, London W1H 1DP
E casting@drbentertainment.co.uk

ROWAN, Amy CASTING　　T 00 353 1 2140514
PO Box 10247, Blackrock
Co. Dublin, Ireland
F 00 353 1 2802005

ROWE, Annie CASTING　　T 020 8354 2699
98 St Albans Avenue, London W4 5JR
E annie@annierowe-casting.com
W www.annierowe-casting.com

ROYAL SHAKESPEARE
COMPANY　　T 020 7845 0530
Contact: Hannah Miller, Head of Casting (CDG Member),
Helena Palmer (CDG Member), Janine Snape (CDG
Member)
Casting Department, 1 Earlham Street
London WC2H 9LL
F 020 7845 0505
E suggestions@rsc.org.uk
W www.rsc.org.uk

RUBIN, Shaila EUROPEAN
CASTING SERVICE　　T 00 39 06 72901906
Cinecitta Studios Via Tuscolana 1055
00173 Roma, Teatro 6/7 Stanza 8, Italy
F 00 39 06 72905183
E semass@gmail.com

RYCROFT CASTING　　T 07958 540815
Contact: Amy Rycroft
20B Turners Road, London E3 4LE
E amy@rycroftcasting.co.uk
W www.rycroftcasting.co.uk

SPOTLIGHT

Casting from start to finish

Spotlight Database

Browse over 40,000 actors, actresses, presenters, stunt artists, children and dancers

View performer CVs, photos, showreels, portfolios and contact details

Know that every Spotlight performer has professional training or experience

Spotlight Rooms & Studios

Six meeting rooms and three state-of-the-art casting studios

Hold your auditions in the heart of central London

Post DVD quality audition clips online in minutes

Spotlight Website

Email casting calls to hundreds of UK agents and performers and receive responses in minutes

Find exactly the right performer for the part with our award-winning search engine

www.spotlight.com   020 7437 7631   casting@spotlight.com

SALBERG, Jane   T 01303 239277
86 Stade Street, Hythe
Kent CT21 6DY
T 07931 932103
E janesalberg@aol.com

SCHILLER, Ginny   T 020 8806 5383
CDG Member
53 Clapton Common
London E5 9AA
E ginny.schiller@virgin.net

SCHOFIELD, Gilly
CDG Member
E gillyschofield1@btinternet.com

SCOTT, Laura   T 020 7978 6336
CDG Member
56 Rowena Crescent
London SW11 2PT
F 020 7924 1907
E laurascottcasting@mac.com
W www.thecdg.co.uk

SEARCHERS THE   T 07958 922829
70 Sylvia Court
Cavendish Street
London N1 7PG
F 020 7684 5763
E waynesearcher@mac.com

SEECOOMAR, Nadira   T 020 8892 8478
E nadira.seecoomar@gmail.com

SELECT CASTING LTD   T 07956 131494
PO Box 748, London NW4 1TT
F 020 8203 2007
E info@selectcasting.co.uk
W www.selectcasting.co.uk

SHAW, David
See KEOGH, Beverley CASTING LTD

SHAW, Phil   T 020 8715 8943
Contact: By Post. Commercials. Film. Stage. Television
Suite 476, 2 Old Brompton Road
South Kensington, London SW7 3DQ
E shawcastlond@aol.com

SHEPHERD, Debbie CASTING   T 020 7240 0400
Suite 16, 63 St Martin's Lane
London WC2N 4JS
E casting@debbieshepherd.com

SID PRODUCTIONS   T 01932 863194
110 Sandringham Flats
Charing Cross Road
London WC2H 0BP
E casting@sidproductions.co.uk
W www.sidproductions.co.uk

SIMPSON, Georgia   T 028 9147 0800
88 Ashley Drive, Bangor
Co Down, Northern Ireland BT20 5RD
E georgia@georgiasimpson.com
W www.georgiasimpson.com

SINGER Sandra ASSOCIATES   T 01702 331616
Contact: By e-mail
21 Cotswold Road
Westcliff-on-Sea, Essex SS0 8AA
E sandrasingeruk@aol.com
W www.sandrasinger.com

SMITH, Michelle CASTING LTD   T 0161 439 6825
*Contact: Michelle Smith (CDG Member). By Post. Accepts
Showreels/Voicereels. Animation. Commercials. Corporate.
Film. Television*
220 Church Lane, Stockport SK7 1PQ
F 0161 439 0622
E michelle.smith18@btinternet.com

SMITH, Suzanne   T 020 7278 0045
CDG Member
3rd Floor, 15 Crinan Street, York Way, London N1 9SQ
E zan@dircon.co.uk

SNAPE, Janine
CDG Member. See ROYAL SHAKESPEARE COMPANY

SOLOMON, Alison   T 0121 245 2023
Birmingham Repertory Theatre
Centenary Square
Broad Street, Birmingham B1 2EP

SPORTSCASTINGS.COM   T 07973 863263
Contact: Penny Burrows
3 Thornlaw Road, London SE27 0SH
E info@sportsmodels.com
W www.sportsmodels.com

STAFFORD, Aaron   T 020 8372 0611
Freelance. Commercials. Film. Television
14 Park Avenue, Enfield
Middlesex EN1 2HP
E aaron.stafford@blueyonder.co.uk

STAFFORD, Emma CASTING   T 0161 833 4263
T 020 7866 5424
E info@emmastafford.tv
W www.emmastafford.tv

STAFFORD, Helen   T 020 8360 6329
14 Park Avenue, Enfield
Middlesex EN1 2HP
F 020 8372 0611
E helen.stafford@blueyonder.co.uk

STARK CASTING   T 020 8800 0060
T 07956 150689
E anna@starkcasting.com
W www.starkcasting.com

STEVENS, Gail CASTING   T 020 7253 6532
CDG Member
Greenhill House, 90-93 Cowcross Street
London EC1M 6BF
E office@gailstevenscasting.com

**STEVENS MILLEFIORINI,
Danny**   T 00 39 389 4352200
Via Sillaro 14, Cerveteri, Rome 00052, Italy
E dannystevens62@gmail.com

STEVENSON, Sam
CDG Member
E sam@hancockstevenson.com

STEWART, Amanda CASTING   T 020 7485 7973
Apartment 1, 35 Fortess Road
London NW5 1AD

STOLL, Liz   T 020 8228 8285
BBC DRAMA SERIES CASTING
BBC Elstree, Room N223
Neptune House, Clarendon Road
Borehamwood, Herts WD6 1JF
F 020 8228 8311

STYLE, Emma T 01628 483740
CDG Member
1 Overton Cottages, Kings Lane
Cookham, Maidenhead SL6 9BA

SUMMERS, Mark CASTING T 020 7229 8413
Formerly Casting Unlimited
1 Beaumont Avenue
West Kensington
London W14 9LP
E mark@marksummers.com
W www.marksummers.com

SYERS, Michael
See CASTING CONNECTION THE

SYSON GRAINGER CASTING T 020 7287 5327
Contact: Lucinda Syson (CDG Member),
Elaine Grainger (CDG Member)
1st Floor
33 Old Compton Street
London W1D 5JT
F 020 7287 3629
E office@sysongraingercasting.com

TABAK, Amanda
CDG Member. See CANDID CASTING

TOPPING, Nicci T 07802 684256
The Media Centre
7 Northumberland Street
West Yorkshire HD1 1RL
T 01484 511988
E general@toppscasting.co.uk
W www.toppscasting.co.uk

TREVELLICK, Jill T 020 8340 2734
CDG Member
92 Priory Road, London N8 7EY
E jill@jilltrevellick.com

TREVIS, Sarah T 020 8354 2398
CDG Member
E info@sarahtrevis.com

VALENTINE HENDRY, Kelly
CDG Member.
See VALENTINE HENDRY & JENKINS

**VALENTINE HENDRY
& JENKINS** T 020 7255 6146
22 Torrington Place
London WC1 7HP
E assistant@vhjcasting.com
W www.vhjcasting.com

VAUGHAN, Sally T 020 7735 6539
CDG Member
2 Kennington Park Place
London SE11 4AS
E svaughan12@btinternet.com

VOSSER, Anne CASTING T 01252 404716
156 Lower Franham Road, Aldershot
Hampshire GU12 4EL
T 07968 868712
E anne@vosser-casting.co.uk
W www.vosser-casting.co.uk

WAUDBY, Melissa T 07957 284709
E mail@vital-productions.co.uk
W www.vital-productions.co.uk

WEIR, Fiona T 020 7727 5600
CDG Member
2nd Floor, 138 Portobello Road
London W11 2DZ

WEST, June
CDG Member
E junewestcasting@gmail.com

WESTERN, Matt CASTING T 020 7602 6646
Contact: By Post. Accepts Showreels. Children.
Commercials. Film. Television
150 Blythe Road, London W14 0HD
E matt@mattwestern.co.uk
W www.mattwestern.co.uk

WHALE, Toby T 020 8993 2821
CDG Member
80 Shakespeare Road, London W3 6SN
F 020 8993 8096
E toby@whalecasting.com
W www.whalecasting.com

WHITTINGHAM, Ian Zachary T 020 3246 0088
The Manic Media Group UK
77A Brick Lane, London E1 6QL
F 020 3246 0081
E zach@themanicmediagroup.co.uk
W www.manictv.co.uk

WILDMANHALL CASTING T 020 7373 2036
Contact: Vicky Wildman, Buffy Hall
1 Child's Place, London SW5 9RX
E wildmanhall@mac.com

WILLIS, Catherine T 020 7255 6130
CDG Member. Contact: By e-mail
The Heals Building, 22 Torrington Place
London WC1E 7HP
E catherine@cwcasting.co.uk

YOUNGSTAR CASTING T 023 8047 7717
Children & Teenagers only
5 Union Castle House, Canute Road SO14 3FJ
E info@youngstar.tv
W www.youngstar.tv

ZIMMERMANN, Jeremy CASTING T 020 7478 5161
36 Marshall Street, London W1F 7EY
F 020 7437 4747

ACADEMY OF PERFORMANCE
COMBAT THE T 07963 206803
Teaching Body of Stage Combat
Ivy Villa, 250 Lees New Road
Lees, Lancs OL4 5PP
E info@theapc.org.uk
W www.theapc.org.uk

ACADEMY OF PERSONAL
TRAINING LTD (APT LTD) T 07776 304511
*Providing Personal Training, Weight Management, Sports
Specific/Conditioning, Corrective Exercise & Injury
Rehabilitation Services to the Film & Media Industry*
West Acre, Hurst Lane, Egham, Surrey TW20 8QJ
E alan@academypt.org

ACE FEATURE FILM - MEDIA INTERNATIONAL
FOUNDATION T 07765 927008
*Contact: Margaret Cooper (Executive Producer). Sourcing
Investors. Product Placement for Films*
227 Earl's Court Road, London SW5 9BL
E acefilm1@yahoo.com
W www.i-mf.co

ACTING AUDITION SUCCESS T 020 8731 6686
Audition Speeches for Top UK Drama Schools
53 West Heath Court, London NW11 7RG
E philiprosch1@hotmail.com
W www.philiprosch.com

ACTING BUDDY
E info@actingbuddy.com
W www.actingbuddy.com

ACTORS ADVICE SURGERY T 07968 011163
Contact: Yvonne l'Anson (Consultant)
E yvonne@actorsadvicesurgery.co.uk
W www.actorsadvicesurgery.co.uk

ACTOR'S ONE-STOP SHOP THE T 020 8888 7006
Showreels for Performing Artists
1st Floor, Above The Gate Pub
Station Road, London N22 7SS
E info@actorsonestopshop.com
W www.actorsonestopshop.com

AGENTFILE T 07050 683662
Software for Agents
E admin@agentfile.com
W www.agentfile.com

AKA T 020 7836 4747
*Advertising. Design. Digital. Marketing.
Promotions. Sales & Ticketing*
1st Floor, 115 Shaftesbury Avenue
Cambridge Circus, London WC2H 8AF
F 020 7836 8787
E aka@akauk.com
W www.akauk.com

ARIAS, Enrique T 07956 261568
Subtitles. Translations. Voice Overs
E enriqueag@gmail.com
W www.rnwlondon.com/eag

ARTS VA THE T 01789 552559
*Contact: Bronwyn Robertson (Experienced PA).
Admin Support*
T 07815 192135
E bronwyn@theartsva.com
W www.theartsva.com

ASSOCIATED STUDIOS THE T 020 8237 1080
Riverside Studios, Crisp Road
London W6 9RL
E info@associatedstudios.co.uk
W www.associatedstudios.co.uk

AUDIO DESCRIPTION T 07747 655215
*For Blind & Visually Impaired Audiences.
West End & on Tour*
E info@theatredescription.com

AUTOMOBILE ASSOCIATION
(THE AA) T 01256 492640
Fanum House, Basing View
Basingstoke RG21 4EA
E lindsey.szegota@theaa.com

BARTERCARD T 0845 2197000
Lakeside House, 1 Furzeground Way
Stockley Park East, Uxbridge UB11 1BD
E info@uk.bartercard.com
W www.bartercard.co.uk

BIG PICTURE T 020 7371 4455
Contact: Bridget Kelly. Field Marketing
13 Netherwood Road, London W14 0BL
E humanresources@ebigpicture.co.uk
W www.ebigpicture.co.uk

BOARDMAN, Emma T 07976 294604
Creative Events. Entertainment. Media Expert
143 Talgarth Road, Barons Court
London W14 9DA
E ideas@emmaboardman.net
W www.emmaboardman.net

BRITISH ASSOCIATION
OF DRAMATHERAPISTS T/F 01242 235515
Waverley, Battledown Approach
Cheltenham, Glos GL52 6RE
E enquiries@badth.org.uk
W www.badth.org.uk

BUTCHER, Litz T 020 8401 6234
Psychic Medium
Cromer Mansions, Cheam Road, Sutton SM1 2SR
E litz@litzbutcher.co.uk

BYFORD, Simon PRODUCTION MANAGEMENT
SERVICES T 01273 623972
Production & Event Management
22 Freshfield Place, Brighton
East Sussex BN2 0BN
F 01273 606402
E simon@simonbyfordpms.com

BYRNE, John T 07758 609747
One-to-one Advice from The Stage's Career Advisor
E johnbyrnecontact@gmail.com
W www.showbusiness-success.com

CAP PRODUCTION
SOLUTIONS LTD T 07973 432576
Technical Production Services
116 Wigmore Road, Carshalton, Surrey SM5 1RQ
F 07970 763480
E leigh@leighporter.com

CASTLE MAGICAL SERVICES T/F 01904 709500
Contact: Michael Shepherd. Magical Effect Consultants
Broompark, 131 Tadcaster Road
Dringhouses, York YO24 1QJ
E info@castlemagicalservices.co.uk

CAULKETT, Robin Dip SM MIIRSM T 07970 442003
Abseiling. Rope Work
3 Churchill Way, Mitchell Dean
Glos GL17 0AZ
E robincaulkett@talktalk.net

CELEBRITIES WORLDWIDE LTD T 020 7637 4178
Celebrity Contacts & Booking
E claire@celebritiesworldwide.com
W www.celebritiesworldwide.com

CHAPERONE T/F 020 8650 8997
For Children in Performing Arts
31 Whitecroft Way, Beckenham, Kent BR3 3AQ
T 07930 353381
E elaineboyle@msn.com

CHAPERONE AGENCY THE T 07960 075928
E chaperoneagency@hotmail.co.uk
W www.chaperoneagency.com

CHAPERONES & TUTORS T 07896 651552
141 Main Road, Nottingham
Nottinghamshire NG16 5GQ
E chaperonesandtutors@hotmail.co.uk
W www.chaperonesandtutors.co.uk

**CHILD CHAPERONE -
DENISE SMITH** T 07956 427442
Stage, Television & Film Industry
E denisesmith916@btinternet.com
W www.childchaperone.co.uk

**CLASS - CARLINE LUNDON
ASSOCIATES** T 07853 248957
25 Falkner Square, Liverpool L8 7NZ
E carline.lundon@ukonline.co.uk

COBO MEDIA LTD T 020 8291 7079
Performing Arts, Entertainment & Leisure Marketing
43A Garthorne Road, London SE23 1EP
F 020 8291 4969
E admin@cobomedia.com
W www.cobomedia.com

COLCLOUGH, John T 020 8873 1763
Practical Independent Guidance for Actors & Actresses
E john@johncolclough.org.uk
W www.johncolclough.co.uk

COMBAT INTERNATIONAL T 01259 731010
27 High Street, Kincardine, Alloa FK10 4RJ
E info@clanranald.org
W www.clanranald.org

CREATIVE CULTURE T 020 7193 3076
21E Heathmans Road, London SW6 4TJ
E m.chevalier@creativecultureint.com
W www.creativecultureint.com

**CREATIVE INDUSTRIES
DEVELOPMENT AGENCY (CIDA)** T 01484 483140
*Professional Development & Business Support for Artists &
Creative Businesses*
Media Centre, Huddersfield, West Yorkshire HD1 1RL
F 01484 483150
E info@cida.org
W www.cida.org

**CREATIVE MAGIC DIRECTOR
(TONY MIDDLETON)** T 01727 838656
67 De Tany Court, St Albans
Herts AL1 1TX
T 07738 971077
E tony@force10magic.co.uk
W www.consultantmagician.com

CROFTS, Andrew T/F 01403 864518
Book Writing Services
Westlands Grange, West Grinstead
Horsham, West Sussex RH13 8LZ
E croftsa@aol.com
W www.andrewcrofts.com

**EARLE, Kenneth
PERSONAL MANAGEMENT** T 020 7274 1219
214 Brixton Road, London SW9 6AP
F 020 7274 9529
E kennethearle@agents-uk.com

EQUIP T 01708 479898
11 Balmoral Road, Gidea Park
Romford, Essex RM2 5XD
E sales@equip-u.com
W www.equip-u.com

ES GLOBAL LTD T 020 7055 7200
Bell Lane, North Woolwich Road
London E16 2AB
F 020 7055 7201
E info@esglobalsolutions.com
W www.esglobalsolutions.com

EYENNCEE.COM T 020 7557 6650
Professional Networking Site
I.N.C. Space, 9-13 Grape Street
Covent Garden, London WC2H 8ED
F 020 7557 6656
E chris@international-collective.com
W www.eyenncee.com

FACADE T 020 8291 7079
Creation & Production of Musicals
43A Garthorne Road
London SE23 1EP
F 020 8291 4969
E facade@cobomedia.com

FERRIS ENTERTAINMENT MUSIC T 0845 4724725
Music for Film & Television. London. Cardiff. Belfast
Number 8, 132 Charing Cross Road
London WC2H 0LA
E info@ferrisentertainment.com
W www.ferrisentertainment.com

**FIGHT CHOREOGRAPHER &
ACTION DIRECTOR** T 07739 184418
*Contact: Nic Main (Professional Actor, Film Fighting
Choreographer).*
Based in the South East,
E nicmain@nicmain.com
W www.nicmain.com

**FLAMES MARTIAL ARTS
ACADEMY** T 07950 396389
Contact: Adam Richards
Unit 2, 128 Milton Road Business Park
Gravesend, Kent DA12 2PG
E stunts@adamrichardsstunts.co.uk
W www.kuentao.com

FRANCO THE MAGICIAN T/F 020 8202 4940
Flat 1, 79 Brent Street
London NW4 2EA
E franco@francomagic.co.uk
W www.francomagic.co.uk

GHOSTWRITER/AUTHOR T 01227 721071
Contact: John Parker
Dove Cottage, The Street
Ickham CT3 1QP
E ghostwriterforyourbook@ymail.com
W www.ghostwriteruk.info

GILMOUR Rev/Prof.em/Dr Glenn MscD SHsc.D
Dip.Coun. BCMA.Reg T 0114 321 6500
Fully Qualified/International Medium & Clairvoyant. Healer/
Counsellor. Holistic Therapist. Consultant
Paranormal/Metaphysics/Occult for Radio & Television
E drglenngilmour@yahoo.com
W www.drglenngilmour.com

GLOBAL ACCESS
IMMIGRATION SERVICES T 001 323 936 7100
5657 Wilshire Boulevard, Suite 390
Los Angeles 90036, USA
F 001 323 936 7197
E lara@globalaxs.net

GOLDIELLE PROMOTIONS T 07977 936826
Event Management & Entertainment
68 Lynton Drive, Hillside
Southport, Merseyside PR8 4QQ
T 01704 566604
E goldielle@yahoo.co.uk
W www.goldiellepromotions.com

HANDS UP PUPPETS T 07909 824630
Contact: Marcus Clarke
7 Cavendish Vale, Nottingham NG5 4DS
E enquiries@handsuppuppets.com
W www.handsuppuppets.com

HARLEY PRODUCTIONS T 020 7580 3247
68 New Cavendish Street, London W1G 8TE
F 020 8202 8863
E harleyprods@aol.com

HAYES, Susan T 07721 927714
Choreographer
46 Warrington Crescent, London W9 1EP
E susan22@btconnect.com

HERITAGE RAILWAY
ASSOCIATION T 01993 883384
10 Hurdeswell, Long Hanborough
Witney, Oxfordshire OX29 8DH
W www.heritagerailways.com

HITWAVE T 0844 8700496
Unit 1, 52 Churchfield Road
Acton, London W3 6DA
E info@hitwave.co.uk
W www.hitwave.co.uk

IMAGE DIGGERS T 020 8455 4564
Slide/Stills/Audio/Video Library. Theme Research
618B Finchley Road, London NW11 7RR
E lambhorn@gmail.com
W www.imagediggers.netfirms.com

IMPACT AGENCY THE T 020 7580 1770
Public Relations
3 Bloomsbury Place
London WC1A 2QL
F 020 7580 7200
E mail@impactagency.co.uk
W www.theimpactagency.com

I R A - INDEPENDENT REVIEWS
ARTS SERVICES T 07956 212916
Stories from the Art World
E critic@independentradioarts.com

JACKSON, Kim T 0116 253 3429
Forum Theatre Practitioner
Transforum, Studio B402
LCB Depot, 31 Rutland Street
Leicester LE1 1RW
E kim@transforum.co.uk

JENKINS, Andrew LTD T 07977 425518
Accountancy Services. Audience Research.
General Management
E andrew@andrewjenkinsltd.com
W www.andrewjenkinsltd.com

JOHNSON, Gareth LTD T 01239 891368
Plas Hafren, Eglwyswrw
Crymych, Pembrokeshire SA41 3UL
T 07770 225227
E gjltd@mac.com

JORDAN, Richard
PRODUCTIONS LTD T 020 7243 9001
Festivals. General Management. Production Consultancy.
UK & International Productions
Mews Studios, 16 Vernon Yard
London W11 2DX
F 020 7313 9667
E richard.jordan@virgin.net

KEAN LANYON LTD T 020 7354 3362
Contact: Sharon Kean, Iain Lanyon.
PR & Web/Graphic Consultants
Rose Cottage, Aberdeen Centre
22 Highbury Grove, London N5 2EA
F 020 7359 0199
E sharon@keanlanyon.com
W www.keanlanyon.com

KELLER, Don T 020 8800 4882
Marketing Consultancy. Project Management
65 Glenwood Road, Harringay
London N15 3JS
E don@donkeller.co.uk

KIEVE, Paul T 020 7502 2213
Magical Effects for Film & Stage
2 St Philip's Road, London E8 3BP
E mail@stageillusion.com
W www.stageillusion.com

LAMBOLLE, Robert T 020 8455 4564
Script Evaluation & Editing
618B Finchley Road, London NW11 7RR
E lambhorn@gmail.com
W www.readingandrighting.netfirms.com

LAWINSPORT.COM T 020 7193 1877
Contact: Sean Cottrell (Editor). Online sports law publication
providing articles of legal opinion, case law, events listings &
other sports law related directories
E sean.cottrell@lawinsport.com
W www.lawinsport.com

LAWSON LEAN, David T 01932 230273
Chaperone Service for Children in Entertainment
72 Shaw Drive, Walton-on-Thames
Surrey KT12 2LS
E dlawsonlean@aol.com
W www.davidlawsonlean.com

LEEP MARKETING & PR T 020 7439 9777
Marketing. Press. Publicity
5 Nassau House, 122 Shaftesbury Avenue
London W1D 5ER
F 020 7439 8833
E philip@leep.biz

Magus Lynius Shadeè

Psychic ~ International ~ Occult Investigator & Consultant

Specialist in:

Psychic Research • Paranormal Phenomena • Practical Ritual Workings • Hauntings
Physical Mediumship • Materialisations • Direct Voice Communications
Exorcisms • Transcendental Magic • Witchcraft • White & Black Magic • The Occult

Suite 362   110 Great Russell Street   London WC1B 3BC   Tel: 020 8378 6844   Mob: 07740 043156
email: maguslyniusshadee@hotmail.com   www.occultcentre.com   www.lifeafterdeath.net

LEO MEDIA & ENTERTAINMENT
GROUP THE   T 020 7183 3177
Executive Production. Film, Television & Literary
Consultancy. Legal Work
PO Box 68006, London NW4 9FW
F 07006 057893
E info@leomediagroup.com
W www.leomediagroup.com

LOCATION TUTORS
NATIONWIDE   T 020 7978 8898
Fully Qualified & Experienced Teachers working with
Children on Film Sets & Covering all Key Stages of National
Curriculum
16 Poplar Walk, Herne Hill
London SE24 0BU
F 020 7207 8794
E locationtutorsnationwide@gmail.com
W www.locationtutors.co.uk

LONDON COMPUTER DOCTOR   T 020 7652 4296
Computer Support
66 Heath Road, Clapham
London SW8 3BD
E joe@londoncomputerdoctor.com
W www.londoncomputerdoctor.com

LOVE, Billie
HISTORICAL PHOTOGRAPHS   T 01983 812572
Picture Research. Formerly 'Amanda' Theatrical Portraiture
3 Winton Street, Ryde
Isle of Wight PO33 2BX
E billielove@tiscali.co.uk

LUXFACTOR GROUP (UK) THE   T 0845 3700589
Fleet Place, 12 Nelson Drive
Petersfield, Hampshire GU31 4SJ
F 0845 3700588
E info@luxfactor.co.uk
W www.luxfactor.co.uk

MAGICIANS.CO.UK   T 0845 0062442
Entertainers. Magic Consultants
Burnhill House, 50 Burnhill Road
Beckenham BR3 3LA
F 0845 0062443
E mail@magicians.co.uk

MAIN, Nic   T 07739 184418
Experienced Stage, Television & Film
Action/Fight Director/Actor
62 Kingsway, Blackwater
Camberley, Surrey GU17 0JB
E nicmain@nicmain.com
W www.nicmain.com

MATT-LX LTD   T 0845 6808692
Audio Visual. Health & Safety. Lighting. Production Design
Unit 3, Vinehall Business Centre, Vinehall Road
Robertsbridge, East Sussex TN32 5JW
E intray@mattlx.com
W www.mattlx.com

MATT-LX HEALTH &
SAFETY TRAINING   T 0845 6808692
Gunnery House, 9 Gunnery Terrace
London SE18 6SW
E intray@mattlx.com
W www.mattlx.com

MAYS, Lorraine   T 01494 771029
Children's Licensed Chaperone
Park View, Stanley Avenue
Chesham, Bucks HP5 2JF
T 07778 106552
E lorrainebmays@aol.com

McKENNA, Deborah LTD   T 020 8846 0966
Celebrity Chefs & Lifestyle Presenters only
64-66 Glentham Road, London SW13 9JJ
F 020 8846 0967
E deborah@deborahmckenna.com
W www.deborahmckenna.com

MEDIA LEGAL   T 01732 460592
Jurisconsults
Town House, 5 Mill Pond Close
Sevenoaks, Kent TN14 5AW

MILDENBERG, Vanessa   T 07796 264828
Choreographer. Director. Movement Director
Flat 6, Cameford Court
New Park Road, London SW2 4LH
E vanessamildenberg@me.com
W http://web.me.com/vanessamildenberg

MILITARY ADVISORY &
INSTRUCTION SPECIALISTS T 01904 491198
Contact: John Sessions. Advice on Weapons, Drill, Period
to Present. Ex-Army Instructors. Health & Safety. IOSH.
Military Bugler & Drummer. Actor. PSV License
38 Knapton Close, Strensall
York YO32 5ZF
E johnmusic1@hotmail.com

MINIMAL RISK   T 01432 360643
Security Consultancy
Wye Valley Court, Netherwood Road
Hereford HR2 6JG
E admin@minimalrisk.co.uk
W www.minimalrisk.co.uk

MINISTRY OF FUN THE   T 020 7407 6077
Entertainment. Promotions. PR Marketing Campaigns
Unit 1, Suffolk Studios
127-129 Great Suffolk Street
London SE1 1PP
F 020 7407 5763
E james@ministryoffun.net
W www.ministryoffun.net

MORGAN, Jane
ASSOCIATES (JMA)   T 020 7263 9867
Marketing. Media
8 Heathville Road, London N19 3AJ
E jma@janemorganassociates.com

MUSIC SOLUTIONS LTD   T 020 7866 8160
Garden Studios, 11-15 Betterton Street
London WC2H 9BP
E mail@musicsolutionsltd.com

NEATE, Rodger
PRODUCTION MANAGEMENT   T 020 7609 9538
15 Southcote Road, London N19 5BJ
E rneate@dircon.co.uk

NEXTSTOPLAX   T 001 323 798 5103
Relocation of Entertainment Industry Professionals
1210 Poinsettia Drive, West Hollywood
CA 90046, USA
T 001 323 798 5102
E info@nextstoplax.com
W www.nextstoplax.com

NORTHERNALLSTARS.CO.UK   T 07980 507690
Resources for Actors
2 Prince's Gardens, Sunderland SR6 8DF
E info@northernallstars.co.uk
W www.northernallstars.co.uk

ORANGE TREE STUDIO LTD &
MUSIC SERVICES   T 07768 146200
Original Music/Composition & Production. Saxophonist &
Brass Section For Hire. Live or in Studio
31A New Road, Croxley Green
Herts WD3 3EJ
E richard@orangetreestudio.com
W www.redhornz.co.uk

PENROSE, Scott   T 07767 336882
Magic for Film, Stage & Television
17 Berkeley Drive, Billericay
Essex CM12 0YP
E mail@stagemagician.com
W www.stagemagician.com

PINEWOOD NET   T 07882 794583
Networking Group
86 Hurst Farm Road, East Grinstead
West Sussex RH19 4DH
W www.pinewoodnet.net

PSYCHOLOGY GROUP THE   T 0870 6092445
Assessments. Counselling. Expert Opinion. Presentation.
Psychotherapy
F 0845 2805243
E info@psychologygroup.co.uk
W www.psychologygroup.co.uk

PUKKA PRESENTING   T 020 8455 1385
Training in Television Presenting & Presentation Techniques
Appletree Cottage, 51 Erskine Hill
London NW11 6EY
E kathryn@pukkapresenting.co.uk
W www.pukkapresenting.co.uk

PUPPET CENTRE TRUST   T 020 7228 5335
Development & Advocacy Agency for Puppetry & Related
Animated Theatre
BAC, Lavender Hill
London SW11 5TN
E pct@puppetcentre.org.uk
W www.puppetcentre.org.uk

RAINBOW BIGBOTTOM &
CO LTD   T 01494 771029
Children's Warm-up Artists for Stage & Television
Park View, Stanley Avenue
Chesham, Bucks HP5 2JF
E lorrainebmays@aol.com
W www.mrpanda.co.uk

REACH TO THE SKY LTD   T 0843 2892503
Contact: Dr T.W.S. Johnson. Success Life Coach
Maxet House, Liverpool Road
Luton, Bedfordshire LU1 1RS
T 07961 911027
E drtwsj@reachtothesky.com
W www.wix.com/mylifecoach/dr

RED HOT ID - THE BRANDING
SERVICE FOR ACTORS   T 020 7635 8988
Unit 6, Farriers Mews
London SE15 3XP
E id@redhotentertainment.biz
W www.redhotentertainment.biz

RICHARDS, Adam   T 07950 396389
Fight Director
Unit 2, 128 Milton Road Business Park
Gravesend, Kent DA12 2PG
E stunts@adamrichardsstunts.co.uk
W www.adamrichardsfightdirector.com

RIPLEY-DUGGAN
PARTNERSHIP THE   T 020 7436 1392
Tour Booking
26 Goodge Street, London W1T 2QG
E info@ripleyduggan.com

ROSCH, Philip   T 020 8731 6686
Audition Speeches for Top UK Drama Schools
53 West Heath Court
London NW11 7RG
E philiprosch1@hotmail.com
W www.philiprosch.com

SHADEÈ, Magus Lynius   T 020 8378 6844
Psychic. Occult Investigator & Consultant
Suite 362, 110 Great Russell Street
London WC1B 3BC
T 07740 043156
E maguslyniusshadee@hotmail.com
W www.occultcentre.com

SHAW, Jennifer EVENTS   T 0845 1309517
Event Management & Promotions
15 Ladyhouse Lane, Milnrow OL16 4EH
E jennifer@jennifershawevents.co.uk
W www.jennifershawevents.co.uk

SHOWBIZ FRIENDS
Social Networking Website for Professional Showbiz People
W www.showbizfriends.com

SINCLAIR, Andy   T 07831 196675
Mime
E andynebular@hotmail.com
W www.andyjsinclair.co.uk

**SNODE, Chris SPORTS
PROMOTIONS LTD**   T 020 8771 4700
Production Advisors. Safety. Sport. Stunts
56 Church Road, Crystal Palace, London SE19 2EZ
F 020 8771 4704
E agent@sportspromotions.co.uk
W www.sportspromotions.co.uk

SOUTHAM FERRARI, Maggie   T 01730 814177
6 Oak Tree Court, Meadway
Midhurst, West Sussex GU29 9SE
T 07758 052325
E margaret.ferrari@virgin.net

STAGE CRICKET CLUB   T 020 7402 7543
Cricketers & Cricket Grounds
39-41 Hanover Steps, St George's Fields
Albion Street, London W2 2YG
F 020 7262 5736
E brianjfilm@aol.com
W www.stagecc.co.uk

**STUNT ACTION
SPECIALISTS (S.A.S.)**   T 01273 230214
Corporate & Television Stunt Work
110 Trafalgar Road, Portslade
East Sussex BN41 1GS
F 01273 708699
E mail@stuntactionspecialists.co.uk
W www.stuntactionspecialists.co.uk

**STYLES, John -
MAGICAL MART**   T/F 020 8300 3579
Magic, Ventriloquism & Punch & Judy Consultant
42 Christchurch Road, Sidcup
Kent DA15 7HQ
W www.johnstylesentertainer.co.uk

SYNCREDIBLE MEDIA   T 020 7117 6776
Licensing & Media Marketing Communications
26-28 Hammersmith Grove, Hammersmith
London W6 7BA
E contact@syncredible.com
W www.syncredible.com

TALENT SCOUT THE   T 01924 464049
Referral Service. Agents & Managers
19 Edge Road, Thornhill
Dewsbury, West Yorkshire WF12 0QA
E connect@thetalentscout.org

**THEATRE PROJECTS
CONSULTANTS**   T 020 7482 4224
4 Apollo Studios, Charlton Kings Road
London NW5 2SW
F 020 7284 0636
E uk@theatreprojects.com
W www.theatreprojects.com

**THERAPEDIA LONDON
BRIGHTON**   T 07941 300871
93 Gloucester Place, London W1U 6JQ
E info@gregmadison.net
W www.gregmadison.net

TODD, Carole   T 01584 819005
Choreographer. Director
c/o Chris Davis Management Ltd
Tenbury House, 36 Teme Street
Tenbury Wells, Worcs WR15 8AA
F 01584 819076
E cdavis@cdm-ltd.com

TWINS WORLDWIDE LTD   T 0845 0523683
Special Effects for Film, Stage & Television Productions
T 07971 589186
E info@thetwinfx.com
W www.thetwinsfx.com

UK THEATRE AVAILABILITY   T 020 8455 3278
Bookings Service for Theatre Producers
1 Hogarth Hill, London NW11 6AY
E info@uktheatreavailability.co.uk
W www.uktheatreavailability.co.uk

**UNITED KINGDOM
COPYRIGHT BUREAU**   T 01273 277333
Script Services
110 Trafalgar Road, Portslade
East Sussex BN41 1GS
E info@copyrightbureau.co.uk
W www.copyrightbureau.co.uk

VERNON, Doremy   T/F 020 8767 6944
Archivist. Author 'Tiller Girls'. Dance Routines Tiller Girl Style
16 Ouseley Road
London SW12 8EF

VOCALEYES   T 020 7375 1043
Audio Description "Describing The Arts"
1st Floor, 54 Commercial Street
London E1 0LT
E enquiries@vocaleyes.co.uk
W www.vocaleyes.co.uk

VOICEATWORK   T 07973 871479
Voice Coach
5 Anhalt Road, London SW11 4NZ
E kateterris@voiceatwork.co.uk
W www.voiceatwork.co.uk

WELBOURNE, Jacqueline   T 07977 247287
Choreographer. Circus Trainer. Consultant
43 Kingsway Avenue
Kingswood
Bristol BS15 8AN
E jackie.welbourne@gmail.com

WEST END WORKSHOPS   T 07828 821871
Educational Arts Workshops. Audition Coaching
E info@westendworkshops.co.uk
W www.westendworkshops.co.uk

WHITE, Leonard   T 01273 514473
Stage & Television Credits
Highlands, 40 Hill Crest Road
Newhaven, Brighton, East Sussex BN9 9EG
E leoguy.white@virgin.net

WILKINSON, Gavin   T 01245 200555
Children's Director
E enquiries@tomorrowstalent.co.uk
W www.tomorrowstalent.co.uk

**WISE MONKEY FINANCIAL
COACHING**   T 0845 6346713
Contact: Simonne Gnessen
14 Eastern Terrace Mews
Brighton BN2 1EP
E simonne@financial-coaching.co.uk
W www.financial-coaching.co.uk

YOUNGBLOOD   T 020 7193 3207
Fight Coordinators & Directors
E info@youngblood.co.uk
W www.youngblood.co.uk

ACADEMY COSTUMES　　　T 020 7620 0771
50 Rushworth Street, London SE1 0RB
F 020 7928 6287
E info@academycostumes.com
W www.academycostumes.com

AJ COSTUMES LTD　　　T 0871 2003343
Theatrical Costume Hire, Design & Making
Sullom Lodge, Sullom Side Lane
Barnacre, Garstang PR3 1GH
F 01253 407715
E info@squiresjohns.com
W www.squiresjohns.com

ALL-SEWN-UP　　　T/F 01422 843407
Mechanics Institute, 7 Church Street
Heptonstall, West Yorks HX7 7NS
E nwheeler_allsewnup@hotmail.com
W www.allsewnup.org.uk

AND SEW TO DANCE　　　T 01268 285050
Unit 11, Cornwallis House, Howard Chase
Basildon, Essex SS14 3BB
E andsewtodance@blueyonder.co.uk

ANELLO & DAVIDE　　　T 020 7938 2255
Handmade Shoes
15 St Albans Grove, London W8 5BP
W www.handmadeshoes.co.uk

ANGELS　　　T 020 7836 5678
Fancy Dress. Revue
119 Shaftesbury Avenue, London WC2H 8AE
F 020 7240 9527
E fun@fancydress.com
W www.fancydress.com

ANGELS THE COSTUMIERS　　　T 020 8202 2244
1 Garrick Road, London NW9 6AA
F 020 8202 1820
E angels@angels.uk.com
W www.angels.uk.com

ANGELS WIGS　　　T 020 8202 2244
Facial Hair Suppliers. Wig Hire/Makers
1 Garrick Road, London NW9 6AA
F 020 8202 1820
E wigs@angels.uk.com
W www.angels.uk.com

ANTOINETTE COSTUME HIRE　　　T 020 8699 1913
Events. Film. Stage
High Street Buildings, 134 Kirkdale, London SE26 4BB
E antoinettehire@aol.com
W www.costumehirelondon.com

ARMS & ARCHERY　　　T 01920 460335
*Armour. Banners. Chainmail. Medieval Tents. Warrior
Costumes. Weaponry*
Thrift Lane, Off London Road
Ware, Herts SG12 9QS
E armsandarchery@btconnect.com

COSTUME-MAKERS FOR STAGE & SCREEN

tel: 020 8444 8801
RON BRIGGS DESIGN
1 Bedford Mews, London N2 9DF
e.mail: costumes@ronbriggs.com
www.ronbriggs.com

ATTLE COSTUMIERS LTD　　　T 020 8540 3044
Contact: Jamie Attle. Designs, Makes & Hires Costumes
4 Toynbee Road, Wimbledon
London SW20 8SS
E aalexiscolby@aol.com

BAHADLY, R.　　　T 01625 615878
Hair & Make-up Artist, incl. Bald Caps, Ageing & Casualty
47 Ploughmans Way, Macclesfield
Cheshire SK10 2UN
T 07973 553073
E rosienico@hotmail.co.uk

BERTRAND, Henry　　　T 020 7424 7000
London Stockhouse for Silk
52 Holmes Road, London NW5 3AB
F 020 7424 7001
E sales@henrybertrand.co.uk
W www.henrybertrand.co.uk

BIRMINGHAM COSTUME HIRE　　　T 0121 622 3158
Suites 209-210, Jubilee Centre
130 Pershore Street, Birmingham B5 6ND
F 0121 622 2758
E info@birminghamcostumehire.co.uk

BISHOP, Kerry　　　T 07759 704394
Hair & Make-up Artist
Flat 4, 49 Upper Rock Gardens
Brighton, East Sussex BN2 1QF
E kerrybishop@email.com

BRIGGS, Ron DESIGN　　　T 020 8444 8801
Costume Design & Making. Embroidery. Rhinestones
1 Bedford Mews, London N2 9DF
E costumes@ronbriggs.com

BRODY, Shirley　　　T 07717 855684
14 Jenner House, London WC1N 1BL
E s.brody@blueyonder.co.uk

BURLINGTONS　　　T 0844 8008884
Hairdressers
14 John Princes Street, London W1G 0JS
E ccm@newidstudios.co.uk
W www.newidstudios.co.uk

CALICO FABRICS　　　T 020 8541 5274
*Suppliers of Unbleached Calico & other Fabrics for Stage,
Costumes, Backdrops etc*
3 Ram Passage, High Street
Kingston-upon-Thames, Surrey KT1 1HH
F 020 8546 7755
E sales@calicofabrics.co.uk
W www.calicofabrics.co.uk

CAPEZIO LONDON　　　T 020 7379 6042
Dance Products
33 Endell Street, London WC2H 9BA
E capeziolondon@capezio.com
W www.capezio.com

CHRISANNE LTD　　　T 020 8640 5921
Specialist Fabrics & Accessories for Dance & Stage
Chrisanne House, 110-112 Morden Road
Mitcham, Surrey CR4 4XB
F 020 8640 2106
E sales@chrisanne.com
W www.chrisanne.com

CLANRANALD COSTUME　　　T 01259 731010
27 High Street, Kincardine, Alloa FK10 4RJ
E info@clanranald.org
W www.clanranald.org

COLTMAN, Mike
See COSTUME CONSTRUCTION

COOK, Sheila TEXTILES　　　T 020 7603 3003
Vintage Textiles, Costumes & Accessories for Sale/Hire
26 Addison Place, London W11 4RJ
E sheilacook@sheilacook.co.uk
W www.sheilacook.co.uk

COSPROP LTD   T 020 7561 7300
Accessories. Costumes
469-475 Holloway Road, London N7 6LE
F 020 7561 7310
E enquiries@cosprop.com
W www.cosprop.com

COSTUME BOUTIQUE   T 020 7193 6877
Costume Hire for Events & Parties
38 Great Western Studios, 65 Alfred Road
London W2 5EU
T 07973 794450
E costumeboutique@me.com
W www.costumeboutique.co.uk

COSTUME CONSTRUCTION   T/F 01242 581847
Costumes. Masks. Props. Puppets
Studio 1, Croft Street, Cheltenham GL53 0EE
E mike@costumeconstruction.co.uk
W www.costumeconstruction.co.uk

COSTUME CREATIONS   T 01902 738282
10 Olinthus Avenue, Wolverhampton WV11 3DE
E yourcostume@googlemail.com
W www.costumecreations.co.uk

COSTUME GUIDE THE   T 020 7602 2857
Products & Suppliers Directory
E tp@tessap.plus.com

COSTUME SOLUTIONS   T 020 7603 9035
43 Rowan Road, London W6 7DT
E karen@costumesolutions.co.uk
W www.costumesolutions.co.uk

COSTUME STORE LTD THE   T 01273 479727
Costume Accessories
16 Station Street, Lewes, East Sussex BN7 2DB
F 01273 477191
E enquiries@thecostumestore.co.uk
W www.thecostumestore.co.uk

COSTUME STUDIO LTD   T 020 7275 9614
Costumes. Wigs
Montgomery House, 159-161 Balls Pond Road
London N1 4BG
T/F 020 7923 9065
E costume.studio@btconnect.com
W www.costumestudio.co.uk

COSTUMEGENIE.CO.UK   T 01702 617918
113 Norwich Avenue, Southend
Essex SS2 4DH
E costume-genie@hotmail.com
W www.costumegenie.co.uk

COUTURE BEADING &
EMBELLISHMENT   T 020 8925 2714
108 Hiltongrove Business Centre, Hatherley Mews
Walthamstow, London E17 4QP
T 07866 939401
E enquiries@couturebeading.com
W www.couturebeading.com

CRAZY CLOTHES CONNECTION   T 020 7221 3989
1920's-1980's for Sale or Hire
134 Lancaster Road, Ladbroke Grove
London W11 1QU
W www.crazy-clothes.co.uk

DANCIA INTERNATIONAL   T 020 7831 9483
168 Drury Lane, London WC2B 5QA
E dancialondon@btconnect.com
W www.dancia.co.uk/london

DARCY CLOTHING   T 01273 471586
2 Mount Place, Lewes
East Sussex BN7 1YH
F 01273 783884
E sales@darcyclothing.com
W www.darcyclothing.com

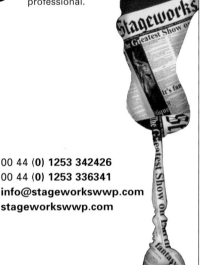

DAVIES, Bryan Philip
COSTUMES   **T** 01273 481004
Lavish Pantomime. Musical Shows. Opera
68 Court Road, Lewes
East Sussex BN7 2SA
T 07931 249097
E bryan@bpdcostumes.co.uk
W www.bpdcostumes.co.uk

DELAMAR ACADEMY   **T/F** 020 8579 9511
Make-up Training
Ealing Studios, Building D, 2nd Floor
Ealing Green, London W5 5EP
E info@delamaracademy.co.uk
W www.delamaracademy.co.uk

DESIGNER ALTERATIONS   **T** 020 7498 4360
Restyling & Remodelling of Clothes & Costumes
220A Queenstown Road, Battersea, London SW8 4LP
F 020 7622 4148
E info@designeralterations.com
W www.designeralterations.com

DR. BOO   **T** 020 8693 4823
22 North Cross Road, East Dulwich
London SE22 9EU
E boogirls@hotmail.co.uk
W www.drboo.co.uk

EASTON, Derek   **T/F** 01273 588262
Wigs For Film, Stage & Television
1 Dorothy Avenue, Peacehaven
East Sussex BN10 8LP
T 07768 166733
E wigs@derekeastonwigs.co.uk
W www.derekeastonwigs.co.uk

EIA MILLINERY DESIGN   **T** 001 773 975 5959
1620 West Nelson Street, Chicago
Illinois 60657, USA
E info@eiahatart.com

EVOLUTION SETS &
COSTUMES LTD   **T** 01304 615333
Set & Costume Hire
Langdon Abbey, West Langdon, Dover, Kent CT15 5HJ
F 01304 615353
E dorcas@evolution-productions.co.uk

FOX, Charles H. LTD   **T** 020 7240 3111
The Professional Make-up Centre
22 Tavistock Street, London WC2E 7PY
F 020 7379 3410
E makeup@charlesfox.co.uk
W www.charlesfox.co.uk

FOXTROT PRODUCTIONS LTD   **T** 020 8964 3555
Armoury Services. Costume & Prop Hire. Firearms
3B Brassie Avenue, East Acton
London W3 7DE
E info@foxtrot-productions.co.uk
W www.foxtrot-productions.co.uk

FREED OF LONDON   **T** 020 7240 0432
Dance Shoes. Dancewear
94 St Martin's Lane, London WC2N 4AT
F 020 7240 3061
E shop@freed.co.uk
W www.freedoflondon.com

FUNN LTD   **T** 0870 8743866
*Silk, Cotton & Wool Stockings. Opaque Opera Tights. 40's
Rayon Stockings*
PO Box 102, Steyning, West Sussex BN44 3EB
F 0870 8794450
E funnsales@lycos.com

GAMBA THEATRICAL
See THEATRICAL FOOTWEAR COMPANY LTD THE

GAV NICOLA
THEATRICAL SHOES   **T** 07961 974278
T 00 34 673803783
E gavnicola@yahoo.com
W www.theatricalshoes.com

GILLHAM, Felicite   **T** 01761 437142
Wig Makers for Film, Opera & Stage
Gallis Ash, Kilmersdon, Near Bath, Somerset BA3 5SZ
T 07802 955908
E felicite@gillywigs.co.uk

GREASEPAINT SCHOOL OF
MAKE-UP & HAIR   **T** 020 8840 6000
143 Northfield Avenue, Ealing, London W13 9QT
F 020 8840 3983
E info@greasepaint.co.uk
W www.greasepaint.co.uk

GROVE, Sue DESIGNS   **T** 023 8078 6849
Costume Designers & Makers. Historical Specialist
12 Ampthill Road, Shirley
Southampton, Hants SO15 8LP
E sue.grove1@tiscali.co.uk

HAIRAISERS   **T** 020 8965 2500
Hair Extensions. Wigs
32-34 Sunbeam Road
Park Royal, London NW10 6JL
F 020 8963 1600
E info@hairaisers.com
W www.hairaisers.com

HAND & LOCK   **T** 020 7580 7488
Bespoke Embroidery for Costumes, Fashion & Interiors
86 Margaret Street, London W1W 8TE
F 020 7580 7499
E enquiries@handembroidery.com
W www.handembroidery.com

HARVEYS OF HOVE   **T** 01273 430323
Military Specialists. Theatrical Costumes
110 Trafalgar Road
Portslade, Sussex BN41 1GS
F 01273 708699
E harveys.costume@ntlworld.com
W www.harveysofhove.co.uk

HENRY, Lewis LTD   **T** 020 7636 6683
Dress Makers
111-113 Great Portland Street, London W1W 6QQ
E info@lewishenrydesigns.com

HIREARCHY   **T** 01202 394465
Classic & Contemporary Costume
45-47 Palmerston Road, Boscombe
Bournemouth, Dorset BH1 4HW
E hirearchy1@aol.com
W www.hirearchy.co.uk

Derek Easton Wigs

for Theatre, Film and Television

www.derekeastonwigs.co.uk
wigs@derekeastonwigs.co.uk
T/F: 01273 588262   M: 07768 166733

1 Dorothy Avenue East Sussex Peacehaven BN10 8LP

HISTORY IN THE MAKING LTD   T 023 9225 3175
Bespoke Tailoring. Costume Hire. Military Specialists
4A Aysgarth Road, Waterlooville
Hampshire PO7 7UG
E jean@history-making.com
W www.history-making.com

HODIN, Annabel   T 020 7431 8761
Costume Designer & Stylist
12 Eton Avenue, London NW3 3EH
T 07836 754079
E annabelhodin@aol.com

HOPKINS, Trisha   T 01704 873055
6 Willow Grove, Formby L37 3NX
T 07957 368598
E trisha_hopkins@hotmail.co.uk

**INTERNATIONAL DANCE
SUPPLIES/GRISHKO UK LTD**   T 01223 861425
Importer & Distributor of Dance Shoes & Dancewear
9 Ballard Close, Milton, Cambridge CB24 6DW
F 01223 280388
E info@grishko.co.uk
W www.grishko.co.uk

JULIETTE DESIGNS   T 020 7263 7878
Diamante Jewellery Manufacturers
90 Yerbury Road, London N19 4RS
F 020 7281 7326
E juliettedesigns@hotmail.com
W www.stagejewellery.com

KATIE'S WIGS   T 07900 250853
Wig Supplier & Maker
15 Birchwood Gardens, Idle Park
Bradford BD10 9EW
E katie.hunt@katieswigs.com

KIDD, Ella J.   T 020 8539 2786
*Bespoke Millinery, Wigs & Head-dresses for Film,
Stage & Television*
W www.ellajkidd.co.uk

**LARGER THAN LIFE
STAGEWEAR**   T 020 8466 9010
Theatrical Costumes for Hire
55C Croydon Road, Elmers End
Beckenham, Kent BR3 4AB
T 07802 717714
E info@largerthanlifestagewear.co.uk
W www.largerthanlifestagewear.co.uk

LOCK, Josie   T 07722 358425
Make-up Artist
Flat 2, Liwood House, 217 Kennington Lane
Kennington, London SE11 5QT
E hello@josielock.co.uk
W www.josielockmakeup.co.uk

**MADDERMARKET THEATRE
COSTUME HIRE**   T 01603 626292
Costume & Wig Hire. Period Clothing
St John's Alley
Norwich NR2 1DR
F 01603 661357
E mmtheatre@btconnect.com
W www.maddermarket.co.uk

**MAKE-UP ARTIST &
HAIR STYLIST**   T 07973 216468
Freelancer
16 Tempest Avenue, Potters Bar
Hertfordshire EN6 5JX
E magui@magui.co.uk
W www.mm-mua.co.uk

MAKEUP 4 DANCERS   T 01795 556003
82 Recreation Way, Kemsley
Sittingbourne, Kent ME10 2TG
E jill@makeup4dancers.co.uk
W www.makeup4dancers.co.uk

**MARSDEN, Chloe COSTUMES &
MILLINERY**   T 07786 427386
1st Floor, 61 Loftus Road
London W12 7EL
E mail@chloemarsden.co.uk
W www.chloemarsden.co.uk

MASK, Kim   T 0845 0568482
Costume & Make-up Protection Masks
E info@kimmask.com
W www.kimmask.com

MASTER CLEANERS THE   T 020 7431 3725
Dry Cleaning of Theatrical Costumes & Antique Garments
189 Haverstock Hill
London NW3 4QG
E info@themastercleaners.com
W www.themastercleaners.com

McCORMACK, Mitsuki   T 07940 517757
Media Make-up Artist
London, SW11
E mitsukimccormack@yahoo.co.uk
W www.mitsukimccormack.webs.com

MEANANDGREEN.COM   T 0845 8991133
87 Darlington Street
Wolverhampton WV1 4EX
E custserv@meanandgreen.com
W www.meanandgreen.com

MORRIS, Heather
Hair Replacement. Wigs
Fortyseven, 47A Westow Street
Crystal Palace, London SE19 3RW
W www.fortysevenhair.co.uk

NATIONAL THEATRE   T 020 7735 4774 (Costume)
Costume, Furniture & Props Hire
Chichester House, Kennington Park Estate
1-3 Brixton Road, London SW9 6DE
T 020 7820 1358 (Props)
E costume_hire@nationaltheatre.org.uk

NEW ID   T 0870 8701299
Makeover & Photographic Studios
2 Lacemaker Court, London Road
Old Amersham HP7 0HS
E bookings@newidstudios.co.uk
W www.newidstudios.co.uk

NORMAN, Sam   T 07932 397465
Hair. Make-up
E sam@samnorman.co.uk
W www.samnorman.co.uk

ORIGINAL KNITWEAR   T 01726 844807
Contact: Gina Pinnick. Inc. Fake Fur
Avalon, Tregoney Hill
Mevagissey, Cornwall PL26 6RG
T 07957 376855
E okgina@btinternet.com
W www.originalknitwear.co.uk

PACE, Terri MAKE-UP DESIGN   T 07939 698999
E info@terripace.com
W www.terripace.com

PALMER, Johnny   T 07786 101360
Wardrobe Master & Supplier
Based in Glasgow
E jonboyjohnny@yahoo.co.uk

PATEY (LONDON) LTD   T 020 8291 4820
The Hat Workshop
Connaught Business Park
Malham Road, London SE23 1AH
F 020 8291 6275
E trevor@pateyhats.com
W www.pateyhats.com

PEARCE, Kate   T 07749 283802
Costume Maker
Thistledown, Wellfield Road
Marshfield, Near Newport CF3 2UB
E kpearce55@hotmail.com

PINK POINTES DANCEWEAR   T/F 01708 438584
1A Suttons Lane, Hornchurch
Essex RM12 6RD
E pink.pointes@btconnect.com

POLAND DENTAL STUDIO   T 020 7935 6919
Film/Stage Dentistry
1 Devonshire Place, London W1G 6HH
F 020 7486 3952
E robpoland@btconnect.com

PORSELLI   T 0845 0170817
4 Frensham Road
Sweet Briar Industrial Estate, Norwich NR3 2BT
F 01603 406676
E porselliuk@aol.com
W www.dancewear.co.uk

PROBLOOD   T/F 01728 723865
11 Mount Pleasant, Framlingham
Suffolk IP13 9HQ

RAINBOW PRODUCTIONS LTD   T 020 8254 5300
Manufacture & Handling of Costume Characters
Unit 3, Green Lea Park, Prince George's Road
London SW19 2JD
F 020 8254 5306
E info@rainbowproductions.co.uk
W www.rainbowproductions.co.uk

REPLICA WAREHOUSE   T/F 01477 534075
Costumiers. Props
200 Main Road, Goostrey
Cheshire CW4 8PD
E lesleyedwards@replicawarehouse.co.uk
W www.replicawarehouse.co.uk

ROBBINS, Sheila   T/F 01865 735524
Wig Hire
Broombarn, 7 Ivy Cottages
Hinksey Hill, Oxford OX1 5BQ

ROLANDI, Gianluca   T 07990 637299
Hair. Make-up
83 Deroy Lodge, Wicklow Street
London WC1X 9LF
E info@glmakeup.com
W www.glmakeup.com

ROSE, Eda MILLINERY   T 01491 837174
Ladies' Hats. Design & Manufacture
Lalique, Mongewell, Wallingford, Oxon OX10 8BP
F 01491 835909
E edarose.lawson@btconnect.com

ROUSSINOV, Sarah   T 07747 777493
20 Isabella Place
Kingston Upon Thames KT2 5PB
E sarahroussinov@aol.com
W www.sarahroussinov.co.uk

**ROYAL EXCHANGE THEATRE
COSTUME HIRE**   T/F 0161 819 6660
Period Costumes & Accessories
47-53 Swan Street, Manchester M4 5JY
E costume.hire@royalexchange.co.uk
W www.royalexchange.co.uk

**ROYER, Hugo
INTERNATIONAL LTD**   T 01252 878811
Hair & Wig Materials
10 Lakeside Business Park, Swan Lane
Sandhurst, Berkshire GU47 9DN
F 01252 878852
E enquiries@royer.co.uk
W www.hugoroyer.com

RSC COSTUME STORE   T/F 01789 205920
28 Timothy's Bridge Road
Stratford Enterprise Park
Stratford-upon-Avon, Warwickshire CV37 9UY
E costume.store@rsc.org.uk

RUMBLE, Jane   T 020 8904 6462
Masks, Millinery & Helmets Made to Order
121 Elmstead Avenue, Wembley
Middlesex HA9 8NT

SAGUARO, Jen   T 07773 385703
35 Southey Street, Bristol BS2 9RE
E jrsaguaro@googlemail.com

SERENDIPITY STUDIO LTD   T 01784 558281
77 High Street, Egham
Surrey TW20 9HY
E chrissie@serendipitystudio.co.uk
W www.serendipitystudio.co.uk

SEXTON, Sally Ann   T 01923 211644
Hair & Make-up Designer
c/o The Harris Agency Ltd, 71 The Avenue
Watford, Herts WD17 4NU
T 07973 802842
E theharrisagency@btconnect.com

SILVESTER, Michaela   T 07595 725047
Chantry, Chapel Lane
Pirbright, Surrey GU24 0JY
E kaylasilvester@hotmail.co.uk

SINGER, Sandra ASSOCIATES   T 01702 331616
Fashion Stylists for Stage & Television. Costume/Designer
21 Cotswold Road, Westcliff-on-Sea
Essex SS0 8AA
E sandrasingeruk@aol.com
W www.sandrasinger.com

SLEIMAN, Hilary   T 020 8555 6176
Specialist & Period Knitwear
72 Godwin Road, London E7 0LG
T 07940 555663
E hilary.sleiman@ntlworld.com

SOFT PROPS   T 020 7587 1116
Costume & Model Makers
92 Fentiman Road, London SW8 1LA
F 020 7207 0062
E jackie@softprops.co.uk

SOLAK, Shenay   T 07771 921931
Make-up Artist. Freelance Production Designer. Art Director
51 Drury House, London SW8 4JL
E shenays@yahoo.de

**STAGEWORKS WORLDWIDE
PRODUCTIONS**   T 01253 342426
Largest Costume Wardrobe in North
525 Ocean Boulevard, Blackpool FY4 1EZ
F 01253 342702
E simone.bolajuzon@stageworkswwp.com
W www.stageworkswwp.com

STRIBLING, Joan   T 0845 4266169
*BAFTA Member. Film & Television Hair, Make-up &
Prosthetics Designer. BAFTA Craft Award. BAFTA Design &
Art Director's Award*
T 07791 758480
E joanstribling@hotmail.com
W www.joanstribling.com

SWINFIELD, Rosemarie   T 07976 965520
Rosie's Make-up Box. Make-up Design & Training
E rosiesmake-up@uw.club.net

TALK TO THE HAND PUPPETS   T 07855 421454
Custom Puppets for Film, Stage & Television
Studio 277, Wimbledon Art Studios, Riverside Yard
Earlsfield, London SW17 0BB
T 07813 682293
E iestynmevans@hotmail.com
W www.talktothehandpuppets.com

**THEATRICAL FOOTWEAR
COMPANY LTD THE**   T 020 8529 9195
Trading as GAMBA Theatrical
Unit 14, Chingford Industrial Centre
Hall Lane, Chingford, London E4 8DJ
F 020 8529 7995
E gambatheatrical1@btconnect.com

**THEATRICAL
SHOEMAKERS LTD**   T 020 7474 0500
Footwear
Unit 7A, Thames Road Industrial Estate
Thames Road, Silvertown, London E16 2EZ
F 020 7476 5220
E ts@shoemaking.co.uk
W www.shoemaking.co.uk

TRYFONOS, Mary MASKS   T 020 7502 7883
Designer & Maker of Masks & Costume Properties
59 Shaftesbury Road, London N19 4QW
T 07764 587433
E marytryfonos@aol.com

**MIKE COLTMAN
COSTUME CONSTRUCTION**

**PROMOTIONAL COSTUMES
PANTO ANIMALS · MASKS
HEADDRESSES · SOFT PROPS
ANIMAL · VEGETABLE · MINERAL**

**PHONE/FAX
01242 581847**

www.costumeconstruction.co.uk

TUTU-TOPIA   T 07999 553021
Lincoln LN1
E sales@tutu-topia.co.uk
W www.tutu-topia.co.uk

**WEST YORKSHIRE
FABRICS LTD**   T/F 0113 225 6550
*Barathea. Crepe. Linen. Stretch Fabrics. Suiting. Venetian.
Cut Lengths*
Unit 5 Milestone Court, Stanningley, Leeds LS28 6HE
E neil@wyfabrics.com

WIG EXPECTATIONS   T 07814 739692
3 Northernhay Walk, Morden, Surrey SM4 4BS
E wigexpectations@aol.com
W www.wigexpectations.com

WIG ROOM THE   T 01256 415737
22 Coronation Road, Basingstoke, Hants RG21 4HA
E darren@wigroom.co.uk

WIG SPECIALITIES LTD   T 020 7724 0020
Hand Made Wigs & Facial Hair, Hair Extensions etc
77 Ashmill Street, London NW1 6RA
F 020 7724 0069
E wigspecialities@btconnect.com
W www.wigspecialities.co.uk

WIGS & MAKE-UP SPECIALIST   T 07516 323000
4A Summerhill Villas, Susan Wood
Chislehurst, Kent BR7 5NG
E rachellisajones@hotmail.co.uk

WILLIAMS, Emma   T 07710 130345
Costume Designer & Stylist. Film, Stage & Television
E emmacoz@dsl.pipex.com

DAILY EXPRESS T 020 8612 7000
Contact: Caroline Jowett (Stage, Film, Dance, Opera),
Matt Baylis (Television)
Northern Shell Building, 10 Lower Thames Street
London EC3R 6EN
E arts.editor@express.co.uk

DAILY MAIL T 020 7938 6000
Contact: Quentin Letts (Stage), Chris Tookey (Film)
Northcliffe House, 2 Derry Street
Kensington, London W8 5TT

DAILY STAR T 020 8612 7000
Contact: Alan Frank (Film & Video), Nigel Pauley (Showbiz
Report)
Northern Shell Building, 10 Lower Thames Street
London EC3R 6EN

DAILY TELEGRAPH T 020 7931 2000
Contact: Charles Spencer, Dominic Cavendish (Stage),
Sukhdev Sandhu, Tim Robey (Film), Gillian Reynolds (Radio),
Richard Dorment (Art), Sarah Crompton (Arts Editor), Mark
Monahan (Dance), Geoffrey Norris, Ivan Hewitt (Music)
111 Buckingham Palace Road, London SW1W 0DT

FINANCIAL TIMES T 020 7873 3000
Contact: Sarah Hemmings, Ian Shuttleworth (Stage),
Nigel Andrews, Karl French (Film), Martin Hoyle, John Lloyd
(Television)
1 Southwark Bridge, London SE1 9HL

GUARDIAN T 020 3353 2000
Contact: Michael Billington (Stage), Nancy Banks-Smith
(Television)
King's Place, 90 York Way
London N1 9GU

INDEPENDENT T 020 7005 2000
Contact: Gerard Gilbert (Television)
2 Derry Street, London W8 5HF

LONDON EVENING STANDARD T 020 3367 7000
Contact: Henry Hitchings, Fiona Mountford, Kieron Quirke
(Stage), Derek Malcolm (Film), Jane Shilling (Television),
Barry Millington (Classical Music & Opera)
Northcliffe House, 2 Derry Street
Kensington, London W8 5TT
W www.thisislondon.co.uk

MAIL ON SUNDAY T 020 7938 6000
Contact: Georgina Brown (Stage), Jason Solomons
(Cinema & DVDs), Matthew Bond (Film),
Simon Garfield (Radio)
Review Section, Northcliffe House
2 Derry Street, London W8 5TT

MIRROR T 020 7510 3000
Contact: Dave Edwards (Film), James Simon, Jim Shelley
(Television Previews)
Mirror Group Newspapers Ltd, 1 Canada Square
Canary Wharf, London E14 5AP

MORNING STAR T 020 8510 0815
Contact: Cliff Cocker (Arts Editor)
William Rust House, 52 Beachy Road
London E3 2NS

OBSERVER T 020 3353 2000
Contact: Susannah Clapp (Stage Contributor), Philip French
(Film Contributor), Sarah Donaldson (Arts Editor), Miranda
Sawyer (Radio Contributor), Luke Jennings (Dance
Contributor), Fiona Maddocks (Opera Contributor)
King's Place, 90 York Way
London N1 9GU

PEOPLE T 020 7293 3000
Contact: Conor Nolan (Film), John Wise (Television & Radio),
Caroline Waterson (Features), Katie Hind (Show Business)
1 Canada Square, Canary Wharf
London E14 5AP

SUN T 020 7782 4000
Contact: Grant Rollings, Ally Ross (Features Writer)
3 Thomas More Square, London E98 1XY

SUNDAY EXPRESS T 020 8612 7000
Contact: Mark Shenton (Stage), Henry Fitzherbert (Film),
David Stephenson (Television), Clare Heal (Radio & Arts)
Northern Shell Building, 10 Lower Thames Street
London EC3R 6EN

SUNDAY MIRROR T 020 7510 3000
Contact: Kevin O'Sullivan (Stage & Television), Mark Adams
(Film), Dean Piper (Show Business)
Mirror Group, 1 Canada Square
Canary Wharf, London E14 5AP

SUNDAY TELEGRAPH T 020 7931 2000
Contact: Tim Walker (Stage), Jenny McCartney (Film),
John Preston (Television)
111 Buckingham Palace Road, London SW1W 0DT

SUNDAY TIMES T 020 7782 5000
Contact: Christopher Hart (Stage), Cosmo Landesman (Film),
A. A. Gill (Television), Paul Donovan (Radio)
3 Thomas More Square, London E98 1XY

TIMES T 020 7782 5000
Contact: Libby Purves (Stage), Kate Muir (Film),
James Jackson (Television), Ed Potton (Music)
3 Thomas More Square, London E98 1XY

D

Dance Companies

How do I become a professional dancer?

Full-time vocational training can start from as young as ten years old. A good starting point for researching the different schools and courses available is CDET (Council for Dance Education & Training) www.cdet.org.uk. There are twenty dance colleges offering professional training accredited by CDET, and nearly three hundred university courses which include some form of dance training. It is estimated that over one thousand dancers graduate from vocational training schools or university courses every year, so it is a highly competitive career. Therefore anyone wanting to be a professional dancer must obtain as many years of training and experience as possible, plus go to see plenty of performances spanning different types and genres of dance. If you require further information on vocational dance schools, applying to accredited dance courses, auditions and funding, contact CDET's information line 'Answers for Dancers' on 020 7240 5703 or see their case study in this section.

What are dance companies?

There are more than two hundred dance companies in the UK, spanning a variety of dance styles including ballet, contemporary, hip hop and African. A dance company will either be resident in a venue, be a touring company, or a combination of both. Many have websites which you can visit for full information. Most dance companies employ ensemble dancers on short to medium contracts, who may then work on a number of different productions for the same company over a number of months. In addition, the company will also employ principal/leading dancers on a role-by-role basis.

What are dance organisations?

There are numerous organisations which exist to support professional dancers, covering important areas including health and safety, career development, networking and legal and financial aspects. Other organisations (e.g. regional/national dance agencies) exist to promote dance within the wider community.

I have already trained to be a dancer. Why do I need further training?

Dance training should not cease as soon as you get your first job or complete a course. Throughout your career you should continuously strive to maintain your fitness levels, enhance and develop your existing skills and keep learning new ones in order to retain a competitive edge. You must also be prepared to continuously learn new dance styles and routines for specific roles. Ongoing training and classes can help you stay fit and active, and if you go through a period of unemployment you can keep your mind and body occupied, ready to take on your next job.

How should I use these listings?

The following pages will supply you with up-to-date contact details for a wide range of dance companies and organisations, followed by listings for dance training and professional classes. Always research schools and classes thoroughly, obtaining copies of prospectuses where available. Most vocational schools offer two and three year full-time training programmes, many also offer excellent degree programmes. Foundation courses offer a sound introduction to the profession, but they can never replace a full-time vocational course. Many schools, organisations and studios also offer part-time/evening classes which offer a general understanding of dance and complementary technique or the opportunity to refresh specific dance skills; they will not, however, enable a student to become a professional dancer.

How else can I find work as a dancer?

Dance also plays a role in commercial theatre, musicals, opera, film, television, live music and video, corporate events and many other industries. Dancers may also want to be represented by an agent. Agents have many more contacts within the industry than an individual dancer can have, and can offer advice and negotiate contracts on your behalf as well as submit you for jobs. A number of specialist dance agencies are listed in the 'Agents: Dance' section.

What is Spotlight Dancers?

Dancers wishing to promote themselves to these types of job opportunities should consider joining Spotlight's specialist casting directory for dancers. This is a central directory of dancers published annually which is used by dance employers throughout the UK to locate dancers and send out casting or audition information. Members receive a page in the directory containing a headshot and body shot, agency contact details and selected credits as well as an online CV. Dancers who attend CDET accredited schools receive a discount when applying in their graduating year. Please see www.spotlight.com/artists/dancers for more information.

What other careers are available in dance?

Opportunities also exist to work as a teacher, choreographer, technician or manager. Dance UK www.danceuk.org is a valuable source of information for anyone considering this type of work.

What should I do to avoid injury?

An injury is more likely to occur if you are inflexible and unprepared for sudden physical exertion. The last thing you want to do is to pick up an injury, however minor, and be prevented from working, so continuous training during both employment and unemployment will help you to minimise the risk of an injury during a performance or rehearsal. If you do sustain an injury you will want to make sure it does not get any worse by getting treatment with a specialist. The British Association for Performing Arts Medicine (BAPAM) provides specialist health support for performers, free health assessment clinics and a directory of performing arts health practitioners and specialists. Visit their website www.bapam.org.uk for more information. You may also find their case study in the 'Health & Wellbeing' section of Contacts useful.

I'm not a professional dancer but I enjoy dancing. Why should I use these listings?

People don't just dance to perform, teach or advise within the industry. Dance can be pursued for fun, recreation, social reasons and for health. Training and professional advice should still be pursued to ensure that you do not injure yourself while dancing and prevent yourself from working. You can also use the 'Dance Training & Professional Classes' listings to find suitable dance lessons in your area, which you could attend to make friends, keep fit and stay occupied.

Where can I find more information?

For further advice about the dance industry, you could try contacting CDET (www.cdet.org.uk) for training information, Dance UK (www.danceuk.org) regarding the importance and needs of dance and dancers, or BAPAM (www.bapam.org.uk) for health issues. You may want to get involved with Move It! – the UK's biggest dance exhibition which takes place every year in March. Visit www.moveitdance.co.uk for more information. If you are looking for a dance agent to promote you to job opportunities, please see the 'Agents: Dance' section of Contacts.

Dance Companies

The Council for Dance Education and Training (CDET) is the quality assurance agency of the dance and musical theatre industries. It is the first point of contact for students and others seeking information on the quality of education and training in the United Kingdom. CDET negotiates with government agencies in this country and overseas to ensure the accredited private dance and musical theatre sectors are represented vigorously and consistently at all levels of national and international decision making.

What is a CDET Accredited School?

A CDET accredited school is a vocational school or college offering full-time courses in dance, musical theatre or dance teaching to students over the age of 16.

What is a CDET AMS School?

A CDET Application for Membership School (AMS) is a vocational school or college that is working towards accreditation but has not yet received an accreditation visit by a professional CDET assessment panel. All AMS schools meet CDET's initial criteria for accreditation.

What makes CDET accredited education and training so special?

Every CDET accredited institution has been inspected by a trained panel of dance and musical theatre professionals to ensure it meets the needs of both the industry and the student.

What is a CDET Dance Awarding Organisation?

Dance Awarding Organisations are examining institutions offering graded and vocational graded qualifications in dance and musical theatre. Dance teachers who hold a teaching qualification from an awarding organisation may enter students for the examinations of that body. CDET has two categories of membership for Awarding Organisations:

1. Validated Dance Awarding Organisations
2. Corporate Members

Corporate Members are member organisations of CDET currently working towards validation.

What are the CDET *Recognised Awards?*

CDET's *Recognised Awards* are four industry-recognised awards available to dance and musical theatre schools and/or teachers meeting the standards of professional practice of CDET. The awards recognise dance and musical theatre schools and teachers who have committed themselves to upholding safe and professional standards. Students choosing a *Recognised* dance school or teacher may be confident in their professional standards knowing they have met CDET's nine *Requirements* of professional practice.

Competition for places at CDET accredited dance and musical theatre schools is fierce; consequently students will sometimes consider an offer from an unaccredited vocational trainer. Students should always ensure they will receive the quality of training they expect, that studio facilities and medical resources are suitable for the teaching of dance or musical theatre and that they have requested a written explanation as to why the school does not hold CDET accreditation prior to enrolling on any course.

What resources are available to me?

CDET publishes the annual *UK Guide of Accredited Courses in Dance and Musical Theatre*. A downloadable PDF version of the guide is available on the CDET website www.cdet.org.uk. Hard copies are also available, free of charge, from French's Theatre Bookshop, London. The Council offers a comprehensive and free information service, *Answers for Dancers*, on all aspects of dance education and training. E-mail answersfordancers@cdet.org.uk or call the CDET office on 020 7240 5703.

Whatever your query regarding dance or musical theatre education and training visit the CDET website at www.cdet.org.uk or telephone the CDET office on 020 7240 5703.

Dance Companies

Paul Harris is a choreographer in film, television and theatre, whose very varied credits include the wand combat sequences in Harry Potter And The Order of The Phoenix, the famous laser scenes for Catherine Zeta-Jones in Entrapment and The Other Boleyn Girl as well as many period dramas for TV over the past decade including the BAFTA-winning Bleak House and The Way Live Now. In theatre he choreographed the 50th anniversary production of The Entertainer at The Old Vic, Liberty at the Globe and many regional and touring productions. Much of Paul's work is dance in the context of acting.

The nature of film and television means that producers and directors want dance sequences to be filmed as quickly and as painlessly as possible! Ball sequences can be very tricky to film and, in my view, it is essential that the choreographer knows every single person who is dancing on the set. I feel it is very important for me to keep an extensive database so that I can call upon people with the exact skills required for a particular job, as the choreographer will need to choose exactly the right combination of people to make the scene work and to be able to pull everything together quickly.

Many choreographers hold frequent auditions, but I do not. I tend to 'collect people' and I keep a database of CVs and photographs of dancers and actors who can dance, as well as the CVs of some of the students I have personally taught. I read carefully every CV that is sent to me and I keep the CVs and photographs of anyone I think I may be able to use – even if it is for the future – and I have a very detailed memory for dancers with the skills I tend to use.

An example of this was an actor who had quite specific dance skills and who wrote to me for a TV drama casting in 2001 (for which I was holding an audition). Although he was too late for that particular job, I kept his CV and photograph and remembered him five years later when I was casting for an actor who could dance in a trailer for a well known TV series. The actor was called in to meet the director – and he got the job!

This brings me on to CVs. The actor mentioned remained in my memory because his CV contained words and information that enabled me to understand that his particular dance skills were suitable for much of the work that I do. It is vital that CVs are very clear with regard to dance skills. For example, if a CV states 'partner work', this is not clear as to whether the person is referring to Pas de Deux or Ballroom dancing! It is also often useful to name the people they have trained with on their CVs, as the teachers will often be known to me and other choreographers.

For me personally, the most useful combination of skills is a high level broad dance training, combined with extensive knowledge of socially related dances from the last 500 years. This can be anything from Argentine Tango to Salsa, Swing, Ballroom or Historical dance. These dance styles, when combined with good formal dance training, can be a formidable combination. What is vital though is that the exact knowledge of the dancer is identified on the CV. Tango, for example, comes in more than one form and Latin American can mean either Salsa (and its related forms) or Ballroom-style Latin American. This should always be made clear as they are very different.

Dancers should also be clear with their agents and encourage their agents not to submit them for work they are not right for. Whenever dancers have written to me directly, their descriptions of their skills have usually proved to be more accurate than when submitted by an agent. My own agent is very careful when selecting dancers and choreographers for a particular job and always tries to marry the job with the right dancer/choreographer, rather than just submit everyone for everything.

I hope this is useful advice and I wish anyone entering the industry the very best of luck!

Please visit www.paulharris.uk.com for further information.

Dance Companies

AKADEMI
SOUTH ASIAN DANCE UK   T 020 7691 3210
213 Haverstock Hill
Hampstead Town Hall
Haverstock Hill, London NW3 4QP
F 020 7691 3211
E info@akademi.co.uk
W www.akademi.co.uk

ANJALI DANCE COMPANY   T 01295 251909
The Mill Arts Centre, Spiceball Park
Banbury, Oxford OX16 5QE
E info@anjali.co.uk
W www.anjali.co.uk

BALLET CYMRU   T 01633 253985
30 Glasllwch Crescent, Newport
South Wales NP20 3SE
E dariusjames@welshballet.co.uk
W www.welshballet.co.uk

BALLETBOYZ   T 020 7278 5508
Sadler's Wells, Rosebery Avenue
Islington, London EC1R 4TN
E dance@balletboyz.com
W www.balletboyz.com

BALLROOM,
LONDON THEATRE OF   T 020 8722 8798
Contact: Paul Harris® (Artistic Director)
24 Montana Gardens, Sutton
Surrey SM1 4FP
T 07958 784462
E office@londontheatreofballroom.com
W www.londontheatreofballroom.com

BIRMINGHAM ROYAL BALLET   T 0121 245 3500
Thorp Street
Birmingham B5 4AU
F 0121 245 3570
E brbinfo@brb.org.uk
W www.brb.org.uk

CANDOCO DANCE COMPANY   T 020 7704 6845
2T Leroy House, 436 Essex Road
London N1 3QP
F 020 7704 1645
E info@candoco.co.uk
W www.candoco.co.uk

CHOLMONDELEYS &
FEATHERSTONEHAUGHS THE   T 020 7375 0100
Toynbee Studios
28 Commercial Street
London E1 6AB
E admin@thecholmondeleys.org
W www.thecholmondeleys.org

COMPANY OF CRANKS   T 07963 617981
1st Floor, 62 Northfield House
London SE15 6TN
E mimetic16@yahoo.com
W www.mimeworks.com

CREATIVE KIDZ & CO   T 07958 377595
9 Weavers Terrace, Fulham
London SW6 1QE
T 07908 144802
E info@creativekidzandco.co.uk

DANCE SOUTH WEST/
PAVILION DANCE   T 01202 203630
Pavilion Theatre, Westover Road
Bournemouth BH1 2BU
E paviliondance@dancesouthwest.org.uk
W www.paviliondance.org.uk

DAVIES, Siobhan DANCE   T 020 7091 9650
85 St George's Road
London SE1 6ER
F 020 7091 9669
E info@siobhandavies.com
W www.siobhandavies.com

DV8 PHYSICAL THEATRE   T 020 7655 0977
Artsadmin, Toynbee Studios
28 Commercial Street
London E1 6AB
F 020 7247 5103
E dv8@artsadmin.co.uk
W www.dv8.co.uk

ENGLISH NATIONAL
BALLET LTD   T 020 7581 1245
Markova House, 39 Jay Mews
London SW7 2ES
F 020 7225 0827
E comments@ballet.org.uk
W www.ballet.org.uk

ENGLISH YOUTH BALLET   T 01689 856747
Appledowne, The Hillside
Orpington, Kent BR6 7SD
T 07732 383600
E misslewis@englishyouthballet.co.uk
W www.englishyouthballet.co.uk

FRANCOIS', Ryan
SWING X-TREME   T 07590 695361
Orchard View, Love Lane
Iver, Bucks SL0 9QT
E ryan@swingextreme.co.uk
W www.swingextreme.co.uk

GREEN CANDLE
DANCE COMPANY   T 020 7739 7722
Oxford House, Derbyshire Street
Bethnal Green, London E2 6HG
E info@greencandledance.com
W www.greencandledance.com

IJAD DANCE COMPANY   T 07930 378639
22 Allison Road, London N8 0AT
E ijaddancecompany@gmail.com
W www.ijad.freeserve.co.uk

JEYASINGH, Shobana
DANCE COMPANY   T 020 7697 4444
Moving Arts Base
134 Liverpool Road, Islington, London N1 1LA
E admin@shobanajeyasingh.co.uk
W www.shobanajeyasingh.co.uk

KHAN, Akram COMPANY   T 020 7354 4333
Unit 232A, 35A Britannia Row
London N1 8QH
F 020 7354 5554
E office@akramkhancompany.net
W www.akramkhancompany.net

KOSH THE　　T/F 020 8374 0407
Physical Theatre
59 Stapleton Hall Road, London N4 3QF
E info@thekosh.com

LUDUS DANCE　　T 01524 35936
Assembly Rooms, King Street
Lancaster LA1 1RE
F 01524 847744
E info@ludusdance.org
W www.ludusdance.org

NEW ADVENTURES　　T 020 7713 6766
Sadler's Wells, Rosebery Avenue
London EC1R 4TN
E info@new-adventures.net
W www.new-adventures.net

NORTHERN BALLET　　T 0113 220 8000
2 St Cecilia Street, Quarry Hill
Leeds LS2 7PA
F 0113 220 8001
E info@northernballet.com
W www.northernballet.com

PHOENIX DANCE THEATRE　　T 0113 236 8130
2 St Cecilia Street, Quarry Hill
Leeds LS2 7PA
E info@phoenixdancetheatre.co.uk
W www.phoenixdancetheatre.co.uk

PLACE THE　　T 020 7121 1000
17 Duke's Road, London WC1H 9PY
F 020 7121 1142
E info@theplace.org.uk
W www.theplace.org.uk

PMB PRESENTATIONS LTD　　T 020 7368 3337
Vicarage House
58-60 Kensington Church Street
London W8 4DB
F 020 7368 3338
E p@triciamurraybett.com
W www.pmbpresentations.co.uk

RAMBERT DANCE COMPANY　　T 020 8630 0600
94 Chiswick High Road, London W4 1SH
F 020 8747 8323
E rdc@rambert.org.uk
W www.rambert.org.uk

ROTIE, Marie-Gabrielle
PRODUCTIONS
1 Christchurch Square, London E9 7HU
E rotieproductions@googlemail.com
W www.rotieproductions.com

ROYAL BALLET THE　　T 020 7240 1200 Ext 712
Royal Opera House
Covent Garden
London WC2E 9DD
F 020 7212 9121
E balletcompany@roh.org.uk
W www.roh.org.uk

SCOTTISH BALLET　　T 0141 331 2931
Tramway, 25 Albert Drive
Glasgow G41 2PE
W www.scottishballet.co.uk

SCOTTISH DANCE THEATRE　　T 01382 342600
Dundee Repertory Theatre
Tay Square
Dundee DD1 1PB
F 01382 228609
E achinn@dundeereptheatre.co.uk
W www.scottishdancetheatre.com

SLOVAK
DANCE THEATRE　　T/F 00 421 2 54645811
Pribinova 25
811 09 Bratislava
Slovakia
E sdt@sdt.sk
W www.sdt.sk

SPLITZ THEATRE ARTZ　　T 01223 880389
5 Cow Lane, Fulbourn
Cambridge CB21 5HB
E clare@splitz-ta.net
W www.splitz-ta.co.uk

SPRINGS DANCE COMPANY　　T 01634 817523
65 John Kennedy Court
Newington Green Road
London N1 4RT
T 07775 628442
E info@springsdancecompany.org.uk
W www.springsdancecompany.org.uk

TRANSITIONS
DANCE COMPANY　　T 020 8469 9471
Creekside
London SE8 3DZ
E transitions@trinitylaban.ac.uk
W www.trinitylaban.ac.uk

TWITCH EVENT
CHOREOGRAPHY　　T 07747 770816
T 07932 656358
E info@twitch.uk.com
W www.twitch.uk.com

UNION DANCE　　T 020 7836 7837
Top Floor, 6 Charing Cross Road
London WC2H 0HG
F 020 7836 7847
E info@uniondance.co.uk
W www.uniondance.co.uk

**ACCELERATE
PRODUCTIONS LTD**   T 07782 199181
374 Ley Street, Ilford IG1 4AE
E info@accelerate-productions.co.uk
W www.accelerate-productions.co.uk

**AKADEMI
SOUTH ASIAN DANCE UK**   T 020 7691 3210
Hampstead Town Hall, 213 Haverstock Hill
London NW3 4QP
F 020 7691 3211
E info@akademi.co.uk
W www.akademi.co.uk

ALLIED DANCING ASSOCIATION   T 0151 724 1829
137 Greenhill Road, Mossley Hill
Liverpool L18 7HQ
E carolparryada@yahoo.co.uk

**ASSOCIATION OF DANCE OF
THE AFRICAN DIASPORA**   T 020 7841 7357
Urdang, The Old Finsbury Town Hall
Rosebery Avenue, London EC1R 4QT
F 020 7833 2363
E info@adad.org.uk
W www.adad.org.uk

BENESH INSTITUTE THE   T 020 7326 8035
36 Battersea Square, London SW11 3RA
T 020 7326 8031
E beneshinstitute@rad.org.uk
W www.benesh.org

**BLUE EYED SOUL
DANCE COMPANY**   T 01743 210830
Closing March 2012
The Lantern, Meadow Farm Drive
Shrewsbury SY1 4NG
E admin@besdance.com
W www.besdance.com

BRITISH ARTS THE   T 01708 756263
12 Deveron Way, Rise Park
Romford RM1 4UL
W www.britisharts.org

**BRITISH ASSOCIATION OF
TEACHERS OF DANCING**   T 0141 427 3699
Pavilion, 8 Upper Level
Watermark Business Park
315 Govan Road, Glasgow G51 2SE
E enquiries@batd.co.uk
W www.batd.co.uk

**BRITISH BALLET
ORGANISATION**   T 020 8748 1241
Dance Examining Society. Teacher Training
Woolborough House, 39 Lonsdale Road
Barnes, London SW13 9JP
E info@bbo.org.uk
W www.bbo.org.uk

**BRITISH THEATRE
DANCE ASSOCIATION**   T 0845 1662179
Garden Street, Leicester LE1 3UA
F 0845 1662189
E info@btda.org.uk
W www.btda.org.uk

CHISENHALE DANCE SPACE   T 020 8981 6617
64-84 Chisenhale Road, Bow
London E3 5QZ
F 020 8980 9323
E mail@chisenhaledancespace.co.uk
W www.chisenhaledancespace.co.uk

**COUNCIL FOR DANCE
EDUCATION & TRAINING (CDET)**   T 020 7240 5703
Old Brewer's Yard, 17-19 Neal Street
Covent Garden, London WC2H 9UY
F 020 7240 2547
E info@cdet.org.uk
W www.cdet.org.uk

DANCE4   T 0115 941 0773
3-9 Hockley, Nottingham NG1 1FH
F 0115 941 0776
E info@dance4.co.uk
W www.dance4.co.uk

**DANCE BASE NATIONAL
CENTRE FOR DANCE**   T 0131 225 5525
14-16 Grassmarket, Edinburgh EH1 2JU
E dance@dancebase.co.uk
W www.dancebase.co.uk

DANCE CITY   T 0191 261 0505
National Dance Agency
Temple Street
Newcastle-upon-Tyne NE1 4BR
E info@dancecity.co.uk
W www.dancecity.co.uk

DANCE DIGITAL   T 01245 346036
2 Bond Street, Chelmsford
Essex CM1 1GH
E admin@dancedigital.org.uk
W www.dancedigital.org.uk

DANCE EAST   T 01473 295230
Jerwood Dance House
Foundry Lane
Ipswich IP4 1DW
E info@danceeast.co.uk
W www.danceeast.co.uk

DANCE HOUSE   T 0141 552 2442
The Briggait, 141 Bridgegate
Glasgow G1 5HZ
E info@dancehouse.org
W www.dancehouse.org

DANCE IN DEVON   T 01392 667050
County Dance Development Agency
Exeter Phoenix, Bradninch Place
Gandy Street, Exeter EX4 3LS
E info@danceindevon.org.uk
W www.danceindevon.org.uk

**DANCE INITIATIVE
GREATER MANCHESTER**   T 0161 232 7179
Zion Arts Centre, Stretford Road
Hulme, Manchester M15 5ZA
F 0161 232 7483
E info@digm.org.uk
W www.digm.org

**DANCE SOUTH WEST/
PAVILION DANCE**   T 01202 203630
Pavilion Theatre, Westover Road
Bournemouth BH1 2BU
E paviliondance@dancesouthwest.org.uk
W www.paviliondance.org.uk

DANCE UK   T 020 7713 0730
Including the Healthier Dancer Programme
The Old Finsbury Town Hall, Rosebery Avenue
London EC1R 4QT
F 020 7833 2363
E info@danceuk.org
W www.danceuk.org

DANCE UMBRELLA　　T 020 7407 1200
1 Brewery Square, London SE1 2LF
F 020 7378 8405
E mail@danceumbrella.co.uk
W www.danceumbrella.co.uk

**DANCERS' CAREER
DEVELOPMENT**　　T 020 7831 1449
Plouviez House
19-20 Hatton Place
London EC1N 8RU
F 020 7242 1462
E admin@thedcd.org.uk
W www.thedcd.org.uk

DANCEXCHANGE　　T 0121 689 3170
National Dance Agency
Birmingham Hippodrome, Thorp Street
Birmingham B5 4TB
E info@dancexchange.org.uk
W www.dancexchange.org.uk

DAVIES, Siobhan DANCE　　T 020 7091 9650
Professional Development for Dance Artists & Education
85 St George's Road
London SE1 6ER
F 020 7091 9669
E info@siobhandavies.com
W www.siobhandavies.com

EAST LONDON DANCE　　T 020 8279 1050
Stratford Circus, Theatre Square
London E15 1BX
F 020 8279 1054
E office@eastlondondance.org
W www.eastlondondance.org

EVERYBODY DANCE　　T 07590 032294
*Contact: Rachel Freeman. Aerial & Community Dance for
Disabled & Non-disabled Artists of All Ages*
Longlands Barn, Whitbourne
Worcester, Worcestershire WR6 5SG
E rfeverybodydance@gmail.com

**FAME ACADEMY OF
PERFORMING ARTS**　　T 020 8882 7849
Arts Education. Event Management. Projects
450A Green Lanes, Palmers Green
London N13 5XD
E famearts@yahoo.com
W www.fameapa.org.uk

**FOUNDATION FOR
COMMUNITY DANCE**　　T 0116 253 3453
LCB Depot, 31 Rutland Street
Leicester LE1 1RE
F 0116 261 6801
E info@communitydance.org.uk
W www.communitydance.org.uk

GREENWICH DANCE　　T 020 8293 9741
The Borough Hall, Royal Hill
London SE10 8RE
E info@greenwichdance.org.uk
W www.greenwichdance.org.uk

**IDTA (INTERNATIONAL DANCE TEACHERS'
ASSOCIATION)**　　T 01273 685652
International House, 76 Bennett Road
Brighton, East Sussex BN2 5JL
F 01273 674388
E info@idta.co.uk
W www.idta.co.uk

COUNCIL FOR DANCE
EDUCATION & TRAINING

The Council for Dance Education and Training (CDET)

- accredits professional training programmes in vocational dance and musical theatre schools
- validates the qualifications of Dance Awarding Organisations
- recognises, by means of its *Recognised Awards* scheme, dance and performing arts schools and teachers working with students under the age of sixteen that can demonstrate compliance to the Council's standards of professional practice

CDET also

- offers a comprehensive and free information service, *Answers for Dancers*, to students, parents, teachers, dance artists and employers on all aspects of dance education and training
- holds the CDET searchable database containing the details of all *Recognised Schools* and dance teachers belonging to one or more of CDET's Validated Awarding Organisations or Corporate Members

For more information on CDET please contact:

Council for Dance Education and Training
Old Brewer's Yard, 17-19 Neal Street, Covent Garden, London, WC2H 9UY
Tel 020 7240 5703　**Email** info@cdet.org.uk　**Website** www.cdet.org.uk

LANGUAGE OF DANCE CENTRE T 020 7749 1131
Oxford House, Derbyshire Street
London E2 6HG
E info@lodc.org
W www.lodc.org

**LONDON CONTEMPORARY
DANCE SCHOOL** T 020 7121 1111
16 Flaxman Terrace, London WC1H 9AT
F 020 7121 1142
E lcds@theplace.org.uk
W www.lcds.ac.uk

LUDUS DANCE T 01524 35936
The Assembly Rooms, King Street
Lancaster LA1 1RE
F 01524 847744
E info@ludusdance.org
W www.ludusdance.org

**MERSEYSIDE DANCE
INITIATIVE** T 0151 708 8810
National Dance Agency
24 Hope Street, Liverpool L1 9BX
E info@mdi.org.uk
W www.mdi.org.uk

**MIDLAND INTERNATIONAL
DANCE ARTS ASSOCIATION** T 0121 694 0012
29A Sycamore Road
Birmingham B23 5QP
F 0121 694 0013
E midaa.hq@hotmail.com
W www.abdance.net

**NATIONAL RESOURCE
CENTRE FOR DANCE** T 01483 689316
University of Surrey, Guildford GU2 7XH
F 01483 689500
E nrcd@surrey.ac.uk
W www.surrey.ac.uk/nrcd

PLACE THE T 020 7121 1000
17 Duke's Road
London WC1H 9BY
F 020 7121 1142
E info@theplace.org.uk
W www.theplace.org.uk

**PROFESSIONAL TEACHERS
OF DANCING** T 01935 848547
Contact: Jo Pillinger
The Studios, Morcombelake
Dorset DT6 6DY
E ptdenquiries@msn.com
W www.ptdance.com

SOUTH EAST DANCE T 01273 696844
*National Development Organisation for Dance
in South East England*
28 Kensington Street
Brighton BN1 4AJ
F 01273 697212
E info@southeastdance.org.uk
W www.southeastdance.org.uk

SWINDON DANCE T 01793 601700
National Dance Agency
Town Hall Studios
Regent Circus
Swindon SN1 1QF
E info@swindondance.org.uk
W www.swindondance.org.uk

YORKSHIRE DANCE T 0113 243 9867
National Dance Agency
3 St Peters Buildings
St Peters Square
Leeds LS9 8AH
F 0113 259 5700
E admin@yorkshiredance.com
W www.yorkshiredance.com

**ACADEMY FOR
THEATRE ARTS THE**   T 01782 631895
1 Vale View, Porthill
Newcastle under Lyme, Staffordshire ST5 0AF
F 01782 610363
E no1theacademy@aol.com
W www.jillclewes.com

AIRCRAFT CIRCUS LTD   T 020 8317 8401
Unit 7A, Mellish House
Harrington Way, London SE18 5NR
E moira@aircraftcircus.com
W www.aircraftcircus.com

**ARTS EDUCATIONAL
SCHOOLS, LONDON**   T 020 8987 6666
Cone Ripman House, 14 Bath Road
Chiswick, London W4 1LY
E receptionist@artsed.co.uk
W www.artsed.co.uk

AVIV DANCE STUDIOS   T/F 01923 250000
Watford Boys Grammar School, Rickmansworth Road
Watford WD18 7JF
E info@avivdance.com
W www.avivdance.com

**BALLROOM, LONDON
THEATRE OF**   T 020 8722 8798
Artistic Director: Paul Harris® (Mentor "Faking It")
24 Montana Gardens, Sutton, Surrey SM1 4FP
T 07958 784462
E office@londontheatreofballroom.com
W www.londontheatreofballroom.com

BELFAST TALENT SCHOOL   T 028 9024 3324
*Cheerleading, Musical Theatre Dance & Pop Style for
Children & Adults*
The Crescent Arts Centre, 2-4 University Road
Belfast, Antrim BT7 1NH
E info@belfasttalent.com
W www.belfasttalentschool.com

BHAVAN CENTRE   T 020 7381 3086
*Training in Indian Classical Music, Dance,
Languages & Yoga*
4A Castletown Road, London W14 9HE
E info@bhavan.net
W www.bhavan.net

**BIRD COLLEGE DANCE MUSIC &
THEATRE PERFORMANCE**   T 020 8300 6004
Dance & Theatre Performance HE & FE Programmes
The Centre, 27 Station Road
Sidcup, Kent DA15 7EB
F 020 8308 1370
E performance@birdcollege.co.uk
W www.birdcollege.co.uk

BODENS STUDIOS   T 020 8447 0909
Performing Arts Classes
Bodens Studios & Agency, 99 East Barnet Road
New Barnet, Herts EN4 8RF
T 07545 696888
E info@bodens.co
W www.bodens.co

BRIGHTON DANCE DIVERSION   T 01903 770304
93 Sea Lane, Rustington
West Sussex BN16 2RS
E info@brightondancediversion.com
W www.brightondancediversion.com

**CAMBRIDGE PERFORMING
ARTS AT BODYWORK**   T 01223 314461
Bodywork Company Dance Studios
25-29 Glisson Road
Cambridge CB1 2HA
E admin@bodyworkds.co.uk
W www.bodywork-dance.co.uk

CANDOCO DANCE COMPANY   T 020 7704 6845
2T Leroy House, 436 Essex Road, London N1 3QP
E info@candoco.co.uk
W www.candoco.co.uk

**CENTRAL SCHOOL
OF BALLET**   T 020 7837 6332
*Full Time Vocational Training. Open Classes
Beginner/Professional Level*
10 Herbal Hill, Clerkenwell Road, London EC1R 5EG
F 020 7833 5571
E info@csbschool.co.uk
W www.centralschoolofballet.co.uk

**CENTRE - PERFORMING ARTS
COLLEGE THE**   T 020 8855 6661
681 Maidstone Road, Rochester, Kent ME1 3QJ
E dance@thecentrepac.com
W www.thecentrepac.com

**COLLECTIVE DANCE
& DRAMA**   T/F 020 8428 0037
The Studio, Rectory Lane
Rickmansworth, Herts WD3 1FD
E info@collectivedance.co.uk
W www.collectivedance.co.uk

**CONTI, Italia ACADEMY OF
THEATRE ARTS**   T 020 7608 0044
*Courses: 3 yr Performing Arts Diploma. 3 yr Performing
Arts with Teacher Training. 1 yr Intensive Performing Arts.
1 yr Foundation Performing Arts. 3 yr BA (Hons) Acting.
2 yr Foundation Acting. 1 yr Singing. Theatre Arts School
(academic yrs 7-11)*
Italia Conti House, 23 Goswell Road, London EC1M 7AJ
F 020 7253 1430
E admin@italiaconti.co.uk
W www.italiaconti.com

FUNDING AVAILABLE

Photography by Nicholas Dawkes

Paul Harris®

Choreographer: "The Other Boleyn Girl" "Harry Potter 5" (Wand Combat)
Choreography and Coaching in Period and Contemporary Social Dance
office@paulharris.uk.com   www.paulharris.uk.com

Swing ✦ Waltz ✦ Salsa
Tango ✦ Charleston
Quadrille

**COUNCIL FOR DANCE
EDUCATION & TRAINING (CDET)**   T 020 7240 5703
Old Brewer's Yard, 17-19 Neal Street
Covent Garden, London WC2H 9UY
F 020 7240 2547
E info@cdet.org.uk
W www.cdet.org.uk

CPA STUDIOS   T 01708 766007
The Studios, 219B North Street
Romford, Essex RM1 4QA
F 01708 766077
E college@cpastudios.co.uk
W www.cpastudios.co.uk

**D & B SCHOOL OF
PERFORMING ARTS**   T 020 8698 8880
Central Studios, 470 Bromley Road
Bromley, Kent BR1 4PQ
E bonnie@dandbmanagement.com
W www.dandbperformingarts.co.uk

**DANCE BASE NATIONAL
CENTRE FOR DANCE**   T 0131 225 5525
14-16 Grassmarket, Edinburgh EH1 2JU
E dance@dancebase.co.uk
W www.dancebase.co.uk

DANCE HOUSE   T 0141 552 2442
The Briggait, 141 Bridgegate
Glasgow G1 5HZ
E info@dancehouse.org
W www.dancehouse.org

**DANCE RESEARCH COMMITTEE - IMPERIAL
SOCIETY OF TEACHERS
OF DANCING**   T 01233 712469
Training in Historical Dance
c/o Ludwell House, Charing
Kent TN27 0LS
F 01233 712768
E n.gainesarmitage@tiscali.co.uk
W www.istd.org

DANCE STUDIO LEEDS LTD THE   T 0113 242 1550
Mill 6, 1st Floor
Mabgate Mills, Leeds, West Yorkshire LS9 7DZ
E katie@thedancestudioleeds.com
W www.thedancestudioleeds.com

DANCEWORKS   T 020 7629 6183
Also Fitness, Yoga & Martial Arts Classes
16 Balderton Street, London W1K 6TN
E info@danceworks.net
W www.danceworks.net

DAVIES, Siobhan STUDIOS   T 020 7091 9650
Daily Professional Classes. Open Dance & Body
Conditioning Classes for Wider Community
85 St George's Road, London SE1 6ER
F 020 7091 9669
E info@siobhandavies.com
W www.siobhandavies.com

**DIRECTIONS THEATRE ARTS
CHESTERFIELD LTD**   T/F 01246 854455
1A-2A Sheffield Road, Chesterfield, Derbyshire S41 7LL
E julie.cox5@btconnect.com
W www.directionstheatrearts.org

D M ACADEMY   T 01274 585317
The Studios, Briggate
Shipley, Bradford, West Yorks BD17 7BT
F 01274 592502
E info@dmacademy.co.uk
W www.dmacademy.co.uk

**DUFFILL, Drusilla
THEATRE SCHOOL**   T 01444 232672
Grove Lodge, Oakwood Road
Burgess Hill, West Sussex RH15 0HZ
F 01444 232680
E drusilladschool@btclick.com
W www.drusilladuffilltheatreschool.co.uk

EAST LONDON DANCE   T 020 8279 1050
Stratford Circus, Theatre Square
London E15 1BX
F 020 8279 1054
E office@eastlondondance.org
W www.eastlondondance.org

**EDINBURGH'S
TELFORD COLLEGE**   T 0131 559 4000
350 West Granton Road, Edinburgh EH5 1QE
F 0131 559 4111
E mail@ed-coll.ac.uk
W www.ed-coll.ac.uk

ELIE, Mark DANCE FOUNDATION   T 07947 484021
Portobello Dance School
The Tabernacle, Powis Square
London W11 2AY
E markeliedancefoundation@uk2.net
W www.portobellodance.org.uk

**ELMHURST SCHOOL
FOR DANCE**   T 0121 472 6655
249 Bristol Road, Edgbaston
Birmingham B5 7UH
F 0121 472 6654
E enquiries@elmhurstdance.co.uk
W www.elmhurstdance.co.uk

**ENGLISH NATIONAL
BALLET SCHOOL**   T 020 7376 7076
Carlyle Building, Hortensia Road
London SW10 0QS
F 020 7376 3404
E info@enbschool.org.uk
W www.enbschool.org.uk

**EXPRESSIONS ACADEMY
OF PERFORMING ARTS**   T 01623 424334
3 Newgate Lane, Mansfield
Nottingham NG18 2LB
F 01623 647337
E expressions-uk@btconnect.com
W www.expressionsperformingarts.co.uk

**FANTASY FEET DANCE & MUSICAL THEATRE
ACADEMY**   T 07947 345434
The Dance Studio, Merthyr Leisure Centre
Merthyr Tydfil Leisure Village
Merthyr Tydfil, Wales CF48 1UT
T 07894 164104
E fantasyfeetdanceacademy@yahoo.co.uk
W www.fantasyfeetdance.co.uk

 **Aircraft Circus**

Specialist in Circus Training and Consultancy

★ Classes in Trapeze ★ Silks ★ Bungee ★ Rope ★ Acrobatics

Circus training for Actors

★ Circus consultancy for shows and events
★ Performer Flying, Manual and Automated
★ Stunt Flying for Film and TV ★ Corporate Workshops

Contact Alex Frith - 07951 896945
alex@aircraftcircus.com www.aircraftcircus.com

Hangar Arts Trust, Unit 7A, Mellish House
Harrington Way, London SE18 5NR

**GEORGIE SCHOOL OF
THEATRE ARTS** T/F 01484 606994
101 Lane Head Road, Shepley
Huddersfield, West Yorkshire HD8 8DB
E donna.george@virgin.net

GREASEPAINT ANONYMOUS T 020 8886 2263
4 Gallus Close, Winchmore Hill, London N21 1JR
F 020 8882 9189
E info@greasepaintanonymous.co.uk
W www.greasepaintanonymous.co.uk

HAMMOND SCHOOL THE T 01244 305350
Hoole Bank, Mannings Lane, Chester CH2 4ES
F 01244 305351
E info@thehammondschool.co.uk
W www.thehammondschool.co.uk

HARRIS, Paul T 020 8722 8798
*Contact: Paul Harris®. Choreography. Movement for Actors.
Tuition in Period & Contemporary Social Dance*
24 Montana Gardens, Sutton
Surrey SM1 4FP
T 07958 784462
E office@paulharris.uk.com
W www.paulharris.uk.com

HOOPLA IMPRO T 07976 975348
*Commedia Dell'Arte, Improvised Comedy, Mask & Narrative
Classes. Various Venues Around London*
E roezone@hotmail.com
W www.hooplaimpro.com

ISLINGTON ARTS FACTORY T 020 7607 0561
2 Parkhurst Road, London N7 0SF
F 020 7700 7229
E info@islingtonartsfactory.org
W www.islingtonartsfactory.org

LAINE THEATRE ARTS T 01372 724648
The Studios, East Street, Epsom, Surrey KT17 1HH
F 01372 723775
E webmaster@laine-theatre-arts.co.uk
W www.laine-theatre-arts.co.uk

**LEARN SALSA, CHA CHA CHA & MERENGUE
WITH PATRICE** T 07748 676670
Mondays & Fridays, 6-7pm
The Hendon Methodist Church, The Burroughs
Hendon Central Station, London NW4 4EH
E salsawithpatrice@gmail.com
W www.myspace.com/salsaisback

**LEE, Lynn THEATRE
SCHOOL THE** T 01268 795863
48 Brook Road, Benfleet, Essex SS7 5JF
E lynn@leetheatre.fsnet.co.uk

LIVERPOOL THEATRE SCHOOL T 0151 728 7800
Musical Theatre & Professional Classes
19 Aigburth Road, Liverpool, Merseyside L17 4JR
T 07515 282877
E info@liverpooltheatreschool.co.uk
W www.liverpooltheatreschool.co.uk

**LONDON CONTEMPORARY
DANCE SCHOOL** T 020 7121 1111
Full-time Vocational Training at Degree & Postgraduate Level
16 Flaxman Terrace, London WC1H 9AT
F 020 7121 1145
E lcds@theplace.org.uk
W www.lcds.ac.uk

LONDON SCHOOL OF CAPOEIRA T 020 7281 2020
Unit 1-2 Leeds Place
Tollington Park, London N4 3RF
E info@londonschoolofcapoeira.com
W www.londonschoolofcapoeira.com

LONDON STUDIO CENTRE T 020 7837 7741
42-50 York Way, London N1 9AB
F 020 7837 3248
E info@london-studio-centre.co.uk
W www.london-studio-centre.co.uk

**MANN, Stella COLLEGE OF
PERFORMING ARTS LTD** T 01234 213331
Professional Training Course for Performers & Teachers
10 Linden Road, Bedford
Bedfordshire MK40 2DA
F 01234 217284
E info@stellamanncollege.co.uk
W www.stellamanncollege.co.uk

**MGA ACADEMY OF
PERFORMING ARTS THE** T 0131 466 9392
The MGA Company, 207 Balgreen Road
Edinburgh EH11 2RZ
E info@themgacompany.com
W www.themgaacademy.com

**MIALKOWSKI, Andrzej - BALLROOM
& LATIN AMERICAN** T 01604 239755
Choreographer. Teacher. IDTA Member
Step By Step Dance School
24 Henry Street
Northampton, Northamptonshire NN1 4JE
T 07849 331430
E info@danceschool-stepbystep.com
W www.danceschool-stepbystep.com

**MIDLANDS ACADEMY OF
DANCE & DRAMA** T/F 0115 911 0401
Century House, Building B
428 Carlton Hill
Nottingham NG4 1QA
E admin@maddcollege.supanet.com
W www.maddcollege.co.uk

**MILLENNIUM PERFORMING
ARTS LTD** T 020 8301 8744
29 Thomas Street, Woolwich
London SE18 6HU
E info@md2000.co.uk
W www.md2000.co.uk

**NEW LONDON PERFORMING
ARTS CENTRE** T 020 8444 4544
*Performing Arts Classes (3-19 yrs). All Dance Styles. GCSE
Course. RAD & ISTD Exams*
76 St James Lane, Muswell Hill
London N10 3DF
F 020 8444 4040
E nlpac@aol.com
W www.nlpac.co.uk

ERIC RICHMOND
PHOTOGRAPHY

www.ericrichmond.net
tel: 020 8880 6909

NORTH LONDON DANCE STUDIO   T 020 8360 5700
843-845 Green Lanes, Winchmore Hill
London N21 2RX
F 020 8364 2009
E thedancestudio@btconnect.com
W www.thedancestudio.co.uk

NORTHERN ACADEMY OF PERFORMING ARTS   T 01482 310690
Anlaby Road, Hull HU1 2PD
F 01482 212280
E napa@northernacademy.org.uk
W www.northernacademy.org.uk

NORTHERN BALLET SCHOOL   T 0161 237 1406
The Dancehouse, 10 Oxford Road
Manchester M1 5QA
F 0161 237 1408
E enquiries@northernballetschool.co.uk
W www.northernballetschool.co.uk

NORTHERN SCHOOL OF CONTEMPORARY DANCE THE   T 0113 219 3000
98 Chapeltown Road, Leeds LS7 4BH
E info@nscd.ac.uk
W www.nscd.ac.uk

PENS PEOPLE   T 01708 457443
75 Victor Walk, Hornchurch
Essex RM12 4XQ
E penny@penspeople.co.uk
W www.penspeople.co.uk

PERFORMERS COLLEGE   T 01375 672053
Southend Road, Corringham
Essex SS17 8JT
F 01375 672353
E lesley@performerscollege.co.uk
W www.performerscollege.co.uk

PINEAPPLE DANCE STUDIOS   T 020 7836 4004
7 Langley Street
London WC2H 9JA
F 020 7836 0803
W www.pineapple.uk.com

PLACE THE   T 020 7121 1000
17 Duke's Road
London WC1H 9BY
F 020 7121 1142
E info@theplace.org.uk
W www.theplace.org.uk

PROFESSIONAL TEACHERS OF DANCING   T 01935 848547
Contact: Jo Pillinger
The Studio, Morcombelake
Dorset DT6 6DY
E ptdenquiries@msn.com
W www.ptdance.com

RAMBERT SCHOOL OF BALLET & CONTEMPORARY DANCE   T 020 8892 9960
Clifton Lodge, St Margaret's Drive
Twickenham, Middlesex TW1 1QN
F 020 8892 8090
E info@rambertschool.org.uk
W www.rambertschool.org.uk

RIDGEWAY STUDIOS PERFORMING ARTS CENTRE   T 01992 633775
Cheshunt & Cuffley Studios
Office: 106 Hawkshead Road
Potters Bar, Hertfordshire EN6 1NG
E info@ridgewaystudios.co.uk
W www.ridgewaystudios.co.uk

RIVERSIDE REFLECTIONS BATON TWIRLING TEAM   T/F 01322 410003
34 Knowle Avenue, Bexleyheath
Kent DA7 5LX
T 07958 617976
E c.johnson717@ntlworld.com
W www.riverside-reflections.webs.com

ROEBUCK, Gavin   T 020 7370 7324
Classical Ballet
51 Earls Court Square, London SW5 9DG
E info@gavinroebuck.com

ROJO Y NEGRO   T 020 8520 2726
Argentine Tango School of Dance
Union Tavern
Above 52 Lloyd Baker Street
Farringdon, Kings Cross
London WC1X 9AA
E info@rojoynegroclub.com
W www.rojoynegroclub.com

ROJO Y NEGRO   T 020 8520 2726
Argentine Tango School of Dance
Latvian Club, 1st Floor
72 Queensborough Terrace
London W2 3HS
E info@rojoynegroclub.com
W www.rojoynegroclub.com

ROYAL ACADEMY OF DANCE   T 020 7326 8000
36 Battersea Square, London SW11 3RA
F 020 7924 3129
E info@rad.org.uk
W www.rad.org.uk

SAFREY ACADEMY OF PERFORMING ARTS   T 07956 920813
10 St Julians Close, London SW16 2RY
F 020 8488 9121
E info@safreyarts.co.uk
W www.mbkonline.co.uk

TIFFANY THEATRE COLLEGE   T 01702 710069
969-973 London Road, Leigh on Sea
Essex SS9 3LB
E info@tiffanytheatrecollege.com
W www.tiffanytheatrecollege.com

TRINITY LABAN CONSERVATOIRE OF MUSIC & DANCE   T 020 8691 8600
Creekside, London SE8 3DZ
F 020 8691 8400
E info@trinitylaban.ac.uk
W www.trinitylaban.ac.uk

URDANG ACADEMY THE   T 020 7713 7710
Finsbury Town Hall, Rosebery Avenue
London EC1R 4RP
F 020 7278 6727
E info@theurdangacademy.com
W www.theurdangacademy.com

VALLÉ ACADEMY OF PERFORMING ARTS   T 01992 622862
The Vallé Academy Studios, Wilton House
Delamare Road, Cheshunt, Herts EN8 9SG
F 01992 622868
E enquiries@valleacademy.co.uk
W www.valleacademy.co.uk

YOUNG, Sylvia THEATRE SCHOOL   T 020 7258 2330
1 Nutford Place, London W1H 5YZ
F 020 7258 3915
E syoung@syts.co.uk
W www.syts.co.uk

ALRA (ACADEMY OF LIVE & RECORDED ARTS) T 020 8870 6475
Studio 24, The Royal Victoria Patriotic Building
John Archer Way, London SW18 3SX
F 020 8875 0789
E info@alra.co.uk
W www.alra.co.uk

ARTS EDUCATIONAL SCHOOLS LONDON T 020 8987 6666
14 Bath Road, London W4 1LY
F 020 8987 6699
E receptionist@artsed.co.uk
W www.artsed.co.uk

BIRMINGHAM SCHOOL OF ACTING T 0121 331 7220
Level 0, Millennium Point
Curzon Street, Birmingham B4 7XG
F 0121 331 7221
E info@bsa.bcu.ac.uk
W www.bcu.ac.uk/bsa

BRISTOL OLD VIC THEATRE SCHOOL T 0117 973 3535
1-2 Downside Road, Clifton
Bristol BS8 2XF
F 0117 980 9258
E enquiries@oldvic.ac.uk
W www.oldvic.ac.uk

CENTRAL SCHOOL OF SPEECH & DRAMA, UNIVERSITY OF LONDON T 020 7722 8183
Eton Avenue, Swiss Cottage
London NW3 3HY
E enquiries@cssd.ac.uk
W www.cssd.ac.uk

CONTI, Italia ACADEMY OF THEATRE ARTS T 020 7733 3210
Avondale, 72 Landor Road
London SW9 9PH
F 020 7737 2728
E acting@lsbu.ac.uk
W www.italiaconti-acting.co.uk

CYGNET TRAINING THEATRE T/F 01392 277189
New Theatre, Friars Gate
Exeter, Devon EX2 4AZ
E cygnetarts@btconnect.com
W www.cygnetnewtheatre.com

DRAMA CENTRE LONDON T 020 7514 8778
Central Saint Martins College of Art & Design
Granary Building
1 Granary Square, London N1C 4AA
F 020 7514 8777
E drama@arts.ac.uk
W www.csm.arts.ac.uk/drama

DRAMA STUDIO LONDON T 020 8579 3897
Grange Court, 1 Grange Road
London W5 5QN
F 020 8566 2035
E admin@dramastudiolondon.co.uk
W www.dramastudiolondon.co.uk

EAST 15 ACTING SCHOOL T 020 8508 5983
Hatfields, Rectory Lane, Loughton IG10 3RY
F 020 8508 7521
E east15@essex.ac.uk
W www.east15.ac.uk

GSA, GUILDFORD SCHOOL OF ACTING T 01483 560701
University of Surrey, Stag Hill Campus
Guildford, Surrey GU2 7XH
E gsaenquiries@gsa.surrey.ac.uk
W www.gsauk.org

GUILDHALL SCHOOL OF MUSIC & DRAMA T 020 7628 2571
Silk Street, Barbican
London EC2Y 8DT
E info@gsmd.ac.uk
W www.gsmd.ac.uk

LAMDA T 020 8834 0500
155 Talgarth Road
London W14 9DA
F 020 8834 0501
E enquiries@lamda.org.uk
W www.lamda.org.uk

LIVERPOOL INSTITUTE FOR PERFORMING ARTS THE T 0151 330 3000
Mount Street
Liverpool L1 9HF
F 0151 330 3131
E reception@lipa.ac.uk
W www.lipa.ac.uk

MANCHESTER SCHOOL OF THEATRE AT MANCHESTER METROPOLITAN UNIVERSITY T 0161 247 1305
The Mabel Tylecote Building
Cavendish Street
Manchester M15 6BG
E theatre@mmu.ac.uk
W www.theatre.mmu.ac.uk

MOUNTVIEW T 020 8881 2201
Academy of Theatre Arts
Ralph Richardson Memorial Studios
1 Kingfisher Place
Clarendon Road, London N22 6XF
F 020 8829 0034
E enquiries@mountview.org.uk
W www.mountview.org.uk

OXFORD SCHOOL OF DRAMA THE T 01993 812883
Sansomes Farm Studios
Woodstock, Oxford OX20 1ER
F 01993 811220
E info@oxforddrama.ac.uk
W www.oxforddrama.ac.uk

ROSE BRUFORD COLLEGE T 020 8308 2600
Lamorbey Park
Burnt Oak Lane
Sidcup, Kent DA15 9DF
F 020 8308 0542
E enquiries@bruford.ac.uk
W www.bruford.ac.uk

ROYAL ACADEMY OF DRAMATIC ART T 020 7636 7076
62-64 Gower Street
London WC1E 6ED
F 020 7323 3865
E reception@rada.ac.uk
W www.rada.ac.uk

ROYAL CONSERVATOIRE OF SCOTLAND T 0141 332 4101
100 Renfrew Street
Glasgow G2 3DB
E dramaadmissions@rcs.ac.uk
W www.rcs.ac.uk

ROYAL WELSH COLLEGE OF MUSIC & DRAMA T 029 2039 1361
Drama Department
Castle Grounds
Cathays Park
Cardiff CF10 3ER
F 029 2039 1301
E admissions@rwcmd.ac.uk
W www.rwcmd.ac.uk

THE CONFERENCE OF DRAMA SCHOOLS

The Conference of Drama Schools comprises Britain's leading Drama Schools. CDS exists to set and maintain the highest standards of training within the vocational drama sector and to make it easier for prospective students to understand the range of courses on offer and the application process. CDS member schools offer courses in Acting, Musical Theatre, Directing and Technical Theatre training.

CDS members offer courses which are:
Professional – you will be trained to work in the theatre by staff with professional experience and by visiting professionals.
Intensive – courses are full-time
Work Orientated – you are being trained to do a job – these courses are practical training for work.

CDS publishes *The Conference of Drama Schools – Guide to Professional Training in Drama and* *Technical Theatre 2012* and *The CDS Guide to Careers Backstage*.

For links to CDS schools please visit the website at **www.drama.ac.uk**

The full texts of both guides are available on the website – if you would like a hard copy please contact French's Theatre Bookshop, by phone on 020 7255 4300 or by emailing **theatre@samuelfrench-london.co.uk** or by visiting the shop at 52 Fitzroy Street, London W1T 5JR. Single copies will be sent free of charge to UK addresses.
To contact CDS please visit the website or write to the Executive Secretary, CDS Ltd, P.O. Box 34252, London NW5 1XJ.

in association with

VOICE CONSULTANT & COACH

Jessica Higgs

Mobile: 079-4019 3631   Email: Juhiggs@aol.com

Vocal technique, voice & text
sight-reading and auditions

2PRODUCTION T 020 7993 4675
Professional Management. Voice-Over Direction & CDs
80 Netherlands Road, New Barnet
Herts EN5 1BS
E voice@2production.com
W www.2production.com

**A B ACADEMY
THEATRE SCHOOL** T/F 0161 429 7413
Act Out Ltd, 22 Greek Street
Stockport, Cheshire SK3 8AB
E ab22actout@aol.com

ABBI ACTING MA BA Hons T 07977 050223
*Drama School Tutor/Actress. 1-2-1 Sessions in
Auditioning, Corporate Presentation, Public Speaking,
Relaxation, Shakespeare & Text & Voice*
Based in London NW10
E stephanie.schonfield@googlemail.com

ABOMELI TUTORING T 07960 954904
*Contact: Charles Abomeli BA LLAM. Development Coach.
Stage & Screen Acting Technique*
E charlesabm@aol.co.uk
W www.charlesabomeli.com

**ACADEMY ARTS THEATRE
SCHOOL & AGENCY** T 01245 422595
6A The Green, Writtle, Chelmsford, Essex CM1 3DU
E info@academyarts.co.uk
W www.academyarts.co.uk

**ACADEMY OF
CREATIVE TRAINING** T 01273 818266
Contact: Janette Eddisford
8-10 Rock Place, Brighton, East Sussex BN2 1PF
T 07740 468338
E janette@actbrighton.org
W www.actbrighton.org

ACADEMY OF PERFORMANCE COMBAT THE
T 07963 206803
Teaching Body of Stage Combat
Ivy Villa, 250 Lees New Road
Lees, Lancs OL4 5PP
E info@theapc.org.uk
W www.theapc.org.uk

**ACADEMY OF THE SCIENCE OF ACTING &
DIRECTING THE** T 020 7272 0027
9-15 Elthorne Road, London N19 4AJ
F 020 7272 0026
E info@asad.org.uk
W www.asad.org.uk

**ACADEMY SCHOOL OF
PERFORMING ARTS THE** T 0161 287 9700
Dance. Drama. Singing
T 07950 212901
E theacademy@ntlworld.com
W www.academy-sopa.co.uk

**ACKERLEY STUDIOS OF SPEECH,
DRAMA & PUBLIC SPEAKING** T 0151 724 3449
Est. 1919. Contact: Margaret Parsons
16 Fawley Road, Allerton
Liverpool L18 9TF
E johnmutch@talktalk.net

ACT 2 CAM T 0191 280 1345
14 Percy Road, Whitley Bay
Newcastle, Tyne and Wear NE26 2AX
E info@act2cam.com
W www.act2cam.com

ACT ONE DRAMA STUDIO T 07904 339024
PO Box 4776, Sheffield S11 0EX
E info@actonedramastudio.co.uk
W www.actonedramastudio.co.uk

ACT UP T 020 7924 7701
*Acting Classes for Everyone. Acting Workshops. Audition
Technique. Pre-Drama School (18+ yrs). Public Speaking.
Vocal Coaching*
Unit 88, Battersea Business Centre
99-109 Lavender Hill, London SW11 5QL
F 020 7924 6606
E info@act-up.co.uk
W www.act-up.co.uk

ACTING ANGEL THE T 07807 103295
*Acting, Audition & Career Coaching, Industry Talks &
Training Products for Young Adult & Graduate Actors*
E info@theactingangel.co.uk
W www.theactingangel.co.uk

COURT
Theatre Training Company

train for a life in the theatre by working in the theatre...

BA (Hons) Acting
Intensive 2 Year Course

P.G. Dipl.
• Technical Theatre
• Acting
• Directing
1 Year Courses

address: Court Theatre Training Company, The Courtyard Theatre, Bowling Green Walk, 40 Pitfield St, London N1 6EU
phone/fax: 020 7739 6868   **email:** info@thecourtyard.org.uk   **web:** www.courttheatretraining.org.uk

Drama Training

Why do I need drama training?

The entertainment industry is an extremely competitive one, with thousands of performers competing for a small number of jobs. In such a crowded market, professional training will increase an actor's chances of success, and professionally trained artists are also more likely to be represented by agencies. Drama training can begin at any age and should continue throughout an actor's career.

I have already trained to be an actor. Why do I need further training?

Drama training should not cease as soon as you graduate or get your first job. Throughout your career you should strive to enhance your existing skills and keep up-to-date with the techniques new actors are being taught, even straight after drama school, in order to retain a competitive edge.
You must also be prepared to learn new skills for specific roles if required. Ongoing drama training and classes can help you stay fit and active, and if you go through a period of unemployment you can keep your mind and body occupied, ready to take on your next job.

What kind of training is available?

For the under 18's, stage schools provide specialist training in acting, singing and dancing. They offer a variety of full and part-time courses. After 18, students can attend drama school. The standard route is to take a three-year, full-time course, in the same way you would take a university degree. Some schools also offer one or two-year courses.

What is the Conference of Drama Schools (CDS)?

The Conference of Drama Schools was founded in 1969 and comprises Britain's leading Drama Schools. It exists in order to strengthen the voice of the member schools, to set and maintain the highest standards of training within the vocational drama sector, and to make it easier for prospective students to understand the range of courses on offer and the application process. The member schools listed in the section 'Drama Schools: Conference Of' offer courses in Acting, Musical Theatre, Directing and Technical Theatre training. For more information you can visit their website www.drama.ac.uk

What is NCDT?

The National Council for Drama Training was established in 1976 and is a unique collaborative partnership of employers in the theatre, broadcast and media industry, employee representatives and training providers. Its aim is to champion and support professional drama training and education working to safeguard the highest standards and quality assurance through accreditation for vocational drama courses in the UK. This provides students with the confidence that the courses they choose are recognised by the drama profession as being relevant to the purposes of their employment. For more information please see www.ncdt.co.uk

How should I use these listings?

The following listings provide up-to-date contact details for a wide range of performance courses, classes and coaches. Every company listed is done so by written request to us. Some companies have provided contact names, areas of specialisation and a selection of courses on offer.

I want to apply to join a full-time drama course. Where do I start?

Your first step should be to research as many different courses as possible. Have a look on each school's website and request a prospectus. Ask around to find out where other people have trained or are training now and who they recommend. You would be advised to begin your search by considering CDS courses. Please refer to the *CDS Guide to Professional Training in Drama & Technical Theatre* for a description of each school, its policy and the courses it offers together with information about funding, available from www.drama.ac.uk

What types of courses are available?

Drama training courses generally involve three-year degree or diploma courses or one-year postgraduate courses if you have already attended university or can demonstrate a certain amount of previous experience. Alternatively, short-term or part-time foundation courses are available, which can serve as an introduction to acting but are not a substitute for a full-time drama course.

When should I apply?

Deadlines for applications to drama courses vary between schools so make sure you check each school's individual deadlines. Most courses start in September. If the school you are considering requires you to apply via UCAS, you must submit your application between mid-September 2011 and 15th January 2012 to guarantee that your application will be considered for a course beginning in 2012. You can apply after that until 30th June, but the school is then under no obligation to consider your application.

See www.ucas.ac.uk/students/startapplication/whentoapply or contact the individual school for more details.

What funding is available to me?

Drama courses are unavoidably expensive. Most students have to fund their own course fees and other expenses, whether from savings, part-time work or a student loan. However, if you are from a low-income household you may qualify for a maintenance grant from the government to cover some of the costs. Some NCDT accredited courses offer a limited number of students Dance and Drama Awards (DaDA) scholarships, introduced to increase access to dance, drama and stage management training for talented students. These scholarships include help with both course fees and living expenses. Find out what each school offers in terms of potential financial support before applying. Visit www.ncdt.co.uk/guidetotraining/funding for a useful guide to drama school funding.

Another possibility is to raise funds from a charity, trust or foundation. As with applying to agents and casting professionals for representation and work, do your research first and target your letters to explain how your needs meet each organisation's objectives, rather than sending a generalised letter to everyone. You are much more likely to be considered if you demonstrate that you know the background of the organisation and what they can offer performers. You will find further advice and a list of charities and foundations you could approach at www.ncdt.co.uk/guidetotraining/funding/fundraising

How can my child become an actor?

If your child is interested in becoming an actor, they should try to get as much practical experience as possible. They could also join a stage school or sign with an agent. Contact details for stage schools can be found among the listings in this section. Please also see the Agents: Children's & Teenagers' section for more information.

What about other forms of training?

Building on your initial acting course is essential for both new and more experienced actors. There are so many new skills you can learn – you could take stage fighting classes, hire a vocal coach, attend singing and dance lessons, and many more. These will enhance your CV and will give you a competitive edge. It is also extremely useful to take occasional 'refresher' courses on audition skills, different acting techniques and so on in various forms such as one-to-one lessons, one-off workshops or evening classes, to make sure you are not rusty when your next audition comes along.

Where can I find more information?

The Actors Centre runs approximately 1700 classes and workshops a year to encourage performers to develop their talent throughout their career in a supportive environment. They also run introductory classes for people who are interested in becoming actors but currently have no training or experience. Visit their website www.actorscentre.co.uk for more information. You may also want to refer to the 'Dance Training & Professional Classes' to add additional skills to your CV as well as keep fit. If you are interested in a career behind rather than in front of the camera or stage, please see the CDS Guide to Careers Backstage, available from www.drama.ac.uk

Drama Training

Freelance journalist and former teacher, Susan Elkin is Education and Training Editor at The Stage.

So you want to train as a performer?

If you've done GCSE drama, taken part in lots of productions in and out of school and are now so head over heels in love with performing that you now desperately want to earn your living in the industry, you have two broad choices.

First, you can go down the traditional route by applying for some form of full-time specialist vocational training at age 16 or 18.

If you're 18 this could mean drama school. The best known are the 21 highly regarded schools registered with the Conference of Drama Schools (www.drama.ac.uk). These operate like small universities and some are part of larger universities. No two are the same and they are not all, in fact, drama schools. Some specialise in musical theatre and others are also music conservatoires.

There is a wide range of courses at most of these schools, some but not all of which are accredited by National Council of Drama Training (www.ncdt.co.uk). Whether or not a course is NCDT accredited affects the availability of funding.

Fees for most CDS schools are in the region of £9,000 per year as for most university courses. Drama and other performance students on accredited courses in CDS schools are eligible for the usual student loans or, for some courses in some schools, a limited number of Dance and Drama Awards which are, effectively, grants. Most schools also offer some scholarships and bursaries for the most talented applicants.

There are also some excellent schools which are not part of CDS but well worth considering. They too will charge around £9,000 per year and there may be scholarships, but not usually any entitlement to state funding. But beware. Not all schools are up to scratch.

If you are interested in a particular school start asking questions. The three crucial things you need to know are:

1. How many hours of teaching – actually in studios and other practical work spaces being instructed by a tutor – will you get each week? On a good vocational course it should be 25-30 hours.

2. What is the professional experience of the tutors and how recent is it? In this business you want to be taught by people who are still actively involved in the industry.

3. What are recent graduates of the course you're interested in doing now? Ideally they should be signed by agents and getting plenty of work.

If you're 16 you might go to a specialist college to do some sort of pre-vocational training. This could, for example, be a Foundation or BTec course. Some people sometimes move straight into paid work from these. Others use it as a preparatory stepping stone between school and drama school.

The second option – which may be favoured by your school careers advisor and parents – comes in two forms. Either you go to university to do a 'proper' degree in, say, maths or French, do lots of student drama while you're there and then (if you haven't gone off the idea) try your hand at a short post-graduate performing arts course in three years' time. Alternatively, you do a drama degree at university and regard that as your training.

Both these have worked well for some very successful actors. Emma Thompson, Ian McKellen, Imogen Stubbs and Simon Russell Beale all did English degrees before starting their professional lives, for instance. But post-graduate training is very expensive because it almost always has to be self-funded – when you already have substantial debts incurred by the three years you've just spent in university.

Most – but not all – university drama students report that there is simply not enough practical work and teaching for someone wanting to perform professionally. There are exceptions to this, of course, so if you decide on this route make sure you know exactly what you're getting and that it is right for you.

Good luck!

Drama Training

Members of the Conference of Drama Schools offer their students the highest quality training in the industry. Graduates from these schools are in a strong position to advise anyone thinking of following in their path. We have asked two recent graduates from CDS schools to share their thoughts on the benefits of drama training.

Kurt Egyiawan

Kurt recently graduated from Guildhall School of Music & Drama where he achieved a BA Hons in Acting. He won the Spotlight Prize at the Spotlight Showcase 2011.

Photo: Alex George

I went to drama school three years after completing a degree in Drama and Theatre Arts at Goldsmiths College. I worked with a small theatre company formed at university for two years before I got a big break performing at Shakespeare's Globe Theatre.

I decided to go into training because I wanted guaranteed work for three years in an environment where I could challenge myself. My decision to go to Guildhall was based mainly on the level of teaching and the creative atmosphere the school has. From my first visit to the school I was aware of this wonderful energy about the place, which supports risk taking, vulnerability and the power of a group of actors as an ensemble.

I would say one of the most important decisions to make when choosing a drama school is selecting one which you feel will challenge you to take risks.

Although predominantly offering thorough classical training, the course is full of opportunities including working with Guildhall musicians on projects and European directors in Italy at the Prima Del Teatro Festival. I had many highlights at Guildhall, but the opportunities to play so many exciting roles such as Uncle Vanya, Oedipus and Richard III created priceless experiences.

I would say one of the most important decisions to make when choosing a drama school is selecting one which you feel will challenge you to take risks. The three years spent there are a luxurious opportunity for any actor to investigate, as well as develop, their skills and choices – one not often available in our competitive industry.

Kirsty Oswald

Kirsty recently graduated from Rose Bruford College where she achieved a First Class BA Hons in Acting. She won the Highly Commended Actor award at the Spotlight Showcase 2011.

Photo: Wolf Marloh

A question you will be asked a lot during your career is "why did you become an actor?" It's a bit like being asked "why do you love the people that you do?" Basically, there is nothing else I *could* do every day for the rest of my life. I think you'll know when you go to a drama school for an open day/audition whether it's "for you" or not. Rose Bruford attracted me because they were interested in the individual. They didn't want to break us down and build us back up to be the same acting machine. We are all very different actors; in fact, you've never seen a more eclectic bunch in all your life. But we worked very hard and very well together, learning from each other.

Your third year at drama school is generally geared towards preparing you to leave: mock auditions, mock interviews, shows and meeting industry professionals. But nothing can fully prepare you. Every experience will be different but that's a perk of the job – you never stop learning. Prepare as much as you can for auditions and absorb as much as you can from each job.

The highlight of my training would be hard to pin down. I love the process of rehearsal. I think that's when you really put things into practice. I enjoyed working within a company and watching a bunch of people – sweaty and nervous in a first read through – making something great over a few weeks. There's a wonderful feeling when you all do something you're proud of.

I think you'll know when you go to a drama school for an open day/audition whether it's "for you" or not.

Since graduating I entered the Carleton Hobbs Radio competition in March and won a freelance contract with BBC Radio drama. I signed with Jessica Carney Associates after my showcase, and have been auditioning and done a bit of TV and radio work since then. Right now is an exciting time.

My advice to drama students? Stop worrying about being a "good actor" and make LOADS of mistakes! Commit, fail, explore and don't be self-conscious. Be *interested* and enjoy yourself – it makes you a better actor. That's what I find anyway. If you're passionate, committed and talented, you will enjoy a stimulating and exciting career doing what you love to do.

RICK LIPTON DIALECT, DIALOGUE AND VOICE COACH

- American Accent Coaching from an American in London
- Digital Recordings of your sessions provided
- Film, Television, Theatre, Auditions, Private Lessons
- 10+ years experience, 1000+ actors trained and coached

07961445247   rl@ricklipton.com   www.ricklipton.com

ACTING AUDITION SUCCESS   T 020 8731 6686
Contact: Philip Rosch (Assoc. Guildhall Teachers / Actor).
Audition Speeches for Top UK Drama Schools. Effective
Sight-reading. Expert Career Guidance. Improvisation.
Shakespeare Made Easy
53 West Heath Court, London NW11 7RG
E philiprosch1@hotmail.com
W www.philiprosch.com

ACTING BUDDY
E info@actingbuddy.com
W www.actingbuddy.com

ACTING COACH SCOTLAND   T/F 0800 7569535
Contact: Mark Westbrook. Acting Workshops. Audition
Technique. Drama School Preparation. Private Acting
Classes. Courses: Developing Acting Skills, Intro to
Practical Aesthetics, Rehearsal Technique, Scene Study,
All 10 weeks, Part-time
2nd Floor, 19 Queen Street
Glasgow, Lanarkshire G20 6HQ
E mark@actingcoachscotland.co.uk
W www.actingcoachscotland.co.uk

ACTION LAB   T 020 8810 0142
Contact: Miranda French, Peter Irving. Part-time Acting
Courses & Private Coaching. London & West Dorset
34 Northcote Avenue, London W5 3UT
T 07979 623987
E miranda@mirandafrench.com

ACTOR WORKS   T 020 7702 0909
Contact: Daniel Brennan, Wendy Smith. Courses: 1 Year
Intensive, Evening & Weekend. 15 Week Foundation, Day.
1 Year Part-time, Evening. Drama School (Over 18s)
1st Floor, Raine House
Raine Street, Wapping, London E1W 3RJ
E ask@theactorworks.co.uk
W www.theactorworks.co.uk

ACTORS CENTRE THE   T 020 7632 8001
Accent/Dialect Coaching. Acting for Camera. Audition
Technique. Beginners & Professional Workshops. Meisner.
Shakespeare. Singing. Television Presenting
1A Tower Street, London WC2H 9NP
E reception@actorscentre.co.uk
W www.actorscentre.co.uk

ACTORS PLATFORM LTD
Contact: Melissa Osborne. Courses: Agent Workshops,
Quarterly. Casting Workshops, Weekly, 3 hrs. Industry
Showcases, Quarterly
Based in Central London
E melissa@actorsplatform.com
W www.actorsplatform.com

ACTORS STUDIO   T 01753 650951
Acting Workshops. Audition Technique. Dialect/Accent
Coaching. Elocution. Improvisation. Language Tutoring.
Private Acting Classes. Public Speaking. Stage School for
Children. Vocal Coaching
Pinewood Film Studios, Pinewood Road
Iver Heath, Bucks SL0 0NH
F 01753 655622
E info@actorsstudio.co.uk
W www.actorsstudio.co.uk

ACTOR'S TEMPLE THE   T 020 3004 4537
13-14 Warren Street, London W1T 5LG
E info@actorstemple.com
W www.actorstemple.com

ACTORS' THEATRE SCHOOL   T 020 8450 0371
Foundation Course
32 Exeter Road, London NW2 4SB
F 020 8450 1057
E info@theactorstheatreschool.co.uk
W www.theactorstheatreschool.co.uk

ACTS   T 020 8360 0352
Ayres-Clark Theatre School
c/o 12 Gatward Close
Winchmore Hill, London N21 1AS
E actsn21@talktalk.net

**ADVANCED PERFORMERS
STUDIO**   T 020 8237 1080
Workshops & Courses for Actors, Musical Theatre Singers
& Opera Singers
Riverside Studios, Crisp Road, London W6 9RL
E info@associatedstudios.co.uk
W www.advancedperformersstudio.com

ALEXANDER, Helen   T 020 8543 4085
Audition Technique. Drama School Entry
14 Chestnut Road, Raynes Park
London SW20 8EB
E helen-alexander@virginmedia.com

**ALL EXPRESSIONS
THEATRE SCHOOL**   T 020 8898 3321
153 Waverley Avenue
Twickenham, Middlesex TW2 6DJ
E info@allexpressions.co.uk
W www.allexpressions.co.uk

ALLSORTS - DRAMA   T/F 020 8969 3249
Part-time Courses & Drama Training (3-18 yrs).
Kensington, Notting Hill, Hampstead
Fulham, Putney
34 Crediton Road, London NW10 3DU
E info@allsortsdrama.com
W www.allsortsdrama.com

ALRA (ACADEMY OF LIVE & RECORDED ARTS)
See DRAMA SCHOOLS: Conference Of

**AMERICAN MUSICAL THEATRE
ACADEMY OF LONDON**   T 020 7247 7110
11 Plough Yard, London EC2A 3LP
E info@americanacademy.co.uk
W www.americanacademy.co.uk

AMERICAN VOICES   T 07875 148755
Contact: Lynn Bains. Acting Teacher & Director. American
Accent/Dialect Coach
20 Craighall Crescent
Edinburgh EH6 4RZ
E mail@lynnbains.com

AND ALL THAT JAZZ   T 020 8993 2111
Contact: Eileen Hughes. Accompanist. Vocal Coaching
165 Gunnersbury Lane, Acton Town
London W3 8LJ

ᦉ Eileen Benskin ᦉ
Dialect/Dialogue Coach
R.A.D.A. dip., C.P.E.P. University College London

FILMS • TELEVISION • THEATRE
*Specialist in Standard British English (R.P.)
and American, British & Foreign Accents & Dialects*
Tel/Fax: 020-8455 9750 or Spotlight 020-7437 7631   Mobile 07785 791715

ANNA SCHER THEATRE
See SCHER, Anna THEATRE

**ARABESQUE SCHOOL OF
PERFORMING ARTS**　　　T/F 01243 531144
Quarry Lane, Chichester PO19 8NY
E info@aspauk.com
W www.aspauk.com

**ARDEN SCHOOL OF
THEATRE THE**　　　T 0161 909 6655
*Professional Stage Practice in Acting Studies & Musical
Theatre. HNC in Drama. FD in Theatre Practice*
The Manchester College, Ashton Old Road
Openshaw, Manchester M11 2WH
E enquiries@themanchestercollege.ac.uk
W www.themanchestercollege.ac.uk

**ARTEMIS SCHOOL OF
SPEECH & DRAMA**　　　T/F 01342 321330
Peredur Centre of The Arts, West Hoathly Road
East Grinstead, West Sussex RH19 4NF
E office@artemisspeechanddrama.org.uk
W www.artemisspeechanddrama.org.uk

ARTEMIS STUDIOS　　　T 01344 429403
30 Charles Square, Bracknell, Berkshire RG12 1AY
E info@artemis-studios.co.uk
W www.artemis-studios.co.uk

ARTS EDUCATIONAL SCHOOLS LONDON
See DRAMA SCHOOLS: Conference Of

ASH, Samantha Jane　　　T 07805 091361
Acting Workshops. Short Films
2 Stanley Street, Chadderton, Oldham OL9 0ED

**ASHCROFT ACADEMY OF
DRAMATIC ART THE**　　　T/F 0844 8005328
Dance ISTD. Drama LAMDA. Singing (4-18 yrs)
Malcolm Primary School
Malcolm Road
Penge, London SE20 8RH
T 07799 791586
E info@ashcroftacademy.com
W www.ashcroftacademy.com

**ASHFORD, Clare BSc PGCE LLAM
ALAM (Recital) ALAM (Acting)**　　T 020 8660 9609
20 The Chase, Coulsdon
Surrey CR5 2EG
E clareashford@rocketmail.com

AUDITION COACH　　　T 0161 969 1444
*Contact: Martin Harris. Acting Workshops.
Audition Techniques. Group Evening Classes.
Private Acting Classes*
32 Baxter Road
Sale
Manchester M33 3AL
T 07788 723570
E martin@auditioncoach.co.uk
W www.auditioncoach.co.uk

AUDITIONS: A PRACTICAL GUIDE
W www.auditionsapracticalguide.com

AVERY-CLARK, Kenneth　　　T 020 7247 7110
Musical Theatre. Voice Coach
32 Brookfield Road
London E9 5AH
T 07734 509810
E ken@americanacademy.co.uk

**BAC
(BATTERSEA ARTS CENTRE)** T 020 7326 8219
*Young People's Theatre Workshops & Performance Projects
(12-25 yrs)*
Lavender Hill, London SW11 5TN
F 020 7978 5207
E bacypt@bac.org.uk
W www.bac.org.uk

**BATE, Richard MA (Theatre)
LGSM (TD) PGCE (FE) Equity** T 07940 589295
*Audition Technique. Drama School Entry.
Vocal & Acting Training*
45 Derngate, Northampton, Northamptonshire NN1 1UE
E rich.bate@yahoo.co.uk

BATES, Ms Esme TEFL GTLLS T 0118 958 9330
*Director, UK Drama Education. BA Hons Drama Education,
Central School of Speech & Drama. Associate of LAMDA
Teachers. LAMDA Speech & Drama Exam Coach
(Specialising in Individuality & Equality). Plays in a week.
Youth Theatre Director*
2 Baron Court, Western Elms Avenue
Reading, Berks RG30 2BP
T 07941 700941
E ukdramaeducation@live.co.uk
W www.ukdramaeducation.com

BELFAST TALENT SCHOOL T 028 9024 3324
*Adults. Children. Teenagers. Classes in Acting & Dance.
Saturday Stage School*
The Crescent Arts Centre, 2-4 University Road
Belfast, Antrim BT7 1NH
E info@belfasttalent.com
W www.belfasttalentschool.com

**BENCH Paul MEd LGSM ALAM FRSA LJBA
(Hons) PGCE ACP (Lings) (Hons) MASC
(Ph) MIFA (Reg)** T/F 01743 233164
*Audition Technique. Corporate Vocal Presentation. LAMDA
Exams, Grades to Diploma Level. Private Acting Classes.
Public Speaking. Stress Management. Vocal Coaching*
1 Whitehall Terrace, Shrewsbury, Shropshire SY2 5AA
E pfbench@aol.com
W www.paulbench.co.uk

BENSKIN, Eileen T 020 8455 9750
Dialect Coach
T 07785 791715

BERKERY, Barbara T 020 7281 3139
Dialogue/Dialect Coach for Film & Television

BEST THEATRE ARTS T 01727 759634
PO Box 749, St Albans AL1 4YW
E bestarts@aol.com   W www.besttheatrearts.com

BIG LITTLE THEATRE SCHOOL T 01202 434499
*Acting Examination & Audition Prep (LAMDA). Early Years
Drama & Dance. Performance in Education Workshops.
Professional Development Programme. RAD Ballet, ISTD
Tap & Modern. Singing Technique Classes & Private
Lessons. Skills Development Classes. Summer Schools.
Youth Theatre Companies*
Garnet House, 2A Harvey Road
Bournemouth, Dorset BH5 2AD
E info@biglittle.biz
W www.biglittle.biz

**BIG TALENT SCHOOL &
AGENCY THE** T 01656 841841
Contact: Shelley Barrett-Norton
Ynyslas Uchaf Farm
Blackmill, Bridgend CF35 6DW
T 07886 020923
E info@thebigtalent.co.uk
W www.thebigtalentschool.co.uk

BIG VOICE - LITTLE VOICE T 01706 812420
*Contact: Russell Richardson LLAM DipDram. Audition
Techniques. Drama School Preparation. LAMDA Speech
Exams. Private Acting Classes. Public Speaking.
Vocal Coaching*
The Mill House, 3 Clough Mill
Walsden, West Yorkshire OL14 7QX
T 07939 215458
E russell@richardsonassoc.co.uk
W www.russrichardson.co.uk

BIRD COLLEGE T 020 8300 6004
Drama/Musical Theatre College
The Centre
27 Station Road
Sidcup, Kent DA15 7EB
F 020 8308 1370
E admin@birdcollege.co.uk
W www.birdcollege.co.uk

BIRMINGHAM SCHOOL OF ACTING
See DRAMA SCHOOLS: Conference Of

**BIRMINGHAM THEATRE
SCHOOL THE** T 0121 440 1665
The Old Fire Station, 285-287 Moseley Road
Highgate, Birmingham B12 0DX
E info@birminghamtheatreschool.co.uk
W www.birminghamtheatreschool.co.uk

BODENS STUDIOS T 020 8447 0909
*Contact: Adam Boden. Acting Workshops. Audition
Technique. Dancing. Improvisation. Part-time Performing
Arts Classes. Singing*
Bodens Studios & Agency
99 East Barnet Road
New Barnet, Herts EN4 8RF
E info@bodens.co
W www.bodens.co

BOWES, Sara T 07830 375389
Child Acting Coach for Film & Commercials
25 Holmes Avenue, Hove BN3 7LA
E saracrowe77@gmail.com

BOYD, Beth T 020 8398 6768
Private Acting Coaching
10 Prospect Road
Long Ditton, Surbiton, Surrey KT6 5PY

BRADSHAW, Irene T 020 7794 5721
Private Coach. Voice & Audition Preparation
Flat F, Welbeck Mansions
Inglewood Road
West Hampstead, London NW6 1QX
T 07949 552915
E irene@irenebradshaw.fsnet.co.uk
W www.voice-power-works.co.uk

Theatre, Films & TV

Dee Forrest PGDVS Dip.DV.
VOICE & DIALECT COACH

• Auditions • Projection • Interpretation • Vocal Problems
• Phonetics • Presentation Skills • NLP Coaching
Sessions in London & Brighton
07957 211065   dee_forrest@yahoo.com   www.projecturvoice.com

---

BRAITHWAITE'S
ACROBATIC SCHOOL   T 020 8954 5638
8 Brookshill Avenue, Harrow Weald, Middlesex HA3 6RZ

BRANSTON, Dale   T 020 8696 9958
Audition Technique. Repertoire. Singing Teacher
Ground Floor Flat, 16 Fernwood Avenue
Streatham, London SW16 1RD
T 07767 261713   E branpickle@yahoo.co.uk

BRIDGE THEATRE TRAINING
COMPANY THE   T 020 7424 0860
*Contact: Mark Akrill. Audition Technique. Dancing. Drama
School (over 18s). Improvisation. Singing. Courses: Post-
graduate Professional Acting Course, 1 yr Full-time,
Diploma. Professional Acting Course, 2 yrs Full-time,
Diploma*
Cecil Sharp Hse, 2 Regent's Park Rd, London NW1 7AY
F 020 7424 9118
E admin@thebridge-ttc.org   W www.thebridge-ttc.org

BRISTOL OLD VIC THEATRE SCHOOL
See DRAMA SCHOOLS: Conference Of

B.R.I.T. SCHOOL FOR PERFORMING ARTS &
TECHNOLOGY THE   T 020 8665 5242
60 The Crescent, Croydon CR0 2HN
F 020 8665 8676
E admin@brit.croydon.sch.uk W www.brit.croydon.sch.uk

BRITISH AMERICAN
DRAMA ACADEMY   T 020 7487 0730
14 Gloucester Gate, Regent's Park, London NW1 4HG
F 020 7487 0731
E info@badaonline.com   W www.badaonline.com

BROWN, Michael BA MFA   T 07963 171385
*Acting Technique (Meisner). Audition Technique/Preparation.
Private Acting Coach. Physical Performance Skills (Lecoq).
Workshops: Clown, Commedia, Mask Performance.
Teacher at LAMDA & LISPA*
75 Palmerston Road, London SW14 7QA
E brown.michaelanthony@gmail.com

CADDY, Julian ACTING TRAINING T 07905 120431
Sweet Studio, 42 Theobalds Road, London WC1X 8NW
E training@juliancaddytraining.com
W www.sweet-uk.net

CAMERON BROWN, Jo PGDVS   T 07970 026621
*Dialect. Dialogue. Voice Coaching for Film, Stage,
Television & Auditions*
E jocameronbrown@me.com
W www.imdb.com/name/nm0131472

CAMPBELL, Jon   T 07854 697971
36 Fentiman Road, London SW8 1LF
E joncampbell@joncampbell.co.uk
W www.joncampbell.co.uk

CAMPBELL, Ross ARCM
Dip RCM (Perf)   T 01252 510228
*Head of Singing & Music, GSA. Professor, Royal Academy
of Music. Head of GSA Musical Theatre, Singing, Exams &
Diplomas*
17 Oldwood Chase, Farnborough, Hants GU14 0QS
T 07956 465165   E rosscampbell@ntlworld.com

CAPITAL ARTS
THEATRE SCHOOL   T/F 020 8449 2342
Contact: Kathleen Shanks
Wyllyotts Centre, Darkes Lane
Potters Bar, Herts EN6 2HN
T 07885 232414
E capitalarts@btconnect.com
W www.capitalarts.org.uk

CAPITAL SCREEN ARTS   T 07583 175120
*Courses in Screen-Acting. 1 Day Master Classes
& Private Coaching*
1st Floor, 75 Brownlow Road, London N11 2BN
E info@capitalscreenarts.co.uk
W www.capitalscreenarts.co.uk

CAPO FERRO FIGHT ENSEMBLE T 07791 875902
*Contact: Paul Yardley. Acting Workshops. Drama School
(over 18s). Improvisation. Private Acting Classes. Stage
School for Children. Courses: Basic Introduction to Stage
Fighting. Fight Choreography. Stage Combat Past &
Present. Stage Combat with Weapons & Props. All Abilities.
All Courses Day/Half Day*
168 Richmond Road, Sheffield, Yorkshire S13 8TG
E cassonsue@hotmail.com

CARSHALTON COLLEGE   T 020 8544 4444
Nightingale Road, Carshalton, Surrey SM5 2EJ
F 020 8544 4440
E cs@carshalton.ac.uk   W www.carshalton.ac.uk

CARTER, Lauren   T 07879 352382
Vocal Coach for Singing
7 Oxberry Avenue, London SW6 5SP
E lauren@laurencarteronline.com
W www.laurencarteronline.com

CELEBRATION THEATRE
COMPANY FOR THE YOUNG   T 020 8994 8886
*Contact: Neville Wortman. Drama School (over 18s). Drama
School Preparation. Private Acting Classes. Summer
School. Vocal Coaching. Courses: Audition Interview
Technique, 4 weeks Part-time. Shakespeare Today,
Speaking in Public, The Confident Voice, All 10 weeks
Part-time*
48 Chiswick Staithe, London W4 3TP
T 07976 805976
E neville@speakwell.co.uk   W www.speakwell.co.uk

CELEBRITY TALENT ACADEMY T 0845 1162355
2A Tileyard Studios, Tileyard Road
Kings Cross, London N7 9AH
E celebritytalentacademy@gmail.com
W www.celebritytalentacademy.com

CENTRAL SCHOOL OF SPEECH & DRAMA,
UNIVERSITY OF LONDON
See DRAMA SCHOOLS: Conference Of

CENTRE STAGE ACADEMY
THEATRE SCHOOL   T 07773 416593
*Weekend Theatre School in Midhurst &
Chichester (5-20 yrs)*
9 Beech Grove, Midhurst West Sussex GU29 9JA
E brett.east@hotmail.com
W www.csa-theatreschool.co.uk

Bodens
Studios & Agency
the best place for performing arts

Singing . Acting . Dancing . Musical Theatre
For Children & Young Adults
020 8447 0909 www.bodens.co

PURPOSE BUILT PERFORMING ARTS STUDIOS
Classes Held in Barnet & Enfield

CENTRE STAGE SCHOOL
OF PERFORMING ARTS T 020 8886 4264
Students (4-18 yrs). North London
The Croft, 7 Cannon Road
Southgate, London N14 7HE
F 020 8886 7555
E carole@centrestageuk.com
W www.centrestageuk.com

CENTRESTAGE SCHOOL OF
PERFORMING ARTS T 020 7328 0788
Drama School Auditions. Private Coaching for Professionals.
Summer Courses
Centrestage House, 117 Canfield Gardens
London NW6 3DY
E vickiwoolf@centrestageschool.co.uk
W www.centrestageschool.co.uk

CENTRESTAGE SCHOOL
OF PERFORMING ARTS T 020 7328 0788
Drama School Auditions. Private Coaching for Professionals.
Summer Courses
Holy Trinity School
Trinity Walk, London NW3 5SQ
E vickiwoolf@centrestageschool.co.uk
W www.centrestageschool.co.uk

CHARD, Verona LRAM
Dip RAM (Musical Theatre) T 020 8992 1571
Teacher at Central School of Speech & Drama.
Singing Tutor
Ealing House, 33 Hanger Lane
London W5 3HJ
E verona@veronachard.com

CHARKHAM, Esta T 020 8741 2843
16 British Grove, Chiswick
London W4 2NL
E esta@clara.co.uk

CHARRINGTON, Tim T 020 7987 3028
Dialect/Accent Coaching
54 Topmast Point
Strafford Street, London E14 8SN
T 07967 418236
E tim.charrington@gmail.com

CHASE, Stephan
PRODUCTIONS LTD T 020 8878 9112
Private Coach for Acting, Auditions, Public Speaking &
Script Work. Originator of Managing Authentic Presence
The Studio, 22 York Avenue, London SW14 7LG
E stephan@stephanchase.com
W www.stephanchase.com

CYGNET TRAINING THEATRE Patron: Peter Brook

PROFESSIONAL
ACTING TRAINING
CYGNET students train and tour as a company playing at a wide variety of venues. The training gives high priority to voice technique, musical skills and the acting methods of Stanislavsky and Michael Chekhov.

www.cygnetnewtheatre.com

The Tempest

ENTRY (over 18) by audition workshop and interview
Apply to: New Theatre, Friars Gate, Exeter EX2 4AZ

Member of The Conference of Drama Schools   Registered Charity No. 1081824

CYGNET
NEW THEATRE
PATRON: PETER BROOK

Jurgen Schwarz German Speech Consultant and Coach

German Speech for Film, TV and Theatre • German Singing for Lieder, Recitals and Opera
t: 020 3411 4951   e: contact@liedercoach.com   www.liedercoach.com

CHEKHOV, Michael
CENTRE UK   T 020 8696 7372
Acting Workshops. Audition/Casting Technique. Film/
Television Acting. Private Acting sessions. Vocal Training.
Group Training: The Awakening, The Deepening
E admin@michaelchekhov.org.uk
W www.michaelchekhov.org.uk

CHEKHOV, Michael
STUDIO LONDON   T 020 8696 7372
Contact: Graham Dixon. Acting Workshops. Private Acting
Classes. Summer School. Vocal Coaching. Courses:
Creative Imagination (November). Improvisation & Ensemble
(January). Atmosphere & Feelings (February). Character &
Characterisation (March)
E info@michaelchekhovstudio.org.uk
W www.michaelchekhovstudio.org.uk

CHRISKA STAGE SCHOOL T 01928 739166
37-39 Whitby Road, Ellesmere Port, Cheshire L64 8AA
E chrisbooth41@hotmail.com
W www.chriska.co.uk

CHRYSTEL ARTS
THEATRE SCHOOL   T 01494 785589
Part-time classes for Children, Teenagers & Young Adults in
Dance, Drama & Musical Theatre. ISTD & LAMDA
Examinations
Edgware Parish Hall, Rectory Lane
Edgware, Middlesex HA8 7LG
T 020 8952 6010
E chrystelarts@waitrose.com

CHUBBUCK TECHNIQUE   T 020 7732 1774
Private Coaching. Workshops
E coaching@chubbucktechnique.co.uk
W www.chubbucktechnique.co.uk

CHURCHER, Mel MA   T 07778 773019
Acting & Vocal Coach
E melchurcher@hotmail.com
W www.melchurcher.com

CHURCHER, Teresa
(Life Coach MASC)   T 07807 103295
Acting, Audition, Career & Life Coaching, Industry Talks &
Training Products for Young Adult & Graduate Actors
Based in London, Milton Keynes & Northampton
E info@theactingangel.co.uk
W www.theactingangel.co.uk

CIRCOMEDIA   T/F 0117 947 7288
Centre for Contemporary Circus & Physical Performance
Britannia Road, Kingswood, Bristol BS15 8DB
E info@circomedia.com
W www.circomedia.com

CITY LIT THE   T 020 7492 2542
Accredited & Non-Accredited Part-time & Full-time Day &
Evening Courses. Acting Workshops. Audition Technique.
Bi-Media. Camera Training. Dancing. Dialect/Accent
Coaching. Directing. Elocution Coaching. Improvisation.
Presenting. Professional Preparation. Public Speaking.
Role-play Training. Singing. Story Telling
Keeley Street, Covent Garden, London WC2B 4BA
E drama@citylit.ac.uk
W www.citylit.ac.uk

CLANRANALD TRUST:
COMBAT INTERNATIONAL T 01259 731010
27 High Street, Kincardine, Alloa FK10 4RJ
E info@clanranald.org
W www.clanranald.org

CLEMENTS, Anne
MA LGSM FRSA   T 020 7435 1211
Audition Technique. Back to Basics for Professional Actors.
Dialect/Accent Coaching. Preparation for Drama School
Entry. Vocal Coaching
Based in Hampstead
E woodlandcreature10@hotmail.com

COLDIRON, M J   T 07941 920498
Audition Preparation & Presentation Skills. Private Coaching
54 Millfields Road, London E5 0SB
E jiggs@blueyonder.co.uk
W www.web.me.com/mcoldiron

COLGAN, Valerie   T 020 7267 2153
Audition Technique. Voice Production
The Green, 17 Herbert Street, London NW5 4HA

COMBER, Sharrone
BA (Hons) MAVS (CSSD) PGCE T 07752 029422
Audition Technique. Dialect/Accent Coaching. Elocution.
Presentation Skills. Private Acting Classes. Public Speaking.
Vocal Coaching
E sharronecomber@hotmail.com

COMEDY COACH   T 01494 772908
Contact: Jack Milner
43 Church Street, Chesham, Buckinghamshire HP5 1HU
E jack@standanddeliver.co.uk
W www.standanddeliver.co.uk

COMPLETE WORKS THE   T 020 7377 7280
The Old Truman Brewery, 91 Brick Lane, London E1 6QL
F 020 7247 7405
E jacinta@tcw.org.uk
W www.tcw.org.uk

CONTI, Italia ACADEMY OF THEATRE ARTS
See DRAMA SCHOOLS: Conference Of

CONTI, Italia ACADEMY
OF THEATRE ARTS   T 020 7608 0044
Courses: 3 yr Performing Arts Diploma. 3 yr Performing
Arts with Teacher Training. 1 yr Intensive Performing Arts.
1 yr Foundation Performing Arts. 3 yr BA (Hons) Acting.
2 yr Foundation Acting. 1 yr Singing. Theatre Arts School
(academic yrs 7-11)
Italia Conti House, 23 Goswell Road, London EC1M 7AJ
F 020 7253 1430
E admin@italiaconti.com
W www.italiaconti.com

CORNER, Clive AGSM LRAM T 01305 860267
Qualified Teacher. Audition Training. Private Coaching
'The Belenes', 60 Wakeham, Portland DT5 1HN
E cornerassociates@btconnect.com

CORONA THEATRE SCHOOL T 020 8758 2553
3 Thameside Centre, Kew Bridge Road
Brentford, Middlesex TW8 0HF
E info@coronatheatreschool.com
W www.coronatheatreschool.com

COURT THEATRE TRAINING COMPANY T/F 020 7739 6868
The Courtyard Theatre, Bowling Green Walk
40 Pitfield Street, London N1 6EU
E info@thecourtyard.org.uk
W www.courttheatretraining.org.uk

COX, Gregory BA Joint Hons T 07931 370135
Bristol Old Vic Graduate with 30 Years' Experience. Audition Coaching. Drama Coaching. Sight Reading Skills. Voice Work
Based in South West London
E gregoryedcox@hotmail.com

COX, Jerry MA PGCE BA (Hons) T 07957 654027
Acting Coach. Audition Technique. Preparation/Entry for Drama School. Private Acting Classes
4 Stevenson Close, London EN5 1DR
E jerrymarwood@hotmail.com

CPA COLLEGE T 01708 766007
Full-time 3 yr Performing Arts College
The Studios, 219B North Street
Romford, Essex RM1 4QA
F 01708 766077
E college@cpastudios.co.uk
W www.cpastudios.co.uk

CREATIVE PERFORMANCE LTD T 020 8908 0502
Mobile Workshop in Circus Skills & Drama TIE. Events Management for Libraries, Schools, Youth Clubs & Play Schemes
20 Pembroke Road
North Wembley, Middlesex HA9 7PD
E creative.performance@yahoo.co.uk

CROSKIN, Phil T 07837 712323
Auditions & Presentation Skills
E teamactivate@fastmail.fm
W www.teamactivate.com

CROWE, Ben T 07952 784911
Accent, Acting & Audition Tuition
25 Holmes Avenue, Hove BN3 7LA
E bencrowe@hotmail.co.uk

CYGNET TRAINING THEATRE
See DRAMA SCHOOLS: Conference Of

D & B SCHOOL OF PERFORMING ARTS T 020 8698 8880
Central Studios, 470 Bromley Road
Bromley BR1 4PQ
E bonnie@dandbmanagement.com
W www.dandbperformingarts.co.uk

GORDON FAITH B.A., IPA., Dip.R.E.M. Sp., L.R.A.M.
SPEECH AND VOICE TEACHER
• Ex BBC Repertory   • All Speech Work Undertaken
020-7328 0446   www.gordonfaith.co.uk   1 Wavel Mews, Priory Rd. London NW6 3AB

DALLA VECCHIA, Sara   T 07877 404743
Italian Teacher
13 Fauconberg Road, London W4 3JZ

DAVIDSON, Clare   T 020 8348 0132
30 Highgate West Hill, London N6 6NP
E clare@claredavidson.co.uk
W www.claredavidson.co.uk

DE BURGH, Luan
BA (Hons) MA, MA Dip   T 07976 809693
Accent Softening. Elocution. Improvisation. Presentation
Skills. Public Speaking. Vocal Coaching. Voice & Text
E luan@luandeburgh.com
W www.luandeburgh.com

DEBUT THEATRE SCHOOL
OF PERFORMING ARTS   T 01274 618288
12 Tenterfields House, Meadow Road
Apperley Bridge, Bradford BD10 0LQ
E jacqui.debut@btinternet.com
W www.debuttheatreschool.co.uk

DE COURCY, Bridget   T 020 8883 8397
Singing Teacher
19 Muswell Road, London N10
E bridgetdecourcy@fsmail.net

De FLOREZ, Jane LGSM PG Dip   T 020 7803 0835
Singing Teacher: Auditions. Classical. Jazz. Musical Theatre.
Technique, Performance & Repertory
Waterloo, London SE1 8LT
E janedeflorez@gmail.com
W www.singingteacherlondon.com

DIGNAN, Tess MA   T 020 8691 4275
Audition, Text & Voice Coach
004 Oregon Building, Deals Gateway
Lewisham SE13 7RR
E tess.dignan@gmail.com

DIRECTIONS THEATRE ARTS
(CHESTERFIELD) LTD   T/F 01246 854455
Musical Theatre School
Studios: 1A-2A Sheffield Road
Chesterfield, Derby S41 7LL
T 07973 768144
E julie.cox5@btconnect.com
W www.directionstheatrearts.org

DOGGETT, Antonia   T 07814 155090
Flat 2/2, 131 Queen Margaret Drive, Glasgow G20 8PD
E antonia.doggett@googlemail.com
W www.antoniadoggett.co.uk

DONKER CURTIUS, Jill   T 07970 753289
W www.jilldonkercurtius.co.uk

DORSET SCHOOL OF
ACTING THE   T 01202 922675
c/o Lighthouse, 21 Kingland Road
Poole, Dorset BH15 1UG
E admin@dorsetschoolofacting.co.uk
W www.dorsetschoolofacting.co.uk

DRAMA ASSOCIATION
OF WALES   T 029 2045 2200
Summer Courses for Amateur Actors & Directors
Unit 2, The Malting
East Tyndall Street, Cardiff Bay, Cardiff CF24 5EA
E gary@dramawales.org.uk

DRAMA CENTRE LONDON
See DRAMA SCHOOLS: Conference Of

DRAMA COACHING   T 07950 720868
Audition Technique. Text Analysis. Trinity Guildhall
Examinations. Vocal Presentation Skills
Based in SW18
E euniceroberts1@gmail.com

DRAMA STUDIO
EDINBURGH THE   T 0131 453 3284
Children's Weekly Drama Workshops
19 Belmont Road
Edinburgh EH14 5DZ
E info@thedramastudio.com
W www.thedramastudio.com

DRAMA STUDIO LONDON
See DRAMA SCHOOLS: Conference Of

DULIEU, John   T 020 8696 9958
Acting Coach. Audition & Role Preparation
16 Fernwood Avenue
Streatham, London SW16 1RD
T 07803 289599
E john_dulieu@yahoo.com

DUNMORE, Simon
Acting & Audition Tuition
E simon.dunmore@btinternet.com
W www.simon.dunmore.btinternet.co.uk

DURRENT, Peter   T 01787 373483
Audition & Rehearsal Pianist. Vocal Coach
Blacksmiths Cottage, Bures Road, Little Cornard
Sudbury, Suffolk CO10 0NR
E tunefuldurrent@gmail.com

DYSON, Kate LRAM   T 01273 607490
Audition Technique Coaching. Drama
39 Arundel Street, Kemptown BN2 5TH
T 07812 949875
E kate.dyson@talktalk.net

EARNSHAW, Susi
THEATRE SCHOOL   T 020 8441 5010
Acting Workshops. Audition Technique. Singing. Courses:
Acting for Camera, 1 hr per week. Saturday Theatre School,
3½ hrs per week. Stage School, (academic yrs 7-11),
GCSEs, Full-time. Summer School, 1 week, Full-time
The Bull Theatre, 68 High Street
Barnet, Herts EN5 5SJ
F 020 8364 9618
E info@sets.org.uk
W www.susiearnshaw.co.uk

EAST 15 ACTING SCHOOL
See DRAMA SCHOOLS: Conference Of

EASTON Helena
BPSA MA ATC (CSSD)   T 07985 931473
Acting Coach
103 Red Square, Carysfort Road
London N16 9AG
E helena.easton@gmail.com

EASTON, Lydia   T 07977 511621
Singing Teacher
72 Palmerston Road, London N22 8RF
E lydzeaston@yahoo.com

ONE and TWO YEAR ACTING COURSES
and SUMMER ACTING COURSES

DRAMA STUDIO LONDON

- Intensive training in all aspects of the acting profession.
- The teaching is passionate, personal and always relevant.
- We teach you not just how to act, but how to be an actor.

020 8579 3897
admin@dramastudiolondon.co.uk
www.dramastudiolondon.co.uk

Accredited by the NCDT
Validated by Trinity College London
Member of the Conference of Drama Schools
Dance and Drama Awards Scheme

ÉCOLE INTERNATIONALE DE THÉÂTRE JACQUES LECOQ T 00 33 1 47704478
Acting Workshops. Drama School (over 21 yrs). Mime. Movement & Creative Theatre. Play Writing
57 rue du Faubourg Saint-Denis
75010 Paris, France
F 00 33 1 45234014
E contact@ecole-jacqueslecoq.com
W www.ecole-jacqueslecoq.com

EDINBURGH LIGHTING & SOUND SCHOOL (ELSS) T 0131 551 0204
c/o Black Light, West Shore Trading Estate
West Shore Road, Edinburgh EH5 1QF
E contact@edinburghlightingandsoundschool.co.uk
W www.edinburghlightingandsoundschool.co.uk

ELLIOTT-CLARKE THEATRE SCHOOL & COLLEGE T 0151 709 3323
Full-time Vocational & Saturday/Evening Classes
35 Sefton Street
Liverpool L8 5SL
E contact@elliottclarke.co.uk

EXPRESSIONS ACADEMY OF PERFORMING ARTS T 01623 424334
3 Newgate Lane
Mansfield
Notts NG18 2LB
F 01623 647337
E expressions-uk@btconnect.com
W www.expressionsperformingarts.co.uk

DIALECT COACH

LINDA JAMES R.A.M. Dip. Ed., I.P.D. (Lon Univ), L.R.A.M.

FILMS, T.V., STAGE & PRIVATE COACHING, ERADICATION OF ACCENT
AUTHOR OF BESTSELLER "GET RID OF YOUR ACCENT"
020 8568 2390

FAIRBROTHER, Victoria
MA CSSD LAMDA Dip   T 07877 228990
Audition Technique. Improvisation. Private Acting Classes.
Public Speaking. Vocal Coaching
15A Devonport Road, Shepherd's Bush
London W12 8NZ
E victoriafairbrother1@hotmail.com

FAITH, Gordon BA IPA
Dip.REM.Sp LRAM   T 020 7328 0446
Speech & Voice
1 Wavel Mews, Priory Road
West Hampstead, London NW6 3AB
E gordon.faith@tiscali.co.uk
W www.gordonfaith.co.uk

FERRIS, Anna
MA (Voice Studies, CSSD)   T 01258 881098
Audition Technique. Private Acting Classes. Vocal Coaching
Based in South West England
E atcferris@gmail.com

FERRIS ENTERTAINMENT
PERFORMING ARTS   T 0845 4724725
London. Belfast. Cardiff
Number 8, 132 Charing Cross Road
London WC2H 0LA
E info@ferrisentertainment.com
W www.ferrisentertainment.com

FINBURGH, Nina   T 020 7435 9484
Sight Reading Specialist (Masterclasses & Individuals).
Audition Technique (Equity Members only)
1 Buckingham Mansions, West End Lane
London NW6 1LR
E ninafinburgh@aol.com

FOOTSTEPS THEATRE SCHOOL T/F 01274 616535
Dance, Drama & Singing Training
1st Floor, Morrisons Enterprise, 5 Bradford Road
Bradford, West Yorkshire BD10 8EW
E gwestman500@btinternet.com

FORD, Carole Ann ADVS   T 020 8815 1832
Acting Coach. Communication Skills
Based in N10
E emko2000@aol.com

FOREMAN, Giles
CENTRE FOR ACTING   T 020 8968 3772
Formerly CARAVANSERAI PRODUCTIONS & ACTING
STUDIO. Acting Workshops. Audition Technique.
Improvisation. Private Acting Classes. Summer School.
Courses: Acting - All Levels, 12 weeks Part-time. Diploma,
1 yr Full-time. Movement/Voice, 10 weeks Part-time.
Professional Actors Classes, 10 sessions, Part-time
Basement, Townsend House
22-25 Dean Street, London W1D 3RX
E info@gilesforeman.com
W www.gilesforeman.com

FRANKLIN, Michael   T/F 020 8979 9185
Meisner Technique
Correspondence: c/o Spotlight, 7 Leicester Place
London WC2H 7RJ
E info@acteach.info

FRANKLYN, Susan   T 01306 884913
Audition Speeches. Confidence. Interview Technique.
Presentation. Sight Reading
T 07780 742891
E susan.franklyn1@btinternet.com

FURNESS, Simon   T 07702 619665
Contact: Simon Furness. Actor Training (Sanford Meisner
Technique). Audition Preparation & Technique.
Private Acting Classes
c/o The Actors' Temple, 13-14 Warren Street
London W1T 5LG
E simonfurness@googlemail.com

GLASGOW ACTING ACADEMY   T 0141 222 2942
Contact: Maureen Cairns, Allan Jones
2nd Floor, 34 Argyle Arcade Chambers
Buchanan Street, Glasgow G2 8BD
E info@glasgowactingacademy.com

GLYNNE, Frances
THEATRE STUDENTS   T 07950 918355
Flat 9, Elmwood
6 The Avenue, Hatch End, Middlesex HA5 4EP
E franandmo@gmail.com

GMA TELEVISION
PRESENTER TRAINING   T 01628 673078
Presenting for Television, Radio, Live Events. Autocue.
Improvisation. Scriptwriting. Talkback. Vocal Coaching
86 Beverley Gardens, Maidenhead, Berks SL6 6SW
T 07769 598625
E geoff@gma-training.co.uk

GRAYSON, John   T 07702 188031
Acting Workshops. Audition Technique. Improvisation.
Private Acting Classes. Public Speaking. Singing.
Vocal Coaching
2 Jubilee Road, St Johns, Worcester WR2 4LY
E jgbizzybee@btinternet.com

GREASEPAINT ANONYMOUS   T 020 8886 2263
Youth Theatre & Training Company. Part-time Theatre
Workshops run weekly through School Term Time. Holiday
Courses at Easter & Summer. Acting Workshops. Dancing.
Singing (4-30 yrs)
4 Gallus Close, Winchmore Hill, London N21 1JR
F 020 8882 9189
E info@greasepaintanonymous.co.uk

GROUT, Philip   T 020 8881 1800
Theatre Director. Drama Coaching. Tuition for Students &
Professionals
81 Clarence Road, London N22 8PG
E philipgrout@hotmail.com

GSA, GUILDFORD SCHOOL OF ACTING
See DRAMA SCHOOLS: Conference Of

GUILDHALL SCHOOL OF MUSIC & DRAMA
See DRAMA SCHOOLS: Conference Of

HANCOCK, Allison LLAM   T/F 020 8891 1073
Acting. Audition Coach. Dramatic Art. Elocution. Speech
Correction. Voice
38 Eve Road, Isleworth, Middlesex TW7 7HS

explore different techniques and new ways of working in over 1700 classes a year, taught by top industry professionals

extend your skills and your networks with advanced workshops and groundbreaking labwork led by leading actors and directors

excel at your craft with one-to-one tuition and expert advice, all at prices that won't break the bank

The Actors Centre has been the UK's premiere resource for actors for over 30 years.

Discover what becoming a member can do for you and your career at www.actorscentre.co.uk

the actors centre

ACADEMY OF PERFORMANCE COMBAT
STAGE COMBAT FOR THE 21ST CENTURY
Patrons: Sir Tom Courtenay - Kay Mellor OBE - Braham Murray - Henry Winkler OBE

Teaching includes: RSC Open Stages

Chairman: Renny Krupinski
Address: Ivy Villa,
          250 Lees New Road
          Lees,
          Lancs,
          OL4 5PP

Website: www.theapc.org.uk
E-mail: info@theapc.org.uk
Phone: 07963 206803

**HARLEQUIN STUDIOS PERFORMING
ARTS SCHOOL**   T 01273 581742
Drama & Dance Training
122A Phyllis Ave, Peacehaven, East Sussex BN10 7RQ

**HARRIS, Sharon NCSD LRAM LAM STSD IPA Dip
DA (London Univ)**   T 01923 211644
*Speech & Drama Specialist Teacher. Private Acting Coach
for Screen and Stage. Training for RADA, LAMDA and ESB
Exams. Audition Technique. Drama School and National
Youth Theatre Audition Preparation*
71 The Avenue, Watford, Herts WD17 4NU
T 07956 388716
E theharrisagency@btconnect.com

HARRISON, Abigail   T 07847 420882
Audition & Acting Coach
E creativeacting@hotmail.co.uk

**HARRISON RUTHERFORD, Lucie MA
Voice Studies, BA (Hons) Drama**   T 07773 798440
Voice Tutor & Acting Coach
Based in Richmond upon Thames
E info@lucieharrison.co.uk   W www.lucieharrison.co.uk

HASS, Leontine
Vocal Coach
E leontine@associatedstudios.co.uk
W www.leontinehass.co.uk

HEALING VOICES   T 07939 143721
*Contact: Felicitas Ste. Croix. Singing. Voice Coach.
Coaches many Actors, Church Musicians & other
Professional Singers in the UK, France & USA*
E healing.voices@yahoo.com

HESTER, John LLCM (TD)   T 020 8393 5705
*Member of The Society of Teachers of Speech & Drama.
Acting Courses for All Ages. Acting Workshops. Audition
Technique. Dialect/Accent Coaching. Drama School
Auditions (over 18s). Elocution Coaching. Private Acting
Classes. Public Speaking. Stage School for Children.
Vocal Coaching*
105 Stoneleigh Park Road, Epsom, Surrey KT19 0RF
E hjohnhester@aol.com

HETHERINGTON, Caro   T 07723 620728
7 Dodcott Barns, Burleydam
Whitchurch, Cheshire SY13 4BQ
E carolinehetherington@gmail.com
W www.carohetherington.co.uk

HIGGS, Jessica   T 07940 193631
Voice
34 Mary Batchelor House
2D Camberwell Grove
London SE5 8FB   E juhiggs@aol.com

**H. J. A.
(HERBERT JUSTICE ACADEMY)**   T 020 8249 3299
Inspiration House, 38 Croydon Road
Beckenham, Kent BR3 4BJ
F 020 8650 8365
E mail@hjaworld.com   W www.hjaworld.com

HOFFMANN-GILL, Daniel   T 020 8888 6045
Acting & Audition Tuition
T 07946 433903   E danielhg@gmail.com

HONEYBORNE, Jack   T 020 8993 2111
Accompanist. Coach
The Studio,165 Gunnersbury Lane, London W3 8LJ

HOOKER, Jennifer Jane   T 07725 977146
Private Acting Coach
Flat 3, 16 Cosway Street, London NW1 5NR
E jjanehooker@yahoo.com   W www.jjhooker.com

HOPE STREET LTD   T 0151 708 8007
*Professional Development Opportunities for Emerging &
Established Artists*
13A Hope Street, Liverpool L1 9BQ
F 0151 709 3242
E peter@hope-street.org   W www.hope-street.org

HOPNER, Ernest LLAM   T 0151 625 5641
Elocution. Public Speaking. Vocal Coaching
70 Banks Road, West Kirby CH48 0RD

HOUSEMAN, Barbara   T 07767 843737
*Ex-RSC Voice Dept. Author 'Finding Your Voice' & 'Tackling
Text'. Voice. Text. Acting. Confidence*
E barbarahouseman@hotmail.com
W www.barbarahouseman.com

HOWARD, Ashley BA MA   T 07821 213752
Voice Coach
5 St John's Street, Aylesbury, Bucks HP20 1BS
E ashleyhowardvoicecoach@yahoo.co.uk
W www.accentsofteningandelocution.com

HUDSON, Mark   T 0161 238 8900
Film & Television Acting Coach
14-32 Hewitt Street, Manchester M15 4GB
E actorclass@aol.com

HUGHES, Dewi   T 07836 545717
Accents. Auditions. Bodywork. Text. Voice
Flat 2, 4 Fielding Road, London W14 0LL
E dewi.hughes@gmail.com

HUGHES-D'AETH, Charlie   T 07811 010963
*RSC Voice Coach. Acting Workshops. Audition Technique.
Public Speaking*
22 Osborne Road, Brighton BN1 6LQ
E chdaeth@aol.com

IDENTITY DRAMA SCHOOL   T 020 7470 8711
The UK's First Black Drama School
73-75 Shacklewell Lane, London E8 2EB
E space@identitydramaschool.com
W www.identitydramaschool.com

IMPULSE COMPANY THE   T/F 07525 264173
Meisner-Based Core Training
PO Box 158, Twickenham TW1 3WG
E info@impulsecompany.co.uk

**INDEPENDENT THEATRE
WORKSHOP THE**   T 00 353 1 2600831
8 Terminus Mills, Clonskeagh, Dublin 6, Ireland
E info@independent-theatre-workshop.com
W www.independent-theatre-workshop.com

INTERACT   T 07961 982198
*Contact: Lauren Bigby (LGSM). Acting Workshops. Audition
Technique. Elocution Coaching. Private Acting Classes.
Public Speaking*
18 Knightsbridge Walk, Billericay, Essex CM12 0HP
E renbigby@hotmail.com

INTERNATIONAL PERFORMING ARTS & THEATRE LTD   T 07760 666788
Specialises in Triple Threat (Dance, Singing & Acting)
57 Old Compton Street, Westminster, London W1D 6HP
E london@i-path.biz   W www.i-path.biz

INTERNATIONAL SCHOOL OF SCREEN ACTING   T 020 8555 5775
3 Mills Studios, Unit 3, 24 Sugar House Lane
London E15 2QS
E office@screenacting.co.uk
W www.screenacting.co.uk

JACK, Andrew   T 07836 615839
Dialect Coach
Vrouwe Johanna, 24 The Moorings
Willows Riverside, Windsor, Berks SL4 5TG
W www.andrewjack.com

JACK, Paula   T 07836 615839
Dialect Coach. Language Specialist
Vrouwe Johanna, 24 The Moorings
Willows Riverside, Windsor, Berks SL4 5TG
W www.paulajack.com

JAM THEATRE COMPANY   T 01628 487773
21 Beechtree Avenue, Marlow, Bucks SL7 3NH
E office@jamtheatre.co.uk   W www.jamtheatre.co.uk

JAMES, Linda
RAM Dip Ed IPD LRAM   T 020 8568 2390
Dialect & Speech Coach
25 Clifden Road, Brentford, Middlesex TW8 0PB

JAQUARELLO, Roland BA   T/F 020 8741 2446
Audition Technique. Drama School Entrance.
Radio Coaching
41 Parfrey Street, London W6 9EW
T 07808 742307
E roland@jaquarellofulham.freeserve.co.uk
W www.rolandjaquarello.com

JG DANCE LTD   T 01491 572000
Melody House, 198 Grey's Road, Gillott's Corner
Henley-on-Thames, Oxon RG9 1QU
E info@jgdance.co.uk   W www.jgdance.co.uk

JIGSAW PERFORMING ARTS SCHOOLS   T 020 8447 4530
Head Office: 64-66 High Street, Barnet, Herts EN5 5SJ
E admin@jigsaw-arts.co.uk
W www.jigsaw-arts.co.uk

JINGLES, Jo   T 01494 778989
1 Boismore Road, Chesham, Bucks HP5 1SH
E headoffice@jojingles.co.uk
W www.jojingles.com

TIM CHARRINGTON ACCENT & DIALECTS

Dip. C.S.S.D., A.D.V.S., ACTOR & TEACHER

t: 020 7987 3028   m: 07967 418236   tim.charrington@gmail.com

---

JONES, Desmond   T/F 020 8747 3537
Courses in Dynamic Acting, The Total Actor. Introduction to Mime & Physical Theatre. Physical Story Telling for the Theatre. Private Classes & Consultant. Freelance Choreography. Coach. Director. Teacher
20 Thornton Avenue, London W4 1QG
E enquiries@desmondjones.com
W www.desmondjones.com

JORDAN, Daniel   T 07803 684375
E daniel_jordan27@hotmail.com

**JUDE'S DRAMA ACADEMY
& MANAGEMENT**   T 0161 624 5378
Manor House, Oldham Road
Springhead, Oldham OL4 4QJ
E judesdrama@yahoo.co.uk
W www.judesdrama.co.uk

KENT YOUTH THEATRE   T 01227 730177
Contact: Richard Andrews. Stage & Screen Academy. Courses in Drama, Dance, Musical Theatre, Singing, Film Acting/Making. Improvisation. Private Acting Classes. Stage School for Children
Office: Mulberry Croft, Mulberry Hill, Chilham CT4 8AJ
T/F 07967 580213
E richard@kentyouththeatre.co.uk
W www.kentyouththeatre.co.uk

KERR, Louise   T 020 8509 2767
Voice Coach
20A Rectory Road, London E17 3BQ
T 07780 708102
E louise@louisekerr.com   W www.resonancevoice.com

**KINGSTON JUNIOR
DRAMA COMPANY**   T 01932 230273
Workshops. 10-14 yrs
72 Shaw Drive, Walton-on-Thames, Surrey KT12 2LS
E kingstonjdc@aol.com   W www.davidlawsonlean.com

KIRKLEES COLLEGE   T 01484 437047
Courses in Acting, Dance & Musical Theatre (BTec)
Highfields Annexe, New North Road
Huddersfield HD1 5NN
E info@kirkleescollege.ac.uk

KNYVETTE, Sally   T 07958 972425
Drama School Preparation. Drama Tuition. Specialising in Shakespeare. All Levels
52 Burnfoot Avenue, London SW6 5EA
E salkny@aol.com   W www.sallyknyvette.co.uk

KRIMPAS, Titania   T 07957 303958
One-to-one Tuition, all levels. Tailored to suit experienced actors and beginners
The Garden Flat, 23 Lambolle Road, London NW3 4HS
E titania@krimpas.freeserve.co.uk

KSA PERFORMING ARTS   T 020 8090 5801
Beckenham Halls, 4 Bromley Road, Beckenham BR3 5JE
E info@ksapa.co.uk   W www.ksapa.co.uk

KTPAS   T 020 8799 6157
Performing Arts School. Full-time, Saturday & Summer Courses
KT Summit House, 100 Hanger Lane, London W5 1EZ
E info@kt.org
W www.kt.org/ktpas

LAINE THEATRE ARTS   T 01372 724648
The Studios, East Street
Epsom, Surrey KT17 1HH
F 01372 723775
E info@laine-theatre-arts.co.uk
W www.laine-theatre-arts.co.uk

LAMDA
See DRAMA SCHOOLS: Conference Of

**LAMONT DRAMA SCHOOL &
CASTING AGENCY**   T 07736 387543
Contact: Diane Lamont. Acting Skills. Audition Technique. Coaching. Part-time Lessons
2 Harewood Avenue, Ainsdale, Merseyside PR8 2PH
E diane@lamontcasting.co.uk
W www.lamontcasting.co.uk

LAURIE, Rona   T 020 7262 4909
Coach for Auditions. Public Speaking. Voice & Speech Technique
Flat 1, 21 New Quebec Street, London W1H 7SA

**LEAN, David Lawson
BA Hons PGCE**   T 01932 230273
Acting Tuition for Children. LAMDA Exams. Licensed Chaperone
72 Shaw Drive, Walton-on-Thames, Surrey KT12 2LS
E dlawsonlean@aol.com
W www.davidlawsonlean.com

LEE THEATRE SCHOOL THE   T 01268 795863
Office: 48 Brook Road, Benfleet, Essex SS7 5JF
E lynn@leetheatre.fsnet.co.uk
W www.lynnlee.co.uk

LESLIE, Maeve   T 020 7834 4912
Classical & Musicals. Presentations. Singing. Voice Production
60 Warwick Square, London SW1V 2AL

LEVENTON, Patricia BA Hons   T 020 7624 5661
Audition & Dialect Coach
113 Broadhurst Gardens, West Hampstead
London NW6 3BJ
T 07703 341062
E patricia@lites2000.com

LIEDERCOACH.COM   T 020 3411 4951
Contact: Jurgen Schwarz. German Singing for Lieder, Recitals & Opera. German Speech for Film, Television & Theatre
E contact@liedercoach.com
W www.liedercoach.com

**LINCOLN ACADEMY OF
DRAMATIC ARTS**   T 01522 837242
6-18 yrs
Sparkhouse Studios
Rope Walk, Lincoln, Lincs LN6 7DQ
F 01522 837201
E info@lada.org.uk
W www.lada.org.uk/academy

LIPTON, Rick   T 07961 445247
Dialect/Accent Coaching
14 Lock Road, Richmond, Surrey TW10 7LH
E info@ricklipton.com
W www.ricklipton.com

LIVERPOOL INSTITUTE FOR PERFORMING ARTS THE
See DRAMA SCHOOLS: Conference Of

LLOYD, Gabrielle　T 020 8946 4042
Audition Technique. Drama School Entrance. LAMDA Exams. Private Acting Classes. Public Speaking. Vocal Coaching
Based in South West London
E gubilloyd@hotmail.com

LOCATION TUTORS NATIONWIDE　T 020 7978 8898
Fully Qualified/Experienced Teachers Working with Children on Film Sets & Covering all Key Stages of National Curriculum
16 Poplar Walk, Herne Hill SE24 0BU
F 020 7207 8794
E locationtutorsnationwide@gmail.com
W www.locationtutors.co.uk

LONDON ACTORS WORKSHOP　T 07748 846294
Workshop Studio Based in Endell Street, Covent Garden
Enquiries: 29B Battersea Rise, London SW11 1HG
E info@londonactorsworkshop.co.uk
W www.londonactorsworkshop.co.uk

LONDON DRAMA SCHOOL　T 020 8830 0074
Acting. Singing. Speech Training
30 Brondesbury Park, London NW6 7DN
F 020 8830 4992
E enquiries@startek-uk.com
W www.startek-uk.com

LONDON INTERNATIONAL SCHOOL OF PERFORMING ARTS　T 020 8215 3390
The Old Lab, 3 Mills Studios
Three Mill Lane, London E3 3DU
F 020 8215 3392
E welcome@lispa.co.uk
W www.lispa.co.uk

LONDON LANGUAGE EXPERIENCE　T 07941 468639
English language courses & private tuition specialising in natural, conversational English, pronunciation & intonation by native speaking trained actor & language tutor
Flat 1, 143 Albion Road, London N16 9JU
E luke@londonlanguageexperience.com

LONDON REPERTORY COMPANY ACADEMY　T/F 020 7258 1944
PO Box 59385, London NW8 1HL
E academy@londonrepertorycompany.com
W www.londonrepertorycompany.com/academy

LONDON SCHOOL OF DRAMATIC ART　T 020 7581 6100
Foundation & Advanced Diplomas in Acting (Full & Part-time). Drama School (over 18s). Short Summer Courses
4 Bute Street, South Kensington, London SW7 3EX
E enquiries@lsda-acting.com
W www.lsda-acting.com

LONDON SCHOOL OF FILM, MEDIA & PERFORMANCE　T 020 7487 7505
Regent's College, Inner Circle
Regent's Park, London NW1 4NS
F 020 7487 7425
E lsfmp@regents.ac.uk　　W www.regents.ac.uk/lsfmp

LONDON SCHOOL OF MUSICAL THEATRE　T/F 020 7407 4455
83 Borough Road, London SE1 1DN
E enquiries@lsmt.co.uk

LONDON STUDIO CENTRE　T 020 7837 7741
Courses in Theatre Dance (3 yrs), Full-time, BA. Evening & Saturday Classes. Summer Course
42-50 York Way, London N1 9AB
F 020 7837 3248
E info@london-studio-centre.co.uk
W www.london-studio-centre.co.uk

Charlie Hughes-D'Aeth ✍

Based in London, Brighton & Stratford-Upon-Avon.

Voice Coach - CSSD trained; 20 years' experience in theatre / actor training / business; RSC Text and Voice Coach since 2009, currently working on 'Matilda'.

07811 010963   CHDAETH@aol.com   charliehughesdaeth.co.uk

**LONG OVERDUE THEATRE
SCHOOL THE**   T 07870 832562
16 Butterfield Drive, Amesbury, Wiltshire SP4 7SJ
E school@longoverdue.co.uk
W www.longoverdue.co.uk

LONGMORE, Wyllie   T 0161 881 6440
Acting Techniques. Voice & Speech. Presentation Skills
Based in Manchester,
E info@wyllielongmore.co.uk
W www.wyllielongmore.co.uk

MACKINNON, Alison   T 07973 562132
Accent. Audition Preparation. Presentation. Voice
Based in London SE6
E alison.mackinnon@bruford.ac.uk

MADDERMARKET THEATRE   T 01603 628600
Contact: Education Officer
Education Department, St John's Alley, Norwich NR2 1DR
F 01603 661357
E mmtedu@btconnect.com   W www.maddermarket.co.uk

**MANCHESTER SCHOOL
OF ACTING**   T/F 0161 238 8900
14-32 Hewitt Street, Manchester M15 4GB
E info@manchesterschoolofacting.co.uk
W www.manchesterschoolofacting.co.uk

**MANCHESTER SCHOOL OF THEATRE AT
MANCHESTER METROPOLITAN UNIVERSITY**
See DRAMA SCHOOLS: Conference Of

MARLOW, Chris   T 07792 309992
Voice & Speech Teacher
RDDC, 52 Bridleway, Waterfoot
Rossendale, Lancashire BB4 9DS
E rddc@btinternet.com   W www.rddc.co.uk

MARLOW, Jean LGSM   T 020 8450 0371
32 Exeter Road, London NW2 4SB

**MARTIN, Liza GRSM GRSM (Recital) ARMCM
(Singing & Piano)**   T 020 8348 0346
Piano Accompanist. Singing Tuition

**MARTIN, Mandi
SINGING TECHNIQUE**   T 020 8950 7525
*Previously at London Studio Centre. Currently Coaching at
Millennium Dance 2000 & Bodywork at Cambridge
Performing Arts*
T 07811 758656
E mandi.martin@sky.com

**MASTERS PERFORMING
ARTS COLLEGE LTD**   T 01268 777351
Musical Theatre/Dance Course
Arterial Road, Rayleigh, Essex SS6 7UQ
E info@mastersperformingarts.co.uk

MAVERICK YOUTH ACADEMY   T 07531 138248
12 Lydney Grove, Northfield, Birmingham B31 1RB
E academy@mavericktheatre.co.uk
W www.mavericktheatre.co.uk

MAY, Maggie DRAMA   T 07984 745323
The Epsom Playhouse, Ashley Avenue
Epsom, Surrey KT18 5AL
E office@maggiemayltd.com   W www.maggiemayltd.com

McDAID, Marj   T 020 7923 4929
1 Chesholm Road, Stoke Newington, London N16 0DP
T 07815 993203
E marjmcdaid@hotmail.com
W www.voicings.co.uk

**McDONAGH, Melanie MANAGEMENT (ACADEMY
OF PERFORMING ARTS
& CASTING AGENCY)**   T 01254 392560
14 Apple Tree Way, Oswaldtwistle
Accrington, Lancashire BB5 0FB
T 07909 831409
E mcdonaghmgt@aol.com
W www.mcdonaghmanagement.co.uk

McKEAND, Ian   T 01522 805966
Audition Technique. Drama School Entry
12 Linnet Close, Birchwood
Lincoln LN6 0JQ
E ian.mckeand@ntlworld.com
W http://homepage.ntlworld.com/ian.mckeand1

McKELLAN, Martin   T 07973 437237
*Acting Workshops. Dialect/Accent Coaching. Private Acting
Classes. Vocal Coaching*
Covent Garden, London WC2H 9PA
E martinmckellan@yahoo.co.uk

MELLECK, Lydia   T 020 7794 8845
*Pianist & Coach for Auditions & Repertoire, RADA,
Mountview. Accompanist. Singing for Beginners. Vocal
Coaching. Workshops on Sondheim*
10 Burgess Park Mansions, London NW6 1DP
E lyd.muse@yahoo.co.uk

**MGA ACADEMY OF
PERFORMING ARTS THE**   T 0131 466 9392
The MGA Company, 207 Balgreen Road
Edinburgh EH11 2RZ
E info@themgacompany.com
W www.themgaacademy.com

MICHEL, Hilary ARCM   T 020 8343 7243
*Accompanist. Audition Songs. Diction & Languages for
Songs. Piano, Recorder & Singing Teacher. Technique.
Theory. Vocal Coach*
82 Greenway
Totteridge, London N20 8EJ
T 07775 780182
E hilarymich@hotmail.com

MILLER, Christie   T 020 8525 0111
Acting & Life Coach
32 Brookfield Road, London E9 5AH
E christie.miller@btinternet.com
W www.christiemillercoaching.com

MILLER, Robin   T 07957 627677
Audition Technique. Dialect/Accent Coaching
Based in South West London
E robinjenni@hotmail.com

MONTAGE THEATRE ARTS   T 020 8692 7007
*Contact: Judy Gordon (Artistic Director). Dance. Drama.
Singing. Children & Adults*
The Albany, Douglas Way, London SE8 4AG
E office@montagetheatre.com
W www.montagetheatre.com

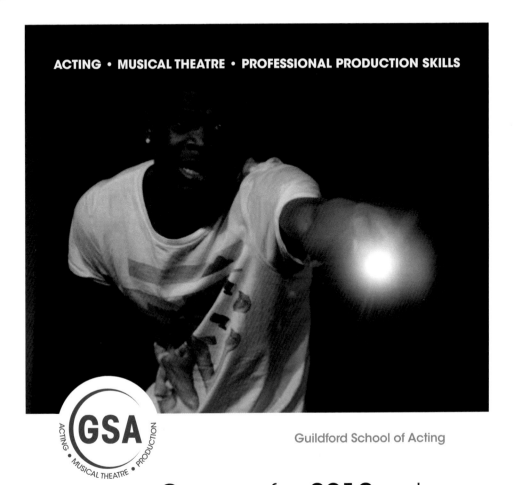

ACTING • MUSICAL THEATRE • PROFESSIONAL PRODUCTION SKILLS

GSA
ACTING • MUSICAL THEATRE • PRODUCTION

Guildford School of Acting

Courses for **2012** entry

Foundation Course

Undergraduate Courses

Postgraduate Courses

Part-time Evening Courses

Easter and Summer Schools

For an application form/further details contact:

Guildford School of Acting
Stag Hill Campus, University of Surrey, Guildford GU2 7XH UK

Tel: (01483) 560701   Fax: (01483) 684040
Email: gsaenquiries@gsa.surrey.ac.uk   Web: www.gsauk.org

UNIVERSITY OF
SURREY

Private Tuition
Solo Projects
Acting Skills
Drama School Auditions
Classical Text Work

GARETH ARMSTRONG
Author of 'So You Want To Do A Solo Show?'
Published by Nick Hern Books
ISBN 978-1-84842-064-7
www.garetharmstrong.com
info@garetharmstrong.com
020 8996 0677

"The most valuable read for any performer who has ever thought "If only I could have some control over the way my career is going."' - Maureen Lipman

---

MORGAN, Katie
BA (Hons) PG Dip PGCE   T 07956 344255
Private Acting Coach. Audition Preparation. Devising. Drama
School Entry. Improvisation. Meisner Technique.
Working the Text
Based in London
E katie080@hotmail.com

MORLEY ADULT EDUCATION
COLLEGE   T 020 7450 1925
Acting School Programme. Day & Evening.
LOCN Accredited
61 Westminster Bridge Road
London SE1 7HT
E dominic.grant@morleycollege.ac.uk
W www.morleycollege.ac.uk

MORRISON, Elspeth   T 07790 919870
Accent & Dialect Coach
E elsp.morrison@talk21.com

MORRISON, Stuart MA Voice Studies FVCM(TD)
(Hons) FIfL FRSA   T 07867 808648
Voice, Speech & Acting Coach
24 Deans Walk
Coulsdon, Surrey CR5 1HR
E stuartvoicecoach@yahoo.co.uk
W www.voiceandspeech.org.uk

MOTHERWELL COLLEGE   T 01698 232323
Courses: Acting, Musical Theatre. HNC/D, BA Hons
1 Enterprise Way, Motherwell ML1 2TX
E information@motherwell.co.uk
W www.motherwell.co.uk

MOUNTVIEW
See DRAMA SCHOOLS: Conference Of

MTA THE (THE MUSICAL THEATRE
ACADEMY)   T 020 8882 8181
T 07904 987493
E info@themta.co.uk
W www.themta.co.uk

MURRAY, Barbara LGSM LALAM   T 01923 823182
129 Northwood Way, Northwood
Middlesex HA6 1RF

MUSICAL KIDZ COMPANY THE   T 07989 353673
Spires Meade, 4 Bridleways
Wendover, Bucks HP22 6DN
F 01296 623696
E themusicalkidz@aol.com
W www.themusicalkidz.co.uk

NATHENSON, Zoe   T 07956 833850
Audition Technique. Film Acting. Sight Reading.
Group Classes
55 St James's Lane, London N10 3DA
E zoe.act@btinternet.com
W www.zoenathenson.com

NEIL, Andrew   T/F 020 7262 9521
Audition Technique. Private Acting Classes. Public Speaking
2 Howley Place
London W2 1XA
T 07979 843984
E andrewneil@talktalk.net

NEW LONDON PERFORMING
ARTS CENTRE   T 020 8444 4544
Courses in Performing Arts (3-19 yrs). Dance. Drama.
GCSE Courses LAMDA ISTD & RAD
76 St James Lane, Muswell Hill, London N10 3DF
F 020 8444 4040
E nlpac@aol.com   W www.nlpac.co.uk

NEWNHAM, Caryll   T 01707 267700
Singing Teacher
35 Selwyn Crescent, Hatfield, Herts AL10 9NL
T 07976 635745
E caryll@ntlworld.com

NICHOLAS, Paul SCHOOL OF
ACTING & PERFORMING ARTS   T 01253 851144
Thornton Little Theatre, Thornton
Cleveleys, Lancashire FY5 3SZ
T 01253 858529
E info@pnsa.co.uk
W www.pnsa.co.uk

NOBLE, Penny
PSYCHOTHERAPY   T 07506 579895
Character-Centred Counselling & Training. Character
Development. Performance Support. Safe Emotion Memory
Work. Script Work. Self-esteem & Confidence
8 Shaftesbury Gardens, Victoria Road
North Acton, London NW10 6LJ
E pennynobletherapy@googlemail.com
W www.pennynoblepsychotherapy.com

NORTHERN ACADEMY OF
PERFORMING ARTS   T 01482 310690
Anlaby Road, Hull HU1 2PD
F 01482 212280
E napa@northernacademy.org.uk
W www.northernacademy.org.uk

NORTHERN FILM & DRAMA   T/F 01977 681949
Acting Workshops. Television Audition Technique. Drama
School. Residential Courses (over 18s). Film & Television
Training. Improvisation. Private Acting Classes. Stage School
for Children
PO Box 76, Leeds LS25 9AG
E info@northernfilmanddrama.com
W www.northernfilmanddrama.com

NPAS @ THE STUDIOS   T/F 00 353 1 8944660
Docklands, Dublin 1, Ireland
E info@npas.ie
W www.npas.ie

OLLERENSHAW, Maggie
BA (Hons) Dip Ed   T 020 7286 1126
Acting Workshops. Audition Technique. Career Guidance.
Private Acting. Television & Theatre Coaching
151D Shirland Road, London W9 2EP
T 07860 492699
E maggieoll@aol.com

OLSON, Lise   T 0121 331 7220
Acting Through Song. American Accents. Vocal Coaching.
Working with Text
c/o Birmingham School of Acting, Millennium Point
Curzon Street, Birmingham B4 7XG
E lise.olson@bcu.ac.uk

Three Year Acting Course

One Year Acting Course

Accredited by the National
Council for Drama Training

Dance and Drama Awards
available

THE OXFORD SCHOOL OF DRAMA

Six Month Foundation Course in Acting

Six Month Foundation Course in
Musical Theatre

For prospectus or further information

The Oxford School of Drama
Sansomes Farm Studios
Woodstock, OX20 1ER

www.oxforddrama.ac.uk
info@oxforddrama.ac.uk
Telephone: 01993 812883

A member of the
Conference of
Drama Schools **CDS**

Funded by:
>lsc
Leading learning and skills

The Oxford School of Drama Trust is a registered charity
The Foundation Courses are run by The Oxford School of Drama Limited

---

OMOBONI, Lino   T/F 020 8741 2038
Private Acting Classes
2nd Floor, 12 Weltje Road
London W6 9TG
T 07525 187468
E bluewand@btinternet.com

OPEN VOICE   T 01875 820175
Contact: Catherine Owen.
Auditions. Consultancy.
Personal Presentations
9 Bellsmains, Gorebridge
Near Edinburgh EH23 4QD
T 07704 704930
E catherineowenopenvoice@googlemail.com

OPPOSITE LEG LTD   T 07950 824123
Contact: David Windle. Acting Workshops. Classroom
Presence for Teachers. Corporate Voice & Body Training.
Improvisation. Presentation Skills Training. Private Acting
Classes. Public Speaking. Teenage Drama Workshops.
Vocal Coaching
132 Bethwin Road, London SE5 0YY
E david@oppositeleg.co.uk
W www.oppositeleg.co.uk

ORAM, Daron   T 07905 332497
Voice/Accent Coaching & Audition Preparation. Senior
Voice Teacher, Arts Educational Schools
Based in W4/SE10
E darono@yahoo.com

LSDA
LONDON SCHOOL OF DRAMATIC ART

The London School of Dramatic Art offers a
range of comprehensive courses designed to
develop individual creative talents and provide
a thorough grounding in all aspects of
performance as part of a student's preparation
for a working life as an actor

020 7581 6100   www.lsda-acting.com

www.zoenathenson.com

ZOË NATHENSON
SCHOOL OF FILM ACTING

• **FILM ACTING, AUDITION
TECHNIQUE & SIGHT READING**

• **GROUP WORKSHOPS AND
INTENSIVE COURSES AVAILABLE**

Zoe Nathenson School of Film Acting
55 St James' Lane, London N10 3DA
Mobile: 07956 833 850 Tel: 020 8883 7554
Email: zoe.act@btinternet.com

Jill Donker Curtius MA

Dip Ed. Dramatic Art
CSSD/University of London
MA Actor Training and Coaching
CSSD/University of London
Association of Lamda Teachers

Recent entries:
LAMDA
Mountview Academy
Guildford School of Acting
Arts Educational
Oxford School of Drama
CSSD

- Audition coaching for drama school entry
- Confidence building and practical support throughout the auditioning process
- Up to date monologue choice according to age and type

m: 07970 753289   www.jilldonkercurtius.co.uk

OSBORNE HUGHES, John   T 020 8653 7735
Spiritual Psychology of Acting
Miracle Tree Productions Training Department
51 Church Road, London SE19 2TE
T 07801 950916
E johughes@miracletreeproductions.com
W www.spiritualpsychologyofacting.com

OSCARS THEATRE ACADEMY   T 01484 545519
Contact: Paula Danholm
Oscars Management, Spring Bank House
1 Spring Bank, New North Road, Huddersfield
West Yorkshire HD1 5NR
E management@oscarsacademy.co.uk

OXFORD SCHOOL OF DRAMA THE
See DRAMA SCHOOLS: Conference Of

PALMER, Jackie STAGE SCHOOL   T 01494 510597
30 Daws Hill Lane, High Wycombe, Bucks HP11 1PW
F 01494 510479   E jackie.palmer@btinternet.com
W www.jackiepalmer.co.uk

PARKES, Frances MA AGSM   T/F 020 8542 2777
*Contact: Frances Parkes, Sarah Upson. Dialect/Accent
Coaching and Script Coach. Interview Skills for Castings.
Presenting. Private Acting Classes. Public Speaking. Speak
English Clearly Programme for Actors with English as a
Second Language*
Suite 5, 3rd Floor, 1 Harley Street, London W1G 9QD
T 01782 827222 (Upson Edwards)
E frances@maxyourvoice.com W www.maxyourvoice.com

PENS PEOPLE   T 01708 457443
75 Victor Walk, Hornchurch, Essex RM12 4XQ
E penny@penspeople.co.uk
W www.penspeople.co.uk

PERFORMANCE BUSINESS THE   T 01932 888885
78 Oatlands Drive, Weybridge, Surrey KT13 9HT
E michael@theperformance.biz
W www.theperformance.biz

**PERFORMANCE FACTORY
STAGE SCHOOL THE**   T 07939 081413
c/o Forge Fach Centre, Hebron Road, Swansea SA6 5EJ
E info@tpfwales.com
W www.theperformancefactorywales.com

PERFORMANCE FREQUENCY   T 07876 298613
9 Tennyson Road, Stoke
Coventry, West Midlands CV2 5HX
E info@performancefrequency.com
W www.performancefrequency.com

PERFORMERS COLLEGE   T 01375 672053
Contact: Brian Rogers, Susan Stephens
Southend Road, Corringham, Essex SS17 8JT
F 01375 672353
E lesley@performerscollege.co.uk
W www.performerscollege.co.uk

PERFORMERS THEATRE SCHOOL   T 0151 708 4000
*Acting Workshops. Dancing. Singing. Stage School for
Children. Summer School*
8 Vernon Street, Liverpool L2 2AY
E info@performerstheatre.co.uk
W www.performerstheatre.co.uk

**PERFORMERS
THEATRE SCHOOL**   T 020 8479 3000
*Acting Workshops. Dancing. Singing. Stage School for
Children. Summer School*
Royal Victoria Patriotic Buildings, London SW18
E info@performerstheatre.co.uk
W www.performerstheatre.co.uk

**PERFORMERZONE
(BRIGHTON & LONDON)**   T 07973 518643
Contact: William Pool (ARCM). Singing. Tuition. Workshops
33A Osmond Road, Hove
East Sussex BN3 1TD
E pool.william@gmail.com
W www.performerzone.co.uk

PG COACHING   T 07786 512841
*One-to-one Coaching by Professional Actress &
Qualified Teacher*
E coaching@pruegillett.com
W www.pruegillet.com/coaching

PILATES INTERNATIONAL LTD   T 020 8348 1442
Pilates Teacher Training (NVQ3 - Cert). Physical Coaching
Unit 1, Broadbent Close
20-22 Highgate High Street, London N6 5JG
E pilates@pilatesinternational.co.uk
W www.pilatesinternational.co.uk

**POLLYANNA CHILDREN'S
TRAINING THEATRE**   T 020 7481 1911
1 Knighten Street
Wapping, London E1W 1PH
E pollyanna_mgmt@btinternet.com
W www.pollyannatheatre.org

POLYDOROU, Anna   T 07833 545292
147C Fernhead Road
Maida Hill, Queens Park W9 3ED
E annahebe@yahoo.co.uk

POOR SCHOOL   T 020 7837 6030
242 Pentonville Road, London N1 9JY
E acting@thepoorschool.com
W www.thepoorschool.com

**POPPIES YOUTH THEATRE
& AGENCY**   T 07795 370678
Stockbrook House, 8 King Street
Duffield, Derbyshire DE56 4EU
E poppies09@live.co.uk
W www.poppies-yta.co.uk

PRECINCT THEATRE THE   T 020 7359 3594
Units 2-3 The Precinct
Packington Square, London N1 7UP
F 020 7359 3660
E theatre@breakalegman.com
W www.breakalegman.com

PRICE, Janis R.   T 07977 630829
Voice Coach
E janis@janisprice.sfnet.co.uk

PRIMOATTO PRODUCTIONS   T 07830 120536
2/21 Culmington Road, Ealing, London W13 9NJ
E mg@primoattoproductions.com
W www.primoattoproductions.com

**LONDON SCHOOL OF
FILM, MEDIA & PERFORMANCE**

RELEASE YOUR POTENTIAL
WITH THE LONDON SCHOOL
OF FILM, MEDIA & PERFORMANCE

- Acting Foundation Course
- BA (Hons) Acting & Global Theatre
- BA (Hons) Creative Industries
- BA (Hons) Film, TV & Digital Media Production
- BA (Hons) Screenwriting & Producing
- MA Writing for Screen & Stage

**NOW ACCEPTING APPLICATIONS FOR SEPTEMBER 2012
SCHOLARSHIPS AVAILABLE**

Tel **+44 (0)20 7487 7505**
Email **lsfmp@regents.ac.uk**
Web **regents.ac.uk/lsfmp**

PROJECTURVOICE.COM   T 01273 204779
*Contact: Dee Forrest (Deputy Head of Voice, Mountview).
Audition Technique. Confidence Building/NLP. Public
Speaking. Vocal Coaching. London & Brighton Studios*
20 Landseer Road, Hove BN3 7AF
T 07957 211065
E dee_forrest@yahoo.com   W www.projecturvoice.com

**QUEEN MARGARET UNIVERSITY,
EDINBURGH**   T 0131 474 0000
Queen Margaret University Drive
Musselburgh, East Lothian EH21 6UU
F 0131 474 0001
E admissions@qmu.ac.uk   W www.qmu.ac.uk

**QUESTORS THEATRE
EALING THE**   T 020 8567 0011
12 Mattock Lane, London W5 5BQ
F 020 8567 2275
E jane@questors.org.uk   W www.questors.org.uk

**RAPIERSHARP
(STAGE & SCREEN COMBAT)**   T 07710 763735
*Performance Combat Services for Stage & Screen. British
Academy of Dramatic Combat Qualifications. Consultancy.
Dramatic Combat Training. Fight Directing.
Weapon Hire. Workshops*
93 Boundaries Road, Balham, London SW12 8HA
E info@rapiersharp.com   W www.rapiersharp.com

RAVENSCOURT THEATRE SCHOOL
See CORONA THEATRE SCHOOL

RAW TALENT TRAINING   T 0131 510 0133
*Contact: Helen Raw. Courses: Acting for Film, Television
& Stage. Cold Reading & Audition Technique. Monologue
& Character Development. Improvisation & Scene Study.
Beginner to Advanced Actors*
E info@therawtalentcompany.co.uk
W www.therawtalentcompany.co.uk

**RAZZAMATAZ
THEATRE SCHOOLS**   T 01228 550129
2nd Floor, Atlas Works, Nelson Street
Denton Holme, Carlisle CA2 5NB
E franchise@razzamataz.co.uk   W www.razzamataz.co.uk

RC-ANNIE LTD   T 020 8123 5936
*Stage and Screen Combat Training & Theatrical
Blood Supplies*
34 Pullman Place, London SE9 6EG
E info@rc-annie.com   W www.rc-annie.com

**REALLY YOUTHFUL
THEATRE COMPANY THE**   T/F 01926 494533
*Audition Technique. LAMDA/Trinity Guildhall. Private Acting
Classes. Stage School for Children. Summer School*
17 West End Court, Crompton Street
Warwick, Warwickshire CV34 6NA
T 07970 627916
E info@rytc.co.uk   W www.rytc.co.uk

**REBEL SCHOOL OF THEATRE ARTS & CASTING
AGENCY LTD**   T 07808 803637
Based in Leeds & Huddersfield
PO Box 169, Huddersfield HD8 1BE
E sue@rebelschool.co.uk   W www.rebelschool.co.uk

**RED ONION PERFORMING
ARTS CENTRE**   T 020 8520 3975
Dance. Drama. Vocal Training Theatre School (3 yrs-Adult)
806 High Street, Leyton, London E10
E info@redonion.uk.com   W www.redonion.uk.com

REDROOFS THEATRE SCHOOL   T 01628 674092
School Lane, Littlewick Green
Maidenhead, Berks SL6 3QY
T 01628 822982
E sam@redroofs.co.uk   W www.redroofs.co.uk

REFLECTIONS AGENCY   T/F 01322 410003
34 Knowle Avenue, Bexleyheath, Kent DA7 5LX
T 07958 617976
E c.johnson717@ntlworld.com
W www.riverside-reflections.webs.com

REP COLLEGE THE   T 0118 942 1144
17 St Mary's Avenue, Purley on Thames, Berks RG8 8BJ
E tudor@repcollege.co.uk
W www.repcollege.co.uk

**RICHMOND
DRAMA SCHOOL**   T 020 8891 5907 ext 4018
*Contact: Dr Fern-Chantele Carter (Course Director). Acting
Workshops. Audition Technique. Drama School (over 18s).
Drama School Preparation. Public Speaking. Courses:
Access to HE Drama, BTEC Ext Cert L2 Performing Arts
(Acting), RACC Certificate, Richmond Drama School
Advanced Certificate, All 1 yr Part-time*
Richmond Adult & Community College, Parkshot
Richmond, Surrey TW9 2RE
E fern-chantelecarter@racc.ac.uk

**RIDGEWAY STUDIOS
PERFORMING ARTS COLLEGE**   T 01992 633775
Office: 106 Hawkshead Road
Potters Bar, Hertfordshire EN6 1NG
E info@ridgewaystudios.co.uk
W www.ridgewaystudios.co.uk

RISING STARS DRAMA SCHOOL   T 0845 2570127
*Contact: Jessica Andrews. Acting Workshops. Audition
Technique. Filming Techniques. Films Made. Improvisation.
LAMDA Examinations*
10 Orchard Way, Measham, Derbyshire DE12 7JZ
E info@risingstarsdramaschool.co.uk
W www.risingstarsdramaschool.co.uk

ROSCH, Philip   T 020 8731 6686
*Confident Improvisation & Effective Sight-reading.
Shakespeare Made Easy. Assoc. Guildhall Teachers*
53 West Heath Court, London NW11 7RG
E philiprosch1@hotmail.com   W www.philiprosch.com

ROSE BRUFORD COLLEGE
See DRAMA SCHOOLS: Conference Of

ROSS, David ACTING LTD   T 07957 862317
*Contact: David Ross. Acting Workshops. Audition
Technique. Dialect/Accent Coaching. Drama School
Preparation. Improvisation. Stage School for Children.
Vocal Coaching*
8 Farrier Close, Sale, Cheshire M33 2ZL
E info@davidrossacting.com
W www.davidrossacting.com

**ROSSENDALE DANCE &
DRAMA CENTRE**　　T 01706 211161
*Contact: Chris Marlow. LAMDA LCM TCL Grade & Diploma
Courses & Exams. Acting Workshops. Audition Technique.
Dancing. Dialect/Accent Coaching. Drama School (over
18s). Elocution. Improvisation. Private Acting Classes. Public
Speaking. Stage School for Children. Vocal Coaching*
52 Bridleway, Waterfoot
Rossendale, Lancs BB4 9DS
E rddc@btinternet.com

ROYAL ACADEMY OF DRAMATIC ART
See DRAMA SCHOOLS: Conference Of

ROYAL ACADEMY OF MUSIC　　T 020 7873 7483
Musical Theatre Department, Marylebone Road
London NW1 5HT
E mth@ram.ac.uk
W www.ram.ac.uk/mth

ROYAL CONSERVATOIRE OF SCOTLAND
See DRAMA SCHOOLS: Conference Of

ROYAL WELSH COLLEGE OF MUSIC & DRAMA
See DRAMA SCHOOLS: Conference Of

RUMBELOW, Sam　　T 020 7622 9742
*Acting & Method Acting Coach.
Classes held at Brick Lane E1*
84 Union Road, London SW4 6JU
E samson@methodacting.co.uk
W www.methodacting.co.uk

RYDER, Richard　　T 07967 352551
Accent & Dialect Coach
9 Kamen House, Magdalen Street
London Bridge, London SE1 2RH
E richard@therichervoice.com
W www.therichervoice.com

SALES, Stephanie　　T 020 8995 9127
61 Brookfield Road, Chiswick, London W4 1DF
E steph@stephaniesales.co.uk
W www.stephaniesales.co.uk/dramacoaching

SAMUELS, Marianne　　T 07974 203001
Accents. Text & Business Voice. Voice Coach
Based in Ealing, West London
E mariannemicallef@hotmail.com

**SCALA SCHOOL OF
PERFORMING ARTS**　　T 0113 250 6823
*Audition Technique. Dancing. Dialect/Accent Coaching.
Improvisation. Singing. Stage School for Children. Vocal
Training*
Office: 42 Rufford Avenue, Yeadon, Leeds LS19 7QR
F 0113 250 8806
E office@scalakids.com
W www.scalakids.com

SCHER, Anna THEATRE　　T 020 3093 5422
St Silas Church, Pentonville
Penton Street, London N1 9UL
E enquiries@nicknightmanagement.com
W www.nicknightmanagement.com

SEMARK, Rebecca LLAM　　T 07956 850330
*Elocution. Voice & Vocal Coaching. Audition Technique.
Drama School Preparation. LAMDA Exams. Private Acting
Classes & Public Speaking for Children & Adults. Stage
School entry for Children including singing*
Epping, Essex
E rebecca@semark.biz
W www.semark.biz

SHAW, Phil　　T 020 8715 8943
*Actors' Consultancy Service. Acting Workshops. Audition
Technique. Drama School Preparation. Private Acting
Classes. Vocal Coaching*
Suite 476, 2 Old Brompton Road
South Kensington, London SW7 3DQ
E shawcastlond@aol.com

John Colclough Advisory

Practical independent guidance for actors and actresses

t: 020 8873 1763   e: john@johncolclough.org.uk   www.johncolclough.co.uk

---

SHENEL, Helena　　　　T 020 7724 8793
Singing Teacher
80 Falkirk House, 165 Maida Vale, London W9 1QX
T 020 7328 2921

**SHINE TIME MUSICAL
THEATRE & ACTING**　　　　T 07880 721689
*Contact: Laura Green. Audition Technique. Dancing. Drama
School Preparation. Improvisation. LAMDA Acting Solo
Examinations. Musical Theatre & Acting Holiday Workshops.
Private Acting Classes. Singing. Stage School for Children.
Vocal Coaching*
Flat 10, Valentine House, Church Road
Guildford, Surrey GU1 4NG
E shinetime@hotmail.co.uk
W www.shinetimeworkshops.com

SHOWSONG ACCOMPANIST　　　　T 020 8993 2111
165 Gunnersbury Lane, London W3 8LJ

**SIMMONS, Jacki
BA (Hons) PGCE MA (CSSD)**　　　　T 07989 389183
*Audition Technique. Drama School Preparation. Private
Acting Classes. Public Speaking*
Based in North London
E jacki_@hotmail.com

SIMMONS, Ros MA　　　　T 020 8347 8089
Accents/Dialects. Voice. Auditions. Presentations
The Real Speaking Company, 120 Hillfield Avenue
Crouch End, London N8 7DN
T 07957 320572
E info@realspeaking.co.uk
W www.realspeaking.co.uk

SIMPKIN, Heather　　　　T 01491 574349
Morriston, Fairmile
Henley-on-Thames, Oxon RG9 2JX
E heathersimpkin@btinternet.com

SINGER, Sandra ASSOCIATES　　　　T 01702 331616
*LAMDA & ISTD Exams. Acting Workshops. Audition
Technique. Dancing. Dialect/Accent Coaching. Part-time
Drama School (over 18s). Improvisation. Private Acting
Classes. Singing. Stage School for Children.
Vocal Coaching*
21 Cotswold Road, Westcliff-on-Sea, Essex SS0 8AA
E sandrasingeruk@aol.com
W www.sandrasinger.com

SINGER STAGE SCHOOL　　　　T 01702 331616
*Part-time Vocational Stage School & Summer School.
Adult Classes (16+ yrs) for Singing, Acting & Tap. Acting
Workshops. Audition Technique. Dancing. Dialect/Accent
Coaching. Drama School (over 18s). Improvisation. ISTD.
Private Acting Classes. Singing. Stage School for Children.
Vocal Coaching*
Office: 21 Cotswold Road
Westcliff-on-Sea, Essex SS0 8AA
E sandrasingeruk@aol.com
W www.sandrasinger.com

SLP COLLEGE　　　　T 0113 286 8136
5 Chapel Lane, Garforth
Leeds, West Yorkshire LS25 1AG
F 0113 287 4487
E info@slpcollege.co.uk　　　　W www.slpcollege.co.uk

**SOCIETY OF TEACHERS OF
SPEECH & DRAMA THE**　　　　T 01623 627636
Registered Office: 73 Berry Hill Road
Mansfield, Notts NG18 4RU
E ann.k.jones@btinternet.com
W www.stsd.org.uk

**SONNETS THEATRE
ARTS SCHOOL**　　　　T 0845 0038910
Thorneycombe, Vernham Dean
Andover, Hampshire SP11 0JY
E sonnetsagency@hotmail.co.uk
W www.sonnets-tas.co.uk

SPEAK EASILY　　　　T 020 7717 9649
32 Bloomsbury Street
London WC1B 3QJ
E info@speak-easily.com
W www.speak-easily.com

**SPEAKE, Barbara
STAGE SCHOOL**　　　　T 020 8743 1306
East Acton Lane, London W3 7EG
F 020 8743 2746
E speakekids3@aol.com
W www.barbaraspeake.com

**SPEED, Anne-Marie Hon ARAM MA
(Voice Studies) CSSD ADVS BA**　　　　T 07957 272554
*Vanguard Estill Practitioner. Accents. Auditions. Coaching.
Vocal Technique-Speaking & Singing*
E info@thevoiceexplained.com
W www.thevoiceexplained.com

**SPIRITUAL PSYCHOLOGY
OF ACTING THE**　　　　T 020 8653 7735
51 Church Road, London SE19 2TE
E info@spiritualpsychologyofacting.com
W www.spiritualpsychologyofacting.com

SPLITZ THEATRE ARTZ　　　　T 01223 880389
5 Cow Lane, Fulbourn, Cambridge CB21 5HB
E clare@splitz-ta.net
W www.splitz-ta.net

SPONTANEITY SHOP THE　　　　T 020 7788 4080
85-87 Bayham Street, London NW1 0AG
E info@the-spontaneity.com
W www.the-spontaneity-shop.com

STAGE2 YOUTH THEATRE　　　　T 07961 018841
Based at: Millennium Point
Curzon Street, Birmingham B4 7XG
E info@stage2.org
W www.stage2.org

STAGE2 YOUTH THEATRE　　　　T 07961 018841
Administration: 12 Valentine Road, Kings Heath
Birmingham, West Midlands B14 7AN
E info@stage2.org
W www.stage2.org

**STAGE 84 YORKSHIRE SCHOOL
OF PERFORMING ARTS**　　　　T 01274 569197
Evening & Weekend Classes & Summer Schools
Old Bell Chapel, Town Lane, Idle, West Yorks BD10 8PR
T 07785 244984
E valeriejackson@stage84.com

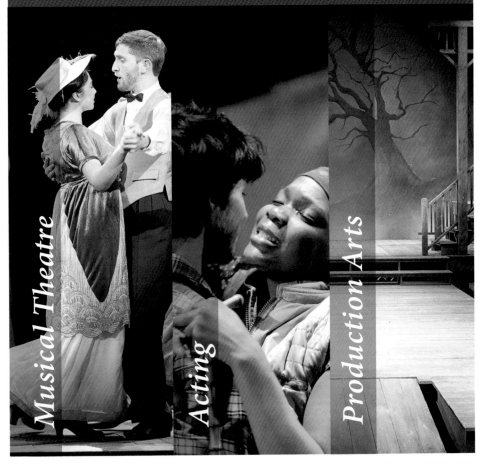

MOUNTVIEW
ACADEMY OF THEATRE ARTS

Ralph Richardson Memorial Studios,
Kingfisher Place, Clarendon Road,
Wood Green, London N22 6XF

Tel: 020 8881 2201
Fax: 020 8829 0034

enquiries@mountview.org.uk
www.mountview.org.uk

Undergraduate & Postgraduate Courses

Plus an exciting programme of Part-time and Summer Courses

CDS MEMBER

Mountview is committed to equal opportunities

Musical Theatre

Acting

Production Arts

Michael Vivian Actor ▮ Director ▮ Writer

Productions at Arts Ed., Mountview, Guildford & Central
Also QDOS, UK Productions & various reps.
Voice Speech & Drama, Audition Coaching, Private Tuition

Tel: 020-8876 2073 Mob: 07958-903911

STAGE CENTRAL THEATRE ARTS T 01423 331478
St John Fisher High School
Harrogate, North Yorkshire HG2 8PT
T 07940 014448
E darren@stagecentral.co.uk
W www.stagecentral.co.uk

STAGECOACH THEATRE ARTS T 01932 254333
The Courthouse, Elm Grove
Walton-on-Thames, Surrey KT12 1LZ
F 01932 222894
E mail@stagecoach.co.uk
W www.stagecoach.co.uk

STAGEFIGHT T 07813 308672
138 Wilden Lane, Stourport-on-Severn
Worcestershire DY13 9LP
E raph@stagefight.co.uk W www.stagefight.co.uk

STE. CROIX, Felicitas T 07939 143721
*Former Assistant to Jack Waltzer. Audition Preparation.
Chekhov. Meisner. Meyerhold. Sense Memories. Coaches
many Professional Actors & Singers in the UK,
France & USA*
E felicitasstecroix@yahoo.com

**STEP ON STAGE ACADEMY
OF PERFORMING ARTS** T 020 8408 0633
*Contact: Emma-Louise Tinniswood. Acting Workshops.
Dancing. Singing. Stage School for Children. Summer
School. Courses: GCSE Drama, 1 yr Part-time, LAMDA, 1
term - 1 yr Part-time*
5 Poulett Gardens, Twickenham, Middlesex TW1 4QS
T 07973 900196
E info@steponstageacademy.co.uk
W www.steponstageacademy.co.uk

**STEPHENSON, Sarah
GMusRNCM PGDip RNCM** T 020 8425 1225
Vocal Coach. Piano Accompanist. Audition Preparation
8A Edgington Road, Streatham, London SW16 5BS
T 07581 716233
E s.stephenson@ntlworld.com

**STEWART, Carola
LRAM NCSD LUD** T 020 8444 5994
*Audition Technique. CV Advice. Dialect/Accent Coaching.
Elocution. Interview Technique. LAMDA Exams. Private
Acting Classes. Public Speaking*
13 Church Lane, East Finchley, London N2 8DX
E carolastewart@msn.com

STIRLING ACADEMY T 0845 0176500
*Contact: Glen Mortimer. Acting Workshops. Audition
Techniques. Audition Training for Camera. Drama School
(over 18's). Improvisation. Private Acting Classes. Showreels*
490 Halliwell Road, Bolton, Lancashire BL1 8AN
F 0844 4128689
E admin@stirlingacademy.co.uk
W www.stirlingacademy.co.uk

**STOCKTON RIVERSIDE
COLLEGE** T 01642 865400
Further Education & Training
Harvard Avenue, Thornaby, Stockton TS17 6FB
W www.stockton.ac.uk

**STOMP! THE SCHOOL
OF PERFORMING ARTS** T 020 8446 9898
*Stage School for Children. Street Dance. Acting &
Singing Classes (6-19 yrs). Evenings & Weekends.
Mill Hill & Finchley Areas*
c/o Suite 2, Fiboard House
5 Oakleigh Gardens, London N20 9AB
E stompschoolnw7@aol.com
W www.stompschool.com

STREETON, Jane T 020 8556 9297
Singing Teacher, RADA
24 Richmond Road, Leytonstone, London E11 4BA
E janestreetonsop@aol.com

STUDIOS THE T 01628 777853
Office: 47 Furze Platt Road, Maidenhead SL6 7NF
E julie.fox@virgin.net

SUPERSTARS IN THE MAKING T 07531 814820
PO Box 187, Barry, Vale of Glamorgan CF63 9EL
E superstars@radio.fm
W www.superstarsinthemaking.com

SUPPORT ACT SERVICES T 07980 300927
*Contact: Ian McCracken. Services for Actors including
Stage Combat Instruction*
197 Church Road, Northolt UB5 5BE
E info@supportact.co.uk
W www.supportact.co.uk

TALENT TIME THEATRE SCHOOL T 07904 771980
Show Company
Parkwood Health & Fitness Centre, Darkes Lane
Potters Bar, Herts EN6 1AA
T 07930 400647
E talenttimeyouth@aol.com
W www.talenttimetheatre.com

**TALENTED KIDS PERFORMING
ARTS SCHOOL & AGENCY** T/F 00 353 4 5485464
*Contact: Maureen V. Ward. Acting Workshops. Audition
Technique. Dance. Drama School (over 18s). Elocution.
Improvisation. Musical Theatre. Singing. Stage School for
Children. Vocal Coaching*
23 Burrow Manor, Calverstown
Kilcullen, Co. Kildare, Ireland
T 00 353 8 72480348
E talentedkids@hotmail.com
W www.talentedkidsireland.com

**THAT'S A WRAP PERFORMING
ARTS SCHOOL** T 01753 650951
*Accompanist. Acting Workshops. Audition Technique.
Dialect & Accent Coaching. Elocution. Improvisation. Private
Acting Classes. Singing. Stage School for Children*
The Actors Studio, Pinewood Studios
Pinewood Road, Iver Heath, Bucks SL0 0NH
E info@actorsstudio.co.uk
W www.actorsstudio.co.uk

THEATRETRAIN T 01327 300498
Annual West End Productions Involving all Pupils (6-18 yrs)
Orchard Studio, PO Box 42
Hitchin, Herts SG4 8FS
E admin@theatretrain.co.uk W www.theatretrain.co.uk

THREE4ALL THEATRE COMPANY   T 020 8402 7858
77 Victoria Road, Bromley BR2 9PL
E alison@three4all.org
W www.three4all.org/dramatraining.php

TIP TOE STAGE SCHOOL   T 07914 899438
Dance, Drama, Singing & Performing Arts Part-time Training
For correspondence only: 65 North Road
South Ockendon, Essex RM15 6QH
E julieecarter@aol.com
W www.tiptoestageschool1.piczo.com

TO BE OR NOT TO BE   T 07958 996227
Contact: Anthony Barnett. LAMDA Exams. Showreels.
Theatre/Audition Pieces. Television/Film Acting Technique
40 Gayton Road, King's Lynn
Norfolk PE30 4EL
E anthony.barnett10@virginmedia.com
W www.showreels.org.uk

TODD, Paul   T 020 7229 9776
Audition Technique. Acting. Drumming. Improvisation.
Vocal Coaching
3 Rosehart Mews, London W11 3JN
T 07813 985092
E paultodd@talk21.com

TOMORROW'S TALENT   T 01245 200555
Contact: Gavin Wilkinson. Acting Workshops. Drama
School Preparation. Stage School for Children.
Summer School
Based in Chelmsford, Essex
E enquiries@tomorrowstalent.co.uk
W www.tomorrowstalent.co.uk

TOP HAT STAGE & SCREEN SCHOOL   T/F 01727 812666
Contact: Warren Bacci. Acting Workshops. Dancing.
Singing. Stage School for Children. Courses: School Term
Weekends, Part-time. Easter & Summer Holidays, Part-time.
Youth Theatre, Weeknights, Part-time. Schools in Potters
Bar, Welwyn, Stevenage, St Albans & Hertford
PO Box 860, St Albans, Herts AL1 9BR
E admin@tophatstageschool.co.uk
W www.tophatstageschool.co.uk

TRING PARK SCHOOL FOR THE PERFORMING ARTS   T 01442 824255
Dance, Drama & Musical Theatre Training School (8-19 yrs)
Tring Park, Tring, Herts HP23 5LX
E info@tringpark.com
W www.tringpark.com

TROLLOPE, Ann   T 07943 816276
Voice/Acting Coach
Harpsford, St. Peters Lane, Solihull B92 0DR
E ann-t@uwclub.net

TROTTER, William BA MA PGDVS   T/F 020 8459 7594
25 Thanet Lodge, Mapesbury Road, London NW2 4JA
E william.trotter@ukspeech.co.uk
W www.ukspeech.co.uk

TUCKER, John   T 07903 269409
Voice Coaching. Singing Lessons. Accents.
Auditions. Role Preparation
503 Mountjoy House, Barbican, London EC2Y 8BP
E mail@john-tucker.com
W www.john-tucker.com

TURNBULL, Mark   T 07742 070122
Private Acting & Vocal Tuition. West End Musical Theatre
Specialist
E sharonturnbull2@btopenworld.com

TV ACTING CLASSES   T 07885 621061
Contact: Elisabeth Charbonneau
E ejcharbonneau@aol.com

TWICKENHAM THEATRE WORKSHOP FOR CHILDREN T 020 8898 5882
29 Campbell Road, Twickenham, Middlesex TW2 5BY
E frabbt@aol.com

URQUHART, Moray T 020 7731 3604
Private Coaching for Auditions, Schools, Showbiz etc
61 Parkview Court, London SW6 3LL
E nmuphelps@yahoo.co.uk

VALLÉ ACADEMY OF PERFORMING ARTS T 01992 622862
The Vallé Academy Studios, Wilton House
Delamare Road, Cheshunt, Herts EN8 9SG
F 01992 622868
E enquiries@valleacademy.co.uk
W www.valleacademy.co.uk

VERRALL, Charles T 020 7833 1971
19 Matilda Street, London N1 0LA
E info@charlesverrall.com
W www.learntoact.co.uk

VISUAL NOISE ARTS CENTRE & WHITE NOISE CASTING T 01253 696990
Performing Arts Centre, 19 Preston Old Road
Blackpool, Lancs FY3 9PR
E info@visualnoiseuk.com

VIVIAN, Michael T 020 8876 2073
Acting Workshops. Audition Technique. Improvisation.
Private Acting Classes. Public Speaking
15 Meredyth Road, Barnes, London SW13 0DS
T 07958 903911
E vivcalling@aol.com

VOCAL CONFIDENCE T 07958 450382
Contact: Alix Longman. Accent & Dialect Coaching. Fast,
Effective Vocal & Acting Technique. Audition Preparation.
Presentation. Singing. Vocal Problems
E alix@vocalconfidence.com
W www.vocalconfidence.com

VOICE MASTER INTERNATIONAL T 020 8455 2211
Creators of the Hudson Voice Technique: the only
Technique in the World for Voiceovers, Actors & Autocue
88 Erskine Hill, London NW11 6HR
E stevehudson@voicemaster.co.uk
W www.voicemaster.co.uk

VOICE & DIALECT COACH T 07723 620728
Contact: Caroline Hetherington
7 Dodcott Barns, Burleydam, Whitchurch SY13 4BQ
E voice@carohetherington.co.uk
W www.carohetherington.co.uk

VOICES & PERFORMANCE T 07712 624083
Contact: Julia Gaunt ALCM TD-Musical Theatre
116 Nottingham Road, Selston, Nottinghamshire
E joolsmusicbiz@aol.com
W www.joolsmusicbiz.com

VOICES LONDON T 01279 655542
Auditions. Technique. Vocal Coaching
36 Wigmore Street, London W1U 2BP
T 07775 810572
E info@voicesvocal.co.uk
W www.voicesvocal.co.uk

VOXTRAINING LTD T 020 7434 4404
Demo CDs. Voice-Over Training
20 Old Compton Street, London W1D 4TW
E info@voxtraining.com
W www.voxtraining.com

WALLACE, Elaine BA T 07856 098334
Voice
249 Goldhurst Terrace, London NW6 3EP
E im@voicebiz.biz

WALSH, Anne T 020 8459 8071
Accents. Dialect. Speech
45B Windsor Road
Willesden Green, London NW2 5DT
T 07932 440043

WALSH, Genevieve T 020 7627 0024
Acting Tuition. Audition Coaching. Voice
37 Kelvedon House, Guildford Road
Stockwell, London SW8 2DN

WALTZER, Jack T 07855 114394 (London)
Professional Acting Workshops
5 Minetta Street Apt 2B
New York NY 10012, USA
T 001 212 840 1234
E jackwaltzer@hotmail.com
W www.jackwaltzer.com

WARD CASTING LTD T 020 8886 5676
Studio 5, 155 Commercial Street
London E1 6BJ
E casting@wardcasting.com
W www.wardcasting.com

WEAKLIAM, Brendan PGDip MusPerf BMusPerf Dip ABRSM T 07724 558955
Singing Teacher. Voice Coach
23 Alders Close, Wanstead
London E11 3RZ
E brendanweakliam@gmail.com

WEBB, Bruce T 01508 518703
Audition Technique. Singing
Abbots Manor, Kirby Cane, Bungay, Suffolk NR35 2HP

WELBOURNE, Jacqueline T 07977 247287
Choreographer. Circus Trainer. Consultant
43 Kingsway Avenue
Kingswood, Bristol BS15 8AN
E jackie.welbourne@gmail.com

WEST END WORKSHOPS T 07828 821871
Educational Arts Workshops. Audition Coaching.
West End Tutors
E info@westendworkshops.co.uk
W www.westendworkshops.co.uk

WESTMINSTER KINGSWAY COLLEGE T 0870 0609800
Performing Arts
Regent's Park Centre
Longford Street, London NW1 3HB
F 020 7391 6400
E courseinfo@westking.ac.uk
W www.westking.ac.uk

WHITE, Chris T 07971 234829
Head of Acting Rose Bruford, BSA, Italia Conti
E chrisjohnwhite40@aol.com

WHITE, Susan BA TEFL LGSM MA Voice Studies Distinction T 020 7244 0402
Coach of Professional Spoken Voice & Personal Presence.
Introductory Voice Days for Individuals and Advanced
Voice & Presence Master Classes
Based in Central London
E susan@per-sona.com
W www.per-sona.com

WILDCATS THEATRE SCHOOL T 07725 915333
Contact: Caz Dolby. Dancing. Public Speaking. Singing.
Stage School for Children. Summer School. Courses:
Acting, Musical Theatre, Public Speaking, Verse & Prose, All
LAMDA, Part-time
PO Box 1198, Stamford, Lincolnshire PE2 2JE
E admin@wildcats-uk.com
W www.wildcatstheatreschool.co.uk

WILDER, Andrea   T 07919 202401
23 Cambrian Drive
Colwyn Bay, Conwy LL28 4SL
F 07092 249314
E andrea@awagency.co.uk
W www.awagency.co.uk

WILSON, Holly   T 020 8878 0015
3 Worple Street, Mortlake, London SW14 8HE
E hbwilson@fastmail.co.uk

WIMBUSH, Martin Dip GSMD   T 020 8877 0086
Audition Technique. Drama School Entry. Elocution.
Public Speaking. Vocal Coaching
Flat 4, 289 Trinity Road
Wandsworth Common
London SW18 3SN
T 07930 677623
E martinwimbush@btinternet.com
W www.martinwimbush.com

WINDSOR, Judith Ph. D   T 01782 827222
American Accents/Dialects
Woodbine, Victoria Road
Deal, Kent CT14 7AS
F 01782 728004
E sarah.upson@voicecoach.tv

WOOD, Tessa Teach Cert
AGSM CSSD PGDVS   T 020 8896 2659
Voice Coach
43 Woodhurst Road, London W3 6SS
E tessaroswood@aol.com

WOODHOUSE, Alan
AGSM ADVS   T 07748 904227
Acting Coach. Acting Workshops. Elocution. Private Acting
Classes. Public Speaking. Voice Coach
33 Burton Road
Kingston upon Thames
Surrey KT2 5TG
E alanwoodhouse50@hotmail.com
W www.woodhouse-voice.co.uk

WOODHOUSE, Nan FLAM(Hon) LGSM (Hons)
LLCM (TD) ALAM (ACT)   T 07812 921625

WORTMAN, Neville   T 020 8994 8886
Speech Coach. Voice Training
11 Mandeville Place, London W1U 3AJ
T 07976 805976
E wortman.speakwell@btinternet.com
W www.speakwell.co.uk

WYNN, Madeleine   T 01394 450265
Acting Workshops. Audition Technique. Directing & Acting
Coach. Drama School (over 18s). LAMDA Exams. Private
Acting Classes. Public Speaking
40 Barrie House
Hawksley Court
Albion Road, London N16 0TX
E madeleine@onetel.com

YOUNG, Sylvia
THEATRE SCHOOL   T 020 7258 2330
Acting Workshops. Audition Technique. Dancing.
Improvisation. Singing. Stage School for Children. Summer
Schools. Vocal Coaching
1 Nutford Place, London W1H 5YZ
F 020 7724 8371
E syoung@syts.co.uk
W www.syts.co.uk

YOUNG ACTORS THEATRE   T 020 7278 2101
70-72 Barnsbury Road, London N1 0ES
F 020 7833 9467
E info@yati.org.uk
W www.yati.org.uk

YOUNGSTAR TELEVISION &
FILM ACTING SCHOOL   T 023 8047 7717
Part-time Schools across the UK (8-20 yrs)
Head Office, 20 Hilldene Way
Westend, Southampton SO30 3DW
F 023 8045 5816
E info@youngstar.tv
W www.youngstar.tv

YOUNGSTARS THEATRE
SCHOOL & AGENCY   T 020 8950 5782
Contact: Coralyn Canfor-Dumas. Part-time Children's
Theatre School (4-18 yrs). Commercials. Dance. Drama.
Film. Singing. Stage. Television. Voice Overs
4 Haydon Dell
Bushey, Herts WD23 1DD
T 07966 176756
E youngstarsagency@gmail.com

ZANDER, Peter   T 020 7437 4767
Acting for Stage, Opera, Screen, Radio. Audition
Preparation. Breathing. Improvisation. Mime. Movement.
Private Acting Classes. Relaxation. Speech/Voice Coaching
in English & German
22 Romilly Street, London W1D 5AG
T 07920 125509
E peterzan.berlin@virgin.net

F

→

Festivals

What do I need to know about the listed festivals?

The festivals listed in this section are all dedicated to creative and performing arts. Festivals are an opportunity for like-minded people to gather together to appreciate and learn from both well-established and new and up-and-coming acts and performers.

Why should I get involved?

Being a spectator at a festival is a chance to see others in action and to see a variety of shows that are not necessarily mainstream. This is an opportunity to see talent in its rawest form, which is exactly why casting directors often attend drama festivals: they may spot someone who is just what they are looking for, who would otherwise have gone unnoticed in a pile of CVs.

Taking part in festivals will be something else to add to your CV and will help develop your skills. This not only means performance skills but social skills as well: you will meet hundreds of new faces with the same passion for their work as you, so this is a great opportunity to make friends and useful contacts in the industry.

What do I need to bear in mind?

Before committing to performing at a festival, there are a number of issues to take into consideration. You will usually be unpaid and you will have to set aside enough money to fund the time spent rehearsing for and performing at the festival, not to mention travel, accommodation and food expenses. Not only that, you must also consider that you will be putting yourself out of the running for any paid work offered to you during this time. Make sure you let your agent know the dates you will be unavailable for work. You may find it helpful to refer to Equity's advice leaflet *Low Pay/No Pay* which is available to all Equity members from their website's members' area.

You may be required to not just perform but help out with any odd jobs involved with your show, such as setting up the stage and handing out flyers. If you are considering taking your own show to a festival, you will have to think well in advance about entrance fees, choosing and hiring a suitable venue, publicising your show, casting if necessary,

finding technicians, buying or hiring props, costumes, sets, and so on. You must weigh up the financial outlays and potential headaches with learning and networking opportunities that come with being involved in festivals.

How can I get involved?

If you are a performer at a festival, casting professionals could be there looking for you! Let them know that you will be performing and where and when. Send them a covering letter giving details and enclose your CV and headshot if you have not already done so in previous correspondence. You could do the same with agents if you are currently searching for new representation.

Spotlight members performing at the Edinburgh Festival Fringe can access a number of free services including a Spotlight VIP area, a series of career advice seminars, one-to-one advice sessions with a Spotlight expert and free Wi-Fi. For full information or to book tickets for seminars please visit www.edfringe.com from June onwards and enter 'Spotlight' in the show/performer field. For full information or to book a one-to-one session please visit www.spotlight.com/artists/booking/EdinburghFestival2012

Most festivals have websites which you can browse for further information on what to expect and how to get involved. Even if you simply go as a spectator to a festival, you will learn a lot and will have the opportunity to network. If you are performing in or organising a show, make sure you know exactly what you are letting yourself in for and make the most of your time there!

Festivals

West End LIVE 2011 was co-presented by Westminster City Council and the Society of London Theatre in association with MasterCard. The festival took place in Trafalgar Square on 18 & 19 June and featured over 40 acts live on stage as well as a variety of interactive activities promoted by many of London's most famous galleries, museums and cultural institutions. 550,000 people descended on Trafalgar Square over the course of the festival weekend.

As the sun comes down on another West End LIVE campaign, I am convinced that festivals are of greater significance than ever before.

Regardless of the size and scope of a festival and whether for commercial gain, community or social enhancement, there are a multitude of benefits that justify the existence of the festival – especially in the current economic climate.

Revisiting the many invoices, contracts, spreadsheets, participation forms and numerous emails involved with my latest venture, I am reminded of the extensive partnerships that are established between trades, organisations, suppliers and participants that are crucial to bringing a festival to life.

And this is what I feel is so magical about the festival environment – the level of interaction that is required to take an initial concept through to reality; a commitment to ensure that every performer or member of the audience leaves having enjoyed a positive experience.

As an Event Director, I feel that the key aspect to organising a festival is passion.

This may sound overly romantic and perhaps slightly naïve – I'm sure many will argue that factors such as budget, content, suppliers, marketing and production all carry greater significance. Whilst I absolutely recognise the necessity of all these aspects, passion is the driving force that ensures things get done, that motivates when times are hard and which provides inspiration at the most random of moments.

In addition to passion, it is essential that you fully understand the festival or event that you wish to organise or are working on – ethos, purpose, motivations and the many audience considerations.

Too often, people embark on organising a festival without addressing these issues and come unstuck. Clichéd as it sounds, knowledge is power and serves as a crucial tool in establishing your event as an attractive proposition to all – suppliers, financiers, performers and of course your audience.

Once the passion and knowledge are ingrained and allied with the necessary finances, suppliers and support network (priceless by the way) then the fun can begin. Organising a festival is incredibly rewarding and allows scope to explore numerous avenues of creativity.

The festival prides itself on offering a unique platform for fresh, undiscovered talent to perform to a vast audience.

The ethos of West End LIVE is to showcase the diversity and quality of entertainment on offer throughout London's West End, allowing me a wide berth when it comes to scheduling the performances at the festival.

Whilst the performances from the West End Musicals are undoubtedly the main attraction of the event 25 performed across the weekend in 2011 - the festival also prides itself on offering a unique platform for fresh, undiscovered talent to perform to a vast audience.

This year we were thrilled to welcome live performances from bands, vocalists, choirs, dance troupes and stage schools to the main stage.

Each year we receive numerous applications from prospective performers, or for work experience from students, graduates and theatre-lovers highlighting the ever-increasing popularity of the event. The selection process for talent and volunteers is quite fluid – there are no strict guidelines – however those who approach in a professional and informed manner are always likely to be more successful. In addition, it makes my job a great deal easier if candidates are able to demonstrate (yes, you've guessed it) a passion for their vocation that substantiates their talent.

Please visit www.westendlive.co.uk for further information.

Festivals

Simon Ginty

Simon recently graduated from the University of Edinburgh with an MA Hons (2:1) in Russian Studies and English Literature. At NSDF 2011 he won the Spotlight Award for Most Promising Actor.

Photo: Faye Thomas

During my four years as a student and aspiring actor in Edinburgh – at a university with a great reputation for theatre (despite offering no drama course) and in the host city of the Edinburgh Festival Fringe – I found that despite the huge interest in the performing arts and the vibrant theatre scene, it was often hard to interpret the mythology that surrounded acting at an industry level. One of the valuable things that NSDF offers is a forum for those in need of real advice from those that know and work in the industry. Workshops or Q&As are held by professionals of all kinds, about all related roles. One finally has the opportunity to put human faces to the gloomy statistics and second-hand horror-stories of the professional sphere. Everyone at the NSDF is there to engage and to help; one could be talking to the casting director of the RSC in the morning, and they could in turn be watching your show in the evening.

This is good enough reason to go, perhaps, but I think the heart of the festival lies beyond this, in performances themselves, and in the companies that bring them. The plays chosen from all over the UK are of a very high standard (in my experience, some are truly great), the crews take real pride in themselves and in each other, and everybody cares – never has it been more fun to watch a play and to talk about it – the collaborative spirit that theatre seems always to provide is multiplied tenfold. This atmosphere is perfect for exploration into new performance modes and possibilities, which many companies take advantage of, and hopefully many more will do so.

Everyone at NSDF is there to engage and to help; one could be talking to the casting director of the RSC in the morning, and they could in turn be watching your show in the evening.

For me, the joy of the festival is in the perfect junction between learning the serious and scary business of just what it is to pursue a career in this industry, and always remembering the reason why we do it.

Elizabeth Bourne

Elizabeth recently graduated from the University of Edinburgh with an MSc in Creative Writing and has also achieved a BA Hons (2:1) in English from the University of Nottingham. At NSDF 2011 she won the Spotlight Award for Most Promising Actress.

Photo: Mihaela Bodlovic

Every actor claims to have a Eureka moment, when they decided acting was 'it': I don't have one. I started performing when I first saw a youth musical and uninhibitedly thought, I'm going to do that - but it's taken me time to acknowledge the significance of my passion because academic studies have always appeared to be my focus. Friends wondered why I rushed off to youth theatre for dozens of plays during my school years. My course-mates question my dedication to both Nottingham University's New Theatre and Edinburgh's Bedlam, blanching at how I manage to get any academic work done. I used to dismiss their worries about my 'acting bug'. But gradually, I've begun to look the unreliable, challenging world of acting in the face, and it's clear that the answer has been there all along.

Participating in NSDF gave me good friends whilst showing me that acting could be much more than extra-curricular. It gave me self-belief.

My first visit to NSDF was with Nottingham's New Theatre in 2008, when I played Claire in 'Proof' by David Auburn. Winning an Acting Commendation and participating in the NSDF Ensemble 2008 gave me good friends whilst showing me, after I'd finally chosen to listen, that acting could be much more than extra-curricular. It gave me self-belief. Student-lead work over the next few years fuelled my resolve, and I've been fortunate enough to meet inspirational friends at both my universities, with whom I share the passionate desire to create and execute performances to the very best of our abilities. NSDF 2011 secured my conviction to act by handing me more opportunities to learn from both professionals in workshops and my talented peer performers in other shows. It showed me that my acting is worth something, and that's it's braver and better to opt for the passion I've constantly been inexorably drawn to, than to get a job I don't like.

My academic studies have nurtured my fascination with literature and creative writing – but even as I put pen to paper to write prose, a play emerges, and what's more I usually want to perform in it. So I guess that's it, then. I do have that acting bug after all.

24:7 THEATRE FESTIVAL T 0845 4084101
Early July 2012
PO Box 247, Manchester M60 2ZT
E info@247theatrefestival.co.uk
W www.247theatrefestival.co.uk

**ALDEBURGH FESTIVAL OF
MUSIC AND THE ARTS** T 01728 687100
8-24 June 2012
Aldeburgh Music
Snape Maltings Concert Hall, Snape Bridge
Nr Saxmundham, Suffolk IP17 1SP
BO 01728 687110
E enquiries@aldeburgh.co.uk
W www.aldeburgh.co.uk

**BARBICAN INTERNATIONAL
THEATRE EVENT (BITE)** T 020 7628 3351
Year-Round Festival
Barbican Theatre
Silk Street, London EC2Y 8DS
F 020 7382 7377
E theatre@barbican.org.uk
W www.barbican.org.uk

**BATH INTERNATIONAL
MUSIC FESTIVAL** T 01225 462231
30 May-10 June 2012
Bath Festivals, Abbey Chambers
Kingston Buildings, Bath BA1 1NT
BO 01225 463362
E info@bathfestivals.org.uk
W www.bathmusicfest.org.uk

BATH LITERATURE FESTIVAL T 01225 462231
2-11 March 2012
Bath Festivals, Abbey Chambers
Kingston Buildings, Bath BA1 1NT
BO 01225 463362
E info@bathfestivals.org.uk
W www.bathlitfest.org.uk

**BRIGHTON DOME &
FESTIVAL LTD** T 01273 700747
*5-26 May 2012 (Provisional). Contact: Andrew Comben
(Chief Executive)*
12A Pavilion Buildings, Castle Square, Brighton BN1 1EE
BO 01273 709709
E info@brightonfestival.org
W www.brightonfestival.org

BUXTON FESTIVAL T 01298 70395
7-25 July 2012
3 The Square, Buxton, Derbyshire SK17 6AZ
BO 0845 1272190
E info@buxtonfestival.co.uk
W www.buxtonfestival.co.uk

**CHESTER SUMMER
MUSIC FESTIVAL** T 01244 405631
*End June - Mid July 2012. Contact: Kate Sawallisch
(Festival Manager)*
Chester Festivals Ltd, Chester Railway Station
1st Floor, West Wing Offices
Station Road, Chester CH1 3NT
BO 0845 2417868
E k.sawallisch@chesterfestivals.co.uk
W www.chesterfestivals.co.uk/site/music

**CHICHESTER FESTIVITIES
(Not Chichester Festival Theatre)** T 01243 785718
29 June - 15 July 2012 (Provisional)
Canon Gate House, South Street
Chichester, West Sussex PO19 1PU
F 01243 528356
E info@chifest.org.uk
W www.chifest.org.uk

DANCE UMBRELLA T 020 7407 1200
*1-29 October 2012. Dance Umbrella brings brave new
dance to London as part of its leading international
dance festival*
1 Brewery Square, London SE1 2LF
F 020 7378 8405
E mail@danceumbrella.co.uk
W www.danceumbrella.co.uk

EDINBURGH FESTIVAL FRINGE T 0131 226 0026
3-27 August 2012
Festival Fringe Society Ltd
180 High Street, Edinburgh EH1 1QS
BO 0131 226 0000
E admin@edfringe.com W www.edfringe.com

**EDINBURGH INTERNATIONAL
FESTIVAL** BO 0131 473 2000
10 August-2 September 2012
The Hub, Castlehill, Edinburgh EH1 2NE
E boxoffice@eif.co.uk W www.eif.co.uk

**HARROGATE INTERNATIONAL
FESTIVAL** T 01423 562303
July 2012
Raglan House, Raglan Street
Harrogate, North Yorkshire HG1 1LE
F 01423 521264
E info@harrogate-festival.org.uk
W www.harrogate-festival.org.uk

HENLEY FRINGE TRUST THE T 07742 059762
16-21 July 2012
Aston Farm House, Remenham Lane
Henley on Thames, Oxon RG9 3DE
E info@henleyfringe.org
W www.henleyfringe.org

KING'S LYNN FESTIVAL   T 01553 767557
15-28 July 2012
5 Thoresby College, Queen Street
King's Lynn, Norfolk PE30 1HX
F 01553 767688
W www.kingslynnfestival.org.uk

LIFT   T 020 7093 6340
11 June-8 July 2012. Biennial Festival
Trinity Buoy Wharf, 60 Orchard Place, London E14 0JW
F 020 7093 1304
E kate@liftfestival.com
W www.liftfestival.com

**LLANDOVERY THEATRE
ARTS FESTIVAL**   T 07814 121827
Autumn 2012. Director: Jaqueline Harrison
Llandovery Theatre, Stone Street
Llandovery, Carmarthenshire SA20 0DQ
W www.llandoverytheatre.com

**LUDLOW FESTIVAL
SOCIETY LTD**   T 01584 875070
25 June-10 July 2012
Festival Office, Castle Square, Ludlow, Shropshire SY8 1AY
BO 01584 872150
E admin@ludlowfestival.co.uk
W www.ludlowfestival.co.uk

MOVE IT 2012   T 020 7288 6463
9-11 March 2012
Olympia Exhibition Centre
Warwick Road, London SW5 9TA
E info@moveitdance.co.uk
W www.moveitdance.co.uk

PERFORM 2012   T 020 7288 6463
9-11 March 2012
Olympia Exhibition Centre
Warwick Road, London SW5 9TA
E info@performshow.co.uk
W www.performshow.co.uk

**SUNDAY TIMES NATIONAL STUDENT DRAMA
FESTIVAL THE**   T 020 7036 9027
22-30 June 2012. Scarborough
Contact: Holly Kendrick (Director)
Woolyard, 54 Bermondsey Street, London SE1 3UD
E info@nsdf.org.uk
W www.nsdf.org.uk

**ULSTER BANK BELFAST
FESTIVAL AT QUEEN'S**   T 028 9097 1034
14-31 October 2012
8 Fitzwilliam Street, Belfast BT9 6AW
BO 028 9097 1197
E festivalservice@qub.ac.uk
W www.belfastfestival.com

**ULSTER BANK DUBLIN
THEATRE FESTIVAL**   T 00 353 1 6778439
29 September-16 October 2012. Contact: Shauna Lyons
44 East Essex Street, Temple Bar, Dublin 2, Ireland
F 00 353 1 6797709
E marketing@dublintheatrefestival.com
W www.dublintheatrefestival.com

WEST END LIVE   T 020 7641 3297
End June 2012 (Provisional)
E westendlive@westminster.gov.uk
W www.westendlive.co.uk

**WINCHESTER HAT FAIR,
FESTIVAL OF STREET THEATRE**   T 01962 849841
6-8 July 2012
5A Jewry Street, Winchester, Hampshire SO23 8RZ
E info@hatfair.co.uk
W www.hatfair.co.uk

NSDF presents
the International
Student Drama Festival
22nd – 30th June 2012
THE SUNDAY TIMES

Photo by Allan Titmuss

*The NSDF is essential, I was
inspired by the drive, idealism and
commitment of the students
and leaders.*
(Christopher Eccleston, Visiting Artist NSDF10)

The National Student Drama Festival is a week-long celebration of theatre and live performance. To celebrate the Olympic year the NSDF, in association with Sheffield Theatres, University of Sheffield and Sheffield Hallam University will present a one-off nine-day International Student Drama Festival (NSDF12 – ISDF) with the most exceptional shows created from young people from around the world alongside workshops from 200 exceptional international professionals, working in collaboration with RSC, LIFT, Old Vic Tunnels and Menier Chocolate Factory amongst others. You can book a ticket for 1, 3, 6 or 9 days at the Festival, where there will be at least 2 shows, 2 workshops and much more every day. Highlights of NSDF11 Workshop and Technical Training Programme included: Richard Wilson, Paul McGann, Janet Suzman, Iain Canning, Thelma Holt, Mannie Manim, RSC, National Theatre Studio, National Theatre of Scotland, Paines Plough, Soho Theatre, Bristol Old Vic Theatre and many more. NSDF12 – ISDF is the only place to be if you are a student who wants to get involved with drama and the creative industries. NSDF12 – ISDF takes place in Sheffield 22nd – 30th June 2012 and is open to any student aged sixteen and over and up to a year after graduating.

To book a ticket for NSDF12 or enter a
production contact:

Holly Kendrick, NSDF Director

T: 020 7036 9027
holly@nsdf.org.uk   www.ideastap.com/nsdf

ACTOR'S ONE-STOP SHOP THE   T 020 8888 7006
Showreels for Performing Artists
1st Floor, Above The Gate Pub
Station Road, London N22 7SS
E info@actorsonestopshop.com
W www.actorsonestopshop.com

ALBANY THE   T 020 8692 4446
Douglas Way, London SE8 4AG
F 020 8469 2253
E hires@thealbany.org.uk
W www.thealbany.org.uk

ANVIL POST PRODUCTION   T 020 8799 0555
Contact: Mike Anscombe (Studio Manager)
Perivale Park, Horsenden Lane South
Perivale UB6 7RL
E mike.anscombe@technicolor.com
W www.technicolor.com

ARRI MEDIA   T 01895 457100
3 Highbridge, Oxford Road
Uxbridge, Middlesex UB8 1LX
F 01895 457101
E info@arrimedia.com
W www.arrimedia.com

CENTRAL FILM FACILITIES   T 01694 771544
Film Unit Drivers & Transport
c/o Myddle Cottage, Plaish
Church Stretton, Shropshire SY6 7HX
T 07966 421878
E mansell323@btinternet.com
W www.centralfilmfacilities.com

CENTRELINE VIDEO LTD   T 0118 941 0033
138 Westwood Road, Tilehurst
Reading RG31 6LL
W www.centrelinevideo.co.uk

CHANNEL 2020 LTD   T 0844 8402020
2020 House, 26-28 Talbot Lane
Leicester LE1 4LR
F 0116 222 1113
E info@channel2020.co.uk
W www.channel2020.co.uk

CHANNEL 2020 LTD   T 0844 8402020
The Clerkenwell Workshops
27/31 Clerkenwell Close
London EC1R 0AT
E info@channel2020.co.uk
W www.channel2020.co.uk

CLICKS MEDIA STUDIOS   T 01634 723838
Contact: Peter Snell
Amp House, Grove Road
Rochester, Kent ME2 4BX
E info@clicksmediastudios.com
W www.clicksmediastudios.com

CRYSTAL MEDIA   T 0131 240 0988
28 Castle Street, Edinburgh EH2 3HT
F 0131 240 0989
E hello@crystal-media.co.uk
W www.crystal-media.co.uk

DE LANE LEA   T 020 7432 3800
Film & TV Sound Dubbing & Editing Suite
75 Dean Street, London W1D 3PU
F 020 7494 3755
E solutions@delanelea.com
W www.delanelea.com

DELUXE 142   T 020 7878 0000
Post-Production Facilities
Film House, 142 Wardour Street
London W1F 8DD
F 020 7878 7800
W www.deluxe142.co.uk

DENMAN PRODUCTIONS   T 020 8891 3461
*3D Computer Animation. Film/Video CD Business Card
Showreels*
60 Mallard Place, Strawberry Vale
Twickenham TW1 4SR
E info@denman.co.uk
W www.denman.co.uk

DIVERSE PRODUCTION LTD   T 020 7603 4567
Pre & Post-Production
Network House, 1 Ariel Way
London W12 7SL
F 020 3189 3200
E reception@diverse.tv
W www.diverse.tv

EXECUTIVE AUDIO VISUAL   T 020 7723 4488
DVD Editing & Duplication Service. Photography Services
E chris.jarvis60@gmail.com

FROME SILK MILL STUDIOS   T 01373 473246
Westbrook House, 33 Vicarage Street
Frome BA11 1PU
T 07811 440584
E silkmillstudios@macace.net

GREENPARK PRODUCTIONS LTD   T 01566 782217
Film & Video Archives
Illand, Launceston
Cornwall PL15 7LS
F 01566 782127
E info@greenparkimages.co.uk
W www.greenparkimages.co.uk

HARLEQUIN PRODUCTIONS   T 020 8653 2333
Suite 5, Woodville Court
31 Sylvan Road
London SE19 2SG
E neill@harlequinproductions.co.uk
W www.harlequinproductions.co.uk

HARVEY HOUSE FILMS LTD   T 07968 830536
Animation. Full Pre/Post Production. Graphics. Showreels
71 Southfield Road, London W4 1BB
E chris@harveyhousefilms.co.uk
W www.harveyhousefilms.co.uk

HIREACAMERA.COM   T 01435 873028
Equipment Hire. Video & Photography. Accessories. Lenses
Unit 5, Wellbrook Farm
Berkeley Road, Mayfield
East Sussex TN20 6EH
F 01435 874841
E info@hireacamera.com
W www.hireacamera.com

HUNKY DORY PRODUCTIONS LTD   T 020 8440 0820
Crew. Facilities. Also Editing: Non-Linear
57 Alan Drive, Barnet
Herts EN5 2PW
T 07973 655510
E adrian@hunkydory.tv
W www.hunkydory.tv

**MPC (THE MOVING
PICTURE COMPANY)**   T 020 7434 3100
Post-Production
127 Wardour Street, London W1F 0NL
F 020 7287 5187
E mailbox@moving-picture.com
W www.moving-picture.com

OCEAN OPTICS   T 01268 523786
Underwater Camera Sales & Operator Rental
Archer Fields, Burnt Mills Industrial Estate
Basildon, Essex SS13 1DL
F 01268 523795
E optics@oceanoptics.co.uk
W www.oceanoptics.co.uk

ONSIGHT LTD   T 020 7637 0888
Film Equipment Rental
Shepperton Studios, Studios Road, Middlesex TW17 0QD
F 01932 592246
E axisfilms@onsight.co.uk
W www.onsight.co.uk

PANAVISION UK   T 020 8839 7333
The Metropolitan Centre, Bristol Road
Greenford, Middlesex UB6 8GD
F 020 8839 7300
W www.panavision.co.uk

PLACE THE   T 020 7121 1000
17 Duke's Road, London WC1H 9BY
F 020 7121 1142
E info@theplace.org.uk
W www.theplace.org.uk

PRO-LINK RADIO SYSTEMS LTD   T 01527 577788
Radio Microphones & Communications
5, B Block, Saxon Business Park
Hanbury Road, Bromsgrove, Worcestershire B60 4AD
F 01527 577757
E service@prolink-radio.com
W www.prolink-radio.com

RICH TV LTD   T 0161 975 6207
Houldsworth Mill, Houldsworth Street
Reddish, Stockport, Cheshire SK5 6DA
E sales@richtv.co.uk
W www.richtv.co.uk

SALON LTD   T 020 8746 7611
Editing Equipment Hire. Post-Production
12 Swainson Road, London W3 7XB
E hire@salonrentals.com
W www.salonrentals.com

SOUNDHOUSE THE   T 0161 832 7299
Unit 1, The Sharp Project
Manchester M40 5BJ
F 0161 832 7266
E mike@thesoundhouse.com
W www.thesoundhouse.tv

TEN80MEDIA   T 07814 406251
Studio: 517 Foleshill Road
Coventry, West Midlands CV6 5AU
E info@ten80media.com
W www.ten80media.com

VIDEO INN PRODUCTION   T 01604 864868
AV Equipment Hire
Glebe Farm, Wooton Road
Quinton, Northampton NN7 2EE
E post@videoinn.co.uk
W www.videoinn.co.uk

**VSI - VOICE & SCRIPT
INTERNATIONAL**   T 020 7692 7700
*Dubbing. DVD Encoding & Authoring Facilities. Editing.
Subtitling. Voice Overs*
132 Cleveland Street
London W1T 6AB
F 020 7692 7711
E info@vsi.tv
W www.vsi.tv

W6 STUDIO   T 020 7385 2272
*Editing Facilities. Music Videos. Photography. Showreels.
Video Production*
359 Lillie Road
Fulham, London SW6 7PA
T 07836 357629
E kazkam@w6studio.fsnet.co.uk
W www.w6studio.co.uk

30 BIRD PRODUCTIONS   T 07970 960995
17 Emery Street, Cambridge CB1 2AX
E info@30birdproductions.org
W www.30birdproductions.org

303 PRODUCTIONS   T 020 7494 0955
11 D'Arblay Street, London W1T 8DT
F 020 7434 1955
E henry@303productions.co.uk

1066 PRODUCTIONS   T 020 7193 6156
8 Blackstone House, Off Bowen Drive
West Dulwich, London SE21 8NY
E admin@1066productions.com
W www.1066productions.com

ACADEMY   T 020 7395 4155
16 West Central Street, London WC1A 1JJ
F 020 7240 0355
E post@academyfilms.com
W www.academyfilms.com

AGILE FILMS   T 020 7000 2882
Unit 1, 68-72 Redchurch Street
London E2 7DP
E info@agilefilms.com
W www.agilefilms.com

AN ACQUIRED TASTE TV CORP   T 020 8686 1188
51 Croham Road, South Croydon CR2 7HD
F 020 8686 5928
E cbennetttv@aol.com

ARIEL PRODUCTIONS LTD
Contact: By Post
46 Melcombe Regis Court, 59 Weymouth Street
London W1G 8NT

ASF PRODUCTIONS LTD   T 07770 277637
Contact: Alan Spencer, Malcolm Bubb. Commercials.
Corporate Videos. Documentaries. Feature Films. Films
38 Clunbury Court, Manor Street
Berkhamsted, Herts HP4 2FF
E info@asfproductions.co.uk

**ASHFORD ENTERTAINMENT
CORPORATION LTD THE**   T 020 8660 9609
Contact: Frazer Ashford. By e-mail. Documentaries. Drama.
Feature Films. Films. Television
20 The Chase, Coulsdon, Surrey CR5 2EG
E info@ashford-entertainment.co.uk
W www.ashford-entertainment.co.uk

ASSOCIATED PRESS   T 020 7482 7400
The Interchange, Oval Road
Camden Lock, London NW1 7DZ
F 020 7413 8312

AVALON TELEVISION LTD   T 020 7598 8000
4A Exmoor Street, London W10 6BD
F 020 7598 7313

BAILEY, Catherine LTD   T 020 7483 3330
110 Gloucester Avenue, Primrose Hill
London NW1 8JA
W www.cbltd.net

BANANA PARK LTD   T 020 7228 7136
Animation Production Company
Banana Park, 6 Cranleigh Mews
London SW11 2QL
F 020 7738 1887
E studio@bananapark.co.uk
W www.bananapark.co.uk

BARFORD PRODUCTIONS   T 020 7324 1466
206-212 St John Street, Clerkenwell
London EC1V 4JY
E info@barford.co.uk
W www.barford.co.uk

BBC WORLDWIDE LTD   T 020 8433 2000
Media Centre, Media Village
201 Wood Lane W12 7TQ
W www.bbcworldwide.com

BLACKBIRD PRODUCTIONS   T 020 7924 6440
6 Molasses Row, Plantation Wharf
Battersea, London SW11 3UX
E enquiries@blackbirdproductions.co.uk

BLUE FISH MEDIA
E ideas@bfmedia.co.uk
W www.bfmedia.co.uk

BRUNSWICK FILMS LTD   T 020 8960 0066
Formula One Motor Racing Archive
26 Macroom Road, Maida Vale
London W9 3HY
F 020 8960 4997
E info@brunswickfilms.com
W www.brunswickfilms.com

BRYANT WHITTLE LTD   T 020 8311 8752
49 Federation Road, Abbey Wood
London SE2 0JT
E amanda@bryantwhittle.com
W www.bryantwhittle.com

BURDER FILMS   T 01202 295395
37 Braidley Road, Meyrick Park
Bournemouth BH2 6JY
E burderfilms@aol.com
W www.johnburder.co.uk

CALDERDALE TELEVISION   T 01484 432389
12 South Avenue, Fartown
Huddersfield HD2 1BY
E ctv@calderdaletv.co.uk

CARDINAL BROADCAST   T 01753 639210
Room 114, N&P Building, Pinewood Studios
Iver Heath, Bucks SL0 0NH
W www.cardinalbroadcast.com

**CENTRAL OFFICE OF
INFORMATION**   T 020 7261 8220
Moving Image
Hercules House, Hercules Road
London SE1 7DU
F 020 7261 8776
E eileen.newton@coi.gsi.gov.uk
W www.coi.gov.uk

CENTRE SCREEN PRODUCTIONS   T 0161 832 7151
Eastgate, Castle Street
Castlefield, Manchester M3 4LZ
F 0161 832 8934
E info@centrescreen.co.uk
W www.centrescreen.co.uk

CHANNEL 2020 LTD   T 0844 8402020
2020 House, 26-28 Talbot Lane
Leicester LE1 4LR
F 0116 222 1113
E info@channel2020.co.uk
W www.channel2020.co.uk

**CHANNEL TELEVISION
PRODUCTION**   T 01534 816816
The Television Centre, La Pouquelaye
St Helier, Jersey JE1 3ZD
F 01534 816817
E production@channeltv.co.uk
W www.channelonline.tv

CHANNEL X LTD   T 0845 9002940
4 Candover Street, London W1W 7DJ
F 020 7580 8016
E gary.matsell@channelx.co.uk
W www.channelx.co.uk

CHILDREN'S FILM & TELEVISION FOUNDATION LTD   T 07887 573479
E annahome@cftf.org.uk

CINEMANX LTD   T 020 7637 2612
3rd Floor, 12 Great Portland Street, London W1W 8QN
F 020 7636 5481

CLASSIC MEDIA   T 01932 561316
Bence Cottage, The Bence
Rosemary Lane, Thorpe TW20 8QD
F 01932 563207
E robert.garofalo@classic-media-group.com

CLASSIC MEDIA   T 020 8762 6200
3rd Floor, Royalty House
72-74 Dean Street, London W1D 3SG
F 020 8762 6299
E enquiries@classicmedia.tv
W www.classicmedia.tv

CLAW FILMS LTD   T 020 7470 8809
11-15 Betterton Street, London WC2H 9BP
F 020 7470 8810
E info@clawfilms.com
W www.clawfilms.com

CLEVER BOY MEDIA LTD   T 01753 650951
Pinewood Film Studios, Pinewood Road
Iver Heath, Bucks SL0 0NH
E tim@cleverboymedia.com
W www.cleverboymedia.com

COLLINGWOOD O'HARE PRODUCTIONS LTD   T 020 8993 3666
10-14 Crown Street, Acton, London W3 8SB
F 020 8993 9595
E info@crownstreet.co.uk
W www.collingwoodohare.com

COMMERCIAL BREAKS   T 0844 8816789
Anglia House, Norwich NR1 3JG
F 0844 8816790
E commercialbreaks@itv.com
W www.commercialbreaks.co.uk

COMMUNICATOR LTD   T 020 7700 0777
Omnibus Business Centre
39-41 North Road
London N7 9DP
E info@communicator.ltd.uk

COMPLETE WORKS CREATIVE COMPANY LTD THE   T 020 7377 0280
The Old Truman Brewery
91 Brick Lane
London E1 6QL
F 020 7247 7405
E film@tcw.org.uk
W www.tcw.org.uk

COMTEC LTD   T 0844 8805238
Tandridge Court Farm, Tandridge Lane
Oxted, Surrey RH8 9NJ
F 0844 8805239
E info@comtecav.co.uk
W www.comtecav.co.uk

COURTYARD PRODUCTIONS   T 01732 700324
TV Production Company
Little Postlings Farmhouse
Four Elms, Kent TN8 6NA
E courtyard@mac.com

CPL PRODUCTIONS LTD   T 020 7240 8101
38 Long Acre, London WC2E 9JT
F 020 7836 9633
E info@cplproductions.co.uk
W www.cplproductions.co.uk

CREATIVE PARTNERSHIP THE   T 020 7439 7762
13 Bateman Street, London W1D 3AF
F 020 7437 1467
W www.creativepartnership.co.uk

CROFT TELEVISION   T 01628 668735
Contact: Nick Devonshire. By e-mail. Commercials.
Corporate Videos. Live Events
Croft House, Progress Business Centre
Whittle Parkway
Slough, Berkshire SL1 6DQ
F 01628 668791
E nick@croft-tv.com
W www.croft-tv.com

CROSSROADS FILMS   T 020 7395 4848
2nd Floor, 83 Long Acre
London WC2E 9NG
F 020 7395 4849
E info@crossroadsfilms.co.uk
W www.crossroadsfilms.co.uk

CUPSOGUE PICTURES   T 020 3411 2058
40 Hayway, Irthlingborough
Wellingborough NN9 5QP
E enquiries@cupsoguepictures.com
W www.cupsoguepictures.com

CUTHBERT, Tony
PRODUCTIONS   T 020 7836 3432
Suite 14, 7 Dials Court
3 Shorts Gardens, London WC2H 9AT
E tonycuthbert@btconnect.com
W www.tonycuthbert.com

DALTON FILMS LTD   T 020 7328 6169
127 Hamilton Terrace, London NW8 9QR
E robindalton1@gmail.com

DANCETIME LTD   T/F 020 8742 0507
1 The Orchard, Chiswick
London W4 1JZ
E berry@tabletopproductions.com
W www.tabletopproductions.com

DARLOW SMITHSON
PRODUCTIONS LTD   T 020 7482 7027
1st Floor
Shepherd's Building Central
Charecroft Way
Shepherd's Bush, London W14 0EE
F 020 7482 7039
E mail@darlowsmithson.com
W www.darlowsmithson.com

DELUXE 142   T 020 7878 0000
Film House, 142 Wardour Street
London W1F 8DD
F 020 7878 7800
W www.deluxe142.co.uk

DIALOGICS   T 020 8960 6069
249-251 Kensal Road, London W10 5DB
E dialogue@dialogics.com
W www.dialogics.com

DIDA MEDIA   T 020 7353 4205
89 Fleet Street, London EC4Y 1DH
E info@didamedia.com
W www.didamedia.com

DISNEY, Walt COMPANY THE   T 020 8222 1000
3 Queen Caroline Street, Hammersmith
London W6 9PE
F 020 8222 2795
W www.disney.co.uk

DLT ENTERTAINMENT UK LTD   T 020 7631 1184
10 Bedford Square, London WC1B 3RA
F 020 7636 4571

DRAMATIS PERSONAE LTD   T 020 7834 9300
Contact: Nathan Silver, Nicolas Kent
19 Regency Street, London SW1P 4BY
E ns@nathansilver.com

DREAMING WILL
INITIATIVE THE   T/F 020 7793 9755
PO Box 38155, London SE17 3XP
E londonswo@hotmail.com
W www.lswproductions.co.uk

ECOSSE FILMS LTD   T 020 7371 0290
Brigade House, 8 Parsons Green, London SW6 4TN
F 020 7736 3436
E info@ecossefilms.com
W www.ecossefilms.com

EDGE PICTURE
COMPANY LTD THE   T 020 7836 6262
20-22 Shelton Street, London WC2H 9JJ
F 020 7836 6949
E ask.us@edgepicture.com
W www.edgepicture.com

EFFINGEE PRODUCTIONS LTD   T 0141 443 9301
Contact: Lesley Kiernan. By e-mail. Television
PO Box 7615, Glasgow G42 2FY
E info@effingee.com
W www.effingee.com

ENDEMOL UK PLC   T 0870 3331700
Including Endemol UK Productions, Initial, Brighter Pictures,
Victoria Real, Remarkable & Zeppotron
Shepherds Building Central, Charecroft Way
Shepherd's Bush, London W14 0EE
F 0870 3331800
E info@endemoluk.com
W www.endemoluk.com

ENGINE CREATIVE   T 01604 453177
The Church Rooms, Agnes Road
Northampton, Northants NN2 6EU
E wecancreate@enginecreative.co.uk
W www.enginecreative.co.uk

ENLIGHTENMENT INTERACTIVE   T 01695 727555
East End House, 24 Ennerdale
Skelmersdale WN8 6AJ
W www.trainingmultimedia.co.uk

EON PRODUCTIONS LTD   T 020 7493 7953
Eon House, 138 Piccadilly, London W1J 7NR
F 020 7408 1236

EXTRA DIGIT LTD
10 Wyndham Place, London W1H 2PU
W www.extradigit.com

EYE FILM & TELEVISION   T 0845 6211133
Epic Studios, 112-114 Magdalen Street
Norwich NR3 1JD
E production@eyefilmandtv.co.uk
W www.eyefilmandtv.co.uk

FARNHAM FILM COMPANY THE   T 01252 710313
34 Burnt Hill Road, Lower Bourne, Farnham GU10 3LZ
F 01252 725855
E info@farnfilm.com
W www.farnfilm.com

FEELGOOD FICTION LTD   T 020 8746 2535
49 Goldhawk Road, London W12 8QP
F 020 8740 6177
E feelgood@feelgoodfiction.co.uk
W www.feelgoodfiction.co.uk

FERRIS ENTERTAINMENT FILMS   T 0845 4724725
London. Belfast. Cardiff
Number 8, 132 Charing Cross Road, London WC2H 0LA
E info@ferrisentertainment.com
W www.ferrisentertainment.com

London Academy of Media Film TV

TV Presenter - Acting - Voice - Film - Photography - Make-up - Radio

100 courses Offering an extensive range of full-time, part-time evening and day courses taught by **celebrities and industry professionals.**

www.media-courses.com   0870 62 65 100

FESTIVAL FILM &
TELEVISION LTD   T 020 8297 9999
Festival House, Tranquil Passage
London SE3 0BJ
F 020 8297 1155
E info@festivalfilm.com
W www.festivalfilm.com

FILM & GENERAL
PRODUCTIONS LTD   T 020 7235 4495
Contact: Davina Belling
3 Bradbrook House, Studio Place
London SW1X 8EL

FILMS OF RECORD LTD   T 020 7428 3100
6 Anglers Lane, Kentish Town
London NW5 3DG
F 020 7284 0626
W www.filmsofrecord.com

FIREFLY PRODUCTIONS   T 01725 514462
Twin Oaks, Hale Purlieu
Fordingbridge, Hampshire SP6 2NN
T 07956 675276
E theonlyfirefly@aol.com
W www.fireflyproductions.info

FLASHBACK TELEVISION LTD   T 020 7253 8768
58 Farringdon Road, London EC1R 3BP
F 020 7253 8765
E mailbox@flashbacktv.co.uk
W www.flashbacktelevision.com

FLYING DUCKS GROUP   T 01902 842888
Duck HQ, The Old Mill
The Upper Hattons
Pendeford Hall Lane, Coven WV9 5BD
E enquiries@flyingducks.biz
W www.flyingducks.biz

FOCUS PRODUCTIONS
PUBLICATIONS   T 01789 298948
58 Shelley Road, Stratford-upon-Avon
Warwickshire CV37 7JS
F 01789 294845
E maddern@focuspublishers.co.uk
W www.focusproductions.co.uk

FORSTATER,
Mark PRODUCTIONS   T 07771 665382
11 Keslake Road, London NW6 6DJ
E mforstater@msn.com

FREMANTLEMEDIA
TALKBACKTHAMES   T 020 7691 6000
1 Stephen Street, London W1T 1AL
F 020 7691 6100
W www.freemantlemedia.com

FRICKER, Ian (FILMS) LTD   T 020 7836 3090
146 Strand, London WC2R 1JD
F 020 7836 3078
E mail@ianfricker.com

FUNNY FACE FILMS LTD   T 07415 054442
8A Warwick Road, Hampton Wick
Surrey KT1 4DW
E stevendrew40@hotmail.com

GALA PRODUCTIONS LTD   T 020 8741 4200
25 Stamford Brook Road, London W6 0XJ
F 020 8741 2323
E info@galaproductions.co.uk
W www.galaproductions.co.uk

GALLEON FILMS LTD   T/F 020 8310 7276
Greenwich Playhouse, Station Forecourt
189 Greenwich High Road
London SE10 8JA
E alice@galleontheatre.co.uk
W www.galleonfilms.co.uk

GAY, Noel TELEVISION LTD   T 01344 887507
Orchard Lea, Drift Road
Windsor SL4 4RU
E charles.armitage@virgin.net

GHA GROUP   T 020 7439 8705
33 Newman Street, London W1T 1PY
F 020 7636 4448
E sales@ghagroup.co.uk
W www.ghagroup.co.uk

GLASS PAGE LTD THE   T 0116 249 2199
15 De Montfort Street, Leicester LE1 7GE
F 0116 249 2188
E info@glass-page.com
W www.glass-page.com

GOLDHAWK ESSENTIAL   T 020 7439 7113
Radio Productions
20 Great Chapel Street, London W1F 8FW
F 020 7287 3597
E lucinda@essentialmusic.co.uk

GRANT NAYLOR
PRODUCTIONS LTD   T 01932 592175
David Lean Building, Shepperton Studios
Studios Road, Shepperton
Middlesex TW17 0QD
F 01932 592484

GREAT GUNS LTD   T 020 7692 4444
43-45 Camden Road, London NW1 9LR
F 020 7692 4422
E reception@greatguns.com
W www.greatguns.com

GUERILLA FILMS LTD   T 020 8758 1716
35 Thornbury Road, Isleworth
Middlesex TW7 4LQ
F 020 8758 9364
E david@guerilla-films.com
W www.guerilla-films.com

HAMMERWOOD
FILM PRODUCERS   T 01273 277333
110 Trafalgar Road, Portslade
Sussex BN41 1GS
E filmangels@freenetname.co.uk
W www.filmangel.co.uk

HANDS UP PRODUCTIONS LTD   T 07909 824630
7 Cavendish Vale, Sherwood
Nottingham NG5 4DS
E marcus@handsuppuppets.com
W www.handsuppuppets.com

HARBOUR PICTURES T 020 7287 6289
21-25 St Annes Court, London W1F 0BJ
F 020 7494 4885
E info@harbourpictures.com
W www.harbourpictures.com

HARTSWOOD FILMS T 020 8607 8736
Twickenham Studios, The Barons, St Margaret's
Twickenham, Middlesex TW1 2AW
F 020 8607 8744
W www.hartswoodfilms.co.uk

HEAD, Sally PRODUCTIONS T 020 8607 8730
Twickenham Film Studios, The Barons, St Margaret's
Twickenham, Middlesex TW1 2AW
F 020 8607 8964
E admin@shpl.demon.co.uk

HEAVY ENTERTAINMENT LTD T 020 7494 1000
111 Wardour Street, London W1F 0UH
F 020 7494 1100
E info@heavy-entertainment.com
W www.heavy-entertainment.com

HERMES ENTERTAINMENT INC T 07875 628299
Based in Paris & London
72/6 Grove Lane, Camberwell Green
London SE5 8TW
E moneymodeste@yahoo.com

HIT ENTERTAINMENT LTD T 020 7554 2500
5th Floor, Maple House
149 Tottenham Court Road, London W1T 7NF
F 020 7388 9321
E creative@hitentertainment.com
W www.hitentertainment.com

**HOLMES ASSOCIATES &
OPEN ROAD FILMS** T 020 7813 4333
The Studio, 37 Redington Road
London NW3 7QY
E holmesassociates@blueyonder.co.uk

HUNGRY MAN LTD T 020 7239 4550
1-2 Herbal Hill, London EC1R 5EF
F 020 7239 4589
E ukreception@hungryman.com
W www.hungryman.com

**HUNKY DORY
PRODUCTIONS LTD** T 020 8440 0820
57 Alan Drive, Barnet
Herts EN5 2PW
T 07973 655510
E adrian@hunkydory.tv
W www.hunkydory.tv

HURICA PRODUCTIONS
89 Birchanger Lane, Bishop Stortford CM23 5QF
E huricaproductions@gmail.com
W www.wix.com/hurica/huricaproductions

HURRICANE FILMS LTD T 0151 707 9700
17 Hope Street, Liverpool L1 9BQ
F 0151 707 9149
E info@hurricanefilms.co.uk
W www.hurricanefilms.net

IAMBIC MEDIA LTD T 0117 923 7222
89 Whiteladies Road, Clifton
Bristol BS8 2NT
F 0117 923 8343
E admin@iambic.tv
W www.iambic.tv

ICE PRODUCTIONS LTD T 01926 864800
Warwick Corner, 42 Warwick Road
Kenilworth, Warwickshire CV8 1HE
E admin@ice-productions.com
W www.ice-productions.com

ICON FILMS LTD T 0117 910 2030
3rd Floor College House, 32-36 College Green
Bristol BS1 5SP
F 0117 910 2031
W www.iconfilms.co.uk

IMAGE PRODUCTIONS T 07729 304795
Makes Films with Children for Children
PO Box 133, Bourne
Lincolnshire PE10 1DE
E info@imageproductions.co.uk
W www.imageproductions.co.uk

INFORMATION TRANSFER LLP T 01223 312227
Training Video Packages
Burleigh House, 15 Newmarket Road
Cambridge CB5 8EG
F 01223 310200
W www.informationtransfer.com

JACKSON, Brian FILMS LTD T 020 7402 7543
39-41 Hanover Steps, St George's Fields
Albion Street, London W2 2YG
F 020 7262 5736
W www.brianjacksonfilms.com

J. I. PRODUCTIONS T 07732 476409
90 Hainault Avenue, Giffard Park
Milton Keynes, Bucks MK14 5PE
E jasonimpey@live.com
W www.jasonimpey.co.uk

JMS GROUP LTD THE T 01603 811855
Park Farm Studios, Hethersett
Norwich, Norfolk NR9 3DL
F 01603 812255
E info@jms-group.com
W www.jms-group.com

JUNCTION 15 PRODUCTIONS T 01782 836600
EMMY Award Winners. Corporate. Television
The Burslem School of Art, Queen Street
Stoke-on-Trent, Staffordshire ST6 3EJ
E info@junction15.com
W www.junction15.com

KNOWLES, Dave FILMS LTD T 023 8084 2190
*Contact: Jenny Knowles. Corporate, Training & Project
Documentary Video Productions*
34 Ashleigh Close, Hythe SO45 3QP
E mail@dkfilms.co.uk
W www.dkfilms.co.uk

LANDSEER PRODUCTIONS LTD T 020 7794 2523
27 Arkwright Road, London NW3 6BJ
E ken@landseerproductions.com
W www.landseerfilms.com

**LIGHT AGENCY &
PRODUCTIONS LTD** T 020 8090 0006
*Contact: Lucy Misch. By Post/e-mail/Telephone.
Commercials. Corporate Videos. Documentaries. Music
Videos. Television*
12 Molasses Row, Plantation Wharf
London SW11 3UX
E lucy@lightproductions.tv
W www.lightproductions.tv

LIME PICTURES T 0151 722 9122
Campus Manor, Childwall
Abbey Road, Liverpool L16 0JP
F 0151 722 6839

**MALLINSON TELEVISION
PRODUCTIONS** T 0141 332 0589
Commercials
29 Lynedoch Street, Glasgow G3 6EF
F 0141 332 6190
E shoot@mtp.co.uk

MANIC TV & FILM PRODUCTIONS　T 020 3246 0088
77A Brick Lane, London E1 6QL
F 020 3246 0081
E info@themanicmediagroup.co.uk
W www.manictv.co.uk

MANSFIELD, Mike PRODUCTIONS　T 020 8947 6884
4 Ellerton Road, London SW20 0EP
E mikemantv@aol.com

MANS, Johnny PRODUCTIONS　T 01992 470907
PO Box 196, Hoddesdon, Herts EN10 7WG
T 07974 755997
E johnnymansagent@aol.com
W www.johnnymansproductions.co.uk

MARTIN, William PRODUCTIONS　T 01865 390258
The Studio, Tubney Warren Barns
Tubney, Oxfordshire OX13 5QJ
F 01865 390148
E info@wmproductions.co.uk
W www.wmproductions.co.uk

MAVERICK TELEVISION　T 0121 771 1812
Progress Works, Heath Mill Lane
Birmingham B9 4AL
F 0121 771 1550
E mail@mavericktv.co.uk
W www.mavericktv.co.uk

MAX MEDIA　T 01487 823608
Contact: Martin Franks. Drama. Comedy. Corporate
The Lilacs, West End
Woodhurst, Huntingdon, Cambridge PE28 3BH
F 01487 825299
E martin@therealmaxmedia.com
W www.therealmaxmedia.com

MBP TV　T 01403 741620
Saucelands Barn, Coolham
Horsham, West Sussex RH13 8QG
F 01403 741647
E info@mbptv.com
W www.mbptv.com

McINTYRE, Phil ENTERTAINMENTS　T 020 7291 9001
3rd Floor, 85 Newman Street, London W1T 3EU
F 020 7291 9000
E info@mcintyre-ents.com

MENTORN　T 020 7258 6800
77 Fulham Palace Road, London W6 8JA
F 020 7258 6888
E reception@mentorn.tv

MET FILM PRODUCTION　T 020 8280 9127
Ealing Studios, Ealing Green, London W5 5EP
F 020 8280 9111
E assistant@metfilm.co.uk
W www.metfilm.co.uk

MINAMON FILM　T 020 8674 3957
Contact: Min Clifford. By e-mail/Telephone. Corporate Videos. Documentaries. Drama. Films
117 Downton Avenue, London SW2 3TX
E studio@minamonfilm.co.uk
W www.minamonfilm.co.uk

MINISTRY OF VIDEO　T 020 8369 5956
Contact: Chris, Andy. By e-mail/Telephone. Casting Videos. Children's Entertainment. Commercials. Corporate Videos. Live Events. Live Stage Productions. Music Videos. Showreels
1533 High Road, Whetstone
London N20 9PP
E info@ministryofvideo.co.uk
W www.ministryofvideo.co.uk

MIRA MOTION PICTURES LTD　T 07790 917476
Commercials. Documentaries. Educational/Training. Film. Live Events. Music Videos. Promotional. Based in London & South Wales
20 Vineyard Vale, Valley Road
Saundersfoot SA69 9DA
E miramotionpictures@googlemail.com
W www.miramotionpictures.com

MISTRAL FILMS LTD　T 020 7284 2300
31 Oval Road, London NW1 7EA
F 020 7284 0547
E info@mistralfilm.co.uk

MONITON PICTURES　T 07753 865511
Mercantile Chambers, 2nd Floor
53 Bothwell Street, Glasgow G2 6TS
E andy@monitonpictures.com
W www.monitonpictures.com

MOVE A MOUNTAIN PRODUCTIONS　T 020 8743 3017
5 Ashchurch Park Villas, London W12 9SP
E mail@moveamountain.com
W www.moveamountain.com

MURPHY, Patricia FILMS LTD　T 020 7267 0007
Lock Keepers Cottage, Lyme Street
London NW1 0SF
F 020 7485 0555
E office@patriciamurphy.co.uk

MY SPIRIT PRODUCTIONS LTD　T 01634 323376
Paranormal & Psychic Radio & Television Production
Maidstone TV Studios, Vinters Park
Maidstone ME14 5NZ
E info@myspirittv.com
W www.myspiritradio.com

Height 5 feet 10 inches　(Equity/M.U.)　Photo: Stephen Hough

Peter Durrent

Pianist ~ Accompanist ~ Composer ~ Vocalist
Audition & Rehearsal Pianist ~ Cocktail Pianist

Tel: 01787 373483　Mob: 07810 613 938
tunefuldurrent@gmail.com
or c/o Spotlight

Film, Radio, Television & Video Production Companies

NEAL STREET PRODUCTIONS LTD T 020 7240 8890
1st Floor, 26-28 Neal Street
London WC2H 9QQ
F 020 7240 7099
E post@nealstreetproductions.com
W www.nealstreetproductions.com

NEW MOON TELEVISION T 020 7479 7010
63 Poland Street, London W1F 7NY
F 020 7479 7011
E production@new-moon.co.uk
W www.new-moon.co.uk

NEW PLANET FILMS LTD T 020 8426 1090
PO Box 640, Pinner HA5 9JB
E info@newplanetfilms.com
W www.newplanetfilms.com

NEXUS PRODUCTIONS LTD T 020 7749 7500
*Animation, Mixed Media, Live Action & Interactive
Production for Commercials, Broadcast, Pop Promos & Title
Sequences*
113-114 Shoreditch High Street, London E1 6JN
F 020 7749 7501
E info@nexusproductions.com
W www.nexusproductions.com

NFD PRODUCTIONS LTD T/F 01977 681949
*Contact: By Post/e-mail/Telephone. Children's
Entertainment. Commercials. Corporate Videos. Drama.
Films. Television. Short Films. Showreels*
PO Box 76, Leeds LS25 9AG
T 07966 473455
E info@nfdproductions.com
W www.nfdproductions.com

OMNI PRODUCTIONS LTD T 0117 954 7170
14-16 Wilson Place, Bristol BS2 9HJ
E info@omniproductions.co.uk
W www.omniproductions.co.uk

ON COMMUNICATION/ ONTV OXFORD T 01235 537400
Work across all Media in Business Communications
5 East St Helen Street, Abingdon
Oxford OX14 5EG
F 01235 530581
E info@oncommunication.com
W www.oncommunication.com

ON SCREEN PRODUCTIONS LTD T 01291 636300
Ashbourne House, 33 Bridge Street
Chepstow, Monmouthshire NP16 5GA
F 01291 636301
E action@onscreenproductions.com
W www.onscreenproductions.com

OPEN MIND PRODUCTIONS T 0845 8909192
27 York Road, Teddington
Middlesex TW11 8SL
E production.manager@openmind.co.uk

OPEN SHUTTER PRODUCTIONS LTD T 01753 841309
*Contact: John Bruce. Documentaries. Drama. Films.
Television*
100 Kings Road, Windsor, Berkshire SL4 2AP
T 07753 618875
E openshutterproductions@googlemail.com

OVC MEDIA LTD T 020 7402 9111
*Contact: Eliot M. Cohen. By e-mail. Animation.
Documentaries. Drama. Feature Films. Films. Television*
88 Berkeley Court, Baker Street
London NW1 5ND
F 020 7723 3064
E eliot@ovcmedia.com
W www.ovcmedia.com

P4FILMS T 01242 542760
Film & Video for Television, Commercials. Corporate
Cheltenham Film Studios, Hatherley Lane
Cheltenham, Gloucestershire GL51 6PN
E info@p4films.com
W www.p4films.com

PAPER MOON PRODUCTIONS T/F 01628 829819
Wychwood House
Burchetts Green Lane, Littlewick Green
Maidenhead, Berkshire SL6 3QW
E insight@paper-moon.co.uk

PARADINE, David PRODUCTIONS LTD T 020 7371 3111
The Penthouse, 346 Kensington High Street
London W14 8NS
F 020 7602 0411
E mail@paradine-productions.com

PARK VILLAGE LTD T 020 7387 8077
1 Park Village East, London NW1 7PX
F 020 7388 3051
E info@parkvillage.co.uk

PASSION PICTURES LTD T 020 7323 9933
Animation. Documentary. Television
2nd Floor, 33-34 Rathbone Place, London W1T 1JN
F 020 7323 9030
E info@passion-pictures.com

PATHE PICTURES LTD T 020 7323 5151
4th Floor, 6 Ramillies Place
London W1F 7TY
F 020 7631 3568
W www.pathe.co.uk

PENSIVE PENGUIN PRODUCTIONS T 01204 848333
37 Oldstead Grove, Ferncrest
Bolton, Lancs BL3 4XW
E glenmortimer@btinternet.com
W www.shadowhawkinternational.com/seeingsmokephotos.htm

PICTURE PALACE FILMS LTD T 020 7586 8763
13 Egbert Street, London NW1 8LJ
F 020 7586 9048
E info@picturepalace.com
W www.picturepalace.com

PIER PRODUCTIONS LTD T 01273 691401
8 St Georges Place, Brighton BN1 4GB
E info@pierproductionsltd.co.uk

PINBALL LONDON T 0845 2733893
London N5 2JZ
E info@pinballonline.co.uk
W www.pinballonline.co.uk

PODCAST COMPANY THE T 07956 468344
101 Wardour Street, London W1F 0UG
E info@thepodcastcompany.co.uk
W www.thepodcastcompany.co.uk

PODCAST COMPANY THE T 0844 5041226
3 The Avenue, London N3 2LB
E info@thepodcastcompany.co.uk
W www.thepodcastcompany.co.uk

POSITIVE IMAGE LTD T 01753 842248
25 Victoria Street
Windsor, Berkshire SL4 1HE
F 01753 830878
E theoffice@positiveimage.co.uk

POTBOILER PRODUCTIONS LTD T 020 7734 7372
9 Greek Street, London W1D 4DQ
F 020 7287 5228
E info@potboiler.co.uk
W www.potboiler.co.uk

POZZITIVE TELEVISION LTD T 020 7255 1112
1st Floor, 25 Newman Street
London W1T 1PN
F 020 7255 1116
E pozzitive@pozzitive.co.uk
W www.pozzitive.co.uk

PRETTY CLEVER PICTURES T 01730 817899
Hurst Cottage, Old Buddington Lane
Hollist Lane, Eastbourne, Midhurst
West Sussex GU29 0QN
T 07836 616981
E pcpics@globalnet.co.uk

PRISM ENTERTAINMENT T 020 3463 8630
Television Production & Website Design Company
Euston Tower, 33rd Floor
286 Euston Road, London NW1 3DP
E info@prismdigitalsolutions.com
W www.prismdigitalsolutions.com

PRODUCERS THE T 020 7636 4226
8 Berners Mews, London W1T 3AW
F 020 7636 4099
E info@theproducersfilms.co.uk
W www.theproducersfilms.co.uk

PSA FILMS T 0161 924 0011
52 The Downs, Altrincham WA14 2QJ
F 0161 924 0022
E andy@psafilms.co.uk

PVA MANAGEMENT LTD T 01905 616100
County House, St Marys Street
Worcester WR1 1HB
F 01905 610709
E films@pva.co.uk
W www.pva.co.uk

QUADRILLION T 01628 487522
The Old Barn, Kings Lane
Cookham Dean, Berkshire SL6 9AY
E enqs@quadrillion.tv
W www.quadrillion.tv

READ, Rodney T 020 8891 2875
45 Richmond Road, Twickenham, Middlesex TW1 3AW
T 07956 321550
E rodney_read@blueyonder.co.uk
W www.rodney-read.com

RECORDED PICTURE
COMPANY LTD T 020 7636 2251
24 Hanway Street, London W1T 1UH
F 020 7636 2261
E rpc@recordedpicture.com

RED KITE ANIMATION T 0131 554 0060
89 Giles Street, Edinburgh EH6 6BZ
F 0131 553 6007
E info@redkite-animation.com
W www.redkite-animation.com

RED ROSE CHAIN T 01473 603388
Gippeswyk Hall, Gippeswyk Avenue
Ipswich, Suffolk IP2 9AF
E info@redrosechain.co.uk
W www.redrosechain.co.uk

REDWEATHER PRODUCTIONS T 0117 941 5854
Easton Business Centre, Felix Road
Bristol BS5 0HE
F 0117 941 5851
E production@redweather.co.uk
W www.redweather.co.uk

REEL THING LTD THE T 0844 3576393
20 The Chase, Coulsdon
Surrey CR5 2EG
E info@reelthing.tv
W www.reelthing.tv

REPLAY LTD T 020 7637 0473
Contact: Danny Scollard. Animation. Corporate Videos.
Documentaries. Drama. E-Learning. Live Events.
Script Writing. Web Design
Museum House
25 Museum Street
London WC1A 1JT
E sales@replayfilms.co.uk
W www.replayfilms.co.uk

REUTERS LTD T 020 7250 1122
The Thompson Reuters Building
South Collonade
Canary Wharf, London E14 5EP

REVERE ENTERTAINMENT T 020 7292 8370
91 Berwick Street, London W1F 0NE
F 020 7292 7391

RIVERSIDE TV STUDIOS T 020 8237 1123
Riverside Studios, Crisp Road
London W6 9RL
F 020 8237 1121
E info@riversidetv.co.uk
W www.riversidetv.co.uk

ROEBUCK PRODUCTIONS T 01937 835900
Commer House, Station Road
Tadcaster, North Yorkshire LS24 9JF
F 01937 835901
E john@roebuckproductions.com
W www.roebuckproductions.com

ROOKE, Laurence
PRODUCTIONS T 020 8674 3128
14 Aspinall House, 155 New Park Road
London SW2 4EY
T 07765 652058

RSA FILMS T 020 7437 7426
42-44 Beak Street, London W1F 9RH
F 020 7734 4978
W www.rsafilms.com

SANDS FILMS T 020 7231 2209
82 St Marychurch Street
London SE16 4HZ
F 020 7231 2119
E info@sandsfilms.co.uk
W www.sandsfilms.co.uk

SCALA PRODUCTIONS LTD T 020 7637 5720
2nd Floor, 37 Foley Street
London W1W 7TN
E scalaprods@aol.com

SCIMITAR FILMS LTD   T 020 7734 8385
219 Kensington High Street, London W8 6BD
F 020 7602 9217
E winner@ftech.co.uk

SCREEN FIRST LTD   T 01248 716973
Cil-y-Coed, Llansadwrn
Mensai Bridge LL59 5SE
E paul.madden@virgin.net

SEPTEMBER FILMS LTD   T 020 8563 9393
Glen House, 22 Glenthorne Road
Hammersmith, London W6 0NG
F 020 8741 7214
E september@septemberfilms.com

SEVENTH ART PRODUCTIONS   T 01273 777678
63 Ship Street, Brighton BN1 1AE
F 01273 323777
E info@seventh-art.com
W www.seventh-art.com

SHED PRODUCTIONS   T 020 7239 1010
85 Gray's Inn Road, London WC1X 8TX
F 020 7239 1011
E mail@walltowall.co.uk
W www.shedproductions.com

SHELL FILM & VIDEO UNIT   T 020 7934 3318
Shell Centre, York Road, London SE1 7NA
E jane.poynor@shell.com

SIGHTLINE   T 01483 813311
Videos for the Web. DVDs. E-Learning. Interactive
CD-ROM. Promotion. Touch Screens. Training. Websites.
Based in Guildford
F 01483 813317
E keith@sightline.co.uk
W www.sightline.co.uk

SILK SOUND   T 020 7434 3461
Commercials. Corporate Videos. Documentaries
13 Berwick Street, London W1F 0PW
F 020 7494 1748
E bookings@silk.co.uk
W www.silk.co.uk

SINDIBAD FILMS LTD   T 020 7259 2707
Tower House, 226 Cromwell Road
London SW5 0SW
E info@sindibad.co.uk
W www.sindibad.co.uk

SITCOM SOLDIERS LTD   T 07712 669097
Windy Yetts, Windy Harbour Lane
Bromley Cross, Bolton BL7 9AP
E info@sitcomsoldiers.com
W www.sitcomsoldiers.com

SMITH & WATSON
PRODUCTIONS   T 01803 863033
The Gothic House, Fore Street, Totnes, Devon TQ9 5EH
F 01803 864219
E info@smithandwatson.com
W www.smithandwatson.com

SNEEZING TREE FILMS   T 020 7436 8036
1st Floor, 37 Great Portland Street
London W1W 8QH
F 020 7580 1957
E firstname@sneezingtree.com
W www.sneezingtree.com

SOLOMON THEATRE
COMPANY LTD   T/F 01725 518760
High Street, Damerham
Nr Fordingbridge, Hampshire SP6 3EU
E office@solomon-theatre.co.uk
W www.solomon-theatre.co.uk

SONY PICTURES   T 020 7533 1000
25 Golden Square, London W1F 9LU
F 020 7533 1015

SPACE CITY PRODUCTIONS   T 020 7371 4000
77-79 Blythe Road, London W14 0HP
F 020 7371 4001
E info@spacecity.co.uk
W www.spacecity.co.uk

SPEAKEASY PRODUCTIONS LTD   T 01738 828524
Wildwood House, Stanley, Perth PH1 4NH
F 01738 828419
E info@speak.co.uk
W www.speak.co.uk

SPECIFIC FILMS LTD   T 020 7580 7476
25 Rathbone Street, London W1T 1NQ
F 020 7636 6886
E info@specificfilms.com

SPIRAL PRODUCTIONS LTD   T 020 7428 9948
Unit 17-18, The Dove Centre
109 Bartholomew Road, London NW5 2BJ
F 020 7485 1845
E info@spiral.co.uk
W www.spiral.co.uk

STAFFORD, Jonathan
PRODUCTIONS   T 01932 562611
Shepperton Studios, Studios Road
Shepperton, Middlesex TW17 0QD
E jon@staffordproductions.com

STAMP PRODUCTIONS   T 020 8743 5555
Ugli Campus, 56 Wood Lane
London W12 7SB
E info@stamp-productions.com
W www.stamp-productions.com

STANDFAST FILMS   T 020 8466 5580
The Studio, 14 College Road
Bromley, Kent BR1 3NS

STANTON MEDIA   T 01296 489539
6 Kendal Close, Aylesbury
Bucks HP21 7HR
E info@stantonmedia.com
W www.stantonmedia.com

STONE PRODUCTIONS
CREATIVE LTD   T 01255 822172
Lakeside Studio, 62 Mill Street
St Osyth, Essex CO16 8EW
F 01255 822160
E kevin@stone-productions.co.uk
W www.stone-productions.co.uk

STUDIO AKA   T 020 7434 3581
Animation
30 Berwick Street, London W1F 8RH
F 020 7437 2309
W www.studioaka.co.uk

TABARD PRODUCTIONS LTD   T 020 7497 0830
Contact: John Herbert. By e-mail. Corporate Videos.
Documentaries
Adam House, 7-10 Adam Street
London WC2N 6AA
F 020 7497 0850
E johnherbert@tabard.co.uk
W www.tabardproductions.com

TABLE TOP PRODUCTIONS   T 020 8994 1269
Contact: Ben Berry. By e-mail. Drama. Feature Films
1 The Orchard, Bedford Park
Chiswick, London W4 1JZ
T/F 020 8742 0507
E berry@tabletopproductions.com

TAKE 3 PRODUCTIONS LTD   T 020 7637 2694
Business Design Centre
52 Upper Street
London N1 0QH
E mail@take3.co.uk
W www.take3.co.uk

TAKE FIVE PRODUCTIONS   T 020 7287 2120
37 Beak Street, London W1F 9RZ
F 020 7287 3035
E info@takefivestudio.com
W www.takefivestudio.com

TALKBACKTHAMES   T 020 7861 8000
20-21 Newman Street
London W1T 1PG
F 020 7861 8001
W www.talkbackthames.tv

TALKING PICTURES   T 01753 650000
Pinewood Studios, Pinewood Road
Iver Heath, Bucks SL0 0NH
F 01865 890504
E info@talkingpictures.co.uk
W www.talkingpictures.co.uk

TANDEM CREATIVE   T 01442 261576
Contact: By e-mail. Corporate Videos. Documentaries
Charleston House, 13 High Street
Hemel Hempstead, Herts HP1 3AA
E info@tandem.tv
W www.tandem.tv

THEATRE WORKSHOP   T 0131 555 3854
Film. Theatre
Out of the Blue Drill Hall, 36 Dalmeny Street
Edinburgh EH6 8RG
W www.theatre-workshop.com

THEOTHER COMPANY LTD   T 020 8858 6999
Contact: Sarah Boote. By e-mail. Corporate Videos.
Documentaries. Drama. Music Videos
30 Glenluce Road
Blackheath
London SE3 7SB
E contact@theothercompany.co.uk
W www.theothercompany.co.uk

THIN MAN FILMS   T 020 7734 7372
9 Greek Street, London W1D 4DQ
F 020 7287 5228
E info@thinman.co.uk

TIGER ASPECT PRODUCTIONS   T 020 7434 6700
5 Soho Square, London W1D 3QA
F 020 7434 1798
E general@tigeraspect.co.uk
W www.tigeraspect.co.uk

TOP BANANA   T 01562 700404
The Studio, Stourbridge
West Midlands DY9 0HA
F 01562 700930
E enquiries@top-b.com
W www.top-b.com

TOPICAL TELEVISION LTD   T 023 8071 2233
61 Devonshire Road
Southampton SO15 2GR
F 023 8033 9835
E post@topical.co.uk

TRAFALGAR 1 LTD   T 020 7722 7789
Contact: Hasan Shah. By Post/e-mail. Documentaries.
Feature Films. Films. Music Videos. Television
153 Burnham Towers
Fellows Road, London NW3 3JN
F 020 7483 0662
E t1ltd@blueyonder.co.uk

TREADSTONE 73 LTD   T 07551 556588
Based in London
E info@videoadvert.com
W www.videoadvert.com

TVF   T 020 7837 3000
375 City Road
London EC1V 1NB
F 020 7833 2185

TV PRODUCTION
PARTNERSHIP LTD   T 01264 861440
4 Fullerton Manor, Fullerton, Hants SP11 7LA
E dbj@tvpp.tv
W www.tvpp.tv

TWOFOUR   T 01752 727400
Corporate Videos. Documentaries. Live Events. Television.
Twofour Studios, Estover
Plymouth PL6 7RG
F 01752 727450
E enquiries@twofour.co.uk
W www.twofour.co.uk

TYBURN ENTERTAINMENT LTD   T 01753 516767
Cippenham Court, Cippenham Lane
Cippenham, Nr Slough
Berkshire SL1 5AU
F 01753 691785

VECTOR PRODUCTIONS   T 020 7193 5655 (London)
Inspiring Corporate Video & Television Production
Moulton Park Industrial Estate, Northampton NN3 6AQ
T 0845 0535400 (Northampton)
E production@vectortv.co.uk
W www.vectortv.co.uk

VERA PRODUCTIONS LTD   T 020 7292 1480
165 Wardour Street, London W1F 8WW
F 020 7292 1481
E phoebe@vera.co.uk

VIDEO ARTS   T 020 7400 4800
Elsinore House, 4th Floor
77 Fulham Palace Road
London W6 8JA
F 020 7400 4900
E info@videoarts.co.uk

VIDEO ENTERPRISES   T 01494 534144
Contact: Maurice Fleisher. Corporate Videos.
Documentaries. Live Events. Television
12 Barbers Wood Road
High Wycombe
Bucks HP12 4EP
T 07831 875216
E videoenterprises@ntlworld.com
W www.videoenterprises.co.uk

VIDEOTEL PRODUCTIONS   T 020 7299 1800
Corporate Videos
84 Newman Street, London W1T 3EU
F 020 7299 1818

VILLAGE PRODUCTIONS   T 020 8984 0322
4 Midas Business Centre, Wantz Road
Dagenham, Essex RM10 8PS
F 020 8593 0198
E village000@btclick.com

VSI - VOICE & SCRIPT
INTERNATIONAL   T 020 7692 7700
128-134 Cleveland Street
London W1T 6AB
E info@vsi.tv
W www.vsi.tv

W3KTS LTD   T 01904 647822
10 Portland Street, York YO31 7EH
E chris@w3kts.com

W6 STUDIO   T 020 7385 2272
Editing Facilities. Music Video. Photography.
Video Production
359 Lillie Road, Fulham
London SW6 7PA
E kazkam@w6studio.fsnet.co.uk
W www.w6studio.co.uk

WALKING FORWARD LTD   T/F 020 7359 5249
Studio 6, Aberdeen Centre
22-24 Highbury Grove
London N5 2EA
E info@walkingforward.co.uk
W www.walkingforward.co.uk

WALKOVERS VIDEO LTD   T 01249 750428
Facilities. Production
Kington Langley, Chippenham
North Wiltshire SN15 5NU
T 07831 828022
E walkoversvideo@btinternet.com

WALSH BROS LTD   T/F 020 8858 6870
Contact: By e-mail. Animation. Documentaries. Drama.
Feature Films. Films. Television
29 Trafalgar Grove, Greenwich
London SE10 9TB
E info@walshbros.co.uk
W www.walshbros.co.uk

WALSH, Steve
PRODUCTIONS LTD   T 020 7580 6553
Contact: Wendy Wolfcarius. Animation. Feature Films. Films.
Television
352 Banbury Road, Oxford OX2 7PP
F 020 7580 6567
E info@steve-walsh.com
W www.steve-walsh.com

WARNER BROS
PRODUCTIONS LTD   T 01923 882500
Warner Suite, Leavesden Studios
Aerodrome Way, Leavesden, Herts WD25 7LS

WARNER SISTERS
PRODUCTIONS LTD   T 020 8567 6655
Ealing Studios, Ealing Green, London W5 5EP
E ws@warnercini.com

WEST DIGITAL   T 020 8743 5100
Broadcast Post-Production
65 Goldhawk Road, London W12 8EG
F 020 8743 2345
E luci@westdigital.co.uk

WHITEHALL FILMS   T 020 8785 3737
10 Lower Common South, London SW15 1BP
F 020 8788 2340
E mwhitehall@msn.com

WINNER, Michael LTD   T 020 7734 8385
219 Kensington High Street, London W8 6BD
F 020 7602 9217
E winner@ftech.co.uk

WORKING TITLE FILMS LTD   T 020 7307 3000
26 Aybrook Street, London W1U 4AN
F 020 7307 3001
W www.workingtitlefilms.com

WORLD PRODUCTIONS & WORLD FILM
SERVICES LTD   T 020 3179 1800
Lasenby House, 32 Kingly Street, London W1B 5QQ
F 020 3179 1801
W www.world-productions.com

WORLD WIDE PICTURES   T 020 7613 6580
103 The Timber Yard, Drysdale Street
London N1 6ND
F 020 7613 6581
E info@worldwidepictures.tv
W www.worldwidepictures.tv

WORLD'S END TELEVISION   T 020 7386 4900
16-18 Empress Place, London SW6 1TT
F 020 7386 4901
E info@worldsendproductions.com
W www.worldsendproductions.com

WORTHWHILE MOVIE LTD   T 00 1 416 4690459
Providing the services of Bruce Pittman as Film Director
191 Logan Avenue
Toronto, Ontario, Canada M4M 2NT
E bruce.pittman@sympatico.ca

XINGU FILMS   T 020 7451 0600
12 Cleveland Row, London SW1A 1DH
F 020 7451 0601
W www.xingufilms.com

ZEPHYR FILMS LTD   T 020 7255 3555
33 Percy Street, London W1T 2DF
F 020 7255 3777
E info@zephyrfilms.co.uk

BRIGHTON FILM SCHOOL   T 01273 302166
Contact: Senior Lecturer Franz von Habsburg FBKS (BAFTA).
Member of the National Association for Higher Education in
the Moving Image (NAHEMI) & the University Film & Video
Association (UFVA). Part-time Day or Evening Film Directors'
Courses includes Screen Writing, Cinematography etc
E info@brightonfilmschool.org.uk
W www.brightonfilmschool.org.uk

LEEDS METROPOLITAN
UNIVERSITY   T 0113 812 8000
MA Filmmaking. BA (Hons) Film & Moving Image Production.
Cert HE/FdA Film & Television Production.
BA (Hons) Animation
Northern Film School, Leeds Metropolitan University
Electric Press, 1 Millennium Square, Leeds LS2 3AD
F 0113 812 8080
E filmenquiries@leedsmet.ac.uk
W www.leedsmet.ac.uk

LONDON COLLEGE OF
COMMUNICATION   T 020 7514 6569
Film & Video Course
Elephant & Castle, London SE1 6SB
F 020 7514 6843
E info@lcc.arts.ac.uk
W www.lcc.arts.ac.uk

LONDON FILM ACADEMY   T 020 7386 7711
The Old Church, 52A Walham Grove
London SW6 1QR
F 020 7381 6116
E info@londonfilmacademy.com
W www.londonfilmacademy.com

LONDON FILM SCHOOL THE   T 020 7836 9642
2-year MA Course in Film Making.
1-year MA in Screenwriting
24 Shelton Street, London WC2H 9UB
F 020 7497 3718
E info@lfs.org.uk
W www.lfs.org.uk

MIDDLESEX UNIVERSITY   T 020 8411 5000
School of Arts & Education
Television Production
Trent Park Campus
Bramley Road, London N14 4YZ
W www.mdx.ac.uk

NATIONAL FILM &
TELEVISION SCHOOL   T 01494 731425
MA & Diploma Courses in the Key Filmmaking Disciplines.
Short Courses for Freelancers
Beaconsfield Studios, Station Road
Beaconsfield, Bucks HP9 1LG
F 01494 674042
E info@nfts.co.uk
W www.nfts.co.uk

NORTHERN FILM SCHOOL   T 0113 812 8000
Leeds Metropolitan University
Electric Press
1 Millennium Square, Leeds LS2 3AD
E filmenquiries@leedsmet.ac.uk
W www.leedsmet.co.uk

UNIVERSITY FOR THE
CREATIVE ARTS   T 01252 892883
Pre-degree, Undergraduate & Postgraduate Degrees in
Creative Arts Courses
Falkner Road, Farnham
Surrey GU9 7DS
E enquiries@ucreative.ac.uk
W www.ucreative.ac.uk

UNIVERSITY OF WESTMINSTER SCHOOL OF
MEDIA ARTS & DESIGN   T 020 7911 5000
Undergraduate Courses in Film & Television Production &
Contemporary Media Practice. Postgraduate Courses in
Screenwriting & Producing, Film & Television; Theory,
Culture & Industry
Admissions & Enquiries: Watford Road
Northwick Park, Harrow, Middlesex HA1 3TP
W www.wmin.ac.uk/filmschool

Film & Television Schools

What are Film & Television Schools?

The schools listed in this section offer various courses to those who wish to become part of the behind-camera world of the entertainment industry. These courses include filmmaking, producing, screenwriting and animation, to name a few. Students taking these courses usually have to produce a number of short films in order to graduate. The following advice has been divided into two sections: for potential students and for actors.

Advice For Filmmakers/Writers:

Why should I take a course?

The schools listed here offer courses which enable a budding filmmaker or script writer to develop their skills with practical training. These courses are designed to prepare you for a career in a competitive industry. They also provide you with an opportunity to begin networking and making contacts with industry professionals.

How should I use these listings?

Research a number of schools carefully before applying to any courses. Have a look at the websites of the schools listed first to get an idea of the types of courses on offer, what is expected from students, and the individual values of each school. Request a prospectus from the school if they do not have full details online. Word of mouth recommendations are invaluable if you know anyone who has attended or taught at a school. You need to decide what type of course suits you – don't just sign up for the first one you read about. See what is available and give yourself time to think about the various options.

Advice For Actors:

Why should I get involved?

Student films can offer new performers the chance to develop skills and experience in front of a camera, learning scripts, working with other actors and working with crew members. Making new contacts and learning how to get on with those you are working with, whether in front of or behind camera, is a vital part of getting along in the acting community.

In addition, you are likely to receive a certain amount of exposure from the film. The student filmmaker may show it to teachers, other students, other actors, and most importantly directors when applying for jobs, and you would normally be given your own copy of the film which you can show to agents or casting directors if requested, or use a clip of it in your showreel.

For more experienced actors, working on a student film can offer the opportunity to hone existing skills and keep involved within the industry. It can also be useful to observe new actors and keep up-to-date with new training ideas and techniques.

How do I get involved?

It may be helpful to see if the schools' websites have any advice for actors interested in being considered for parts in student films and suggesting how they should make contact. If there is no advice of this kind, it would be worth either phoning or e-mailing to ask if the school or its students would consider actors previously unknown to them. If this is the case, ask who CVs and headshots should be sent to, and whether they would like to see a showreel or voicereel (for animation courses).

If you are asked to play a role in a student film, make sure you are not going to a student's home and that someone knows where you are going and when. Equity also recommends that actors request a contract when working on any film; you could receive payment retrospectively if the film becomes a success. You may find it helpful to refer to Equity's advice leaflet *Low Pay/No Pay* which is available to all Equity members from their website's members' area.

Should I use a clip of a student film on my showreel?

Casting directors would generally prefer to see some form of showreel than none at all. If you do not have anything else you can show that has been professionally broadcast, or do not have the money to get a showreel made from scratch, then a student film is an acceptable alternative. See the 'Promotional Services' section for more information on showreels.

Where can I find more information?

Students and actors may want to visit Shooting People's website www.shootingpeople.org for further advice and daily e-mail bulletins of student/ short film and TV castings. Filmmakers can upload their films to the site for others to view.

3 MILLS STUDIOS T 020 7363 3336
Three Mill Lane, London E3 3DU
F 08715 944028
E info@3mills.com
W www.3mills.com

ANIMAL PROMOTIONS T 07778 156513
White Rocks Farm, Underriver
Sevenoaks, Kent TN15 0SL
F 01732 763767
E happyhoundschool@yahoo.co.uk
W www.animalpromotions.co.uk

ARDMORE STUDIOS LTD T 00 353 1 2862971
Herbert Road, Bray, Co. Wicklow, Ireland
F 00 353 1 2861894
E film@ardmore.ie
W www.ardmore.ie

BBC TELEVISION T 020 8743 8000
Television Centre, Wood Lane
Shepherds Bush, London W12 7RJ

BRAY FILM STUDIOS T 01628 622111
Down Place, Water Oakley, Windsor, Berkshire SL4 5UG
F 01628 623000

BRIGHTON FILM STUDIOS LTD T 01273 302166
The Brighton Forum, 95 Ditchling Road
Brighton BN1 4ST
E franz@brightonfilmstudios.com
W www.brightonfilmstudios.com

CAPITAL STUDIOS T 07974 921018
Wandsworth Plain, London SW18 1ET
F 020 8877 0234
E info@capitalstudios.com
W www.capitalstudios.com

CLAPHAM ROAD STUDIOS T 020 7582 9664
Animation. Live Action
161 Clapham Road, London SW9 0PU
W www.claphamroadstudios.co.uk

EALING STUDIOS T 020 8567 6655
Ealing Green, London W5 5EP
F 020 8758 8658
E info@ealingstudios.com
W www.ealingstudios.com

ELSTREE STUDIOS T 020 8953 1600
Shenley Road, Borehamwood, Herts WD6 1JG
F 020 8905 1135
E info@elstreestudios.co.uk
W www.elstreestudios.co.uk

LONDON STUDIOS THE T 020 7157 5555
London Television Centre
Upper Ground
London SE1 9LT
F 020 7157 5757
E sales@londonstudios.co.uk
W www.londonstudios.co.uk

PINEWOOD STUDIOS T 01753 651700
Pinewood Road, Iver Heath
Buckinghamshire SL0 0NH
W www.pinewoodgroup.com

REUTERS TELEVISION T 020 7250 1122
The Reuters Thompson Building
South Colonnade
Canary Wharf, London E14 5EP

RIVERSIDE STUDIOS T 020 8237 1000
Crisp Road
London W6 9RL
F 020 8237 1001
E reception@riversidestudios.co.uk
W www.riversidestudios.co.uk

**SANDS FILMS COSTUMES LTD/ROTHERHITHE
STUDIOS** T 020 7231 2209
82 St Marychurch Street
London SE16 4HZ
F 020 7231 2119
E info@sandsfilms.co.uk
W www.sandsfilms.co.uk

SHEPPERTON STUDIOS T 01932 562611
Studios Road, Shepperton
Middlesex TW17 0QD
F 01932 568989
W www.pinewoodgroup.com

TEDDINGTON STUDIOS T 020 8977 3252
Broom Road, Teddington
Middlesex TW11 9NT
F 020 8943 4050
W www.pinewoodgroup.com

TWICKENHAM FILM STUDIOS LTD T 020 8607 8888
The Barons
St Margaret's
Twickenham
Middlesex TW1 2AW
F 020 8607 8889
E enquiries@twickenhamstudios.com
W www.twickenhamstudios.com

Film London

Supports over 1,000 film, TV and advertising projects every year. Make us your first point of contact for filming in the capital.

www.filmlondon.org.uk

MAYOR OF LONDON

Awarding funds from
The National Lottery®

G

Good Digs Guide

Compiled by Janice Cramer
and David Banks

This is a list of digs recommended by those
who have used them.

To keep the list accurate please send
recommendations for inclusion to:

Good Digs Guide
Spotlight, 7 Leicester Place
London WC2H 7RJ

E contacts@spotlight.com

If you are a digs owner wishing
to be listed, your application must
contain a recommendation from
a performer who has stayed
in your accommodation.

BLACKPOOL

VERY HIGH STANDARD - *en suite studios & apartments*
- Wi-Fi • Central Heating • Cooker • Fridge • Microwave & TV - **all new**
- Beds • Linen provided • 'Highly recommended' by members of the profession • 10 minutes walk to the Theatre

Irene Chadderton, 22 Barton Avenue, Blackpool FY1 6AP
Tel/Fax: 01253 346743 www.blackpool-somerset-apartments.co.uk

Somerset Apartments

visit**Britain** ☆☆☆

ABERDEEN: Milne, Mrs A T 01224 638951
5 Sunnyside Walk, Aberdeen AB24 3NZ

ABERDEEN: Woods, Pat T 01224 586324
62 Union Grove, Aberdeen AB10 6RX

ABERYSTWYTH:
Vegetarian Penrhin T 07837 712323
Farmhouse near Aberystwyth Providing Accommodation &
Vegetarian Breakfasts
Penrhin, Llanafan
Aberystwyth, Dyfed SY23 4BA
E penrhin@fastmail.fm
W www.vegetarianpenrhin.com

AYR: Dunn, Sheila T 01292 284531
The Dunn-Thing Guest House,
13 Park Circus, Ayr KA7 2DJ
T 07887 928685

BATH: Hutton, Mrs Celia T 01225 830830
Bath Holiday Homes, Terranova
Shepherds Walk, Bath BA2 5QT
E bhh@virgin.net
W www.bathholidayhomes.co.uk

BATH: Tapley, Jane T 01225 446561
Camden Lodgings
3 Upper Camden Place
Bath BA1 5HX
E peter@tapley.ws

BIRMINGHAM: Hurst, Mr P T 0121 449 8220
41 King Edward Road, Moseley
Birmingham B13 8HR
E phurst1com@aol.com

BIRMINGHAM:
Mountain, Marlene P T 0121 454 5900
268 Monument Road, Edgbaston
Birmingham B16 8XF

BIRMINGHAM: Wilson, Mrs T 0121 440 5182
17 Yew Tree Road, Edgbaston
Birmingham B15 2LX

BLACKPOOL: Lees, Jean T 01253 621059
Ascot Flats, 6 Hull Road
Central Blackpool FY1 4QB

BLACKPOOL:
Somerset Apartments T/F 01253 346743
22 Barton Avenue, Blackpool FY1 6AP
W www.blackpool-somerset-apartments.co.uk

BLACKPOOL:
Waller, Veronica & Bob T 01253 627003
The Brooklyn Hotel, 7 Wilton Parade
Blackpool FY1 2HE
W enquiries@brooklynhotel.co.uk

BOLTON: Duckworth, Paul T 07762 545129
19 Burnham Avenue, Bolton BL1 6BD
E pauljohnathan@msn.com

BOURNEMOUTH: Sitton, Martin T 01202 293318
Flat 2, 9 St Winifreds Road
Meyrick Park, Bournemouth BH2 6NX

BRADFORD: Smith, Theresa T 01274 778568
8 Moorhead Terrace, Shipley
Bradford BD18 4LA
E theresaannesmith@hotmail.com

BRIGHTON: Benedict, Peter T 020 7703 4104
19 Madeira Place, Brighton BN2 1TN
T 07752 810122
E peter@peterbenedict.co.uk
W www.madeiraplace.co.uk

BRIGHTON:
Chance, Michael & Drinkel, Keith T 01273 779585
6 Railway Street, Brighton BN1 3PF
T 07876 223359
E mchance@lineone.net

BRIGHTON: Dyson, Kate T 01273 607490
39 Arundel Street, Kemptown BN2 5TH
T 07812 949875
E kate.dyson@talktalk.net

BRISTOL: Ham, Phil & Jacqui T 0117 902 5213
78 Stackpool Road, Bristol BS3 1NN
T 07956 962422
E jacqui@tiptopmusic.com

BRISTOL: Walsh, Karen T 07966 282398
The Courtyard, 8 Royal York Crescent
Clifton, Bristol BS8 4JZ

BURY ST EDMUNDS: Bird, Mrs S T 01284 754492
30 Crown Street, Bury St Edmunds
Suffolk IP33 1QU
E josandsue@homebird2.plus.com

BURY ST EDMUNDS:
Harrington-Spier, Sue T 01284 768986
39 Well Street, Bury St Edmunds
Suffolk IP33 1EQ
E sue.harringtonspier@googlemail.com

BUXTON: Kitchen, Mrs G T 01298 26555
Silverlands Holiday Apartments
c/o 156 Brown Edge Road
Buxton, Derbyshire SK17 7AA
T 01298 79381
E swiftcaterequip2@aol.com

CAMBRIDGE: Dunn, Anne T 01954 210291
The Dovecot, 1 St Catherine's Hall
Coton, Cambridge CB23 7GU
T 07774 131797
E dunn@annecollet.fsnet.co.uk

CANTERBURY: Ellen, Nikki T 01227 720464
Crockshard Farmhouse, Wingham
Canterbury CT3 1NY
E crockshard_bnb@yahoo.com
W www.crockshard.com

CARDIFF: Blade, Mrs Anne T 029 2022 5860
25 Romilly Road, Canton
Cardiff CF5 1FH

CARDIFF: Kelly, Sheila T 029 2039 5078
166 Llandaff Road, Canton
Cardiff CF11 9PX
E mgsmkelly1@yahoo.co.uk

CARDIFF: Kennedy, Rosie T 07746 946118
Duffryn Mawr Farm House, Pendoylan
Vale of Glamorgan
E rosie@duffrynmawrcottages.com
W www.duffrynmawrcottages.co.uk

Good Digs Guide

CARDIFF: Lewis, Nigel T 029 2049 4008
66 Donald Street, Roath
Cardiff CF24 4TR
T 07813 069822
E nigel.lewis66@btinternet.com

CHESTERFIELD:
Cook, Linda & Chris T 01246 202631
27 Tennyson Avenue, Chesterfield
Derbyshire
T 07929 850561
E chris_cook@talk21.com

CHESTERFIELD:
Foston, Mr & Mrs T 01246 235412
Anis Louise Guest House
34 Clarence Road
Chesterfield S40 1LN
E anislouise@gmail.com
W www.anislouiseguesthouse.co.uk

CHESTERFIELD:
Popplewell, Mr & Mrs T 01246 201738
Alfred House, 23 Tennyson Avenue
Chesterfield S40 4SN

CHICHESTER: Potter, Iain & Lyn T 01243 783375
Hunston Mill Cottages
Selsey Road
Chichester PO20 1AU
E hunstonmill@aol.com
W www.hunstonmill.co.uk

COVENTRY:
Snelson, Paddy & Bob T 01926 852850
Banner Hill Farmhouse, Rouncil Lane
Kenilworth CV8 1NN

DARLINGTON: George Hotel T 01325 374576
Contact: Reception
Piercebridge
Darlington DL2 3SW
W www.georgeontees.co.uk

DARLINGTON: Bird, Mrs T 01748 822771
Gilling Old Mill, Gilling West
Richmond, N Yorks DL10 5JD
E admin@yorkshiredales-cottages.com

DARLINGTON: Graham, Anne T 01325 374280
Holme House, Piercebridge
Darlington DL2 3SY
E graham.holmehouse@gmail.com
W www.holmehouse.com

DERBY: Boddy, Susan T 01332 701384
St Wilfrids, Church Lane
Barrow-upon-Trent, Derbyshire DE73 7HB

DERBY: Coxon, Mary T 01332 347460
Short Term Accommodation. Theatricals Only
1 Overdale Road
Derby DE23 6AU
T 07850 082943
E marycoxon@hotmail.co.uk

DUNDEE: Hill, Mrs J T 01382 450831
Ash Villa, 216 Arbroath Road
Dundee DD4 7RZ
E ashvilla_guesthouse@talk21.com

EASTBOURNE: Allen, Peter T 01323 416861
Flat 1, 16 Enys Road
Eastbourne BN21 2DN
T 07712 439289

EASTBOURNE: Guess, Maggie T 01323 736689
3 Hardy Drive, Langney Point
Eastbourne
East Sussex BN23 6ED
T 07710 273288
E guesswhom@btinternet.com

EDINBURGH: ACS Properties T 01620 840900
Contact: Ashley Smith, Carole Smith.
Short Term Letting in Edinburgh
Office: 7 St Martins Place
Haddington
East Lothian EH41 4NF
T 07875 667752
E ashley@acs-properties.com
W www.acs-properties.com

EDINBURGH: Glen Miller, Edna T 0131 556 4131
25 Bellevue Road, Edinburgh EH7 4DL

EDINBURGH: Tyrrell, Helen T 0131 229 7219
Two single rooms overlooking park. 10 mins walk from
several Edinburgh theatres
9 Lonsdale Terrace, Edinburgh EH3 9HN
T 07929 960510
E hkmtyrrell@gmail.com

GLASGOW: Baird, David W T 0141 423 1340
6 Beaton Road, Maxwell Park
Glasgow G41 4LA
T 07842 195597
E b050557@yahoo.com

GLASGOW:
Leslie-Carter, Simon T 0845 2305252
52 Charlotte Street, Glasgow G1 5DW
F 01436 810520
E slc@52charlottestreet.co.uk
W www.52charlottestreet.co.uk

HASTINGS: Estall, Jane T 07703 550006
37 Madeira Drive, Hastings
East Sussex TN34 2NH
E thejaneestallagency@gmail.com

INVERNESS: Blair, Mrs T 01463 232878
McDonald House Hotel, 1 Ardross Terrace
Inverness IV3 5NQ

INVERNESS:
Kerr-Smith, Jennifer T 01463 233131
Ardkeen Tower, 5 Culduthel Road
Inverness IV2 4AD

IPSWICH: Ball, Bunty T 01473 256653
56 Henley Road, Ipswich IP1 3SA

IPSWICH: Bennett, Liz T 01473 623343
Gayfers, Playford
Ipswich IP6 9DR
E lizzieb@clara.co.uk

IPSWICH: Hyde-Johnson, Anne T 01473 823110
64 Benton Street, Hadleigh
Ipswich, Suffolk IP7 5AT

ISLE OF WIGHT: Ogston, Sue T 01983 280940
Windward House, 69 Mill Hill Road
Cowes, Isle of Wight PO31 7EQ
E sueogston1@tiscali.co.uk

KESWICK: Bell, Miss A T 07740 949250
Flat 4, Skiddaw View
Penrith Road, Keswick CA12 5HF

LEEDS: Baker, Mrs M T 0113 275 8735
2 Ridge Mount, (off Cliff Road)
Leeds LS6 2HD
E ridgemountleeds@googlemail.com

LEEDS: Byrne, Ralph T 0113 249 5303
16 Oakwell Crescent, Leeds LS8 4AF
T 07763 572183
E ralphjbyrne@googlemail.com

LEEDS: Cannon, Rosie T 0113 262 3550
14 Toronto Place, Chapel Allerton
Leeds LS7 4LJ
T 07969 832955

Good Digs Guide

LINCOLN: Carnell, Andrew   T 01522 569892
Tennyson Court Cottages
3 Tennyson Street
Lincoln LN1 1LZ
E andrew@tennyson-court.co.uk
W www.tennyson-court.co.uk

LINCOLN: Sharpe, Mavis S   T 01522 534477
Bight House, 17 East Bight
Lincoln LN2 1QH

LIVERPOOL: Double, Ross   T 0151 708 8821
5 Percy Street, Liverpool L8 7LT

LIVERPOOL: Maloney, Anne   T 0151 734 4839
16 Sandown Lane, Wavertree
Liverpool L15 8HY
T 07977 595040

LLANDUDNO:
Blanchard, Mr D & Mrs A   T 01492 877822
Oasis Hotel, 4 Neville Crescent
Central Promenade
Llandudno LL30 1AT
E oasishotel@unicombox.com

LONDON: Allen, Mrs I   T 020 7723 3979
Flat 2, 9 Dorset Square
London NW1 6QB
E neddyallen@mypostoffice.co.uk

LONDON: Cardinal, Maggie   T 020 7681 7376
17A Gaisford Street, London NW5 2EB

LONDON: Cavanah, Anne Marie   T 07939 220299
Upper Flat
66 Elsinore Road, Forest Hill
London SE23 2SL
E anmariecavanah@aol.com

LONDON: Horn, Cryn   T 020 8470 4868
27 Donald Road, Upton Park
London E13 0QF
E crynhorn@easynet.co.uk

LONDON: Kempton, Victoria   T 020 8888 5595
66 Morley Avenue, London N22 6NG
T 07946 344697
E vjkempton@onetel.com

LONDON: Long, Hilary   T 020 8856 5023
56 Sutlej Road, Charlton
London SE7 7DB
F 07092 315384
E rainbowtheatrelondoneast@yahoo.co.uk

LONDON: Mesure, Nicholas   T 020 8853 4337
16 St Alfege Passage, Greenwich
London SE10 9JS

LONDON: Montagu, Beverley   T 020 7263 3883
13 Hanley Road, London N4 3DU

LONDON: Rothner, Stephanie   T 020 8446 1604
44 Grove Road, North Finchley
London N12 9DY
T 07956 406446

LONDON: Shaw, Lindy   T 020 8567 0877
11 Baronsmede, London W5 4LS
E lindy.shaw@talktalk.net

LONDON: Walsh, Genevieve   T 020 7627 0024
37 Kelvedon House, Guildford Road
Stockwell, London SW8 2DN

LONDON: Warren, Mrs Sally   T 020 8994 0560
28 Prebend Gardens, Chiswick
London W4 1TW

MALVERN: Emuss, Mrs   T 01684 568455
Priory Holme, 18 Avenue Road
Great Malvern WR14 3AR
E prioryholme@fsmail.net

MALVERN: McLeod, Mr & Mrs   T 01684 574994
Sidney House, 40 Worcester Road
Malvern WR14 4AA
E info@sidneyhouse.co.uk
W www.sidneyhouse.co.uk

MANCHESTER: Cox, Lucia   T 0161 860 6005
22 Woodlawn Court, Manchester M16 9RH
T 07805 337742
E lougrand76@hotmail.com

MANCHESTER:
Dyson, Mrs Edwina   T 0161 434 5410
33 Danesmoor Road, West Didsbury
Manchester M20 3JT
E edwinadyson@hotmail.com

MANCHESTER: Heaton, Miriam   T 0161 773 4490
58 Tamworth Avenue, Whitefield
Manchester M45 6UA

MANCHESTER: Higgins, Mark   T 07904 520898
New build less than 1 mile from town
72 Camp Street, Manchester M7 1LG
E icenlemon30@hotmail.com
W www.theatredigsmanchester.co.uk

MANCHESTER:
Jones, Miss P M   T 0161 766 9243
'Forget-me-not Cottages', 12 Livsey Street
Whitefield, Manchester M45 6AE
E cliff.inman@virgin.net

MANCHESTER:
Prichard, Fiona & John   T 0161 434 4877
45 Bamford Road, Didsbury
Manchester M20 2QP
T/F 07771 965651
E fionaprichard@hotmail.com

MANCHESTER: Twist, Susan   T 0161 225 1591
45 Osborne Road, Levenshulme
Manchester M19 2DU

MILFORD HAVEN:
Henricksen, Bruce & Diana   T 01646 695983
Belhaven House Hotel Ltd, 29 Hamilton Terrace
Milford Haven SA73 3JJ
T 07825 237386
E brucehenricksen@mac.com
W www.westwaleshotel.com

NEWCASTLE UPON TYNE:
The Manager   T 0191 281 3363
Rosebery Hotel, 2 Rosebery Crescent
Jesmond, Newcastle upon Tyne NE2 1ET
W www.roseberyhotel.co.uk

NEWPORT: Price, Mrs Dinah   T 01633 420216
Great House, Isca Road
Old Village, Caerleon, Gwent NP18 1QG
E dinahprice123@btinternet.com
W www.greathousebb.co.uk

NORWICH: Busch, Julia   T 01603 612833
8 Chester Street, Norwich NR2 2AY
T 07920 133250
E juliacbusch@aol.com

NOTTINGHAM: Davis, Barbara   T 0115 947 4179
3 Tattershall Drive, The Park
Nottingham NG7 1BX

NOTTINGHAM: Offord, Mrs   T 0115 947 6924
5 Tattershall Drive, The Park
Nottingham NG7 1BX

NOTTINGHAM: Santos, Mrs S   T 0115 966 3018
Eastwood Farm, Hagg Lane
Epperstone, Nottingham NG14 6AX
E info@eastwoodfarm.co.uk

NOTTINGHAM: Seymour Road Studios
Bed & Breakfast　　T 07946 208211
42 Seymour Road, West Bridgford
Nottingham NG2 5EF
E fran@seymourroadstudios.co.uk

NOTTINGHAM: Walker, Christine　T 0115 947 2485
18A Cavendish Crescent North
The Park, Nottingham NG7 1BA
E walker.ce@virgin.net

OXFORD: Petty, Susan　　T 01993 703035
Self-catering Cottages
74 Corn Street, Witney
Oxford OX28 6BS

PETERBOROUGH: Smith, J　　T 01733 211847
Fen-Acre, 20 Barber Drove North
Crowland, Peterborough PE6 0BE
T 07759 661896
E julie@fen-acreholidaylet.com
W www.fen-acreholidaylet.com

PLYMOUTH: Ball, Fleur　　T 01752 670967
3 Hoe Gardens, Plymouth PL1 2JD
E fleurball@blueyonder.co.uk

PLYMOUTH: Carson, Mr & Mrs　　T 01752 872124
6 Beech Cottages
Parsonage Road
Newton Ferrers, Nr Plymouth PL8 1AX
E beechcottages@aol.com

PLYMOUTH:
Humphreys, John & Sandra　　T 01752 220176
Lyttleton House, 4 Crescent Avenue
Plymouth PL1 3AN

PLYMOUTH: Mead, Teresa　　T 01752 664046
Ashgrove House
218 Citadel Road
The Hoe, Plymouth PL1 3BB
E ashgroveho@aol.com

PLYMOUTH:
Spencer, Hugh & Eloise　　T 01752 664066
10 Grand Parade
Plymouth PL1 3DF
T 07966 412839
E hugh.spencer@hotmail.com

POOLE: Saunders, Mrs　　T 01202 741637
1 Harbour Shallows, 15 Whitecliff Road
Poole BH14 8DU
E saunders.221@btinternet.com

RAMSGATE: Waugh, Gilda　　T 01843 448149
4 Bed, 2 Bath 1890's House. Rooms for
Theatricals to Rent
21 Crescent Road, Ramsgate
Kent CT11 9QU
E gildawaugh@hotmail.co.uk

SALISBURY: Brumfitt, Ms S　　T 01722 334877
26 Victoria Road, Salisbury
Wilts SP1 3NG

SHEFFIELD: Slack, Penny　　T 0114 234 0382
Rivelin Glen Quarry
Rivelin Valley Road
Sheffield S6 5SE
E pennyslack@aol.com
W www.quarryhouse.org.uk

SHOREHAM: Cleveland, Carol　　T 01273 567954
Near Brighton
1 Oxen Court, Oxen Avenue
Shoreham-by-Sea BN43 5AS
T 07973 363939
E info@carolcleveland.com

SOUTHSEA & PORTSMOUTH:
Tyrell, Wendy　　T 023 9282 1453
Douglas Cottage
27 Somerset Road
Southsea PO5 2NL

STOKE-ON-TRENT:
Hindmoor, Mrs　　T 01782 264244
Verdon Guest House (Self Catering and B&B)
44 Charles Street
Hanley
Stoke-on-Trent ST1 3JY
W www.verdonguesthouse.co.uk

STOKE-ON-TRENT:
Meredith, Mr K　　T 01782 502160
2 Bank End Farm Cottage
Hammond Avenue
Brown Edge
Stoke-on-Trent, Staffs ST6 8QU
E kenmeredith@btinternet.com

STRATFORD-UPON-AVON:
Caterham House　　T 01789 267309
58-59 Rother Street
Stratford-upon-Avon CV37 6LT
E caterhamhousehotel@btconnect.com

TAUNTON: Parker, Sue　　T 01278 458580
Admirals Rest, 5 Taunton Road
Bridgwater TA6 3LW

TAUNTON: Read, Mary　　T 01823 334148
Pyreland Farm
Cheddon Road
Taunton, Somerset TA2 7QX

WINCHESTER:
South Winchester Lodges　　T 01962 820490
The Green
South Winchester Golf Club
Winchester
Hampshire SO22 5SW

WOLVERHAMPTON:
Riggs, Peter A　　T 01902 844068
'Bethesda', 56 Chapel Lane
Codsall
Nr Wolverhampton WV8 2EJ
T 07930 967809

WORTHING: Stewart, Mollie　　T 01903 206823
School House
11 Ambrose Place
Worthing BN11 1PZ

WORTHING: Symonds, Mrs Val　　T 01903 201557
23 Shakespeare Road
Worthing BN11 4AR
T 07951 183252

YORK: Blacklock, Tom　　T 01904 620487
155 Lowther Street
York YO31 7LZ
E thomas.blacklock@btinternet.com

YORK: Blower, Iris & Dennis　　T 01904 626801
Dalescroft Guest House
10 Southlands Road
York YO23 1NP
E info@dalescroft-york.co.uk
W www.dalescroft-york.co.uk

YORK: Harrand, Greg　　T 01904 637404
Hedley House Hotel & Apts
3 Bootham Terrace
York YO30 7DH
E greg@hedleyhouse.com

Health & Wellbeing

Health & Wellbeing

How should I use these listings?

You will find a variety of companies in this section which could help you enhance your health and wellbeing physically and mentally. They include personal fitness and lifestyle coaches, counsellors, exercise classes and beauty consultants amongst others. It is worth researching any company or service you are considering using. Many of these listings have websites which you can browse. Even if you feel you have your career and lifestyle under control, you may still find the following advice helpful:

Your body is part of your business

Your mental and physical health is vital to your career as a performer. Just from a business perspective, your body is part of your promotional package and it needs to be maintained. Try to keep fit and eat healthily to enhance both your outward appearance and your inner confidence. This is particularly important if you are unemployed. You need to ensure that if you are suddenly called for an audition you look suitable for and feel positive about the part you are auditioning for.

Injury

Keeping fit also helps you to minimise the risk of an injury during a performance. The last thing you want to do is to be prevented from working. An injury is more likely to occur if you are inflexible and unprepared for sudden physical exertion. If you do pick up an injury or an illness you will want to make sure it does not get any worse by getting treatment with a specialist.

Mental health

Mental health is just as important as bodily health. Just as you would for any physical injury or illness, if you suffer from a psychological problem such as stage fright, an addiction or depression, you should make sure that you address your concerns and deal with the issues involved. You may need to see a counsellor or a life coach for guidance and support.

Unemployment

If you are unemployed, it can be difficult to retain a positive mindset. The best thing you can do is to keep yourself occupied. You could join a dance or drama class, which would help to maintain your fitness levels as well as developing contacts and keeping involved within the industry. Improve your CV by learning to speak a new language or play a musical instrument. Think about taking on temporary or part-time work outside of acting to earn money until the next job comes along (see the 'Non-Acting Jobs' section), or you could put yourself forward for acting work in a student film (see 'Film & Television Schools' for more information).

Where can I find more information?

For more information on health and wellbeing you may wish to contact the British Association for Performing Arts Medicine (BAPAM) www.bapam.org.uk. You may also find their case study in this section helpful. Please refer to the 'Drama Training, Schools & Coaches' and 'Dance Training & Professional Classes' sections if you are interested in taking drama or dance courses or lessons to improve your fitness, keep your auditioning skills sharp between jobs and/or stay occupied and motivated.

Health & Wellbeing

Actors who are never out of work are rare creatures. But you can use your resting periods to invest in your physical and mental health. Here are a few suggestions from BAPAM, the charity that provides free health-assessment clinics and reduced-price treatments to artists with performance-related health problems.

Look after your health on a budget

If you can't justify the cost of keeping up your gym membership, go for cheaper forms of exercise:

• **Walk or cycle** instead of driving or using public transport. If you haven't ridden a bike for years, build your confidence by taking a course.
• **Run** in the open air instead of on a treadmill at a gym. It's much better to be in the fresh air – and it's more sociable.

• **Swimming** is a cheap and effective form of exercise. Think about taking lessons to make your stroke more efficient and avoid putting unnecessary pressure on your joints – especially your neck.

• **Team sports** combine fresh air and being sociable; now could be the time to take up football or netball again. Be careful, though – you wouldn't want a sports injury to come between you and your next job!

• Learn a technique to help with **posture,** such as Alexander Technique, Feldenkrais or Pilates. Techniques that are taught one-to-one can be expensive, but you can often find taster sessions at adult education colleges.

• **Take a refresher** in all those stagecraft skills (breathing; warm-up exercises; stage fighting) you learned at drama school. Enrol on a short course or read some books. When the next job comes up you need to be in peak condition and able to perform safely.

Think about your diet while you're resting

Everyone knows that eating well has a positive effect on your mental and physical wellbeing – especially important when you need to keep your spirits up.

• Learn about **healthy eating,** and expand your repertoire of recipes. Farmers' markets save money and you'll learn what's in season. Then you can maintain good habits when you're running around or on tour.

• If you ration your **treats,** you make them more special. If a treat becomes a daily habit you won't enjoy real treats so much.

• Now is the time to **phase out junk food.** Why spend money on processed food when you could eat so much better for less? See the BAPAM factsheet *Sensible eating for performers*.

• Don't rely on **alcohol** to keep you going. You develop expectations around alcohol, and that will take its toll on your liver (and your wallet!).Try to make a drink last longer, or alternate alcohol and water over the course of an evening. See the BAPAM factsheet *The drinks are on me!* for more information about drinking responsibly.

Invest in your mental health too

• Think strategically about your career. Do a **skills** audit, remembering all the skills you've accumulated (numeracy, fundraising, any IT skills). Be creative about how you can put them to use, and fill any skill gaps. Focusing on something developmental can take your mind off your current circumstances.

• Use quiet periods to **organise** your paperwork and electronic filing systems. You will feel empowered when you know everything is in order; it saves time and stress when you do get busy if you already have a workable system in place. Learn to use **spreadsheets** to keep track of your finances. You'll save yourself endless headaches when it's time to file your tax return, *and* you'll save yourself money on an accountant.

• **Volunteering** is great for stopping you feeling isolated. Try and find an activity that involves **physical exercise** – such as working in a community garden. It might even lead to a job!

• Remember, there's no need to suffer alone if being out of work is beginning to get you down. A few sessions with a **counsellor** can make a big difference. Check out the BAPAM Directory online at www.bapam.org.uk to locate aperformer-friendly counsellor in your area.

To find out more about performance-related health issues and BAPAM services, please see the website www.bapam.org.uk

Health & Wellbeing

Dance UK's Healthier Dancer Programme (HDP) has been providing information and resources to support dancers' health for nearly 30 years. HDP Manager Helen Laws conducted the Fit to Dance 2 survey in 2005: a research project to investigate the state of dancers' health in the UK. Erin Sanchez MSc is a member of IADMS and a former dancer and now works with Dance UK's HDP and the Rudolf Nureyev Foundation to promote dancers' health. Now Dance UK's HDP is working to establish the first institute to provide free, world-class, comprehensive, dance-specific health care.

Sometimes dancers don't know where to look for the resources they need to safeguard their health or find treatment when injuries arise. In this age of blogs, websites and YouTube, below are some major health resources for dancers offered by Dance UK's Healthier Dancer Programme and other dancers' health organisations…

Resources: Information Sheets, Books and Links

Dance UK's Information Sheets cover a wide variety of topics essential for keeping dancers fit including warm up and cool down, muscle imbalance, core stability, first aid and common physiotherapy questions. Information sheets are a free benefit of Dance UK membership, or they can be purchased online at Dance UK's shop: www.danceuk.org/shop

The HDP has also reviewed a variety of books about fitness, nutrition and health for dancers. Koutedakis and Sharp's *The Fit and Healthy Dancer* (1999), for example, offers a comprehensive overlook on the dancer's body, and will help you design your own supplementary fitness training programme. Brief reviews and listings of other helpful books can be found online in Dance UK's Resources pages. Information about health-related events and conferences, industry standards, and healthy recipes for dancers are also available on the HDP pages. www.danceuk.org/healthier-dancer-programme

Psychological Approaches and Support

Improving performance can sometimes just be a matter of changing your attitude or finding motivation to improve technical skills. Although clinical topics such as eating disorders and burnout are most commonly associated with seeking mental health support, mental skills such as goal setting, imagery and motivation can help dancers overcome performance anxiety, optimise training and gain confidence. The Foundations for Excellence website has a range of resources on mental training for performers including motivation, developing self-esteem and goal setting. www.foundations-for-excellence.org/resources/preparation-for-performance

Medical Practitioners Directory

Once an injury occurs, finding specific medical advice and treatment for dancers can prove to be a challenge. Dance UK's HDP offers the Medical Practitioners Directory

searchable by area, practitioner type, or practitioner name. The directory is free to everyone and offers a variety of medical and complimentary health practitioners with specific experience caring for dancers. The directory can be found at: www.danceuk.org/medical-practitioners-directory

Expert Health Advice: Ask Ava

If you have a specific health or fitness-related question you can submit your question to Dance UK's resident Agony Aunt for a personal response. Advice is provided by former professional dancer and dance scientist Ava Barron MSc and supported by Dance UK's advisory committees of experienced dance-specific medical practitioners and physiotherapists. The HDP section of the Dance UK website also has answers to dancers' frequently asked health questions: www.danceuk.org/healthier-dancer-programme/health-faqs

International Association of Dance Medicine and Science (IADMS)

IADMS offers resources for teachers and dancers on dance fitness, bone health, nutrition, pointe work, proprioception, and motor learning as well as a Bulletin for Teachers, plus a Studio Teachers Network. They have also partnered with Trinity College London on a Certificate in Safe and Effective Dance Practice for dancers and educators to gain knowledge of anatomy and physiology, injury management and nutrition. More information on the certificate and entering can be found at: www.trinitycollege.co.uk/site/?id=1598

Rudolf Nureyev Foundation Medical Website

This website contains the most up-to-date and relevant information contributed by experienced doctors and scientists about dancers' health, dance medicine and safe practice. Resources include an international listing of health practitioners who specialise in treating dancers, advice on safe practice and caring for common dance injuries and over 300 articles on topics in dancers' health. The website also has listings of events and helpful links, frequently asked questions about dance medicine and science, and a forum in several languages for dancers to ask questions. www.nureyev-medical.org

National Institute for Dance Medicine and Science

Dance UK is also working in partnership with Trinity Laban, Birmingham Royal Ballet's Jerwood Centre for the Prevention and Treatment of Dance Injuries and the University of Wolverhampton to establish centres for all top level dancers to have access to high quality, comprehensive, dance-specific healthcare as well as dance science support services on a par with those enjoyed by elite athletes and the dancers in the very largest ballet companies. For more information check out Dance UK's website: www.danceuk.org/healthier-dancer-programme/healthier-dancer-programme-campaigns/national-institute-dance-medicine-and-science

Please visit www.danceuk.org for any other general dance-related queries and advice.

1ST SUCCESS T 01628 780470
Empowerment, Confidence & Stress Therapies.
Challenge Blocks, Anxieties, Stresses & Fears
10 Gillott Court
St Lukes Road
Maidenhead, Berks SL6 7AD
E joanna@1stsuccess.com
W www.1stsuccess.com

ALEXANDER ALLIANCE T 01727 843633
Alexander Technique. Audition & Voice Coaching
3 Hazelwood Drive
St Albans, Herts
E bev.keech@ntlworld.com
W www.alextech.co.uk

ALEXANDER TECHNIQUE T 020 7731 1061
Contact: Jackie Coote MSTAT
27 Britannia Road, London SW6 2HJ
E jackiecoote@alexandertec.co.uk
W www.alexandertec.co.uk

ALEXANDER TECHNIQUE T 07956 852303
Contact: Robert Macdonald
13 Ascot Lodge, Greville Place
London NW6 5JD
W www.voice.org.uk

ALKALI T 020 8788 8588
Cosmetic Dentistry. Straightening. Whitening
226A Upper Richmond Road
Putney, London SW15 6TG
E hello@alkaliaesthetics.co.uk
W www.alkaliaesthetics.co.uk

ARTS CLINIC THE T 020 7935 1242
Personal & Professional Development.
Psychological Counselling
14 Devonshire Place
London W1G 6HX
F 020 7224 6256
E mail@artsclinic.co.uk

ASPEY ASSOCIATES T 0845 1701300
Executive Coaching. Human Resources.
Management & Team Training
90 Long Acre, Covent Garden
London WC2E 9RZ
E hr@aspey.com
W www.aspey.com

AURA DENTAL SPA T 020 7722 0040
5 Queens Terrace
London NW8 6DX
E info@auradentalspa.com
W www.auradentalspa.com

BLOOMSBURY ALEXANDER
CENTRE THE T 020 7404 5348
Alexander Technique
Bristol House, 80A Southampton Row
London WC1B 4BB
T 07884 015954
E enquiries@alexcentre.com
W www.alexcentre.com

BODY CLINIC THE T 0800 5424809
Skincare Specialists
Harley Street W1G
E info@thebodyclinic.co.uk
W www.thebodyclinic.co.uk

BODY CLINIC THE T 0800 5424809
Skincare Specialists
Gidea Park RM2
E info@thebodyclinic.co.uk
W www.thebodyclinic.co.uk

BODY CLINIC THE T 0800 5424809
Skincare Specialists
South Woodford E18
E info@thebodyclinic.co.uk
W www.thebodyclinic.co.uk

BODYWISE YOGA & NATURAL
HEALTH CENTRE T 020 8981 6938
119 Roman Road, London E2 0QN
E info@bodywisehealth.org
W www.bodywisehealth.org

BOXMOOR HOUSE
DENTAL PRACTICE T 01442 253253
451 London Road
Hemel Hempstead HP3 9BE
F 01442 244454
E d-gardner@btconnect.com

BREATHE FITNESS
PERSONAL TRAINING T 07840 180094
20 Enfield Street, Marylebone
London W1H 1DG
E anthony@breathefitness.uk.com
W www.breathefitness.uk.com

BURGESS, Chris T 07985 011694
Counsellor. Psychotherapist
New Road Consultancy Practice
28 New Road, Brighton BN1 1NG
E chrisburgess@netcom.co.uk

BURT, Andrew T 020 8992 5992
Counselling
74 Mill Hill Road, London W3 8JJ
E burt.counsel@tiscali.co.uk
W www.andrewburtcounselling.co.uk

COGNITIVE BEHAVIOURAL THERAPY (CBT)
Based in West & North London
E info@therapycbt.co.uk
W www.therapycbt.co.uk

CONFIDENT PERFORMER THE T 07859 914501
Based in London & Hertfordshire
E info@theconfidentperformer.com
W www.theconfidentperformer.com

CONSTRUCTIVE TEACHING
CENTRE LTD T 020 7727 7222
Alexander Technique Teacher Training
E constructiveteachingcentre@gmail.com
W www.constructiveteachingcentre.com

CORTEEN, Paola MSTAT T 020 8882 7898
Alexander Technique
10A Eversley Park Road
London N21 1JU
E pmcorteen@yahoo.co.uk

COURTENAY, Julian T 07973 139376
NLP Hypnotherapy
42 Langdon Park Road
London N6 5QG
E julian@mentalfitness.uk.com

CRAIGENTINNY DENTAL CARE   T 0131 669 2114
57 Duddingston Crescent, Milton Road
Edinburgh EH15 3AY
E dentist@craigentinny.co.uk
W www.craigentinny.co.uk

CROWE, Sara   T 07830 375389
Holistic Massage. Pregnancy Treatment. Reflexology
25 Holmes Avenue
Hove BN3 7LB
E saracrowe77@gmail.com

DAVIES, Siobhan
DANCE STUDIOS   T 020 7091 9650
Treatment Room
85 St George's Road
London SE1 6ER
F 020 7091 9669
E info@siobhandavies.com
W www.siobhandavies.com

DREAM   T 07973 731026
Massage, Reflexology & Yoga for the Workplace & Events.
Yoga Holidays in Goa
117B Gaisford Street, London NW5 2EG
E heidi@dreamtherapies.co.uk
W www.dreamtherapies.co.uk

EDGE OF THE WORLD
HYPNOTHERAPY & NLP   T 01206 391050
Contact: Graham Howes. ASHPH GHR Registered. GHSC
Regulated. Gastric Band/Weight Loss Hypnotherapy.
Specialist Help for Performers: Anxiety, Audition/Stage
Fright, Problems with Line Learning, Stress. Quit Smoking
Based in Central London
Essex/Suffolk
T 07875 720623
E info@edgehypno.com
W www.edgehypno.com

EDWARDS, Simon MCAHyp DABCH MHS MHA
MAPHP SQHP   T 020 7467 8498
Hypnotherapy for Professionals in Film, Stage & Television
10 Harley Street, London W1G 9PF
T 07889 333680
E simonedwardsharleystreet@gmail.com
W www.simonedwards.com

ELITE SPORTS SKILLS   T 07527 504052
Personal Training. Sports Coaching.
Level 4 in Fitness & Coaching
E esskills@hotmail.com
W www.elitesportsskills.com

ENLIGHTENED SELF INTEREST   T 07910 157064
45 Hyde Park Square
London W2 2JT
E shevlin-elmore@lcch.co.uk

EXPERIENTIAL FOCUSING
THERAPY SESSIONS   T 07941 300871
Contact: Dr Greg Madison
93-95 Gloucester Place, London W1
E info@gregmadison.net
W www.gregmadison.net

EXPERIENTIAL FOCUSING
THERAPY SESSIONS   T 07941 300871
40 Wilbury Road, Brighton BN1
E info@gregmadison.net
W www.gregmadison.net

EXPLORING U
COUNSELLING LTD   T 01787 829141
Practices in Braintree, Colchester, Sudbury, Saffron Walden,
Stanmore & Birmingham
The Workshop, 9 Hall Street
Long Melford
Nr Sudbury, Suffolk CO10 9JF
T 07841 979450
E euc@exploringUcounselling.co.uk
W www.exploringUcounselling.co.uk

FABULOUS-LIFESTYLES   T 07958 984195
Corporate Impact/Confidence Coach. Hypnotherapy.
Lifestyle & Presentation Coaching. NLP
E nicci@fabulous-lifestyles.com
W www.fabulous-lifestyles.com

FAITH, Gordon
BA MCHC (UK) Dip.REM.Sp   T 020 7328 0446
Focusing. Hypnotherapy. Obstacles to Performing.
Positive Affirmation
1 Wavel Mews
Priory Road
West Hampstead
London NW6 3AB
E gordon.faith@tiscali.co.uk
W www.hypnotherapy.gordonfaith.co.uk

FIT 4 THE PART   T 07702 590464
Contact: Jon Trevor. Celebrity Trainer.
Lifestyle Guru. Media Presenter
Based in North London
E info@fit4thepart.com
W www.fit4thepart.com

FITNESS COACH THE   T 020 7300 1414
Contact: Jamie Baird
Agua at The Sanderson
50 Berners Street, London W1T 3NG
T 07970 782476
E jamie@thefitnesscoach.com

FOOTPRINT COACHING   T 07976 572779
17B Granville Road
Sevenoaks, Kent TN13 1EX
E georgina@georginaburnett.com
W www.footprintcoaching.org.uk

HAMMOND, John
B. Ed (Hons) ICHFST   T/F 01277 632830
Fitness Consultancy. Sports & Relaxation Massage
4 Glencree, Billericay
Essex CM11 1EB
T 07703 185198
E johnhammond69@googlemail.com

HARLEY STREET VOICE
CENTRE THE   T 020 7224 2350
The Harley Street ENT Clinic
109 Harley Street
London W1G 6AN
F 020 7935 7701
E info@harleystreetent.com
W www.harleystreetent.com

HEARING AID DEVICES CENTRE   T 020 7935 5486
Hearing Protection. Invisible Hearing Aids. Tinnitus Maskers
109 Harley Street
London W1G 6AN
E info@hearing-aid-devices.co.uk
W www.hearing-aid-devices.co.uk

HILLSHYPNOTHERAPY   T 07590 466949
30 Tudor Road, Godmanchester
Huntingdon, Cambs PE29 2DP
E adamcharleshills@gmail.com

HILTON HOLISTICS   T 07548 896333
Hilton Hall, Hilton Lane
Essington, Staffordshire WV11 2BQ
E susan@cmc-technologies.co.uk

HYL ENERGISER   T 07768 321092
10 Little Newport Street
London WC2H 7JJ
E info@hylenergiser.com
W www.hylenergiser.com

HYPNOSIS WORKS   T 020 7237 5815
19 Glengall Road, London SE15 6NJ
E sssp@hypnosisdoeswork.net
W www.hypnosisdoeswork.net

IMPLANT & CERAMIC
DENTAL STUDIOS   T 01285 821220
The Club Room, Miserden
Gloucestershire GL6 7JA
E nicolas@ceramiccentre.com
W www.allaboutteeth.co.uk

INSPIRATIONAL WELLBEING   T 01992 576565
Energy Healer
131 Woodland Grove
Epping, Essex CM16 4NG
E inspirationalwellbeing@gmail.com
W www.inspirationalwellbeing.com

INTOUCH LONDON   T 07917 057078
Mobile Massage Therapist
E jade@intouch-london.com
W www.intouch-london.com

JLP FITNESS   T 07930 304809
Personal Trainer. Specialises in Boxing.
Kick/Muay-Thai Boxing. One-to-one or Group Sessions
E jlp@jacquileepryce.com

JOINT PERFORMANCE
OSTEOPATHY   T 07957 165070
Based in Covent Garden
Harley Street, & South East London
E info@jointperformance.co.uk
W www.jointperformance.co.uk

JOSHI CLINIC THE   T 020 7487 5456
Holistic Healthcare
57 Wimpole Street, London W1G 8YW
E reception@joshiclinic.co.uk
W www.joshiclinic.co.uk

LIFE PRACTICE UK LTD   T/F 01462 451473
Specialists in Coaching, NLP & Hypnotherapy
Woodlands, Preston Road
Gosmore, Hitchin, Herts SG4 7QS
E info@lifepractice.co.uk
W www.lifepractice.co.uk

LUCAS, Hazel   T 07870 862939
Qualified Holistic Masseur
119 Brightwell Avenue, Westcliff-on-Sea
Essex SS0 9EQ
E onedaylucas@blueyonder.co.uk

LYONS, Michelle WELLNESS   T 07527 571443
55 Dunn Terrace
Newcastle-upon-Tyne NE6 1AZ
E lyons.a.michelle@gmail.com

MAGIC KEY PARTNERSHIP THE   T 0845 1297401
Contact: Lyn Burgess. Life Coach
151A Moffat Road, Thornton Heath
Surrey CR7 8PZ
E lyn@magickey.co.uk
W www.magickey.co.uk

MATRIX ENERGY
FIELD THERAPY   T 01304 379466
Accredited Healer
Deal Castle House, 31 Victoria Road
Deal, Kent CT14 7AS
T 07762 821828
E donnie@lovingorganization.org

McCALLION, Anna   T 020 7602 5599
Alexander Technique. Voice
Flat 2, 11 Sinclair Gardens
London W14 0AU
E hildegarde007@yahoo.com

MINDSCI CLINIC   T/F 020 8948 2439
Clinical Hypnotism
34 Willow Bank, Ham
Richmond, Surrey TW10 7QX
E bt@mindsci-clinic.com
W www.mindsci-clinic.com

NOBLE, Penny
PSYCHOTHERAPY   T 07506 579895
8 Shaftesbury Gardens, Victoria Road
North Acton, London NW10 6LJ
E pennynobletherapy@googlemail.com
W www.pennynoblepsychotherapy.com

NORTON, Michael R.   T 020 7486 9229
Implant/Reconstructive Dentistry
104 Harley Street, London W1G 7JD
F 020 7486 9119
E linda@nortonimplants.com
W www.nortonimplants.com

NUTRITIONAL THERAPY
FOR PERFORMERS   T 07962 978763
Contact: Vanessa May BSc CNHC NTC & BANT Reg
18 Oaklands Road
Ealing, London W7 2DR
E vanessa@wellbeingandnutrition.co.uk
W www.wellbeingandnutrition.co.uk

OGUNLARU, Rasheed   T 020 7207 1082
Life & Business Coach
The Coaching Studio
223A Mayall Road
London SE24 0PS
E rasheed@rasaru.com
W www.rasaru.com

PEAK PERFORMANCE
TRAINING   T 01628 633509
Contact: Tina Reibl. Hypnotherapy. NLP. Success Strategies
42 The Broadway
Maidenhead, Berkshire SL6 1LU
E tina.reibl@tesco.net
W www.maidenhead-hypnotherapy.co.uk

POLAND, Ken DENTAL STUDIOS   T 020 7935 6919
Film & Stage Dentistry
1 Devonshire Place
London W1G 6HH
F 020 7486 3952
E robpoland@btconnect.com

PSYCHOTHERAPY &
MEDICAL HYPNOSIS   T 020 7794 5843
Contact: Karen Mann DCH DHP. Including Performance
Improvement & Let Go of the Past
10 Harley Street, London W1G 9PF
E emailkarenmann@googlemail.com
W www.karenmann.co.uk

REACH TO THE SKY LTD   T 0843 2892503
Contact: Dr T.W.S. Johnson. Success Life Coach
Maxet House, Liverpool Road
Luton, Bedfordshire LU1 1RS
T 07961 911027
E drtwsj@reachtothesky.com
W www.wix.com/mylifecoach/dr

ROBERTS, Dan -
ELITE PERSONAL TRAINING   T 07958 774541
38 Calverton Street
London SW1V 3AU
E info@danrobertstraining.com
W www.danrobertstraining.com

SEYRI, Kayvan MSc NSCA-CPT*D
CSCS*D NASM-PES CES   T 07881 554636
Athletic Performance Specialist. Master Personal Trainer
E info@ultimatefitpro.com
W www.ultimatefitpro.com

SHENAS, Dr DENTAL STUDIO   T 020 7589 2319
51 Cadogan Gardens, Sloane Square
Chelsea, London SW3 2TH
E info@shenasdental.co.uk
W www.shenasdental.co.uk

SHER SYSTEM THE   T 01784 227805
Helping Skin with Acne & Rosacea
PO Box 573, Staines
Middlesex TW18 9FJ
F 01784 463410
E skincare@sher.co.uk
W www.sher.co.uk

SHIATSU HEALTH CENTRE   T 07905 504418
Moving Arts Base, 134 Liverpool Road
London N1 1LA
E japaneseyoga@btinternet.com
W www.shiatsuhealth.com

SMILE NW   T 020 8458 2333
Contact: Dr Veronica Morris (Cosmetic & General Dentist)
17 Hallswelle Parade, Finchley Road
Temple Fortune, London NW11 0DL
F 020 8458 5681
E enquiries@smile-nw.co.uk
W www.smile-nw.co.uk

SMILE SOLUTIONS   T 020 7449 1760
Dental Practice
24 Englands Lane, London NW3 4TG
F 020 7449 1769
E enquiries@smile-solutions.info
W www.smile-solutions.info

SPORTS MEDICINE
ON SCREEN   T 07796 936442
1 Louis Drive East
London SS6 9DU
E administrator@starinjuries.com
W www.starinjuries.com

STAT (THE SOCIETY OF TEACHERS OF THE
ALEXANDER TECHNIQUE)   T 020 7482 5135
1st Floor Linton House
39-51 Highgate Road
London NW5 1RT
F 020 7482 5435
E enquiries@stat.org.uk
W www.stat.org.uk

THEATRICAL DENTISTRY   T/F 020 7580 9696
Contact: Richard D. Casson (Cosmetic Dentist).
Cosmetic. Orthodontic
6 Milford House
7 Queen Anne Street
London W1G 9HN
E smile@richardcasson.com
W www.richardcasson.com

TOP NOTCH NANNIES   T 020 7824 8209
142 Buckingham Palace Road
London SW1W 9TR
T 020 7881 0893
E jean@topnotchnannies.com
W www.topnotchnannies.com

VITAL TOUCH (UK) LTD THE   T 07976 263691
50 Greenham Road
Muswell Hill
London N10 1LP
E suzi@thevitaltouch.com
W www.thevitaltouch.com

WALK-IN BACKRUB   T/F 020 7436 9875
On-site Massage Company
14 Neals Yard
London WC2H 9DP
E info@walkinbackrub.co.uk
W www.walkinbackrub.co.uk

WELLBEING   T 07957 333921
Contact: Leigh Jones. Personal Training. Tai Chi. Yoga
22 Galloway Close
Broxbourne
Herts EN10 6BU
E williamleighjones@hotmail.com

WOODFORD HOUSE
DENTAL PRACTICE   T 020 8504 2704
162 High Road
Woodford Green
Essex IG8 9EF
E info@improveyoursmile.co.uk
W www.improveyoursmile.co.uk

WORSLEY, Victoria   T 07711 088765
Feldenkrais Practitioner.
Addresses Habits of Moving, Breathing & Thinking which
Limit Range or Cause Pain
32 Clovelly Road
London N8 7RH
E v.worsley@virgin.net
W www.feldenkraisworks.co.uk

N →

Non-Acting Jobs

42ND STREET RECRUITMENT T 020 7734 4422
Linen Hall
162-168 Regent Street
London W1B 5TD
E info@42ndstreetrecruitment.com
W www.42ndstreetrecruitment.com

ACHIEVE RECRUITMENT T 020 7138 3170
Temporary & Permanent Recruitment
271 Regent Street
London SW11 5SQ
F 0845 3632007
E ben.davidson@achieverecruit.co.uk
W www.achieverecruit.co.uk

**AT YOUR SERVICE EVENT
STAFFING LTD** T 020 7610 8610
Temporary Event Staff
Unit 12, The Talina Centre
Bagley's Lane
Fulham, London SW6 2BW
F 020 7610 8616
E sam@ays.co.uk
W www.apply.ays.co.uk

ATTITUDE EVENTS T 020 7953 7935
Event Consultation & Staffing
412 Coppergate House
16 Brune Street
London E1 7NJ
E nikki@attitude-events.com
W www.attitude-events.com

BREEZE PEOPLE T 07903 012859
Promotional Staffing Agency
12 Warren Road
London SW19 2HX
T 07903 012861
E peepz@breezepeople.co.uk
W www.breezepeople.co.uk

**BRISTOW, Lucy
APPOINTMENTS** T 0117 925 5988
Recruitment for Office Staff
12 Orchard Street
Bristol BS1 5EH
E enquire@lucybristow.com
W www.lucybristow.com

CATERINGTEMPS.COM LTD T 020 7713 8772
*Suppliers of Temporary Staff
to the Catering & Hospitality Industry*
108-110 Judd Street
London WC1H 9PX
F 020 7713 6297
E ash@cateringtemps.com
W www.cateringtemps.com

**CENTRAL EMPLOYMENT
AGENCY** T 0191 232 4816
34-36 St Mary's Place
Newcastle upon Tyne NE1 7PQ
F 0191 261 2293
E info@centralemployment.co.uk
W www.centralemployment.co.uk

COVENT GARDEN BUREAU T 020 7734 3374
Recruitment Consultants
5-6 Argyll Street, London W1F 7TE
E cv@coventgardenbureau.co.uk
W www.coventgardenbureau.co.uk

DIAMOND RESOURCING PLC T 020 7929 2977
Generalist Recruitment Consultancy
29-30 Leadenhall Market, London EC3V 1LR
E juliesjobs@diamondresourcing.com
W www.diamondresourcing.com

FAIRYTALE PROMOTIONS T 01636 605291
Event Management, Promotional & Modelling Agency
6 Milton Street, New Balderton
Newark, Nottinghamshire NG24 3AW
E info@fairytalepromotions.com
W www.fairytalepromotions.com

FISHER, Judy ASSOCIATES T 020 7437 2277
Recruitment Consultants
7 Swallow Street, London W1B 4DE
F 020 7434 2696
E margaret@judyfisher.co.uk
W www.judyfisher.c o.uk

FOUR SEASONS RECRUITMENT T 020 8237 8900
Recruitment Company
Landmark House
Hammersmith Bridge Road
London W6 9EJ
F 020 8237 8999
E jo@fsrl.co.uk
W www.fsrl.co.uk

GOGEN T 020 7923 8130
Telephone Fundraising
2A Abbot Street, London E8 3DP
W www.gogen.org

GREEK CONCIERGE T 07763 141470
Event Entertainment
70 Inverness Terrace, London W2 3LB
E members@greek-concierge.com
W www.greekconcierge.com

ID STAFFING T 020 7428 1444
Highgate Studios
53-79 Highgate Road
London NW5 1TL
E recruitment@idstaffing.com
W www.idexperiential.co.uk/idstaffing

JAM STAFFING LTD T 020 7237 2228
Events Company. Part-time Flexible Bar & Waiting Work
Unit 104, The Light Box
111 Power Road, London W4 5PY
E katie@jamstaffing.com
W www.jamstaffing.com

JFL SEARCH & SELECTION T 020 7009 3500
Recruitment Consultants
27 Beak Street, London W1F 9RU
F 020 7734 6501
W www.jflrecruit.com

LEISUREJOBS T 020 7622 8500
*Temporary, Promotional & Permanent
Positions within Leisure*
Cloisters House
8 Battersea Park Road
London SW8 4BG
E info@leisurejobs.com
W www.leisurejobs.com

**LUMLEYS HOSPITALITY
& CATERING** T 020 7630 0545
Private & Corporate Hospitality, Catering & Events
Grosvenor Gardens House
35-37 Grosvenor Gardens
London SW1W 0BS
E admin@lumleyscooks.co.uk
W www.lumleyscooks.co.uk

MORTIMER, Angela T 020 7287 7788
*Recruitment Specialists for Perm & Temp PAs & Support
Staff in the UK & Europe*
37-38 Golden Square
London W1F 9LA
E info@angelamortimer.com
W www.angelamortimer.com

NETWORK THE T 020 8742 4336
Field Marketing & Promotions
Merlin House, 20 Belmont Terrace
Chiswick
London W4 5UG
F 020 8742 4051
E spotlight@thenetwork-uk.com
W www.thenetwork-uk.com

OFF TO WORK T 020 7381 8222
*Non-acting Employment. Promotional Work at Events across
the UK*
3rd Floor, 79 Knightsbridge
London SW1X 7RB
E mariela@offtowork.co.uk
W www.offtowork.co.uk

OFFICETEAM T 020 7389 6900
Grand Buildings, 1-3 Strand
London WC2N 5HR
E london@officeteamuk.com
W www.officeteamuk.com

**PERTEMPS RECRUITMENT
PARTNERSHIP** T 020 7621 1304
Recruitment Consultancy
1st Floor
106 Leadenhall Street
London EC3A 4AA
F 020 7626 6671
E jamie.so@pertemps.co.uk
W www.pertemps.co.uk

PYRAMID PEOPLE T 07792 405929
Suppliers of a range of Acts & Staffing
Unit 00, Mellish Industrial Estate
Harrington Way
London SE18 5NR
E laura@pyramidpeople.co.uk

RSVP (MEDIA RESPONSE LTD)   T 0800 665400
5th Floor
Northern & Shell Tower
4 Selsdon Way
London E14 9GL
E response@rsvp.co.uk
W www.rsvp.co.uk

STAFFWAREHOUSE   T 020 7490 8477
Events Promotional Agency
6-7 Albemarle Way, Farringdon
London EC1V 4JB
F 020 7806 8322
E gavin@staffwarehouse.biz
W www.staffwarehouse.biz

SENSE STAFFING   T 020 7034 2000
Promotional Staffing for Experiential Marketing
2nd Floor, 100 Oxford Street
London W1D 1LN
E staff@senselondon.com
W www.senselondon.com

STUCKFORSTAFF.CO.UK   T 0844 5869595
Promotions, Field Marketing & Brand Experience
Studio 31, Fazeley Studios
191 Fazeley Street, Birmingham
West Midlands B5 5SE
E info@stuckforstaff.com
W www.stuckforstaff.co.uk

SEYNER BENSON   T 020 7813 2121
Temporary Non-acting Positions available in
Museums & Galleries in London
Tudor House
35 Gresse Street
London W1T 1QY
F 020 7813 1414
E admin@seynerbenson.com

TAY ASSOCIATES LTD   T 020 7065 6700
Media Recruitment Agency Specialising in
Support Staff for Arts, Film, Stage & Television
10 Throgmorton Avenue
London EC2N 2DL
E dib@tayassociates.co.uk
W www.tayassociates.com

SMITH, Amanda
RECRUITMENT LTD   T 020 7681 6180
Recruitment of Temporary, Permanent &
Contract Office Support Staff
88 Kingsway, Holborn
London WC2B 6AA
E info@as-recruitment.co.uk

TRIBE MARKETING LTD   T 020 7749 2600
Experiential Marketing & Promotional Staffing Agency
The Tea Building
56 Shoreditch High Street
London E1 6JJ
E dan.campbell@tribemarketing.co.uk
W www.tribemarketing.co.uk

O →

Opera Companies
Organisations

Opera Companies

CAPITAL ARTS OPERA MINOR   T/F 020 8449 2342
Children's Opera Company. For Students aged 6-18
Capital Arts Studio, Wyllyotts Centre
Potters Bar, Herts EN6 2HN
E capitalarts@btconnect.com
W www.capitalarts.org.uk

CARL ROSA OPERA   T 020 7613 0777
359 Hackney Road, London E2 8PR
F 020 7613 0859
E info@carlrosaopera.co.uk
W www.carlrosaopera.co.uk

CO-OPERA CO PRODUCTIONS   T 020 8699 8650
5 Orchard Business Centre
Kangley Bridge Road
London SE26 5AQ
E info@co-opera-co.org
W www.co-opera-co.org

ENGLISH NATIONAL OPERA   T 020 7836 0111
London Coliseum
St Martin's Lane
London WC2N 4ES
F 020 7845 9277
W www.eno.org

ENGLISH TOURING OPERA   T 020 7833 2555
Contact: James Conway
1st Floor
52-54 Rosebery Avenue
London EC1R 4RP
F 020 7713 8686
E admin@englishtouringopera.org.uk
W www.englishtouringopera.org.uk

GARSINGTON OPERA   T 01865 368201
The Old Garage, The Green
Great Milton, Oxford OX44 7NP
F 01865 961545
W www.garsingtonopera.org

GLYNDEBOURNE FESTIVAL OPERA   T 01273 812321
Glyndebourne, Lewes
East Sussex BN8 5UU
W www.glyndebourne.com

GRANGE PARK OPERA   T 01962 737360
24-26 Broad Street, Alresford
Hampshire SO24 9AQ
E info@grangeparkopera.co.uk
W www.grangeparkopera.co.uk

GUBBAY, Raymond LTD   T 020 7025 3750
Dickens House, 15 Tooks Court
London EC4A 1QH
F 020 7025 3751
E info@raymondgubbay.co.uk
W www.raymondgubbay.co.uk

KENTISH OPERA   T 01732 700993
Contact: Sally Langford
Lakefields Farmhouse, Ide Hill Road
Bough Beech, Kent TN8 7PW
E sl.sweald@fsmail.net
W www.kentishopera.fsnet.co.uk

MUSIC THEATRE LONDON   T 07831 243942
c/o Capriol Films
The Old Reading Room
The Street, Brinton
Melton Constable, Norfolk NR24 2QF
E info@capriolfilms.co.uk
W www.capriolfilms.co.uk

OPERA DELLA LUNA   T 01869 325131
7 Cotmore House, Fringford
Bicester, Oxfordshire OX27 8RQ
E enquiries@operadellaluna.org
W www.operadellaluna.org

OPERA NORTH   T 0113 243 9999
Grand Theatre, 46 New Briggate
Leeds LS1 6NU
F 0113 244 0418
E info@operanorth.co.uk
W www.operanorth.co.uk

OPERAUK LTD   T 020 7628 0025
Charity
177 Andrewes House
Barbican, London EC2Y 8BA
E rboss4@aol.com
W www.operauk.co.uk

PEGASUS OPERA COMPANY LTD   T/F 020 7501 9501
The Brix, St Matthew's
Brixton Hill, London SW2 1JF
E admin@pegopera.org
W www.pegopera.org

PIMLICO OPERA   T 01962 737360
24 Broad Street
Alresford
Hampshire SO24 9AQ
E pimlico@grangeparkopera.co.uk
W www.grangeparkopera.co.uk

PMB PRESENTATIONS LTD   T 020 7368 3337
Vicarage House
58-60 Kensington Church Street
London W8 4DB
F 020 7368 3338
E p@triciamurraybett.com
W www.pmbpresentations.co.uk

ROYAL OPERA THE   T 020 7240 1200
Royal Opera House
Bow Street
Covent Garden
London WC2E 9DD
W www.roh.org.uk

SCOTTISH OPERA   T 0141 248 4567
39 Elmbank Crescent
Glasgow G2 4PT
W www.scottishopera.org.uk

WELSH NATIONAL OPERA   T 029 2063 5000
Wales Millennium Centre
Bute Place, Cardiff CF10 5AL
F 029 2063 5099
E marketing@wno.org.uk
W www.wno.org.uk

A STAGE KINDLY
T 07947 074887
Develops & Produces New Musicals
7 Northiam, Cromer Street, London WC1H 8LB
E mail@astagekindly.com
W www.astagekindly.com

ABTT (ASSOCIATION OF BRITISH THEATRE TECHNICIANS)
T 020 7242 9200
4th Floor, 55 Farringdon Road, London EC1M 3JB
F 020 7242 9303
E office@abtt.org.uk
W www.abtt.org.uk

ACADEMY OF PERFORMANCE COMBAT THE
T 07963 206803
Teaching Body of Stage Combat
Ivy Villa, 250 Lees New Road
Lees, Lancs OL4 5PP
E info@theapc.org.uk
W www.theapc.org.uk

ACTORS' ADVISORY SERVICE
T 020 8287 2839
Provides Advice to Actors, Agents, Photographers etc
29 Talbot Road, Twickenham
Middlesex TW2 6SJ

ACTORS' BENEVOLENT FUND
T 020 7836 6378
6 Adam Street, London WC2N 6AD
F 020 7836 8978
E office@abf.org.uk
W www.actorsbenevolentfund.co.uk

ACTORS CENTRE (LONDON) THE
T 020 7632 8001
*Charity. 1700 Classes a year for professional actors.
Advice & information. Introductory Courses*
1A Tower Street, London WC2H 9NP
E reception@actorscentre.co.uk
W www.actorscentre.co.uk

ACTORS CENTRE NORTH
T/F 0161 639 0860
*Contact: Maggie Lackey. Charity. Provides Advice, Support &
Information. Workshops in continuing professional
development for professionally trained actors*
46-50 Oldham Street, Manchester M4 1LE
E info@actorscentrenorth.com
W www.actorscentrenorth.com

ACTORS' CHARITABLE TRUST
T 020 7636 7868
Provides Advice & Support. Grants for Actors' Children
58 Bloomsbury Street
London WC1B 3QT
F 020 7637 3368
E robert@tactactors.org

ACTORS' CHURCH UNION
T 020 7240 0344
St Paul's Church, Bedford Street
London WC2E 9ED
E actors-church.union@tiscali.co.uk

ADVERTISING ASSOCIATION
T 020 7340 1100
7th Floor North, Artillery House
11-19 Artillery Row, London SW1P 1RT
F 020 7222 1504
E aa@adassoc.org.uk
W www.adassoc.org.uk

AGENTS' ASSOCIATION (Great Britain)
T 020 7834 0515
54 Keyes House
Dolphin Square, London SW1V 3NA
E association@agents-uk.com
W www.agents-uk.com

ARTS & BUSINESS
T 020 7378 8143
Nutmeg House, 60 Gainsford Street
Butlers Wharf
London SE1 2NY
F 020 7407 7527
E head.office@aandb.org.uk
W www.artsandbusiness.org.uk

ARTS CENTRE GROUP
T 0845 4581881
c/o Paintings in Hospitals
51 Southwark Street, London SE1 1RU
T 020 7407 1881
E info@artscentregroup.org.uk
W www.artscentregroup.org.uk

ARTS COUNCIL ENGLAND
T 0845 3006200
T 020 7973 6564 (Textphone)
W www.artscouncil.org.uk

ARTS COUNCIL OF NORTHERN IRELAND
T 028 9038 5200
MacNeice House
77 Malone Road, Belfast BT9 6AQ
F 028 9066 1715
E info@artscouncil-ni.org
W www.artscouncil-ni.org

ARTS COUNCIL OF WALES, MID & WEST WALES OFFICE
T 01267 234248
*Ceredigion, Carmarthenshire, Pembrokeshire, Powys,
Swansea, Neath & Port Talbot*
6 Gardd Llydaw, Jacksons Lane
Carmarthen SA31 1QD
F 01267 233084
E midandwest@artswales.org.uk
W www.artswales.org.uk

ARTS COUNCIL OF WALES, NORTH WALES OFFICE
T 01492 533440
*Isle of Anglesey, Gwynedd, Conwy, Denbighshire,
Flintshire, Wrexham*
36 Prince's Drive
Colwyn Bay, Conwy LL29 8LA
F 01492 533677
E north@artswales.org.uk
W www.artswales.org.uk

ARTS COUNCIL OF WALES, SOUTH WALES & CENTRAL OFFICE
T 0845 8734900
*Vale of Glamorgan, Cardiff, Newport, Monmouthshire,
Torfaen, Blaenau Gwent, Caerphilly, Merthyr Tydfil,
Rhonda Cynon Taff, Bridgend*
Bute Place, Cardiff CF10 5AL
F 029 2041 1400
E info@artswales.org.uk
W www.artswales.org.uk

ARTSLINE
T 020 7388 2227
Disability Access Information Service
c/o 21 Pine Court, Wood Lodge Gardens
Bromley BR1 2WA
E admin@artsline.org.uk
W www.artsline.org.uk

ASSOCIATION OF LIGHTING DESIGNERS
T 07817 060189
E office@ald.org.uk
W www.ald.org.uk

ASSOCIATION OF MODEL AGENTS
T 020 7422 0699
11-29 Fashion Street
London E1 6PX
E amainfo@btinternet.com

BASCA - BRITISH ACADEMY OF SONGWRITERS, COMPOSERS & AUTHORS
T 020 7636 2929
2nd Floor, British Music House
26 Berners Street, London W1T 3LR
F 020 7636 2212
E info@basca.org.uk
W www.basca.org.uk

BFI SOUTH BANK
T 020 7928 3535
Belvedere Road, South Bank
London SE1 8XT
W www.bfi.org.uk

WE CAN HELP ACTORS' CHILDREN

Organisations

BRITISH ACADEMY OF FILM
& TELEVISION ARTS   T 020 7734 0022
195 Piccadilly, London W1J 9LN
F 020 7292 5868
E membership@bafta.org
W www.bafta.org

BRITISH ACADEMY OF FILM & TELEVISION
ARTS / LOS ANGELES   T 001 323 658 6590
8533 Melrose Avenue
West Hollywood, CA 90069, USA
F 001 310 854 6002
E office@baftala.org
W www.baftala.org

BRITISH ACADEMY OF STAGE
& SCREEN COMBAT   T 07981 806265
Suite 280, 10 Great Russell Street, London WC1B 3BQ
E info@bassc.org
W www.bassc.org

BRITISH ASSOCIATION FOR PERFORMING ARTS
MEDICINE (BAPAM)   T 020 7404 8444
Charity
4th Floor, Totara Park House
34-36 Gray's Inn Road, London WC1X 8HR
E clinic@bapam.org.uk
W www.bapam.org.uk

BRITISH ASSOCIATION OF
DRAMATHERAPISTS THE   T 01242 235515
Waverley, Battledown Approach
Cheltenham, Glos GL52 6RE
E enquiries@badth.org.uk
W www.badth.org.uk

BRITISH BOARD OF
FILM CLASSIFICATION   T 020 7440 1570
3 Soho Square, London W1D 3HD
F 020 7287 0141
W www.bbfc.co.uk

BRITISH COUNCIL   T 020 7389 3194
Arts Group
10 Spring Gardens, London SW1A 2BN
E arts@britishcouncil.org
W www.britishcouncil.org/arts

BRITISH EQUITY
COLLECTING SOCIETY   T 020 7670 0360
1st Floor, Guild House, Upper St Martin's Lane
London WC2H 9EG
E becs@equity.org.uk
W www.equitycollecting.org.uk

BRITISH FILM INSTITUTE   T 020 7255 1444
21 Stephen Street, London W1T 1LN
F 020 7436 0165
W www.bfi.org.uk

BRITISH LIBRARY
SOUND ARCHIVE   T 020 7412 7676
96 Euston Road, London NW1 2DB
F 020 7412 7609
E sound-archive@bl.uk
W www.bl.uk/soundarchive

BRITISH MUSIC HALL SOCIETY   T 01727 768878
Contact: Daphne Masterton (Secretary). Charity
45 Mayflower Road, Park Street
St Albans, Herts AL2 2QN
W www.music-hall-society.com

CATHOLIC ASSOCIATION OF
PERFORMING ARTS   T 020 7240 1221
Contact: Ms Molly Steele (Hon Secretary). By Post (SAE)
1 Maiden Lane, London WC2E 7NB
E secretary@caapa.org.uk
W www.caapa.org.uk

CELEBRITY BULLETIN THE   T 020 8672 3191
Battersea Studios, Studio G8
80 Silverthorne Road, London SW8 3HE
F 020 8672 2282
E enquiries@celebrity-bulletin.co.uk

CHILDREN'S FILM & TELEVISION
FOUNDATION LTD   T 07887 573479
E annahome@cftf.org.uk

CIDA (CREATIVE INDUSTRIES DEVELOPMENT
AGENCY)   T 01484 483140
Professional Development & Business Support for
Artists & Creative Businesses
Media Centre, Huddersfield
West Yorkshire HD1 1RL
F 01484 483150
E info@cida.org
W www.cida.org

CINEMA & TELEVISION BENEVOLENT FUND
(CTBF)   T 020 7437 6567
22 Golden Square, London W1F 9AD
F 020 7437 7186
E charity@ctbf.co.uk
W www.ctbf.co.uk

CINEMA EXHIBITORS'
ASSOCIATION   T 020 7734 9551
22 Golden Square, London W1F 9JW
F 020 7734 6147
E info@cinemauk.ftech.org.uk
W www.cinemauk.org.uk

CLUB FOR ACTS & ACTORS   T 020 7836 2884
(Members)
Incorporating Concert Artistes Association
20 Bedford Street, London WC2E 9HP
T 020 7836 3172 (Office)
E office@thecaa.org
W www.thecaa.org

COMPANY OF CRANKS   T 07963 617981
1st Floor, 62 Northfield House
Frensham Street, London SE15 6TN
E mimetic16@yahoo.com
W www.mimeworks.com

CONCERT ARTISTES ASSOCIATION
See *CLUB FOR ACTS & ACTORS*

CONFERENCE OF DRAMA SCHOOLS
Contact: Saul Hyman. Comprises Britain's Leading Drama
Schools. Publishes the Guide to Professional Training in
Drama & Technical Theatre
PO Box 34252, London NW5 1XJ
E info@cds.drama.ac.uk
W www.drama.ac.uk

COUNCIL FOR DANCE EDUCATION
& TRAINING (CDET)   T 020 7240 5703
Old Brewer's Yard, 17-19 Neal Street
London WC2H 9UY
F 020 7240 2547
E info@cdet.org.uk
W www.cdet.org.uk

CPMA (CO-OPERATIVE PERSONAL
MANAGEMENT ASSOCIATION)   T 07876 641582
The Secretary, c/o 62 Foulden Road
London N16 7UR
E cpmauk@yahoo.co.uk
W www.cpma.coop

CRITICS' CIRCLE THE   T 020 7483 1181
c/o Catherine Cooper Events
48 De Walden House, Allitsen Road
St John's Wood, London NW8 7BA
W www.criticscircle.org.uk

DANCE HOUSE T 0141 552 2442
The Briggait, 141 Bridgegate
Glasgow G1 5HZ
E info@dancehouse.org
W www.dancehouse.org

DANCE UK T 020 7713 0730
Including the Healthier Dancer Programme & 'The UK Choreographers' Directory'. Professional Body & Charity, providing Advice, Information & Support
The Urdang, The Old Finsbury Town Hall
Rosebery Avenue, London EC1R 4QT
F 020 7833 2363
E info@danceuk.org
W www.danceuk.org

DENVILLE HALL T 01923 825843 (Office)
Provides residential & nursing care to actors & other theatrical professions
62 Ducks Hill Road
Northwood, Middlesex HA6 2SB
T 01923 820805 (Residents)
E office@denvillehall.org.uk
W www.denvillehall.org.uk

DIRECTORS UK T 020 7240 0009
Inigo Place, 31 & 32 Bedford Street
London WC2E 9ED
F 020 7845 9700
E info@directors.uk.com
W www.directors.uk.com

DON'T PLAY ME PAY ME CAMPAIGN T 07554 424022
Campaigning for a Greater Representation of Disabled Talent in the Entertainment Industry
5 Kenwood Road, Shrewsbury, Shropshire SY3 8AJ
E nicola0253@gmail.com
W www.dontplaymepayme.com

D'OYLY CARTE OPERA COMPANY T 0844 6060007
295 Kennington Road, London SE11 4QE
F 020 7820 0240
E ian@doylycarte.org.uk
W www.doylycarte.org.uk

DRAMA ASSOCIATION OF WALES T 029 2045 2200
Specialist Drama Lending Library
Unit 2, The Maltings, East Tyndall Street
Cardiff Bay, Cardiff CF24 5EA
E teresa@dramawales.org.uk
W www.dramawales.org.uk

DRAMATURGS' NETWORK T 07939 270566
UK-wide Voluntary Network of Professional Dramaturgs. Develops Dramaturgy & Supports Practitioners' Development
16 Warner Road, London E17 7DZ
E info@dramaturgy.co.uk
W www.dramaturgy.co.uk

ENGLISH FOLK DANCE & SONG SOCIETY T 020 7485 2206
Cecil Sharp House
2 Regent's Park Road, London NW1 7AY
F 020 7284 0534
E info@efdss.org
W www.efdss.org

EQUITY CHARITABLE TRUST T 020 7831 1926
Plouviez House, 19-20 Hatton Place
London EC1N 8RU
F 020 7242 7995
E info@equitycharitabletrust.org.uk

FILM LONDON T 020 7613 7676
Suite 6.10, The Tea Building
56 Shoreditch High Street, London E1 6JJ
F 020 7613 7677
E info@filmlondon.org.uk
W www.filmlondon.org.uk

GLASGOW FILM OFFICE T 0141 287 0424
Free Advice & Liaison Support for all Productions
City Chambers, Glasgow G2 1DU
F 0141 287 0311
E info@glasgowfilm.com

GRAND ORDER OF WATER RATS T 020 7278 3248
328 Gray's Inn Road, London WC1X 8BZ
F 020 7278 1765
E info@gowr.net
W www.gowr.net

GROUP LINE T 020 7580 6793
Group Bookings for London Theatre
22-24 Torrington Place, London WC1E 7HJ
F 020 7436 6287
E tix@groupline.com
W www.groupline.com

HAMMER FILMS PRESERVATION SOCIETY T 020 8854 7383
Fan Club
14 Kingsdale Road
Plumstead, London SE18 2DG
E braystudios@live.com

INDEPENDENT THEATRE COUNCIL (ITC) T 020 7403 1727
Professional Body offering Advice, Information, Support & Political Representation
12 The Leathermarket, Weston Street, London SE1 3ER
F 020 7403 1745
E admin@itc-arts.org
W www.itc-arts.org

INTERNATIONAL CENTRE FOR VOICE
Central School of Speech & Drama
Eton Avenue, London NW3 3HY
E icv@cssd.ac.uk
W www.icvoice.co.uk

IRVING SOCIETY THE T 020 8566 8301
Contact: Michael Kilgarriff (Hon. Secretary)
10 Kings Avenue, London W5 2SH
E secretary@theirvingsociety.org.uk
W www.theirvingsociety.org.uk

ITC
See INDEPENDENT THEATRE COUNCIL

ITV PLC T 020 7157 3000
London Television Centre
Upper Ground, London SE1 9LT
W www.itv.com

LONDON SCHOOL OF CAPOEIRA THE T 020 7281 2020
Units 1 & 2 Leeds Place, Tollington Park, London N4 3RF
E info@londonschoolofcapoeira.com
W www.londonschoolofcapoeira.com

LONDON SHAKESPEARE WORKOUT T/F 020 7793 9755
PO Box 31855, London SE17 3XP
E londonswo@hotmail.com
W www.lswproductions.co.uk

MANDER & MITCHENSON THEATRE COLLECTION T 0117 331 5086
University of Bristol Theatre Collection
Department of Drama, Cantocks Close, Bristol BS8 1UP
F 0117 331 5082
E theatre-collection@bristol.ac.uk

NATIONAL ASSOCIATION OF YOUTH THEATRES (NAYT) T 01325 363330
Contact: Jo Harker. Founded in 1982, NAYT works with over 1,000 groups & individuals to support the development of youth theatre activity through information & support services, advocacy, training, participation & partnerships
Arts Centre, Vane Terrace
Darlington, County Durham DL3 7AX
F 01325 363313
E nayt@btconnect.com
W www.nayt.org.uk

NATIONAL CAMPAIGN FOR THE ARTS T 020 7287 3777
1 Kingly Street, London W1B 5PA
F 020 7287 4777
E nca@artscampaign.org.uk
W www.artscampaign.org.uk

NATIONAL COUNCIL FOR DRAMA TRAINING T 020 7407 3686
249 Tooley Street, London SE1 2JX
E info@ncdt.co.uk
W www.ncdt.co.uk

NATIONAL RESOURCE CENTRE FOR DANCE T 01483 689316
University of Surrey, Guildford, Surrey GU2 7XH
F 01483 689500
E nrcd@surrey.ac.uk W www.surrey.ac.uk/nrcd

NODA (National Operatic & Dramatic Association)   T 01733 865790
Charity, providing Advice, Information & Support. Largest umbrella body for amateur theatre in the UK offering advice & assistance on all aspects of amateur theatre plus workshops, summer school and social events
Noda House, 58-60 Lincoln Road
Peterborough PE1 2RZ
F 01733 319506
E info@noda.org.uk
W www.noda.org.uk

NORTH WEST PLAYWRIGHTS   T/F 0161 237 1978
Charity. Provides Advice, Information & Support. Regional Agency Developing & Supporting Scriptwriters in All Media
18 Express Networks
1 George Leigh Street
Manchester M4 5DL
E newplaysnw@hotmail.com
W www.northwestplaywrights.co.uk

OFCOM   T 0300 1234000
Ofcom Media Office, Riverside House
2A Southwark Bridge Road
London SE1 9HA
E ofcomnews@ofcom.org.uk
W www.ofcom.org.uk

PACT   T 020 7380 8230
Trade Association for Independent Television, Feature Film & New Media Production Companies
3rd Floor, Fitzrovia House, 153-157 Cleveland Street
London W1T 6QW
E info@pact.co.uk
W www.pact.co.uk

PERFORMING RIGHT SOCIETY LTD   T 020 7580 5544
29-33 Berners Street, London W1T 3AB
F 020 7306 4455
W www.prsformusic.com

RICHARDSON, Ralph & Meriel FOUNDATION   T 020 7636 1616
c/o Suite 23, 19 Cavendish Square, London W1A 2AW
F 020 7664 4489
E manager@sirralphrichardson.org.uk
W www.sirralphrichardson.org.uk

ROYAL TELEVISION SOCIETY   T 020 7822 2810
5th Floor, Kildare House
3 Dorset Rise, London EC4Y 8EN
F 020 7822 2811
E info@rts.org.uk
W www.rts.org.uk

ROYAL THEATRICAL FUND   T 020 7836 3322
11 Garrick Street, London WC2E 9AR
F 020 7379 8273
E admin@trtf.com

SAMPAD SOUTH ASIAN ARTS   T 0121 446 3260
Promotes the appreciation & practice of South Asian Arts
c/o Mac, Cannon Hill Park, Birmingham B12 9QH
E info@sampad.org.uk
W www.sampad.org.uk

SCOTTISH SCREEN   T 0141 302 1700
249 West George Street, Glasgow G2 4QE
F 0141 302 1711
E enquiries@creativescotland.com
W www.creativescotland.com

❖

THE RALPH AND MERIEL RICHARDSON FOUNDATION

Please support us as we provide grants to relieve the need, hardship, or distress of British actors and actresses, their spouses and children.

Please consider including the Foundation in your Will, or sending a donation to the address below, as any amount will be warmly welcomed.

Please help to spread awareness of this very special charity and encourage anyone who needs assistance to be in contact with us.

Address: C/o Suite 23, 19 Cavendish Square, London W1A 2AW
W: sirralphrichardson.org.uk   E: manager@sirralphrichardson.org.uk   T: 020 7636 1616

SOCIETY OF AUTHORS
T 020 7373 6642
Trade Union for Professional Writers. Providing Advice,
Funding, Information & Support
84 Drayton Gardens, London SW10 9SB
E info@societyofauthors.org
W www.societyofauthors.org

SOCIETY OF BRITISH
THEATRE DESIGNERS
T 020 8308 2664
Professional Body. Charity. Providing Advice & Information
Rose Bruford College of Theatre & Performance
Burnt Oak Lane, Sidcup, Kent DA15 9DF
E admin@theatredesign.org.uk
W www.theatredesign.org.uk

SOCIETY OF LONDON
THEATRE (SOLT)
T 020 7557 6700
32 Rose Street, London WC2E 9ET
F 020 7557 6799
E enquiries@solttma.co.uk

SOCIETY OF TEACHERS
OF SPEECH & DRAMA THE
T 01623 627636
Registered Office: 73 Berry Hill Road
Mansfield, Nottinghamshire NG18 4RU
E ann.k.jones@btinternet.com
W www.stsd.org.uk

SOCIETY OF THEATRE
CONSULTANTS
T 020 7419 8767
27 Old Gloucester Street, London WC1N 3AX
W www.theatreconsultants.org.uk

STAGE CRICKET CLUB
T 020 7402 7543
39-41 Hanover Steps, St George's Fields
Albion Street, London W2 2YG
F 020 7262 5736
E brianjfilm@aol.com
W www.stagecc.co.uk

STAGE GOLFING SOCIETY
T 020 8940 8861
Sudbrook Park, Sudbrook Lane
Richmond, Surrey TW10 7AS
E sgs@richmondgolfclub.co.uk

STAGE MANAGEMENT
ASSOCIATION
T 020 7403 7999
Providing Advice, Information & Support. Supports,
represents & promotes stage management and all its
practitioners. Provides help finding work, training &
networking opportunities & advice
89 Borough High Street
London SE1 1NL
E admin@stagemanagementassociation.co.uk
W www.stagemanagementassociation.co.uk

STAGE ONE
T 020 7557 6737
Operating Name of The Theatre Investment Fund Ltd
32 Rose Street, London WC2E 9ET
F 020 7557 6799
E enquiries@stageone.uk.com
W www.stageone.uk.com

THEATRE WRITING
PARTNERSHIP
T 0115 947 4361
Nottingham Playhouse, Wellington Circus
Nottingham NG1 5AF
E info@theatrewritingpartnership.org.uk

THEATREMAD (THEATRE:
MAKING A DIFFERENCE)
T 020 7734 5683
The Make a Difference Trust raises funds to support people
living with HIV, AIDS & other long-term medical conditions.
UK Charity Registration No. 1124014
c/o The Make A Difference Trust, 1st Floor
54 Greek Street, Soho, London W1D 3DS
F 020 7734 0646
E office@madtrust.org.uk
W www.madtrust.org.uk

THEATRES TRUST THE
T 020 7836 8591
Contact: Kate Carmichael (Resources Officer). National
Advisory Public Body for Theatres, Protecting Theatres for
Everyone. Charity. Social Membership. Provides Advice,
Support & Information
22 Charing Cross Road, London WC2H 0QL
F 020 7836 3302
E info@theatrestrust.org.uk
W www.theatrestrust.org.uk

THEATRICAL GUILD THE
T 020 7395 5460
Charity for Backstage & Front of House
Ambassadors Theatre, West Street, London WC2H 9ND
E admin@ttg.org.uk
W www.ttg.org.uk

TMA (THEATRICAL
MANAGEMENT ASSOCIATION)
T 020 7557 6700
32 Rose Street, London WC2E 9ET
F 020 7557 6799
E enquiries@solttma.co.uk
W www.tmauk.org

TYA - UK CENTRE OF ASSITEJ
T 01325 483259
International Association of Theatre for Children & Young
People. Network for makers & promoters of professional
theatre for young audiences
c/o Birmingham Repertory Theatre
Centenary Square, Broad Street, Birmingham B1 2EP
E secretary@tya.uk.org
W www.tya-uk.org

UK CHOREOGRAPHERS' DIRECTORY THE
See DANCE UK

UK THEATRE CLUBS
T 020 8459 3972
54 Swallow Drive, London NW10 8TG
E uktheatreclubs@aol.com

UNITED KINGDOM
COPYRIGHT BUREAU
T 01273 277333
110 Trafalgar Road, Portslade, East Sussex BN41 1GS
E info@copyrightbureau.co.uk
W www.copyrightbureau.co.uk

VARIETY & LIGHT
ENTERTAINMENT COUNCIL
T 020 7798 5622
54 Keyes House, Dolphin Square, London SW1V 3NA
F 020 7821 0261

VARIETY CLUB
CHILDREN'S CHARITY
T 020 7428 8100
Variety Club House, 93 Bayham Street
London NW1 0AG
F 020 7428 8111
E info@varietyclub.org.uk
W www.varietyclub.org.uk

WILLIAMS, Tim AWARDS
T 020 7793 9755
In memory of LSW's late musical director. Seeking to support
excellence in the composition of theatrical song
PO Box 31855, London SE17 3XP
E londonswo@hotmail.com
W www.lswproductions.co.uk

WOMEN IN FILM & TELEVISION
T 020 7287 1400
Contact: Rebecca Brand. WFTV is the premier membership
organisation for women working in the Film, Television and
Digital Media industries in the UK. Provides Advice,
Information, Social Membership & Support
Unit 2, Wedgewood Mews
12-13 Greek Street, London W1D 4BB
E info@wftv.org.uk
W www.wftv.org.uk

YOUTH MUSIC THEATRE
UK (YMT)
T 0844 4154858
40 Parkgate Road, Battersea, London SW11 4JH
E mail@ymtuk.org
W www.youthmusictheatreuk.org

P →

Photographers: Advertisers Only
Promotional Services:
CVs, Showreels, Websites etc
Properties & Trades
Publications: Print & Online
Publicity & Press Representatives

Each photographer listed in this section
has taken an advertisement in this edition.
See Index to Advertisers pages to view
each advertisement.

Photographers

How do I find a photographer?

Having a good quality, up-to-date promotional headshot is crucial for every performer. Make sure you choose your photographer very carefully: do some research and try to look at different examples. Photographers' adverts run throughout this edition, featuring many sample shots, although to get a real feel for their work you should also try to see their portfolio or website since this will give a more accurate impression of the quality of their photography.

If you live in or around London, please feel free to visit the Spotlight offices and look through current editions of our directories to find a style you like. We also have nearly sixty photographers' portfolios available for you to browse, many of them from photographers listed in this edition. Our offices are open Monday - Friday, 10.00am - 5.30pm at 7 Leicester Place, London WC2H 7RJ (nearest tube is Leicester Square).

What should I expect from the photo shoot?

When it comes to your photo shoot, bear in mind that a casting director, agent or production company will want to see a photo of the 'real' you. Keep your appearance as neutral as possible so that they can imagine you in many different roles, rather than type-casting yourself from the outset and limiting your opportunities.

Your eyes are your most important feature, so make sure they are visible: face the camera straight-on and try not to smile too much because it makes them harder to see. Wear something simple and avoid jewellery, hats, scarves, glasses or props, since these will all add character. Do not wear clothes that detract from your face such as polo necks, big collars, busy patterns or logos. Always keep your hands out of the shot.

Also consider the background: some photographers like to do outdoor shots. A contrast between background and hair colour works well, whereas dark backgrounds work less well with dark hair, and the same goes for light hair on light backgrounds.

Which photograph should I choose?

When you get your contact sheet or digital proofs back from the photographer, make sure you choose a photo that looks like you - not how you would like to look. If you are unsure, ask friends or your agent for an honest opinion. Remember, you will be asked to attend meetings and auditions on the basis of your photograph, so if you turn up looking completely different you will be wasting everyone's time.

Due to copyright legislation, you must always credit the photographer when using the photo.

How should I submit my photo to Spotlight and to casting professionals?

All photographs submitted to Spotlight must be of the highest possible quality, otherwise casting professionals will not see you in the best possible light. If you are sending your photo by hard copy, we would expect a 10 x 8 sized print, which is the industry standard. It is not necessary to provide an original print: a high quality, clear focused repro is fine. If you are sending a digital image by e-mail or disk, we have certain technical specifications which can be found on our website. We would recommend that you follow similar guidelines when sending your headshot directly to casting professionals.

What are Spotlight portfolio photographs?

Every Spotlight performer can also add extra photographs onto their web page, in addition to their principal photograph. These are called portfolio photos, and they give you the opportunity to show yourself in a range of different shots and/or roles. Members can upload up to 15 digital photos to their online CV free of charge by logging on to www.spotlight.com with their update PIN.

Please visit www.spotlight.com/artists/ multimedia/photoguidelines for further information.

ACTORHEADSHOTS.CO.UK
T 07740 507970
E info@actorheadshots.co.uk
W www.actorheadshots.co.uk

ALLEN, Stuart
T 07776 258829
W www.stuartallenphotos.com

AM LONDON
T 020 7193 1868
T 07974 188105
W www.am-london.com

ANKER, Matt
T 07835 241835
W www.mattanker.com

ANNAND, Simon
T 07884 446776
W www.simonannand.com

BACON, Ric
T 07970 970799
E ric@ricbacon.co.uk
W www.ricbacon.co.uk

BARTLETT, Pete
T 07971 653994
E info@petebartlett.com
W www.petebartletttheadshots.co.uk

BISHOP, Brandon
T 020 7275 7468
T 07931 383830
W www.brandonbishopphotography.com

BROCKLEHURST, Georgie
T 07950 887895
W www.georgiebrocklehurst.com

BURNETT, Sheila
T 020 7289 3058
W www.sheilaburnett-headshots.com

CABLE, Paul
T 07958 932764
E info@paulcable.com
W www.paulcable.com

CLARK, John
T 020 8854 4069
T 07702 627237
E info@johnclarkphotography.com
W www.johnclarkphotography.com

DAVIES, James
T 07716 515170
W www.jamesdaviesheadshots.com

DAWKES, Nicholas
W www.nicholasdawkesphotography.co.uk

GARDEN, Henrietta
T 07973 825734
E henri.garden@blueyonder.co.uk

GARNIER, George
T 020 7277 9554
T 07796 262368
W www.georgegarnier.com

GRAPE STREET PRODUCTIONS
T 07779 586633
W www.grapestreetproductions.com

GREGAN, Nick
T 020 8533 3003
T 07774 421878
E info@nickgregan.com
W www.nickgregan.com

GROGAN, Claire
T 020 7272 1845
T 07932 635381
E claire@clairegrogan.co.uk
W www.clairegrogan.co.uk

HART, Drew
T 07824 810474
E info@drewhartphotography.com
W www.drewhartphotography.com

HEADSHOT LONDON
T 020 7209 0535
W www.headshotlondon.co.uk

HEMMINGS, Samuel
T 07914 404994
E info@samuelhemmings.com
W www.samuelhemmings.com

HUGHES, Jamie
T 07850 122977
E jhpixx@gmail.com
W www.jamiehughesphotography.com/headshots

HULL, Anna
T 07778 399419
E info@annahullphotography.com
W www.annahullphotography.com

JAMIE, Matt
T 07976 890643
E photos@mattjamie.co.uk
W www.mattjamie.co.uk/portraits

LADENBURG, Jack
T 07932 053743
E info@jackladenburg.co.uk
W www.jackladenburg.co.uk

LATIMER, Carole
T 020 7727 9371
E carole@carolelatimer.com
W www.carolelatimer.com

LAWTON, Steve
T 07973 307487
W www.stevelawton.com

LDW HEADSHOTS
T 07504 696164
E photography@ldwheadshots.com
W www.ldwheadshots.com

LISTER, Robert
M 07909 824893
W www.robertlister.co.uk

M.A.D. PHOTOGRAPHY
T 020 8363 4182
T 07949 581909
W www.mad-photography.co.uk

MERCHANT, Natasha
T 07932 618111
E natashamerchant@mac.com
W www.natashamerchant.com

MP STILLS
T 07872 383897
E info@mpstills.com

MULHOLLAND, Ruth
T 07939 516987
E ruth@ruthmulholland.com
W www.ruthmulholland.com

NAMDAR, Fatimah
T 020 8341 1332
T 07973 287535
E fnamdar@mac.com
W www.fatimahnamdar.com

PIELAK, Alex
T 07817 750560
E alex@alexpielak.com
W www.alexpielak.com

POLLARD, Michael
T 0161 456 7470
E info@michaelpollard.co.uk
W www.michaelpollard.co.uk

POLLEY PHOTOGRAPHY
T 01773 776379
T 07766 274205
W www.familyportraitsmansfield.co.uk

POWELL, Titus
T 07970 972675
W www.tituspowell.com

PROCTOR, Carl
T 07956 283340
E carlphotos@btconnect.com
W www.carlproctorphotography.com

RICHARDSON, Martin
T 07890 149657
E info@martinrichardsonphotography.com
W www.martinrichardsonphotography.com

RICHMOND, Eric
T 020 8880 6909
W www.ericrichmond.net

RUOCCO, Alex
T 07732 293231
W www.alexruoccophotography.co.uk

SAVAGE, Robin
T 07901 927597
E contact@robinsavage.co.uk
W www.robinsavage.co.uk

SAYER, Howard
T 07860 559891
E howard@howardsayer.com
W www.howardsayer.com

SCHWARTZ, Mario
T 07932 036396
E info@marioschwartz.com
W www.marioschwartz.com

SCOTT, Karen
T 07958 975950
E info@karenscottphotography.com
W www.karenscottphotography.com

SELL, David
T 07957 302934
E david@davidsell.co.uk
W www.davidsell.co.uk

SHAKESPEARE LANE, Catherine
T 020 7226 7694
W www.csl-art.co.uk

SHORING, Dan
T 07710 037652
E danshoring@blueyonder.co.uk
W www.danshoring.co.uk

SIMPKIN, Peter
T 020 8364 2634
T 07973 224084
E petersimpkin@aol.com
W www.petersimpkin.co.uk

STEWART, Phil
T 07884 005014
E philheadshots@yahoo.co.uk
W www.headshotsbyphilstewart.co.uk

SUMMERS, Caroline
T 020 7223 7669
T 07931 301234
E carolinesummers@me.com
W www.carolinesummers.co.uk

ULLATHORNE, Steve
T 07961 380969
W www.steveullathorne.com

VALENTINE, Vanessa
T 07904 059541
W www.vanessavalentinephotography.com

VESSEY, Mark
T 07984 829078
E mark@pointandsnap.com
W www.headshots.pointandsnap.com

WADE, Philip
T 020 7226 3088
T 07956 599691
E pix@philipwade.com
W www.philipwade.com

WATERSON, Neil
T 07891 830471
E info@neilwaterson.com
W www.neilwaterson.com

WEBSTER, Caroline
T 07867 653019
E caroline@carolinewebster.co.uk
W www.carolinewebster.co.uk

WHARLEY, Michael
T 07961 068759
W www.michaelwarley.com

WORKMAN, Robert
T 020 7385 5442
W www.robertworkman.demon.co.uk

YOU BEEN PAPPED PHOTOGRAPHY
T 020 8220 6118
T 07944 486800
E youbeenpappedphotography@gmail.com
W www.youbeenpappedphotography.com

10X8PRINTS.COM   T 01561 377377
E info@10x8prints.com
W www.10x8prints.com

2PRODUCTION   T 020 7993 4675
Professional Management Voice Over Direction & CDs
E voice@2production.com
W www.2production.com

A1 VOX LTD   T 020 7434 4404
Audio Clips. Demo CDs. ISDN Links. Spoken Word Audio
20 Old Compton Street
London W1D 4TW
E info@a1vox.com
W www.a1vox.com

ABBEY ROAD STUDIOS   T 020 7266 7000
3 Abbey Road, St John's Wood
London NW8 9AY
F 020 7266 7250
E bookings@abbeyroad.com
W www.abbeyroad.com

ABBEY SHOWREELS   T 020 8544 1944
10B, The 1929 Shop
Merton Abbey Mills, London SW19 2RD
E info@abbeyshowreels.co.uk
W www.abbeyshowreels.co.uk

ABSOLUTE WORKS LTD   T 01525 385400
Danson House, Manor Farm Lane
Ledburn, Bucks LU7 0UG
T 07778 934307
E absoluteworks@btinternet.com
W www.absoluteworks.com

ACTOR SHOWREELS   T 07835 637965
Showreel Service
97B Central Hill, London SE19 1BY
T 07939 241377
E post@actorshowreels.co.uk
W www.actorshowreels.co.uk

ACTORS CENTRE   T 020 7240 3940
1A Tower Street, London WC2H 9NP
E film@actorscentre.co.uk
W www.actorscentre.co.uk

ACTORS INTERACTIVE   T 020 8465 5457
Web Design
10 Frobisher Street, London SE10 9XB
E office@actorsinteractive.com
W www.actorsinteractive.com

ACTOR'S ONE-STOP SHOP THE   T 020 8888 7006
CVs, Photography, Showreels &
Websites for Performing Artists
1st Floor, Above The Gate Pub
Station Road, London N22 7SS
E info@actorsone-stopshop.com
W www.actorsone-stopshop.com

ACTORSHOP.CO.UK   T 07970 381944
E info@actorshop.co.uk
W www.actorshop.co.uk

ACTORSILLUMINATED.COM   T 07769 626074
Contact: Kosha Engler. Websites for People in
the Performing Arts
E mail@actorsilluminated.com
W www.actorsilluminated.com

Promotional Services

What are promotional services?

This section contains listings for companies who provide practical services to help performers promote themselves. You might need to improve or create your CV; record a showreel or voicereel; design your own website; duplicate CDs; or print photographic repros, CVs or Z-cards: all essential ways to create a good impression with those that count in the industry.

Why do I need to promote myself?

Performers need to invest in marketing and promotion as much as any other self-employed businessperson. Even if you have trained at a leading drama school, have a well-known agent, or have just finished work on a popular TV series, you should never sit back and wait for your phone to ring or for the next job opportunity just to knock on your door. In such a competitive industry, successful performers are usually the ones who market themselves pro-actively and treat their careers as a 'business'.

Having up-to-date and well-produced promotional material makes a performer look professional and serious about their career: and hence a desirable person for a director or agent to work with.

Why is my CV important?

Poor presentation, punctuation and grammar create a bad first impression and you risk your CV being dismissed before it is even read. Make sure that you continually update your CV – you don't want it to look as if you haven't been working recently when you have, and you don't want to miss out on an audition because you haven't included skills you have put time and effort into achieving. Your CV should be kept to a maximum of one page and printed on good-quality paper.

Why is my covering letter important?

Always include a covering letter to introduce your CV and persuade casting professionals that it is worth reading. Remember that they receive hundreds each week. Keep your communication concise and be professional at all times. We also recommend that your letter has some kind of focus: perhaps you can tell them about your next showcase, or where they can see you currently appearing on stage. Ideally this should be addressed to an individual, not "Dear Sir or Madam".

Why is my headshot important?

Your CV should feature, or be accompanied by, a recent headshot which is an accurate current likeness. See the 'Photographers' section for more information about promotional photography. You may need to print copies of your headshot through a repro company, some of whom are listed over the following pages.

Why do I need a voicereel?

If you are interested in voice-over and/or radio work, you will need a professional-sounding voicereel to show agents, casting directors and potential employers what your voice is capable of. For commercial and corporate voice-over work this should be no more than two minutes long with a number of short clips demonstrating your range, but showcase the strengths of your natural voice as much as possible. It should contain a mixture of commercials and narrations.

A radio voicereel should be around eight minutes long, with four clips no longer than two minutes each, and read in your natural voice. To achieve a good balance of material, one clip should be 'classical', one 'contemporary', one 'comic' and one a poem. This is designed to give an overview of your suitability to various areas of radio work.

Record your voicereel in a professional studio to ensure a high-quality result, otherwise you are unlikely to be considered in this competitive industry. For further information please see the 'Agents: Voice-Over' and 'Radio' sections.

Why do I need a showreel?

Some casting directors nowadays will only consider a performer for an audition if they have first seen them demonstrating their skills in a showreel. A CV and headshot give some indication of their potential, but can only provide a basic summary.

What should I do if I don't currently have anything on film?

Showreels are expensive to produce if you don't currently have any broadcasted material to use, but it is advisable to get one professionally recorded and edited if at all possible. Showreels help you to promote yourself, but a casting director may be put off by a poor quality one. You might want to consider a Spotlight Intro as a temporary alternative to a full showreel (see below). It may also be worth considering working on a student film. Students are usually willing to let you keep a copy of their film and casting professionals would consider this an acceptable alternative. See 'Film & Television Schools' for further advice and listings.

How long should my showreel be?

We would recommend no more than three or four minutes. Casting professionals receive thousands of CVs and showreels and do not have time to watch every actor for ten minutes each. This is why we suggest you do not send your showreel out with your CV, but instead mention in your covering letter that one is available.

What should I use in my showreel?

Rather than one long excerpt, it is more beneficial to demonstrate your versatility with a number of different clips. Focus on your strongest characters to enable the casting director to picture you in the roles you play best.

The first 30 seconds are the most important in your showreel, and can be the only part a busy casting director or agent has time to look at. You may wish to start with a brief montage summarising the clips that are to follow, or with a headshot of yourself so that they know who to watch out for.

The focus should be on you, not on the other actors, so close-up shots ought to be included. You should be speaking most if not all of the time. A visual contrast is good, whether this means filming in a different location or setting, or changing your outfit. You should avoid well-known scripts in order to prevent drawing comparisons between yourself and previous successful interpretations.

What is a *Spotlight Intro?*

If you are a Spotlight member, a *Spotlight Intro* is your opportunity to give casting professionals a quick introduction to you, your character and your voice with a one or two minute video as part of your Spotlight CV. Think of it as a video version of a covering letter you might enclose with a paper CV. It could also be used as a temporary alternative to a showreel, although ideally you should include both. Please visit www.spotlight.com/spotlightintro for further information.

How should I use these listings?

If you are looking for a company to help you with any of these promotional items, browse through this section carefully and get quotes from a number of places to compare. If you are a Spotlight member, some companies offer a discount on their services. Always ask to see samples of a company's work, and ask friends in the industry for their own recommendations.

Promotional Services

Silver~Tongued Productions has a wealth of experience and understanding in producing voicereels. With over twelve years' experience they know just how intimidating the whole business can be. Here they share advice and information which will help you through the whole process.

Take your time when choosing which company to go with. Listen to examples of their work. A lot of our work comes from recommendations from both actors and agents so ask around and see who your contemporaries have chosen or heard. What do the companies provide? Do they provide bespoke scripts? There's nothing worse than the same old scripts being used over and over again. Do they use copyright free music?

Here are a few things to consider when preparing for your recording session…

Choosing Your Scripts

Commercials, Documentaries, Gaming, Corporate etc.

Male/Female: What sort of product would use a male/female voice? Remember that advertisements, in many ways, play on stereotypes so don't be afraid to use what you've got!

Type of voice: There are many types of voices. From the rich, smooth, velvety voice to the high octane children's TV voice, with many variations in between.

Your age: How old do you sound? The emphasis being on "sound". Your actual age is unimportant but the "age" of your voice is. Choose a product that is relevant to your "voice age". You may have more than one voice age.

Accents: These days casting directors tend to go for the real thing. If you have an authentic accent, use it! If you can do an accent extremely well then include it.

Variety: Try to show a variety of styles: Straight Read, Comedy, Hard Sell, Soft Sell.

So the key points when choosing your adverts are: keep within your capabilities; show off your talent, be it straight read, accents or characters; and try to show variety in the subject matter: this way your finished voicereel will be both entertaining and interesting to listen to.

Narration, Monologue etc.

The readings are your choice, each about a minute long, whether narration, children's narration, monologues etc. If you are stuck, there are many audition books available. Go to www.silver-tongued.co.uk/choosingscripts for more information.

The Recording Day

It's good to discuss your strengths, and work out the best way of conveying them on your voicereel. Don't rush through the recording process; take your time to get it right. When you are satisfied with the take, move on. You should be helped through this process by the director/producer. If there is something you want to change, now is the time to say so.

Mixing and Producing

Some studios will mix the reel for you on the day. That's great, if you need it fast. Other studios, including us, don't like to rush the mix: we think that this ensures good quality results. Your voicereel should be labelled with your photo, running order and contact details.

What to do Next

If your agent is going to represent you for voice-overs, that's great. If not, there are dedicated voice-over agents, many of which can be found in this edition. Now that you have your voicereel, you must get your voice heard. Get duplications made, send them out and upload it onto your Spotlight web page and other sites.

Voice-over work can be very lucrative and the first step is to record your voicereel. Along with your photo, CV and showreel, your voicereel will complete the package and enable you to tap into another aspect of the industry and another source of income.

ACTUALLYACTORS.COM T 020 8325 1946
Websites
3 Milestone Road, London SE19 2LL
E mail@actuallyactors.co.uk
W www.actuallyactors.com

AIR-EDEL RECORDING
STUDIOS LTD T 020 7486 6466
18 Rodmarton Street, London W1U 8BJ
F 020 7224 0344
E tom.bullen@air-edel.co.uk
W www.air-edelstudios.co.uk

ANGEL RECORDING
STUDIOS LTD T 020 7354 2525
311 Upper Street, London N1 2TU
F 020 7226 9624
E bookings@angelstudio.co.uk

ANT FARM STUDIOS
VOICE-OVERS T 01992 714664
Southend Farm, Southend Lane
Waltham Abbey EN9 3SE
E antfarmstudio@yahoo.co.uk
W www.antfarmstudios.co.uk

APPLE VIDEO FACILITIES T 01204 847974
The Studio, 821 Chorley Old Road
Bolton, Lancs BL1 5SL
F 01204 495020
E info@applevideo.co.uk
W www.applevideo.co.uk

ARTS HOSTING T 0845 2508688
46 Glenmore Drive, Birmingham, West Midlands B38 8YR
E hosting@artshosting.co.uk
W www.artshosting.co.uk

ARTUS, William
GRAPHIC DESIGN T 0161 303 8192
20 Crowswood Drive, Stalybridge, Cheshire SK15 3RJ
E williamartus4art@mac.com
W www.gallery.me.com/williamartus4art

BESPOKE REELS T 020 7580 3773
Contact: Charlie Lort-Phillips
3rd Floor, 83 Charlotte Street, London W1T 4PR
T 07538 257748
E charlie@bespokereels.com
W www.bespokereels.com

BEWILDERING PICTURES T 07974 916258
Contact: Graeme Kennedy. Showreel Service & Duplication
Based in West London
E gk@bewildering.co.uk
W www.bewildering.co.uk

BLUE CHECKBOX T 0843 2894414
Website Design
13 Portman House, 136 High Road, London N22 6DF
E contact@bluecheckbox.com
W www.bluecheckbox.com

CAKE & CUSTARD T 020 7503 6216
E info@cakeandcustard.co.uk
W www.cakeandcustard.co.uk

CHANNEL 2020 LTD T 0844 8402020
2020 House, 26-28 Talbot Lane
Leicester LE1 4LR
F 0116 222 1113
E info@channel2020.co.uk
W www.channel2020.co.uk

CHANNEL 2020 LTD T 0844 8402020
The Clerkenwell Workshops
27-31 Clerkenwell Close, London EC1R 0AT
E info@channel2020.co.uk
W www.channel2020.co.uk

CHASE, Stephan
PRODUCTIONS LTD T 020 8878 9112
Producer of Voice Overs & Showreels
The Studio, 22 York Avenue
London SW14 7LG
E stephan@stephanchase.com
W www.stephanchase.com

CLAW FILMS LTD T 020 7470 8809
11-15 Betterton Street, London WC2H 9BP
F 020 7470 8810
E info@clawfilms.com
W www.clawfilms.com

CLICKS MEDIA STUDIOS T 01634 723838
Grove Road, Rochester, Kent ME2 4BX
F 01634 726000
E info@clicksmediastudios.com
W www.clicksmediastudios.com

CONCEPT T 0151 737 1794
99 Thornton Road, Liverpool L16 2LR
E info@soundconcept.co.uk
W www.soundconcept.co.uk

COURTWOOD
PHOTOGRAPHIC LTD T 01736 741222
Photographic Reproduction
Profile Prints, Freepost TO55
Penzance, Cornwall TR20 8DU
F 01736 741255
E images@courtwood.co.uk
W www.courtwood.co.uk

CRICKCRACK PRODUCTIONS   T 01268 416195
*Contact: Charlie Wilson. Professionally Equipped Recording
Facility for Voice Overs*
23 Kings Road, Laindon
Basildon, Essex SS15 4AB
E charlie@crickcrack.com
W www.crickcrackproductions.com

CROWE, Ben   T 07952 784911
Voice Clip Recording
25 Holmes Avenue, Hove BN3 7LB
E bencrowe@hotmail.co.uk

**CRYING OUT LOUD
PRODUCTIONS**   T 07809 549887
Voice Over Specialists. Demo CDs. Voice Training
Studio based in Central London
T 07946 533108
E simon@cryingoutloud.co.uk
W www.cryingoutloud.co.uk

CRYSTAL MEDIA   T 0131 240 0988
28 Castle Street, Edinburgh EH2 3HT
F 0131 240 0989
E hello@crystal-media.co.uk
W www.crystal-media.co.uk

CURTAIN RECORDS   T 020 8983 9117
Studio 3, 59 Dean Street, London W1D 6AN
E info@curtainrecords.com
W www.curtainrecords.com

CUT GLASS PRODUCTIONS   T 020 7267 2339
Voice Over Showreels & Production
169-175 Queens Crescent, Camden
London NW5 4DS
E info@cutglassproductions.com
W www.cutglassproductions.com

DARKSIDE REPROS   T 07990 543370
Photographic Repro Service
E info@darksidephoto.co.uk
W www.darksidephoto.co.uk

DE LANE LEA SOUND   T 020 7432 3800
Post-Production. Re-Recording Studios
75 Dean Street, London W1D 3PU
F 020 7494 3755
E solutions@delanelea.com
W www.delanelea.com

DELUXE 142   T 020 7878 0000
Film House, 142 Wardour Street, London W1F 8DD
F 020 7878 7800
W www.deluxe142.co.uk

DENBRY REPROS LTD   T 01442 242411
Photographic Reproduction
57 High Street, Hemel Hempstead, Herts HP1 3AF
E info@denbryrepros.com
W www.denbryrepros.com

DV2BROADCAST   T 0161 736 5300
3 Carolina Way, Salford M50 2ZY
E info@dv2broadcast.co.uk
W www.dv2broadcast.co.uk

DYNAMIC ISLE STUDIO   T 07956 951090
58 Selhurst New Road, South Norwood
London SE25 5PU
E olympicrecords@tiscali.co.uk
W www.olympicrecordsuk.com

EDGAR, Richard STUDIOS   T 05602 625262
6 Millan Court, Lumphanan, Aberdeenshire AB31 4QF
E richard.edgar@vcstudios.co.uk
W www.vcstudios.co.uk

ELITE SHOWREELS   T 07734 925829
Showreel Production & Editing. Website Design
31 Paynell Court, Lawn Terrace
Blackheath, London SE3 9LN
E info@eliteshowreels.com
W www.eliteshowreels.com

ELMS STUDIOS   T 020 8518 8629
*Contact: Phil Lawrence. Composing/Scoring for Film &
Television. Intel Power Mac. Live Studio*
10 Empress Avenue, London E12 5ES
E info@elmsstudios.com
W www.elmsstudios.com

ESSENTIAL MUSIC   T 020 7439 7113
20 Great Chapel Street, London W1F 8FW
F 020 7287 3597
E david@essentialmusic.co.uk

EXECUTIVE AUDIO VISUAL   T/F 020 7723 4488
DVD Duplication Service. Showreels for Actors & Presenters
E chris.jarvis60@gmail.com

FIREFLY PRODUCTIONS   T 01725 514462
Twin Oaks, Hale Purlieu
Fordingbridge, Hampshire SP6 2NN
T 07956 675276
E theonlyfirefly@aol.com
W www.fireflyproductions.info

FLIXELS LTD   T 020 8960 2577
Unit 7 Rutland Studios, Cumberland Park
Scrubs Lane, London NW10 6RE
E info@flixels.co.uk   W www.flixels.co.uk

FLOURISH NEW BIZ LTD   T 07860 569394
Learn How to Market Yourself
E simone@flourishnewbiz.co.uk
W www.flourishnewbiz.co.uk

**GENESIS TEE SHIRTS
& HOODIES**   T 01654 710137
18 Pendre Enterprise Park
Tywyn
Gwynedd LL36 9LW
F 01654 712461
E info@genesis-uk.com
W www.genesis-uk.com

GLITTERGAL WEBS   T 07931 318021
E info@glittergalwebs.com
W www.glittergalwebs.com

GYROSCOPE STUDIOS   T 00 46 86 459223
Contact: Frank Sanderson
Hökmossevägen 34, SE12638 Hägersten, Sweden
E frank@gyroscope-studios.com
W www.gyroscope-studios.com

HARVEY HOUSE FILMS LTD   T 07968 830536
Animation. Showreels. Video Production
80-82 Chiswick High Road, London W4 1SY
E chris@harveyhousefilms.co.uk
W www.harveyhousefilms.co.uk

HEAVY ENTERTAINMENT LTD   T 020 7494 1000
111 Wardour Street, London W1F 0UH
F 020 7494 1100
E info@heavy-entertainment.com
W www.heavy-entertainment.com

HOTQS CREATIVE T 07903 017819
Animation. Graphics. Showreels. Websites
63 Redchurch Street, London E2 7DJ
E pat@hotqs-creative.com
W www.hotqs-creative.com

HOTREELS T 020 7952 4362
Voice & Showreels
E info@hotreels.co.uk
W www.hotreels.co.uk

IMAGE PHOTOGRAPHIC T 020 7602 1190
Photographic Reproduction
Horizon House, Azalea Drive, Swanley, Kent BR8 8HY
E digital@imagephotographic.com
W www.imagephotographic.com

JMS GROUP LTD THE T 01603 811855
Park Farm Studios, Norwich Road
Hethersett, Norfolk NR9 3DL
F 01603 812255
E info@jms-group.com
W www.jms-group.com

KEAN LANYON LTD T 020 7354 3362
Design of Websites, Print & Front of House,
from Touring to West End
Rose Cottage, The Aberdeen Centre
22 Highbury Grove, London N5 2EA
E iain@keanlanyon.com
W www.keanlanyon.com

KONK STUDIOS T 020 8340 7873
84-86 Tottenham Lane, London N8 7EE
F 020 8348 3952
E linda@konkstudios.com

KORUPT MEDIA T 07791 580600
Specialises in Shooting & Editing Showreels,
Corporate & Music Videos
43 Yewfield Road, London NW10 9TD
E koruptmedia@gmail.com
W www.koruptmedia.com

LONDON SHOWREELS T 020 8144 6750
Based in London N22
T 07986 863550
E sales@londonshowreels.co.uk
W www.londonshowreels.co.uk

MINAMON FILM T 020 8674 3957
Specialist in Showreels
117 Downton Avenue, London SW2 3TX
E studio@minamonfilm.co.uk
W www.minamonfilm.co.uk

MOF STUDIOS T 020 7407 6077
Unit 1 Suffolk Studios
127-129 Great Suffolk Street, London SE1 1PP
E studio@ministryoffun.net
W www.mofstudios.net

MOO.COM
Online Printers. Z-Cards
32-38 Scrutton Street
London EC2A 4RQ
W www.moo.com

MOTIVATION SOUND STUDIOS T 020 7328 8305
35A Broadhurst Gardens
London NW6 3QT
F 020 7624 4879
E info@motivationsound.co.uk
W www.motivationsound.co.uk

MUSIC IN MOTION LTD T 07813 070961
4 Ravenshaw Street
London NW6 1NN
E neil@neilmyers.com
W www.neilmyers.com

MYSTER?Y ENTERTAINMENT -
ACTORS4REEL T 07943 192820
E info@actors4reel.com
W www.actors4reel.com

NICOLINA MARKETING &
COMMUNICATIONS T 07729 757006
Branding. Creative. Marketing. Social Media.
Strategies. Websites
16 The Grange
London SW19 4PS
E consulting@nicolina-online.com
W www.lifestylemarketingcommunications.yolasite.com

PROFESSIONAL SHOWREELS
OF MANCHESTER T 0161 272 1029
10 Old Hall Court
Old Hall Lane
Manchester M45 7JW
T 07738 819880
E showreels@btinternet.com

PROFILE PRINTS T 01736 741222
Photographic Reproduction
Unit 2, Plot 1A
Rospeath Industrial Estate
Crowlas, Cornwall TR20 8DU
F 01736 741255
E sales@courtwood.co.uk
W www.courtwood.co.uk

EVERYTHING

SPECIAL GRADUATE RATES

COMPLETE PORTFOLIO SERVICE

RJ THEATRE ARTS WITH THEOTHER COMPANY LTD

webdesign.rjtheatrearts.com

REAL PRINT & MEDIA   **T** 01622 200123
Printing
36 Hedley Street, Maidstone
Kent ME14 5AD
F 01622 200131
E info@realprintandmedia.com

RED FACILITIES   **T** 0131 555 2288
61 Timber Bush, Leith
Edinburgh EH6 6QH
F 0131 555 0088
E doit@redfacilities.com
W www.redfacilities.com

REEL DEAL
SHOWREEL CO THE   **T** 020 8647 1235
6 Charlotte Road
Wallington
Surrey SM6 9AX
E info@thereel-deal.co.uk
W www.thereel-deal.co.uk

REEL GEEKS.COM THE   **T** 07951 757024
West Kensington
London W14 0DU
E thereelgeeks@hotmail.com
W www.thereelgeeks.com

REEL McCOY THE   **T** 07708 626477
Showreel Editing Service
Flat 2A, Crampton Road
London SE20 7AT
E reelmccoyservice@aol.com
W www.jameshyland.co.uk/reelmccoy

REMOTE LIVE RECORDINGS   **T** 07968 100557
Live Gig, Solo & Studio Recordings.
PA Hire with Engineering. Road Manager
244A Kingston Road, Leatherhead
Surrey KT22 7QA
E info@remoteliverecordings.co.uk
W www.remoteliverecordings.co.uk

REPLAY LTD   **T** 020 7637 0473
Showreels & Performance Recording
Museum House, 25 Museum Street
London WC1A 1JT
E sales@replayfilms.co.uk
W www.replayfilms.co.uk

RESOLUTION LONDON   **T** 0800 4488675
Photography. Web Design
The Diary House, Rickett Street
London SW6 1RU
T 07962 471118
E info@resolutionlondon.co.uk
W www.resolutionlondon.co.uk

RETRO REELS   **T** 07896 299932
Showreels. Voicereels. Websites. Shoots From Scratch
Flat 1, 29 Park Avenue, London NW2 5AN
E mail@retroreels.co.uk
W www.retroreels.co.uk

RJ THEATRE ARTS   **T** 07929 939534
Web Design
7 Greenside Road, Croydon CR0 3PP
E info@rjtheatrearts.com
W www.webdesign.rjtheatrearts.com

**ROUND ISLAND SHOWREELS
& VOICEREELS** T 07939 540458
Contact: Ben Warren, Guy Michaels
T 07973 445328
E mail@roundisland.net
W www.roundisland.net

SCARLET INTERNET T 0870 7771820
15 Red House Yard, Gislingham Road
Thornham Magna, Suffolk IP23 8HH
F 0870 2241418
E info@scarletinternet.com
W www.scarletinternet.com

SETTLE THE SCORE T 07853 643346
E toby@settlethescore.co.uk
W www.settlethescore.co.uk

**SHOOT FROM SCRATCH
SHOWREELS** T 020 8449 7133
Actors Showreels
74 Normandy Avenue, Barnet, Herts EN5 2JA
E info@shootfromscratch.com
W www.shootfromscratch.com

SHOWREEL THE T 020 7043 8660 (Bookings)
Demo Production Services. Voice Over Workshops
140 Buckingham Palace Road
London SW1W 9SA
E info@theshowreel.com
W www.theshowreel.com

SHOWREELS 4 U T 01923 352385
Actors Showreels Filmed & Edited in HD. Voicereels.
Based near Elstree
15 Pippin Close, Shenley, Radlett, Herts WD7 9EU
E showreels4u@hotmail.com
W www.showreels4u.blogspot.com

SHOWREELZ T 020 8994 7927
28 Eastbury Grove, Chiswick, London W4 2JZ
T 07885 253477
E brad@showreelz.com
W www.showreelz.com

**SILVER-TONGUED
PRODUCTIONS** T 020 8309 0659
Specialising in the Recording and Production of Voicereels
Based in Sidcup, Greater London
E contactus@silver-tongued.co.uk
W www.silver-tongued.co.uk

SLICK SHOWREELS T 07543 016194
Monument Street, London EC4R 8AJ
E info@slickshowreels.co.uk
W www.slickshowreels.co.uk

SMALL SCREEN SHOWREELS T 020 8816 8896
The Edit Suite, 17 Knole Road, Crayford, London
E info@smallscreenshowreels.co.uk
W www.smallscreenshowreels.co.uk

SOHO SHOWREELS T 0844 5040731
101 Wardour Street, London W1F 0UG
E info@sohoshowreels.co.uk
W www.sohoshowreels.co.uk

SOHO THIRTY THREE T 020 8123 6085
Video. Voice Overs. Web
E info@sohothirtythree.co.uk
W www.sohothirtythree.co.uk

SONICPOND STUDIO T 020 7690 8561
Specialising in Voicereels. MT Demos. Showreels
70 Mildmay Grove South, Islington, London N1 4PJ
E info@sonicpond.co.uk
W www.sonicpond.co.uk

SOUND T 0117 924 5853
Pembroke House
7 Brunswick Square, Bristol BS2 8PE
E kenwheeler@mac.com
W www.soundat4.com

SOUND COMPANY LTD T 020 7580 5880
23 Gosfield Street, London W1W 6HG
F 020 7580 6454
E bookings@sound.co.uk
W www.sound.co.uk

**SOUND HOUSE POST
PRODUCTION LTD THE** T 0161 832 7299
4th Floor, South Central
11 Peter Street
Manchester M2 5QR
F 0161 832 7266
E mail@thesoundhouse.tv
W www.thesoundhouse.tv

SOUND MARKETING T 01225 701600
Strattons House, Strattons Walk
Melksham, Wiltshire SN12 6JL
F 01225 701601
E nicki@soundm.com
W www.soundm.com

**STAGES CAPTURE
THE MOMENT** T 020 7193 8519
Showreels
31 Evensyde, Croxley Green
Watford, Herts WD18 8WN
T 07786 813812
E info@stagescapturethemoment.com
W www.stagescapturethemoment.com

STAMP PRODUCTIONS T 020 8743 5555
Ugli Campus, 56 Wood Lane
London W12 7SB
E info@stamp-productions.com

SYNCREDIBLE AGENCY T 020 7117 6776
26-28 Hammersmith Grove
London W6 7BA
E contact@syncredible.com
W www.syncredible.com

TAKE FIVE CASTING STUDIO T 020 7287 2120
Showreels
37 Beak Street, London W1F 9RZ
F 020 7287 3035
E info@takefivestudio.com
W www.takefivestudio.com

**TM PHOTOGRAPHY &
DESIGN LTD** T 020 8530 4382
Suites 14-15, Marlborough Business Centre
96 George Lane, South Woodford
London E18 1AD
E info@tmphotography.co.uk
W www.tmphotography.co.uk

TOP TV ACADEMY T 07971 284958
Showreels
Elstree Film & TV Studios
Shenley Road, Herts WD6 1JG
E liz@toptvacademy.co.uk
W www.toptvacademy.co.uk

**TOUCHWOOD AUDIO
PRODUCTIONS** T 0113 278 7180
6 Hyde Park Terrace, Leeds
West Yorkshire LS6 1BJ
T 07745 377772
E bruce@touchwoodaudio.com
W www.touchwoodaudio.com

TV PRESENTER TRAINING -
ASPIRE   T 0800 0305471
3 Mills Studios, Three Mill Lane, London E3 3DU
E info@aspirepresenting.com
W www.aspirepresenting.com

TWITCH FILMS   T 020 7266 0946
Showreels
22 Grove End Gardens
18 Abbey Road, London NW8 9LL
E post@twitchfilms.co.uk
W www.twitchfilms.co.uk

UNIVERSAL SOUND
(JUST PLAY LTD)   T 01494 723400
Old Farm Lane, London Road East
Amersham, Buckinghamshire HP7 9DH
F 01494 723500
E foley@universalsound.co.uk
W www.universalsound.co.uk

VISUALEYES PHOTOREPRO
SERVICES   T 020 7323 7430
Photographic Reproduction
95 Mortimer Street, London W1W 7ST
F 020 7323 7438
E imaging@visualeyes.co.uk
W www.visualeyes.co.uk

VOICE MASTER
INTERNATIONAL   T 020 8455 2211
Creators of the Hudson Voice Technique, the only
Technique in the World for Voice Overs
88 Erskine Hill, London NW11 6HR
E stevehudson@voicemaster.co.uk
W www.voicemaster.co.uk

VOICEREELS.CO.UK   T 07989 602880
Based in London SW16
E rob@voicereels.co.uk
W www.voicereels.co.uk

VSI - VOICE & SCRIPT
INTERNATIONAL   T 020 7692 7700
Foreign Language Specialists. Casting. Dubbing. Editing.
Recording Studios. Subtitling. Translation
132 Cleveland Street
London W1T 6AB
F 020 7692 7711
E info@vsi.tv
W www.vsi.tv

WARWICK HALL OF SOUND   T/F 029 2069 4455
Warwick Hall
Off Banastre Avenue
Heath, Cardiff CF14 3NR
E promotions@cardiffmusicstudios.co.uk
W www.cardiffmusicstudios.co.uk

WARWICK SOUND   T 020 7437 5532
Sound Transfer/Optical & Magnetic
111A Wardour Street, London W1F 0UJ
F 020 7439 0372
E studio@warwicksound.com
W www.warwicksound.com

WORLDWIDE PICTURES LTD   T 020 7613 6580
103 The Timber Yard
Drivedale Street
London N1 6ND
F 020 7613 6581
E anthead@worldwidepictures.tv
W www.worldwidepictures.tv

10 OUT OF 10 PRODUCTIONS LTD   **T** 020 8659 2558
Lighting & Sound. Design. Hire. Installation. Sales
5 Orchard Business Centre
Kangley Bridge Road
London SE26 5AQ
E sales@10outof10.co.uk
W www.10outof10.co.uk

147RESEARCH   **T** 01635 200147
*Will source anything needed for period or
modern productions*
Chaucers, Oare
Hermitage, Thatcham RG18 9SD
T 07778 002147
E jenniferdalton@147research.com
W www.147research.com

3D CREATIONS LTD   **T** 01493 652055
*Production Design. Prop Makers. Scenery Contractors.
Scenic Artists*
Berth 33, Malthouse Lane
Gorleston, Norfolk NR31 0GW
F 01493 443124
E info@3dcreations.co.uk
W www.3dcreations.co.uk

AC FLUTES   **T** 020 8123 5925
*Handmade Native American-style Flutes.
Handmade Wood & Leather Crafts*
E info@acflutes.co.uk
W www.acflutes.co.uk

ACROBAT PRODUCTIONS   **T** 01923 518989
Advisors. Artistes
2 The Grove, Whippendell
Chipperfield, Kings Langley, Herts WD4 9JF
E roger@acrobatproductions.com
W www.acrobatproductions.com

ACTION 99 CARS LTD   **T** 01923 266373
Hyde Meadow Farm, Hyde Lane
Hemel Hempstead HP3 8SA
E david@nineninecars.com
W www.nineninecars.com

ACTION CARS LTD   **T** 01753 785690
Contact: Steven Royffe
Room 49A, D Block, Pinewood Studios
Pinewood Road, Iver Heath, Bucks SL0 0NH
F 01753 652027
E info@actioncars.co.uk
W www.actioncars.co.uk

ADAMS ENGRAVING   **T** 01483 725792
Unit G1A, The Mayford Centre
Mayford Green
Woking GU22 0PP
F 01483 751787
E adamsengraving@pncl.co.uk
W www.adamsengraving.co.uk

AIRBOURNE SYSTEMS INTERNATIONAL   **T** 01245 268772
*All Skydiving Requirements Arranged. Parachute Hire
(Period & Modern)*
8 Burns Crescent, Chelmsford
Essex CM2 0TS

ALCHEMICAL LABORATORIES ETC   **T** 01636 707836
*Medieval Science & Technology Recreated for
Museums & Films*
2 Stapleford Lane, Coddington
Newark, Nottinghamshire NG24 2QZ
W www.jackgreene.co.uk

ALL SCENE ALL PROPS   **T** 01580 211121
Props, Masks, Painting & Scenery Makers
Units 2 & 3, Spelmonden Farm
Goudhurst, Kent TN17 1HE
F 01580 211131
E info@allscene.net
W www.allscene.net

ALL STARS AMERICAN LIMOS   **T** 01797 252528
Fieldgate, Station Road
Northiam, Rye TN31 6QT
E dazwills86@aol.com
W www.limo-hire-sussex-kent.co.uk

AMERICAN DREAMS   **T** 0800 8488032
Vehicle Supply
PO Box 11038, St Osyth
Clacton on Sea, Essex CO16 8SY
E tphj47@aol.com
W www.americandreams.co.uk

ANELLO & DAVIDE   **T** 020 7938 2255
Handmade Shoes
15 St Albans Grove, London W8 5BP
W www.handmadeshoes.co.uk

ANNUAL CLOWNS DIRECTORY THE   **T** 01268 745791
Contact: Salvo The Clown
13 Second Avenue
Kingsleigh Park
Thundersley, Essex SS7 3QD
E salvo@annualclownsdirectory.com
W www.annualclownsdirectory.com

AQUARIUS   **T** 01424 721196
Film & Television Stills Library
PO Box 5
Hastings TN34 1HR
E aquarius.lib@clara.net
W www.aquariuscollection.com

AQUATECH   **T** 01452 740559
Camera Boats
2 Cobbies Rock, Epney
Gloucestershire GL2 7LN
F 01452 741958
E office@aquatech-uk.com
W www.aquatech-uk.com

ARCHERY CENTRE THE   **T** 01424 777183
Tuition
PO Box 39, Battle
East Sussex TN33 0ZT
E sales@archerycentre.co.uk
W www.archerycentre.co.uk

ARMS & ARCHERY   **T** 01920 460335
Armour. Chainmail. Longbows. Tents. Weaponry. X-bows
Thrift Lane, Off London Road
Ware, Herts SG12 9QS
E armsandarchery@btconnect.com

ART *
Art Consultant. Supplier of Paintings & Sculpture
E h@art8star.co.uk
W www.art8star.co.uk

ART DIRECTORS & TRIP PHOTO LIBRARY   **T** 020 8642 3593
Digital Scans & Colour Slides (All Subjects)
57 Burdon Lane, Cheam
Surrey SM2 7BY
F 020 8395 7230
E images@artdirectors.co.uk
W www.artdirectors.co.uk

BAPTY & CO

WWW.BAPTY.CO.UK

Supplying props to the entertainment industry

Bapty & Co.
Witley Gardens, Norwood Green, Middx UB2 4ES
+44 (0)20 8574 7700   +44 (0)20 8571 5700

A. S. DESIGNS T 01279 722416
Theatrical Designer. Costumes, Heads,
Masks, Puppets, Sets etc
E scaddinguk07@aol.com
W www.astheatricaldesign.co.uk

ASH, Riky T 01476 407383
Equity Registered Stunt Performer/Co-ordinator
T 07850 471227
E stuntmanriky@fallingforyou.tv
W www.fallingforyou.tv

AUTOMOTIVE ACTION T 07974 919589
Suppliers of Replica Humvees/H1 Hummers & Prototypes.
Constructor of Specialist Vehicles
E carstunts@hotmail.co.uk
W www.carstunts.co.uk

AWESOME UPHOLSTERY T 01480 461195
Custom Upholstery Specialists
Unit 7, Monsal Works
Somersham Road
St Ives
Cambridgeshire PE27 3LY
E info@awesome.eu.com
W www.awesome.eu.com

BAPTY (2000) LTD T 020 8574 7700
Dressing, Props, Weapons etc
1A Witley Gardens
Norwood Green
Southall, Middlesex UB2 4ES
F 020 8571 5700
E hire@bapty.demon.co.uk
W www.bapty.co.uk

BARNES CATERERS LTD T 01924 896148
9 Ripley Drive, Normanton
Wakefield
West Yorkshire WF6 1QT
F 01924 223730

BEAT ABOUT THE BUSH LTD T 020 8960 2087
Musical Instrument Hire
Unit 23
Enterprise Way
Triangle Business Centre
Salter Street (Off Hythe Road)
London NW10 6UG
F 020 8969 2281
E info@beataboutthebush.com
W www.beataboutthebush.com

**BIANCHI AVIATION
FILM SERVICES**   T 01494 449810
Historic & Other Aircraft
Wycombe Air Park, Booker Marlow
Buckinghamshire SL7 3DP
F 01494 461236
E info@bianchiaviation.com
W www.bianchiaviation.com

BIG BREAK CARDS   T 01386 438952
*Theatrical greetings cards featuring Hamlet the pig, drawn
by Harry Venning, as seen in The Stage.
Made by actors for actors*
E info@bigbreakcards.co.uk
W www.bigbreakcards.co.uk

BLUE MILL LTD   T 0116 248 8130
Dyers. Finishers
84 Halstead Street, Leicester LE5 3RD
F 0116 253 7633
E info@bluemill.co.uk
W www.bluemill.co.uk

BLUEBELL RAILWAY PLC   T 01825 720800
*Period Stations. Pullman Coaches. Steam Locomotives.
Much Film Experience*
Sheffield Park Station, East Sussex TN22 3QL
F 01825 720804
E info@bluebell-railway.co.uk
W www.bluebell-railway.com

**BOLDGATE COMMERCIAL
SERVICES LTD**   T 01753 610525
The Crossbow Centre, 40 Liverpool Road
Slough, Berkshire SL1 4QZ
F 01753 610587
E info@boldgate.co.uk
W www.boldgate.co.uk

BOSCO LIGHTING   T 020 8769 3470
Design/Technical Consultancy
47 Woodbourne Avenue, London SW16 1UX
E boscolx@lineone.net

**BOUNCY CASTLES BY
P. A. LEISURE**   T 01282 453939
Specialists in Amusements & Fairground Equipment
Delph House, Park Bridge Road
Towneley Park
Burnley, Lancs BB10 4SD
T 07968 399053
E paleisure@btconnect.com
W www.paleisure.com

BRISTOL (UK) LTD   T 01923 779333
Scenic Paint & StageFloor Duo Suppliers. VFX Solutions
Unit 3, Sutherland Court
Tolpits Lane, Watford WD18 9SP
F 01923 779666
E tech.sales@bristolpaint.com
W www.bristolpaint.com

BRODIE & MIDDLETON LTD   T 020 7836 3289
Theatrical Suppliers. Glitter, Paints, Powders etc
68 Drury Lane
London WC2B 5SP
F 020 7497 0554
E info@brodies.net
W www.brodies.net

**BRUNEL'S THEATRICAL
SERVICES**   T 0117 907 7855
Removal Services
20A Walnut Lane, Kingswood
Bristol BS15 4JG
E enquiries@brunelsremovalservices.co.uk
W www.brunelsremovalservices.co.uk

CANDLE MAKERS SUPPLIES   T 020 7602 1812
Rear of 102-104 Shepherds Bush Road
(Entrance in Batoum Gardens), London W6 7PD
E candles@candlemakers.co.uk
W www.candlemakers.co.uk

**CARLINE & CREW
TRANSPORTATION**   T 01293 430430
Celebrity Services
12A Bridge Industrial Estate, Balcombe Road
West Sussex RH6 9HU
F 01293 430432
E carlinehire@yahoo.co.uk
W www.carlineprivatehire.co.uk

CAULFIELD PRODUCTIONS LTD   T 07902 974108
Technical & Production Services
71 Turner Road, Walthamstow, London E17 3JG
E office@caulfieldproductions.co.uk
W www.caulfieldproductions.co.uk

**CHASE 55 SUPERHIRE
PROPS LTD**   T 0871 2310900
Prop Hire Specialist. Victorian to Present Day
55 Chase Road, London NW10 6LU
F 020 8965 8107
E trez@superhire.com
W www.superhire.com

CHRISANNE LTD   T 020 8640 5921
Specialist Fabrics & Accessories for Theatre & Dance
Chrisanne House, 110-112 Morden Road
Mitcham, Surrey CR4 4XB
F 020 8640 2106
E sales@chrisanne.com
W www.chrisanne.com

CIRCUS PROMOTIONS   T 01892 537964
Entertainers
36 St Lukes Road, Tunbridge Wells
Kent TN4 9JH
E mike@heypresto.orangehome.co.uk
W www.heyprestoentertainment.co.uk

CLASSIC CAR AGENCY THE   T 01306 731052
Advertising. Film. Promotional. Publicity
PO Box 427, Dorking
Surrey RH5 6WP
T 07788 977655
E theclassiccaragency@btopenworld.com
W www.theclassiccaragency.com

CLASSIC CAR HIRE   T 020 8398 8304
Over 30 Classic & Vintage Vehicles
Unit 2 Hampton Court Estate, Summer Road
Thames Ditton KT7 0RG
F 020 8939 3987
E info@classic-hire.co.uk
W www.classic-hire.co.uk

CLASSIC COLLECTION THE   T 0191 388 2387
Bespoke Wedding Cars
43 Dunstan Close, Chester Le Street DH2 3HX
E info@the-classic-collection.co.uk
W www.the-classic-collection.co.uk

CLASSIC OMNIBUS   T 01303 248999
Vintage Open-Top Buses & Coaches
44 Welson Road, Folkestone, Kent CT20 2NP
W www.opentopbus.co.uk

COBO MEDIA LTD   T 020 8291 7079
Performing Arts, Entertainment & Leisure Marketing
43A Garthorne Road, London SE23 1EP
F 020 8291 4969
E admin@cobomedia.com
W www.cobomedia.com

COMPTON, Mike & Rosi T 020 8680 4364
Costumes. Models. Props
11 Woodstock Road, Croydon, Surrey CR0 1JS
T 07900 258646
E mikeandrosicompton@btopenworld.com

CONCEPT ENGINEERING LTD T 01628 825555
Smoke, Fog, Snow etc
7 Woodlands Business Park, Woodlands Park Avenue
Maidenhead, Berkshire SL6 3UA
F 01628 826261
E info@conceptsmoke.com
W www.concept-smoke.co.uk

COOK, Sheila TEXTILES T 020 7603 3003
Textiles, Costumes & Accessories for Hire/Sale
26 Addison Place, London W11 4RJ
E sheilacook@sheilacook.co.uk
W www.sheilacook.co.uk

**COSTUMES & SHOWS
UNLIMITED** T 01253 827092
Costume Rental & Design. Ice Rink Rental.
Show Production
Crammond, Hillylaid Road
Thornton-Cleveleys, Lancs FY5 4EG
T 07881 970398
E iceshowpro@aol.com
W www.ice-shows-and-costumes-unlimited.co.uk

CREATIVE WORKS T 07976 449681
Floral Design
1 St Arnaud, Doods Way, Reigate, Surrey RH2 0JT
E info@ckworks.net
W www.ckworks.net

CRESTA BLINDS LTD T 01902 714143
Supplier of Vertical Blinds
Unit 23, Hollies Industrial Estate
Graiseley Row, Wolverhampton WV2 4HE
F 01902 715518
E info@crestablindsltd.co.uk
W www.crestablindsltd.co.uk

CROFTS, Andrew T/F 01403 864518
Book Writing Services
Westlands Grange, West Grinstead
Horsham, West Sussex RH13 8LZ
E croftsa@aol.com
W www.andrewcrofts.com

**CUE ACTION POOL
PROMOTIONS** T 07881 828077
Advice for UK & US Pool, Snooker, Trick Shots
4 Hillview Close, Rowhedge, Colchester, Essex CO5 7HT
E sales@cueaction.com
W www.stevedaking.com

CURTAIN TRACKS & DRAPES T 01449 736305
27 The Street, Brettenham
Ipswich, Suffolk IP7 7QP
E piehatch@aol.com
W www.suffolkscenery.info

DAVEY, Brian
See NOSTALGIA AMUSEMENTS

DESIGN PROJECTS T 01883 730262
Perrysfield Farm, Broadham Green
Old Oxted, Surrey RH8 9PG
F 01883 723707
W www.designprojects.co.uk

**DEVEREUX
DEVELOPMENTS LTD** T 01642 560854
Haulage. Removals. Trucking
Daimler Drive, Cowpen Industrial Estate
Billingham, Cleveland TS23 4JD
F 01642 566664
E mikebell@britdev.com

**DORANS PROPMAKERS/
SET BUILDERS** T/F 01335 300064
53 Derby Road, Ashbourne
Derbyshire DE6 1BH
E info@doransprops.com
W www.doransprops.com

DURRENT, Peter T 01787 373483
Audition & Rehearsal Pianist. Cocktail Pianist.
Composer. Vocalist
Blacksmiths Cottage
Bures Road, Little Cornard
Sudbury, Suffolk CO10 0NR
E tunefuldurrent@gmail.com

EAT TO THE BEAT T 01494 790700
Production & Location Caterers
Global Infusion Court
Nashleigh Hill, Chesham, Bucks HP5 3HE
F 01494 790701
E enquiries@eattothebeat.com
W www.globalinfusiongroup.com

ELECTRO SIGNS LTD T 020 8521 8066
97 Vallentin Road, London E17 3JJ
F 020 8520 8127
E info@electrosigns.co.uk

**ELMS LESTERS
PAINTING ROOMS** T 020 7836 6747
Locations. Rehearsal Rooms
1-3-5 Flitcroft Street, London WC2H 8DH
F 020 7379 0789
E info@elmslesters.co.uk

ES GROUP LTD T 020 7055 7200
Event Overlay. Project Management. Staging.
Temporary Structures
Bell Lane, North Woolwich Road
London E16 2AB
F 020 7055 7201
E info@esglobalsolutions.com
W www.esglobalsolutions.com

ESCORT GUNLEATHER T 01268 792769
Custom Leathercraft
602 High Road, Benfleet
Essex SS7 5RW
F 01268 566775
E info@escortgunleather.com
W www.escortgunleather.com

EVANS, Peter STUDIOS LTD T 01582 725730
Scenic Embellishment. Vacuum Forming
12-14 Tavistock Street, Dunstable
Bedfordshire LU6 1NE
F 01582 481329
E sales@peterevansstudios.co.uk
W www.peterevansstudios.co.uk

FACADE T 020 8291 7079
Musical Production Services
43A Garthorne Road, London SE23 1EP
F 020 8291 4969
E facade@cobomedia.com

FAIRGROUND HIRE/ARTWORK T 01722 714786
Halstead, Sutton Mandeville
Salisbury, Wiltshire SP3 5NL
T 07710 287251
E sv@pozzy.co.uk
W www.pozzy.co.uk

FELLOWES, Mark
TRANSPORT SERVICES T 020 7386 7005
Transport. Storage
59 Sherbrooke Road, London SW6 7QL
T 07850 332818
W www.fellowesproductions.com

FILM MEDICAL SERVICES T 020 8961 3222
Units 5 & 7, Commercial Way
Park Royal, London NW10 7XF
F 020 8961 7427
E info@filmmedical.co.uk
W www.filmmedical.co.uk

FINAL CREATION T 01530 249100
Unit 19, The Loft Studio
Hill Lane Industrial Estate, Markfield
Leicestershire LE67 9PN
F 01530 249400
E gemma@finalcreation.co.uk
W www.finalcreation.co.uk

FIREBRAND T/F 01546 870310
Flambeaux Hire & Sales
Leac Na Ban, Tayvallich
By Lochgilphead, Argyll PA31 8PF
E firebrand.props@btinternet.com

FIRST NIGHT DESIGN T 07773 770781
Greeting Cards & Gifts
E info@firstnightdesign.co.uk
W www.firstnightdesign.co.uk

FLAME RETARDING LTD T 01621 818477
Grove Farm, Grove Farm Road
Tolleshunt Major, Maldon, Essex CM9 8LR
F 07092 036931
E email@flameretarding.co.uk
W www.flameretarding.co.uk

FLAMENCO PRODUCTIONS T 01905 424083
Entertainers
Sevilla 4 Cormorant Rise, Lower Wick
Worcester WR2 4BA

FLINT HIRE & SUPPLY LTD T 020 7703 9786
Queen's Row, London SE17 2PX
F 020 7708 4189
E sales@flints.co.uk
W www.flints.co.uk

FLYING BY FOY T 020 8236 0234
Flying Effects for Theatre, TV, Corporate Events etc
Unit 4, Borehamwood Enterprise Centre
Theobald Street, Borehamwood, Herts WD6 4RQ
F 020 8236 0235
E mail@flyingbyfoy.co.uk
W www.flyingbyfoy.co.uk

FRANCO THE MAGICIAN T/F 020 8202 4940
Flat 1, 79 Brent Street, London NW4 2EA
E franco@francomagic.co.uk
W www.francomagic.co.uk

FRANKIE'S YANKEES T 0121 445 5522
Classic 1950s American Cars, Memorabilia,
New Superstretch Limos & Action Vehicles
283 Old Birmingham Road, Bromsgrove B60 1HQ
T 07970 062142
E wow@frankiesyankees.com

FROST, John NEWSPAPERS T 020 8366 1392
Historical Newspaper Archives
22B Rosemary Avenue, Enfield, Middlesex EN2 0SS
E andrew@johnfrostnewspapers.com
W www.johnfrostnewspapers.com

GARRATT, Jonathan FRSA T 01725 517700
Suppliers of Traditional & Unusual Garden Pots &
Installations. Glazed Tableware
Hare Lane Farmhouse, Cranborne
Dorset BH21 5QT
E jonathan.garratt@talk21.com
W www.jonathangarratt.com

GAV NICOLA
THEATRICAL SHOES T 07961 974278
T 00 34 673803783
E gavnicola@yahoo.com
W www.theatricalshoes.com

GET STUFFED T 020 7226 1364
Taxidermy
105 Essex Road, London N1 2SL
T 07831 260062
E taxidermy@thegetstuffed.co.uk
W www.thegetstuffed.co.uk

GHOSTWRITER/AUTHOR T 01227 721071
Contact: John Parker
Dove Cottage, The Street, Ickham CT3 1QP
E ghostwriterforyourbook@ymail.com
W www.ghostwriteruk.info

GORGEOUS GOURMETS LTD T 020 8944 7771
Caterers. Equipment Hire
Gresham Way, Wimbledon SW19 8ED
F 020 8946 1639
E hire@gorgeousgourmets.co.uk
W www.gorgeousgourmets.co.uk

GOULD, Gillian ANTIQUES T 020 8458 7673
Scientific & Marine Antiques & Collectables
38 Denman Drive South, London NW11 6RH
T 07831 150060
E gillgould@dealwith.com
W www.gilliangouldantiques.co.uk

GRADAV HIRE & SALES LTD   T 020 8803 7400
Lighting & Sound Hire/Sales
Units C6 & C9 Hastingwood Trading Estate
Harbet Road, Edmonton, London N18 3HU
F 020 8803 5060
E office@gradav.co.uk

GRAND HIRE   T 020 7281 9555
Short & Long Term Piano Hire
465 Hornsey Road, London N19 4DR
F 020 7263 0154
E piano@grandhire.co.uk
W www.grandhire.co.uk

GRAY, Robin COMMENTARIES   T 01420 23347
Bridles. Hunting Attire. Racing Colours. Saddles
Comptons, Isington
Alton, Hampshire GU34 4PL
T 07831 828424
E comptons1@hotmail.co.uk

GREENPROPS   T 01398 361531
*Prop Suppliers. Artificial Flowers, Fruit, Grass,
Plants, Trees etc*
E trevor@greenprops.org
W www.greenprops.org

GREENSOURCE SOLUTIONS LTD   T 0845 3100200
*Providers of Mobile Phone Props. Supplies & Recycles
Printer Consumables*
14 Kingsland Trading Estate
St Phillips Road, Bristol BS2 0JZ
F 0117 304 2391
E props@greensource.co.uk
W www.greensource.co.uk

HAMPTON COURT HOUSE   T 020 8943 0889
Hampton Court Road
East Molesey KT8 9BS
F 020 8977 5357
W www.hamptoncourthouse.co.uk

HANDS UP PUPPETS   T 07909 824630
7 Cavendish Vale, Nottingham
Nottinghamshire NG5 4DS
E marcus@handsuppuppets.com
W www.handsuppuppets.com

**HARLEQUIN FLOORS
(BRITISH HARLEQUIN PLC)**   T 01892 514888
*Floors for Dance, Display, Entertainment &
the Performing Arts*
Festival House, Chapman Way
Tunbridge Wells, Kent TN2 3EF
T 0800 289932
E enquiries@harlequinfloors.com
W www.harlequinfloors.com

HERON & DRIVER   T 020 7394 8688
Scenic Furniture & Prop Makers
Unit 7, Dockley Road Industrial Estate
Rotherhithe, London SE16 3SF
E mail@herondriver.co.uk
W www.herondriver.co.uk

HI-FLI (Flying Effects)   T 0161 278 9352
18 Greencourt Drive
Manchester M38 0BZ
E mikefrost@hi-fli.co.uk

**HISTORICAL INTERPRETER
& ROLE PLAYING**   T 020 8866 2997
Contact: Donald Clarke
80 Warden Avenue, Rayners Lane
Harrow, Middlesex HA2 9LW
T 07811 606285
E info@historicalinterpretations.co.uk
W www.historicalinterpretations.co.uk

HISTORY IN THE MAKING LTD   T 023 9225 3175
Weapon & Costume Hire
4A Aysgarth Road, Waterlooville
Hampshire PO7 7UG
E enquiries@history-making.com
W www.history-making.com

**HOME JAMES
CHAUFFEUR SERVICE**   T 0121 323 4717
Moor Lane, Witton, Birmingham B6 7HH
E enquiries@homejamescars.com
W www.homejamescars.com

HOMESITE ESTATE AGENTS   T 020 7243 3535
16 Lambton Place, London W11 2SH
F 020 7243 5794
E info@homesite.co.uk
W www.homesite.co.uk

HOTCHPOTCHPROPS   T 07734 685254
21 Silvan Drive, Braunton, Devon EX33 2EQ
E jo@hotchpotchprops.com
W www.hotchpotchprops.com

HOWARD, Rex DRAPES   T 020 8955 6940
Trading division of Hawthorns
Unit F, Western Trading Estate
London NW10 7LU
E hire@hawthorns.uk.com

IMPACT   T 020 8579 9922
Private & Contract Hire of Coaches
1 Leighton Road, Ealing, London W13 9EL
F 020 8840 4880
E sales@impactgroup.co.uk
W www.impactgroup.co.uk

IMPACT PERCUSSION   T 020 8299 6700
Percussion Instruments for Sale
Unit 7 Goose Green Trading Estate
47 East Dulwich Road, London SE22 9BN
F 020 8299 6704
E sales@impactpercussion.com

IMPACT PRINT DISPLAY   T 020 7729 5978
Leaflet & Poster Distribution & Display
Tuscany Wharf, 4B Orsman Road, London N1 5QJ
F 020 7729 5994
E contactus@impactprintdisplay.com
W www.impactprintdisplay.com

IMPACT SCHOOL OF MOTORING   T 01202 666001
Expert Driving Instructors on All Vehicles
85 Dorchester Road, Oakdale
Poole BH15 3QZ
T 07775 713780
E andyd@mail2world.com

JAPAN PROMOTIONS T/F 020 7278 4099
Japanese Costumes & Props
200 Russell Court, 3 Woburn Place
London WC1H 0ND
E info@japan-promotions.co.uk
W www.japan-promotions.co.uk

JULIETTE DESIGNS T 020 7263 7878
Diamante Jewellery Manufacturer: Necklaces, Crowns etc
90 Yerbury Road, London N19 4RS
F 020 7281 7326
E juliettedesigns@hotmail.com
W www.stagejewellery.com

**KEIGHLEY & WORTH VALLEY
LIGHT RAILWAY LTD** T 01535 645214
Crew. Props. Carriages, Engines & Stations
The Railway Station, Haworth
Keighley, West Yorkshire BD22 8NJ
F 01535 647317
E admin@kwvr.co.uk
W www.kwvr.co.uk

**KENSINGTON EYE
CENTRE LTD** T/F 020 7937 8282
Special Eye Effects
37 Kensington Church Street
London W8 4LL
E kensingtoneyecentre@gmail.com

KEW BRIDGE STEAM MUSEUM T 020 8568 4757
Green Dragon Lane, Brentford
Middlesex TW8 0EN
F 020 8569 9978
E info@kbsm.org
W www.kbsm.org

KIRBY'S AFX LTD T/F 020 8723 8552
8 Greenford Avenue, Hanwell
London W7 3QP
T 07958 285608
E mail@afxuk.com
W www.kirbysflying.co.uk

**KNEBWORTH HOUSE,
GARDENS & PARK** T 01438 812661
Knebworth, Herts SG3 6PY
E info@knebworthhouse.com
W www.knebworthhouse.com

LAREDO, Alex T 01306 889423
Expert with Ropes, Bullwhips, Shooting & Riding
29 Lincoln Road, Dorking
Surrey RH4 1TE
T 07745 798118

LAREDO WILD WEST TOWN T 01580 891790
Wild West Entertainment
1 Bower Walk, Staplehurst
Tonbridge, Kent TN12 0LU
T 07947 652771
E colin.winter123@btinternet.com
W www.laredo.org.uk

LEES-NEWSOME LTD T 0845 0708005
Manufacturers of Flame Retardant Fabrics
Ashley Works, Unit 2, Rule Business Park
Grimshaw Lane, Middleton
Manchester M24 2AE
F 0845 0708006
E info@leesnewsome.co.uk
W www.leesnewsome.co.uk

LEIGHTON HALL T 01524 734474
Historic House
Carnforth, Lancashire LA5 9ST
F 01524 720357
E info@leightonhall.co.uk
W www.leightonhall.co.uk

**LEVRANT, Stephen -
HERITAGE ARCHITECTURE LTD** T 020 8748 5501
Architects. Historic Building Consultants
62 British Grove, Chiswick, London W4 2NL
F 020 8748 4992
E info@heritagearchitecture.co.uk

LIMELIGHT ENTERTAINMENT T 020 8853 9570
Theatre Merchandise
Unit 13, The io Centre
The Royal Arsenal, Seymour Street, London SE18 6SX
F 020 8853 0979
E enquiries@thelimelightgroup.co.uk

**LONDON BUSINESS
EQUIPMENT** T 020 8558 0024
Authorised Canon Dealer
527-529 High Road, Leytonstone, London E11 4PB
F 020 8556 4865
E sales@londonbusinessequipment.com
W www.londonbusinessequipment.com

**LONDON QUALITY
DRY CLEANERS LTD** T 020 7935 7316
*Dry Cleaners. Dyers. Launderers.
Costumes & Stage Curtains*
222 Baker Street, London NW1 5RT

LONO DRINKS CO T 0800 8250035
23-24 Failsworth Industrial Estate
Greenhalgh Street
Failsworth, Manchester M35 0BN
E info@lono.co.uk
W www.lono.co.uk

LOS KAOS T/F 01291 680074
Animatronics. Puppetry. Street Theatre
Quay House, Quayside
Brockweir, Gloucestershire NP16 7NQ
E kaos@loskaos.co.uk
W www.loskaos.co.uk

LUCKINGS T 020 8332 2000
Stage Hands. Storage. Transporters
Boston House, 69-75 Boston Manor Road
Brentford, Middlesex TW8 9JJ
F 020 8332 3000
E info@luckings.co.uk
W www.luckings.co.uk

LUCKINGS SCREEN SERVICES T 020 8332 2000
Artists' Trailers/Splits/2-3 Ways
Boston House, 69-75 Boston Manor Road
Brentford, Middlesex TW8 9JJ
F 020 8332 3000
E info@luckings.co.uk
W www.luckings.co.uk

LYON EQUIPMENT T 01539 626250
*Petzl & Beal Rope Access Equipment (PPE) for Industrial &
Theatrical Work*
Junction 38, M6, Tebay, Cumbria CA10 3SS
F 01539 624857
E work.rescue@lyon.co.uk
W www.lyon.co.uk

M A C T 0161 969 8311
Sound Hire
1-2 Attenburys Park, Park Road
Altrincham, Cheshire WA14 5QE
F 0161 962 9423
E hire@macsound.co.uk
W www.macsound.co.uk

MACKIE, Sally LOCATIONS T 01451 830294
Location Finding & Management
Cownham Farm, Broadwell
Moreton-in-Marsh, Gloucestershire GL56 0TT
E sally@mackie.biz
W www.sallymackie-locations.com

GREENPROPS
Foliage * Flowers * Fruit & Veg
Importers, Stockists & Makers

The Artificial STAGE SUPPLIERS, serving The West End, The UK and Europe
T: 01398 361531   trevor@greenprops.org   www.greenprops.org

||||||||||||||||||||||||||||||||||||||||||||||||||||||||||||||||||||||||||||||||||||||||||||||||||||||

MAGICAL MART T/F 020 8300 3579
Magic. Punch & Judy. Ventriloquists' Dolls. Hire & Advising.
Callers by Appointment
42 Christchurch Road, Sidcup, Kent DA15 7HQ
W www.johnstylesentertainer.co.uk

MAINSTREAM LEISURE GROUP T 020 8788 2669
Riverboat/Canal Boat Hire
5 The Mews, 6 Putney Common, London SW15 1HL
F 020 8788 0073
W www.mainstreamleisure.co.uk

MARCUS HALL PROPS T 020 7252 6291
Contact: Chris Marcus, Jonathan Hall
Unit 2B/C Vanguard Court
Rear of 36-38 Peckham Road, London SE5 8QT
E chris@marcushallprops.com
W www.marcushallprops.com

MARKSON PIANOS T 020 7935 8682
8 Chester Court, Albany Street, London NW1 4BU
F 020 7224 0957
E info@marksonpianos.com
W www.marksonpianos.com

MATT-LX LTD T 0845 6808692
Audio Visual. Health & Safety. Lighting. Production Design
Unit 3, Vinehall Business Centre
Vinehall Road, Robertsbridge, East Sussex TN32 5JW
E intray@mattlx.com
W www.mattlx.com

McNEILL, Brian T 01706 812291
Vintage Truck & Coaches
Hawk Mount, Kebs Road
Todmorden, Lancashire OL14 8SB
E autotrans@uk2.net
W www.rollingpast.com

MIDNIGHT ELECTRONICS T 0191 224 0088
Sound Hire
Off Quay Building, Foundry Lane
Newcastle upon Tyne NE6 1LH
F 0191 224 0080
E info@midnightelectronics.co.uk
W www.midnightelectronics.co.uk

**MILITARY, MODELS &
MINATURES** T 020 7700 7036
Model Figures
38A Horsell Road, London N5 1XP
F 020 7700 4624
E miniaturesmodels@aol.com

MODDED MOTORS AGENCY T 07989 128131
Suppliers of Modified Cars
38 Williamson Way, Rickmansworth
Hertfordshire WD3 8GL
E daniellechristie@hotmail.com
W www.moddedmotorsagency.com

MODEL BOX T 01837 54342
Computer Aided Design. Design Services
35 Mill Road
Okehampton
Devon EX20 1PS
E info@modelbox.co.uk
W www.modelboxplans.com

**MOORFIELDS
PHOTOGRAPHIC LTD** T 0151 236 1611
2 Old Hall Street
Liverpool L3 9RQ
E info@moorfieldsphoto.com
W www.moorfieldsphoto.com

MORGAN, Dennis T 07915 662767
Cameraman
241 Crystal Palace Road
London SE22 9JQ
E info@dennismorgan.co.uk

MORTON, G. & L. T 01430 860393
Farming. Horses
Hashome Carr
Holme-on-Spalding Moor
Yorkshire YO43 4BD
E janet_morton@hotmail.com

MOTORHOUSE HIRE LTD T 020 7495 1618
Contact: Michael Geary. Action Vehicles
Oatleys Hall
Turweston
Northants NN13 5JX
F 01280 704944
E michael@motorhouseltd.co.uk

MPG BOOKS GROUP LTD T 01208 73266
Quality Book Manufacturers
Victoria Square, Bodmin
Cornwall PL31 1EB
F 01208 73603
E print@mpg-books.co.uk
W www.mpg-booksgroup.com

NATIONAL MOTOR MUSEUM T 01590 612345
John Montagu Building
Beaulieu, Brockenhurst
Hampshire SO42 7ZN
F 01590 612624
E info@beaulieu.co.uk
W www.beaulieu.co.uk

NATURAL SELECTION T 07543 968238
Things Rustic, Rural & Recycled. Artefacts, Artworks,
Furniture & Tools
E info@naturalselection.gb.com

NEWMAN HIRE COMPANY T 020 8743 0741
Lighting Hire
16 The Vale, Acton
London W3 7SB
E info@newmanhire.co.uk

NORTHERN LIGHT T 0131 622 9100
Assembly Street, Leith
Edinburgh EH6 7RG
F 0131 622 9101
E enquiries@northernlight.co.uk
W www.northernlight.co.uk

NOSTALGIA AMUSEMENTS T 020 8398 2141
Contact: Brian Davey
22 Greenwood Close
Thames Ditton, Surrey KT7 0BG
T 07973 506869

Properties & Trades

**NOTTINGHAM JOUSTING ASSOCIATION
SCHOOL OF NATIONAL
EQUITATION LTD** T 01509 852366
*Jousting & Medieval Tournaments. Horses &
Riders for Films & Television*
Bunny Hill Top, Costock
Loughborough, Leicestershire LE12 6XN
E info@bunnyhill.co.uk
W www.bunnyhill.co.uk

OCEAN LEISURE T 020 7930 5050
Scuba Diving. Watersports Retail
11-14 Northumberland Avenue, London WC2N 5AQ
F 020 7930 3032
E info@oceanleisure.co.uk
W www.oceanleisure.co.uk

OFFSTAGE BOOKS T 020 8444 4717
BlackGull Bookshop, 121 High Road, London N2 8AG
E offstagebooks@gmail.com

PAPERFLOW PLC T 020 8331 2000
Office Equipment. Stationery
Units 5 & 6, Meridian Trading Estate
20 Bugsbys Way, Charlton, London SE7 7SJ
F 020 8331 2001
E info@paperflowgroup.com

PAPERPROPMAKER T 07545 281486
*Paper Props Created for Stage, Film & Television. Letters,
Notebooks, Paper Ephemera etc. Handwritten or Printed.
Any Style or Period Reproduced*
Based in London
E sianwillis@live.co.uk

**PATCHETTS EQUESTRIAN
CENTRE** T 01923 852255
Location
Hillfield Lane, Aldenham
Watford, Herts WD25 8PE
F 01923 859289
E info@patchetts.co.uk
W www.patchetts.co.uk

PATERSON, Helen T 020 7730 6428
Typing Services
40 Whitelands House, London SW3 4QY
E pater@waitrose.com

**PERIOD PETROL
PUMP COLLECTION** T 01379 643978
c/o Diss Ironworks, 7 St Nicholas Street
Diss, Norfolk IP22 4LB
W www.periodpetrolpump.co.uk

PHOSPHENE T 01449 770011
Lighting & Sound. Design. Hire. Sales
Milton Road South
Stowmarket, Suffolk IP14 1EZ
E phosphene@btconnect.com
W www.phosphene.co.uk

PIANO PEOPLE THE T 0845 6076713
Piano Hire & Transport
74 Playford Road, London N4 3PH
E info@pianopeople.co.uk
W www.pianopeople.co.uk

**PICKFORDS MOVING
& STORAGE** T 020 3188 2100
Laxcon Close, London NW10 0TG
E enquiries@pickfords.com
W www.pickfords.com

PICTURES PROPS CO LTD T 020 8749 2434
Film & Television Prop Hire
12-16 Brunel Road, London W3 7XR
F 020 8740 5846
E picturesprops@tiscali.co.uk

PINK POINTES DANCEWEAR T/F 01708 438584
1A Suttons Lane
Hornchurch, Essex RM12 6RD
E pink.pointes@btconnect.com

PLUNGE PRODUCTIONS T 01273 421819
Creative Services. Graphic Design. Props
Unit 3, Bestwood Works
Drove Road, Brighton BN41 2PA
E info@plungeproductions.com
W www.plungeproductions.com

PLUS FILM LTD T 01489 895559
All Periods Vehicle Hire
1 Mill House Cottages
Winchester Road
Bishop's Waltham SO32 1AH
E stephen.lamonby@googlemail.com

**POLAND, Anna: SCULPTOR
AND MODELMAKER** T 023 8040 5166
Sculpture, Models, Puppets, Masks etc
Salterns, Old Bursledon
Southampton, Hampshire SO31 8DH
E polandanna@hotmail.com

POLLEX PROPS / FIREBRAND T/F 01546 870310
Prop Makers
Leac Na Ban, Tayvallich
Lochgilphead, Argyll PA31 8PF
E firebrand.props@btinternet.com

**PRAETORIAN ASSOCIATES/PROCUREMENT
SERVICES - SA** T 020 7096 1827
*Personal Safety & Anti-Stalking Consultancy. Services for
Film & Television Industry within South Africa*
Tintagel, 1 St Clairs Road
St Osyth, Essex CO16 8QG
T 07973 505981
E martin.beale@praetorianasc.com
W www.praetorianasc.com

**PREMIER CHAUFFEUR
SERVICES** T 01925 299112
164 Haydock Street, Newton-le-Willows
Merseyside WA12 9DH
T 07890 661050
E mike.vizard@hotmail.co.uk

PRINTMEDIA GROUP
E info@printmediagroup.eu
W www.printmediagroup.eu

PROBLOOD T/F 01728 723865
11 Mount Pleasant, Framlingham
Suffolk IP13 9HQ

**PROFESSOR PATTEN'S
PUNCH & JUDY** T 01707 873262
Hire & Performances. Advice on Traditional Show
14 The Crest, Goffs Oak
Hertfordshire EN7 5NP
W www.dennispatten.co.uk

PROP FARM LTD T 01909 723100
Contact: Pat Ward
Grange Farm, Elmton
Nr Creswell, North Derbyshire S80 4LX
F 01909 721465
E pat@propfarm.co.uk

PROP STUDIOS LTD T 01444 250088
Unit 3 Old Kiln Works
Ditchling Common Industrial Estate
Hassocks BN6 8SG
F 01444 250089
E info@propstudios.co.uk
W www.propstudios.co.uk

PROPS GALORE T 020 8746 1222
Period Textiles/Jewellery
15 Brunel Road, London W3 7XR
F 020 8354 1866
E propsgalore@farley.co.uk

PUNCH & JUDY PUPPETS
& BOOTHS T/F 020 8300 3579
Hire & Advisory Service. Callers by Appointment
42 Christchurch Road, Sidcup
Kent DA15 7HQ
W www.johnstylesentertainer.co.uk

RAINBOW PRODUCTIONS LTD T 020 8254 5300
Creation & Appearances of Costume Characters.
Stage Shows
Unit 3, Greenlea Park
Prince George's Road, London SW19 2JD
F 020 8254 5306
E info@rainbowproductions.co.uk
W www.rainbowproductions.co.uk

REAL PRINT & MEDIA T 01622 200123
Printing
36 Hedley Street, Maidstone
Kent ME14 5AD
F 01622 200131
E info@realprintandmedia.com

RENT-A-CLOWN T/F 020 7608 0312
Contact: Mattie Faint
37 Sekeforde Street, Clerkenwell
London EC1R 0HA
E mattiefaint@gmail.com

REPLAY LTD T 020 7637 0473
Showreels. Television Facilities Hire
Museum House, 25 Museum Street
London WC1A 1JT
E sales@replayfilms.co.uk
W www.replayfilms.co.uk

ROBERTS, Chris INTERIORS T 07956 512074
Specialist Painters & Decorators to the Film Industry
117 Colebrook Lane, Loughton IG10 2HP

ROOTSTEIN, Adel LTD T 020 7381 1447
Mannequin Manufacturer
9 Beaumont Avenue, London W14 9LP
F 020 7386 9594
W www.rootstein.com

ROYAL HORTICULTURAL HALLS
& CONFERENCE CENTRE THE T 0845 3704606
Film Location: Art Deco & Edwardian Buildings.
Conferences. Events. Exhibitions. Fashion Shows
80 Vincent Square, London SW1P 2PE
F 020 7834 2072
E horthalls@rhs.org.uk
W www.rhhonline.co.uk

RUDKIN DESIGN T 01327 301770
Design Consultants. Advertising, Brochures, Corporate etc
10 Cottesbrooke Park, Heartlands Business Park
Daventry, Northamptonshire NN11 8YL
E arudkin@rudkindesign.co.uk
W www.rudkindesign.com

RUMBLE, Jane T 020 8904 6462
Props to Order. No Hire
121 Elmstead Avenue, Wembley
Middlesex HA9 8NT

SABAH T/F 001 954 566 6219
UK Stylist Based in Florida. Designer. Prop Buyer. Wardrobe
2841 N. Ocean Boulevard Apt 501, Fort Lauderdale
Florida 33308, USA
T 001 954 383 2179
E sabah561@aol.com

SALVO THE CLOWN T 01268 745791
13 Second Avenue, Kingsleigh Park
Thundersley, Essex SS7 3QD
E salvo@annualclownsdirectory.com
W www.annualclownsdirectory.com

SAPEX SCRIPTS T 020 8236 1600
The Maxwell Building
Elstree Film Studios, Shenley Road
Borehamwood, Herts WD6 1JG
F 020 8324 2771
E scripts@sapex.co.uk
W www.sapex.co.uk

SCHULTZ & WIREMU
FABRIC EFFECTS LTD T/F 020 8469 0151
Distressing. Dyeing. Printing
Unit B202 Faircharm Studios
8-12 Creekside
London SE8 3DX
E swfabricfx@london.com
W www.schultz-wiremufabricfx.co.uk

SCRIPTRIGHT T 020 8740 7303
Contact: S.C. Hill. Script & Manuscript Typing Services.
Script Reading Services
6 Valetta Road, London W3 7TN
E samc.hill@virgin.net

SCRIPTS BY ARGYLE T 07905 293319
Play, Film & Book. Binding. Copying. Editing. Word
Processing. London Collection of Manuscript on Request
43 Clappers Lane, Fulking
West Sussex BN5 9ND
E argyle.associates@me.com

SFD T 01923 232425
Ground Floor, Sunningdale
The Belfry, Colonial Way, Watford, Herts WD24 4WH
F 01923 232326
E sales@sfd.co.uk
W www.sfd.co.uk

SHAOLIN WAY T 020 7734 6391
Martial Arts Supplies. Lion Dance & Kung Fu Instruction
10 Little Newport Street
London WC2H 7JJ
T 07768 321092
E shaolinway@btconnect.com
W www.shaolinway.com

SHIRLEY LEAF &
PETAL COMPANY T/F 01424 427793
Flower Makers Museum & Manufacturers
58A/B High Street, Old Town
Hastings, East Sussex TN34 3EN

SIDE EFFECTS T 020 7587 1116
FX. Models. Props
92 Fentiman Road, London SW8 1LA
F 020 7207 0062
E sfx@lineone.net

SNOW BUSINESS T/F 01453 840077
Snow & Winter Effects on Any Scale
The Snow Mill
Bridge Road, Ebley, Stroud
Gloucestershire GL5 4TR
E snow@snowbusiness.com
W www.snowbusiness.com

SOFT PROPS T 020 7587 1116
Modelmakers
92 Fentiman Road, London SW8 1LA
F 020 7207 0062
E jackie@softprops.co.uk

SPUR CREATIVE WORKSHOP T 01435 873755
Unit 1A, North Yard
Pennybridge Lane
Mayfield, East Sussex TN20 6QB
T 07970 805871
E info@spurcreative.co.uk
W www.spurcreative.co.uk

**STANSTED AIRPORT TAXIS
& CHAUFFEURS** T 0845 6436705
55 Croasdaile Road
Stansted Airport
Essex CM24 8DW
E enquiries@stanstedtaxiservice.co.uk
W www.stanstedtaxiservice.co.uk

**STEELDECK RENTALS/
SALES LTD** T 020 7833 2031
Modular Staging. Stage Equipment Hire
Unit 58
T Marchant Trading Estate
42-72 Verney Road
London SE16 3DH
F 020 7232 1780
E rentals@steeldeck.co.uk
W www.steeldeck.co.uk

STEVENSON, Scott T 07739 378579
Prop Maker
60 Ripley Road, Sawmills
Belper, Derbyshire DE56 2JQ
E scott@bodymechprops.co.uk
W www.bodymechprops.co.uk

**STOKE BRUERNE BOAT
COMPANY LTD** T 07966 503609
Passenger & Day Boat Operator
Wharf Cottage, Stoke Bruerne
Northants NN12 7SE
W www.stokebruerneboats.co.uk

SUFFOLK SCENERY T 01449 736305
Curtain Tracks & Drapes only
Pie Hatch Farm
Brettenham Road
Buxall, Stowmarket, Suffolk IP14 3DZ
T 07787 548744
E piehatch@aol.com
W www.suffolkscenery.info

SUPERSCRIPTS T 01256 769376
1 Bluehaven Walk, Hook
Hampshire RG27 9SX
T 07793 160138
E super_scripts@sky.com

SUPERSCRIPTS T 020 8898 7933
Audio Typing. Post-Prod Scripts. Rushes
56 New Road, Hanworth
Middlesex TW13 6TQ
T 07793 160138
E jackie@superscripts.fsnet.co.uk

TALK TO THE HAND PUPPETS T 07855 421454
Custom Puppets for Film, Stage & Television
Studio 277, Wimbledon Art Studios
Riverside Yard
Earlsfield, London SW17 0BB
T 07813 682293

TAYLOR, Charlotte T/F 020 8876 9085
Props Buyer. Stylist
18 Eleanor Grove, Barnes
London SW13 0JN
T 07836 708904
E charlottetaylor1@blueyonder.co.uk

**THAMES LUXURY
CHARTERS LTD** T 020 8780 1562
5 The Mews, 6 Putney Common
London SW15 1HL
F 020 8788 0072
E sales@thamesluxurycharters.co.uk
W www.thamesluxurycharters.co.uk

THEATRESEARCH T 01423 780497
Theatre Consultants
Dacre Hall, Dacre, North Yorkshire HG3 4ET
F 01423 781957
E info@theatresearch.co.uk
W www.theatresearch.co.uk

**THEATRICAL
SHOEMAKERS LTD** T 020 7474 0500
Footwear
Unit 7A
Thames Road Industrial Estate
Thames Road, Silvertown, London E16 2EZ
F 020 7476 5220
E ts@shoemaking.co.uk
W www.shoemaking.co.uk

THEME TRADERS LTD T 020 8452 8518
Props
The Stadium, Oaklands Road
London NW2 6DL
F 020 8450 7322
E mailroom@themetraders.com
W www.themetraders.com

TOP SHOW T/F 01904 750022
Props. Scenery. Conference Specialists
North Lane, Huntington
Yorks YO32 9SU

TRACK THAT T 07941 234254
Tracking Vehicle/Camera Car Supplier
Based in Wandsworth, London SW18
E info@trackthat.co.uk
W www.trackthat.co.uk

TRANSCRIPTS T 07973 200197
*Conferences. Interviews. Post-production Scripts. Proof-
reading. Videos. Working Formats: Digital, CD/DVD, Tapes*
E lucy@transcripts.demon.co.uk

**TRISTAR WORLDWIDE
CHAUFFEUR SERVICES** T 01895 432000
Unit 1-2, Horton Road
West Drayton UB7 8BQ
E reservations@tristarworldwide.com
W www.tristarworldwide.com

GRAND HIRE

020 7281 9555   piano@grandhire.co.uk   www.grandhire.co.uk

TRYFONOS, Mary MASKS   T 020 7502 7883
Mask, Headdress & Puppet Specialist
59 Shaftesbury Road, London N19 4QW
T 07764 587433
E marytryfonos@aol.com

TURN ON LIGHTING   T/F 020 7359 7616
Antique Lighting c1850-1950
11 Camden Passage, London N1 8EA

**UK SAME DAY
DELIVERY SERVICE**   T 07785 717179
Contact: Philip Collings
18 Billingshurst Road, Broadbridge Heath
Horsham, West Sussex RH12 3LW
F 01403 266059
E philcollings60@hotmail.com

UPBEAT EVENT DESIGN   T 01494 790700
Corporate Hospitality Caterers
Global Infusion Court, Nashleigh Hill
Chesham, Bucks HP5 3HE
F 01494 790701
E enquiries@upbeateventdesign.com
W www.upbeateventdesign.com

UPSTAGE   T 020 7403 6510
Live Communications Agency
Studio A, 7 Maidstone Buildings Mews
72-76 Borough High Street, London SE1 1GD
F 020 7403 6511
E post@upstagelivecom.co.uk
W www.upstagelivecom.co.uk

**VELOCITY SUPPLY
CHAIN LOGISTICS**   T 01932 733000
Units 6 & 7, The Heathrow Estate
Silver Jubilee Way, Heathrow TW4 6NF
F 01932 733009
E bhathaway@vscl.co.uk
W www.vscl.co.uk

**VENTRILOQUIST
DOLLS HOME**   T/F 020 8300 3579
Hire & Helpful Hints. Callers by Appointment
42 Christchurch Road, Sidcup, Kent DA15 7HQ
W www.johnstylesentertainer.co.uk

VENTRILOQUIST DUMMY HIRE   T 01707 873262
Contact: Dennis Patten. Hire & Advice
14 The Crest, Goffs Oak, Herts EN7 5NP
W www.dennispatten.co.uk

VINMAG ARCHIVE LTD   T 020 8533 7588
84-90 Digby Road, London E9 6HX
F 020 8525 9209
E piclib@vinmagarchive.com
W www.vinmagarchive.com

VINTAGE CARRIAGES TRUST   T 01535 680425
*Owners of the Museum of Rail Travel at
Ingrow Railway Centre*
Keighley, West Yorkshire BD21 5AX
F 01535 610796
E admin@vintagecarriagestrust.org
W www.vintagecarriagestrust.org

VOCALEYES   T 020 7375 1043
Providers of Audio Description for Theatrical Performance
1st Floor, 54 Commercial Street
London E1 6LT
F 020 7247 5622
E enquiries@vocaleyes.co.uk
W www.vocaleyes.co.uk

WALKING YOUR DOG   T/F 020 8319 1806
Dog Walking & Pet Services for South East London
92 Wricklemarsh Road
London SE3 8DS
T 07867 502333
E info@walkingyourdog.net
W www.walkingyourdog.net

WEB & PRINT   T 020 8838 3555
Suite 14, Space House
Space Business Park
Abbey Road, Park Royal
London NW10 7SU
E info@webandprint.co.uk
W www.webandprint.co.uk

**WEBBER, Peter HIRE/
RITZ STUDIOS**   T 020 8870 1335
Music Equipment Hire. Rehearsal Studios
110-112 Disraeli Road
London SW15 2DX
E ben@peterwebberhire.com

WESTED LEATHERS COMPANY   T 01322 660654
Suede & Leather Suppliers/Manufacturers
Little Wested House, Wested Lane
Swanley, Kent BR8 8EF
F 01322 667039
E wested@wested.com

WESTWARD, Lynn BLINDS   T 020 8742 8333
Window Blind Specialist
458 Chiswick High Road
London W4 5TT
F 020 8742 8444
E info@lynnwestward.com
W www.lynnwestward.com

WHITE ROOM STUDIO   T 020 8674 8151
Unit 03, 45 Morrish Road
London SW2 4EE
E info@whiteroomstudio.co.uk
W www.whiteroomstudio.co.uk

WILTSHIRE A. F. LLP   T 01483 200516
Agricultural Vehicle Engineers, Repairs etc
The Agricultural Centre
Alfold Road
Dunsfold, Surrey GU8 4NP
F 01483 200491
E team@afwiltshire.co.uk

WORBEY, Darryl STUDIOS   T 020 7639 8090
Specialist Puppet Design
Ground Floor, 33 York Grove
London SE15 2NY
F 020 7635 6397
E info@darrylworbeystudios.com

ACADEMY PLAYERS DIRECTORY
See PLAYERS DIRECTORY

A C I D PUBLICATIONS   T/F 07050 205206
The Basement, Minus One House
Lyttelton Road, London E10 5NQ
E acidnews@aol.com

**ACTING: A DRAMA
STUDIO SOURCE BOOK**   T 020 7373 5628
Peter Owen Publishers
20 Holland Park Avenue, London W11 3QU
E info@peterowen.com
W www.peterowen.com

**ACTIONS:
THE ACTORS' THESAURUS**   T 020 8749 4953
By Marina Caldarone & Maggie Lloyd-Williams
Nick Hern Books, The Glasshouse
49A Goldhawk Road, London W12 8QP
F 020 8735 0250
E info@nickhernbooks.demon.co.uk
W www.nickhernbooks.co.uk

ACTORS' YEARBOOK
See BLOOMSBURY PLC

**ANNUAIRE DU
CINEMA BELLEFAYE**   T 00 33 1 42335252
*French Actors' Directory, Production, Technicians &
All Technical Industries & Suppliers*
30 rue Saint Marc, 75002 Paris, France
F 00 33 1 42333303
E contact@bellefaye.com
W www.bellefaye.com

ARTISTES & AGENTS   T 020 7224 9666
Richmond House Publishing Co Ltd, 70-76 Bell Street
Marylebone, London NW1 6SP
F 020 7224 9688
E sales@rhpco.co.uk
W www.rhpco.co.uk

AUDITIONS: A PRACTICAL GUIDE
W www.auditionsapracticalguide.com

AUDITIONS UNDRESSED   T 020 7839 4888
By Dan Bowling
c/o Global Artists, 23 Haymarket, London SW1Y 4DG
E michaelgarrett@globalartists.co.uk

AURORA METRO PRESS (1989)   T 020 3261 0000
*Biography, Drama, Fiction, Humour, Reference & International
Literature in English Translation*
67 Grove Avenue, Twickenham TW1 4HX
E info@aurorametro.com
W www.aurorametro.com

BEAT MAGAZINE   T 01753 866865
Arts & Culture Magazine
c/o Firestation Centre for Arts & Culture, The Old Court
St Leonards Road, Windsor, Berks SL4 3BL
E editor@beatmagazine.co.uk
W www.beatmagazine.co.uk

**BIRTH OF THEATRE THE -
STAGE BY STAGE**   T 020 7373 5628
Drama. History. Reference. Theatre Studies
Peter Owen Publishers
20 Holland Park Avenue, London W11 3QU
F 020 7373 6760
E info@peterowen.com
W www.peterowen.com

BLOOMSBURY PLC   T 020 7494 2111
50 Bedford Square, London WC1B 3DP
F 020 7434 0151
E methuen.drama@bloomsbury.com
W www.methuendrama.com

BOOKTHEACT.COM   T 020 7939 8489
The Entertainment Booking Site & Directory from The Stage
47 Bermondsey Street, London SE1 3XT
F 020 7939 8479
E info@booktheact.com
W www.booktheact.com

**BRITISH PERFORMING
ARTS YEARBOOK**   T 020 7333 1733
Rhinegold Publishing
241 Shaftesbury Avenue, London WC2H 8TF
E bpay@rhinegold.co.uk
W www.rhinegold.co.uk

BRITISH THEATRE DIRECTORY   T 020 7224 9666
Richmond House Publishing Co Ltd
70-76 Bell Street
Marylebone, London NW1 6SP
F 020 7224 9688
E sales@rhpco.co.uk
W www.rhpco.co.uk

BROADCAST   T 020 7728 5542
Greater London House, Hampstead Road
London NW1 7EJ
F 020 7728 5555
W www.broadcastnow.co.uk

CASTCALL   T 01582 456213
Casting Information Services. Incorporating Castfax
106 Wilsden Avenue, Luton LU1 5HR
F 0872 1156975
E admin@castcall.co.uk
W www.castcall.co.uk

CASTWEB   T 020 7720 9002
7 St Luke's Avenue, London SW4 7LG
E info@castweb.co.uk
W www.castweb.co.uk

CELEBRITY BULLETIN THE   T 020 8672 3191
G8 Battersea Studio 1
80 Silverthorne Road
London SW8 3HE
F 020 8672 2282
E enquiries@celebrity-bulletin.co.uk

CHAPPELL OF BOND STREET   T 020 7432 4400
*Sheet Music. Musical Instruments.
Pianos. Synthesizers. Keyboards*
152-160 Wardour Street, London W1F 8YA
F 020 7432 4410
W www.chappellofbondstreet.co.uk

**CONFERENCE &
INCENTIVE TRAVEL MAGAZINE**   T 020 8267 4307
22 Bute Gardens, London W6 7HN
F 020 8267 4442
E cit@haymarket.com
W www.citmagazine.com

CREATIVE REVIEW HANDBOOK   T 020 7970 6455
Centaur Media Plc, 50 Poland Street
London W1F 7AX
W www.crhandbook.com

DANCE DYNAMIC   T 01372 741411
A. E. Morgan Publications Ltd
Resource House, 8A High Street
Epsom, Surrey KT19 8AD
E valerie@aemorgan.co.uk
W www.danceexpression.co.uk

DANCERS SPOTLIGHT   T 020 7437 7631
7 Leicester Place, London WC2H 7RJ
F 020 7437 5881
E questions@spotlight.com
W www.spotlight.com

DIRECTING DRAMA T 020 7373 5628
Peter Owen Publishers
20 Holland Park Avenue
London W11 3QU
E info@peterowen.com
W www.peterowen.com

DODDLE T 01825 840800
Film & Television Resource Guide.
Smartphone app & Website
Pine Lodge, South Street
East Hoathley, East Sussex BN8 6DS
E sales@doddleme.com
W www.doddleme.com

EQUITY MAGAZINE T 020 7670 0211
Guild House, Upper St Martin's Lane
London WC2H 9EG
F 020 7379 7001
E ppemberton@equity.org.uk
W www.equity.org.uk

FILMLOG T 020 7549 2578
Subscriptions
Marketing Department
6-14 Underwood Street
London N1 7JQ
E info@pcrsubscriptions.com
W www.pcrnewsletter.com

FORESIGHT-NEWS T 020 7190 7777
The Profile Group (UK) Ltd
The Johnson Building
77 Hatton Garden, London EC1N 8JS
F 020 7900 3684
E info@foresightnews.co.uk
W www.foresightnews.co.uk

FOURTHWALL MAGAZINE T 020 7701 4536
Incorporating The Drama Student Magazine
Top Floor 3
66 Wansey Street, London SE17 1JP
F 07092 846523
E editor@fourthwallmagazine.co.uk
W www.fourthwallmagazine.co.uk

HERN, Nick BOOKS T 020 8749 4953
Plays. Theatrebooks. Screenplays. Performing Rights
The Glasshouse, 49A Goldhawk Road
London W12 8QP
F 020 8735 0250
E info@nickhernbooks.demon.co.uk
W www.nickhernbooks.co.uk

HOLLYWOOD REPORTER THE T 020 7420 6000
5th Floor, Endeavour House
189 Shaftesbury Avenue, London WC2H 8TJ
F 020 7420 6014
E london_one@eu.hollywoodreporter.com
W www.thr.com

HOW TO BECOME FAMOUS -
A GUIDE FOR
ACTORS IN THE UK T 07932 594312
5 Blanche Street, Canning Town
London E16 4JP
E info@howtobecomefamous.co.uk
W www.howtobecomefamous.co.uk

KAY'S UK & EUROPEAN
PRODUCTION MANUALS T 020 8960 6900
Pinewood Studios, Pinewood Road
Iver Heath, Bucks SL0 0NH
E info@kays.co.uk
W www.kays.co.uk

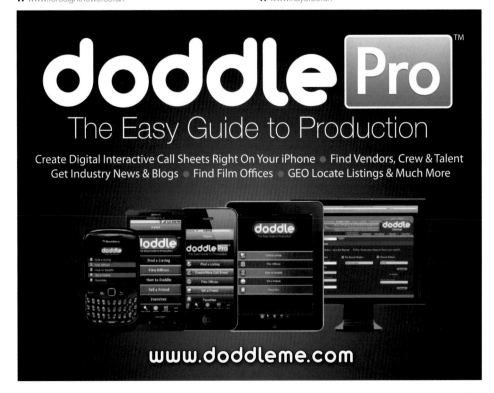

KEMPS GLOBAL T 01342 335779
Reed Business Information
East Grinstead House, East Grinstead
West Sussex RH19 1XA
F 01342 336113
E kemps.marketing@rbi.co.uk
W www.kftv.com

KNOWLEDGE THE T 020 7549 8666
6-14 Underwood Street, London N1 7JQ
F 020 7549 8668
E knowledge@wilmington.co.uk
W www.theknowledgeonline.com

LIMELIGHT THE T 00 27 11 7937231
Limelight Publications, Contacts & Casting Directory
PO Box 760, Randpark Ridge
2156, Gauteng, South Africa
F 00 27 86 5457231
E info@limelight.co.za
W www.limelight.co.za

MAKING OF THE
PROFESSIONAL ACTOR THE T 020 7373 5628
Peter Owen Publishers
20 Holland Park Avenue
London W11 3QU
E info@peterowen.com
W www.peterowen.com

METHUEN DRAMA T 020 7494 2111
50 Bedford Square, London WC1B 3DP
F 020 7434 0151
E methuendrama@bloomsbury.com
W www.methuendrama.com

MOVIE MEMORIES MAGAZINE
Devoted to Films & Stars of the 40s, 50s & 60s
10 Russet Close, Scunthorpe
N. Lincs DN15 8YJ
E crob.mvm@ntlworld.com

MUSIC WEEK DIRECTORY/
MUSIC WEEK T 020 7921 8320
UBM, 3rd Floor, Ludgate House
245 Blackfriars Road, London SE1 9UY
E enquiries@musicweek.com
W www.musicweek.com

MUSICAL STAGES T/F 020 7603 2227
Musical Theatre Magazine
PO Box 8365, London W14 0GL
E editor@musicalstages.co.uk
W www.musicalstages.co.uk

OFFICIAL LONDON
SEATING PLAN GUIDE THE T 020 7224 9666
Richmond House Publishing Co Ltd
70-76 Bell Street
Marylebone, London NW1 6SP
F 020 7224 9668
E sales@rhpco.co.uk
W www.rhpco.co.uk

PA ENTERTAINMENT T 0870 1203200
292 Vauxhall Bridge Road, Victoria
London SW1V 1AE
F 0870 1203201
E events@pressassociation.com
W www.pressassociation.com

PANTOMIME BOOK THE T 020 7373 5628
Peter Owen Publishers, 20 Holland Park Avenue
London W11 EQU
E info@peterowen.com
W www.peterowen.com

PCR
See PRODUCTION & CASTING REPORT

PINTER & MARTIN LTD T 020 7737 6868
6 Effra Parade, Brixton
London SW2 1PS
E info@pinterandmartin.com
W www.pinterandmartin.com

PLAYERS DIRECTORY T 001 310 247 3058
Casting Directory Published in January & July. Hard Copy &
eBook. Contains Actor Photos, Representation, Resume &
Demo Reels. Published since 1937
2210 W. Olive Avenue
Suite 320
Burbank, California 91506, USA
E info@playersdirectory.com
W www.playersdirectory.com

PLAYS INTERNATIONAL T 020 7720 1950
33A Lurline Gardens
London SW11 4DD
W www.playsinternational.org.uk

PRESENTERS CLUB THE T/F 07782 224207
Presenter Promotions
123 Corporation Road, Gillingham
Kent ME7 1RG
E info@presenterpromotions.com
W www.presenterpromotions.com

PRESENTERS SPOTLIGHT T 020 7437 7631
7 Leicester Place
London WC2H 7RJ
F 020 7437 5881
E questions@spotlight.com
W www.spotlight.com

PRODUCTION &
CASTING REPORT T 020 7566 8282
Editorial
PO Box 11, London N1 7JZ
F 020 7566 8284
E info@pcrnewsletter.com
W www.pcrnewsletter.com

PRODUCTION &
CASTING REPORT T 020 7549 2578
Subscriptions
Marketing Department
6-14 Underwood Street
London N1 7JQ
E info@pcrsubscriptions.com
W www.pcrnewsletter.com

RADIO TIMES T 020 8433 3999
201 Wood Lane, London W12 7TQ
F 020 8433 3923
E radio.times@bbc.co.uk
W www.radiotimes.com

RICHMOND HOUSE
PUBLISHING COMPANY LTD T 020 7224 9666
70-76 Bell Street
Marylebone
London NW1 6SP
F 020 7224 9688
E sales@rhpco.co.uk
W www.rhpco.co.uk

ROUTLEDGE PUBLISHING T 020 7017 6000
2 Park Square, Milton Park
Abington, Oxon OX14 4RN
F 020 7017 6336
E book.orders@tandf.co.uk
W www.routledge.com

SBS LTD   **T** 020 7372 6337
Suite 204, 254 Belsize Road
London NW6 4BT
F 020 7372 1992
E office@sbscasting.co.uk

SCREEN INTERNATIONAL   **T** 020 7728 5605
Greater London House
Hampstead Road, London NW1 7EJ
F 020 7728 5555
E mai.le@emap.com
W www.screendaily.com

SHOWBIZ FRIENDS
Social Networking Website for Professional Showbiz People
W www.showbizfriends.com

SHOWCASE   **T** 01892 557825
Annual Handbook for the Worldwide
Music Production Industry
25 Southmead Close, Mayfield
East Sussex TN20 6UJ
E james@showcase-music.com
W www.showcase-music.com

SHOWCAST   **T** 00 61 2 46474166
PO Box 2001
Leumeah, NSW 2560 Australia
F 00 61 2 46474167
E danelle@showcast.com.au
W www.showcast.com.au

SHOWDIGS.CO.UK   **T** 07984 422353
E info@showdigs.co.uk
W www.showdigs.co.uk

SIGHT & SOUND   **T** 020 7255 1444
British Film Institute
21 Stephen Street, London W1T 1LN
E s&s@bfi.org.uk
W www.bfi.org.uk/sightandsound

SO YOU WANT TO BE
AN ACTOR?   **T** 020 8749 4953
By Timothy West & Prunella Scales
Nick Hern Books, The Glasshouse
49A Goldhawk Road, London W12 8QP
F 020 8735 0250
E info@nickhernbooks.demon.co.uk
W www.nickhernbooks.co.uk

SO YOU WANT TO BE
A THEATRE DIRECTOR?   **T** 020 8749 4953
By Stephen Unwin
Nick Hern Books, The Glasshouse
49A Goldhawk Road, London W12 8QP
F 020 8735 0250
E info@nickhernbooks.demon.co.uk
W www.nickhernbooks.co.uk

SO YOU WANT TO BE
A THEATRE PRODUCER?   **T** 020 8749 4953
By James Seabright
Nick Hern Books, The Glasshouse
49A Goldhawk Road, London W12 8QP
F 020 8735 0250
E info@nickhernbooks.demon.co.uk
W www.nickhernbooks.co.uk

SO YOU WANT TO BE
A TV PRESENTER?   **T** 020 8749 4953
By Kathryn Wolfe
Nick Hern Books, The Glasshouse
49A Goldhawk Road, London W12 8QP
F 020 8735 0250
E info@nickhernbooks.demon.co.uk
W www.nickhernbooks.co.uk

SO YOU WANT TO
DO A SOLO SHOW?   **T** 020 8749 4953
By Gareth Armstrong
Nick Hern Books, The Glasshouse
49A Goldhawk Road, London W12 8QP
F 020 8735 0250
E info@nickhernbooks.demon.co.uk
W www.nickhernbooks.co.uk

SPEECH FOR THE SPEAKER   **T** 020 7373 5628
Peter Owen Publishers
20 Holland Park Avenue, London W11 3QU
E info@peterowen.com
W www.peterowen.com

SPOTLIGHT   **T** 020 7437 7631
7 Leicester Place, London WC2H 7RJ
F 020 7437 5881
E questions@spotlight.com
W www.spotlight.com

STAGE NEWSPAPER LTD THE   **T** 020 7939 8483
47 Bermondsey Street
London SE1 3XT
F 020 7939 8478
E editor@thestage.co.uk
W www.thestage.co.uk

SUPERNOVA BOOKS   **T** 020 3261 0000
Contact: Rebecca Gillieron (Publisher/Editor). Publishing
Books on Architecture, Art, Film & Music
67 Grove Avenue
Twickenham TW1 4HX
E rebecca@aurorametro.com
W www.supernovabooks.co.uk

TELEVISUAL MEDIA UK LTD   **T** 020 3008 5750
48 Charlotte Street, London W1T 2NS
F 020 3008 5784
E advertising@televisual.com
W www.televisual.com

THEATRE LIST THE   **T** 020 7557 6700
Society of London Theatre
32 Rose Street
London WC2E 9ET
E enquiries@solttma.co.uk

THEATRE RECORD   **T/F** 01243 539437
131 Sherringham Avenue
London N17 9RU
E editor@theatrerecord.com
W www.theatrerecord.com

TIME OUT GROUP LTD   **T** 020 7813 3000
Universal House
251 Tottenham Court Road
London W1T 7AB
F 020 7813 6001
W www.timeout.com

TV TIMES   **T** 020 3148 5615
IPC Media, Blue Fin Building
110 Southwark Street, London SE1 0SU
F 020 3148 8115

VARIETY NEWSPAPER   **T** 020 7911 1701
Procter House, Procter Street
London WC1V 6EU
F 020 7911 1922
W www.variety.com

WHITE BOOK THE   **T** 020 7772 8300
One Canada Square, Canary Wharf
London E14 5AP
E admin@whitebook.co.uk
W www.whitebook.co.uk

ARTHUR, Leone PR   T 020 7637 2994
The Ground Floor, 3 Charlotte Mews, London W1T 4DZ
F 020 7637 2984
E info@arthurleone.com
W www.arthurleone.com

AVALON PUBLIC RELATIONS   T 020 7598 8000
Arts. Marketing
4A Exmoor Street, London W10 6BD
F 020 7598 7223
E markj@avalonuk.com
W www.avalonuk.com

BEIGE   T 020 7404 3000
65 Clerkenwell Road, London EC1R 5BL
F 020 7404 5000
E beige@beigelondon.com
W www.beigelondon.com

BOLTON, Erica &
QUINN Jane LTD   T 020 7221 5000
6 Addison Avenue, London W11 4QR
F 020 7221 8100
E name@boltonquinn.com
W www.boltonquinn.com

CENTRESTAGE
PUBLIC RELATIONS   T 07838 995736
1 Barricane, St Johns, Woking GU21 7RB
F 0870 2882398
E mail@centrestagepr.com
W www.centrestagepr.com

CHESTON, Judith PUBLICITY   T 01608 661198
30 Telegraph Street, Shipston-on-Stour
Warwickshire CV36 4DA
F 01608 663772
E jacheston@tiscali.co.uk

CLARKE, Duncan PR   T 01904 345247
24 Severus Street, York, North Yorkshire YO24 4NL
E duncanclarkepr@live.co.uk
W www.duncanclarkepr.wordpress.com

CLOUT COMMUNICATIONS LTD   T 020 7851 8625
79 Wardour Street, London W1D 6QD
E info@cloutcom.co.uk
W www.cloutcom.co.uk

DAVEY, Christine ASSOCIATES   T 01753 852619
29 Victoria Road, Eton Wick
Windsor, Berkshire SL4 6LY
F 01753 851123

DDA PUBLIC RELATIONS LTD   T 020 7932 9800
192-198 Vauxhall Bridge Road, London SW1V 1DX
F 020 7932 4950
E info@ddapr.com
W www.ddapr.com

DS MANAGEMENT   T 020 8743 7777
St Martin's Theatre, West Street, London WC2N 9NH
T 07711 245848
E ds@denisesilvey.com

ELSON, Howard PROMOTIONS   T 01494 785873
Management. Marketing. PR
16 Penn Avenue, Chesham, Buckinghamshire HP5 2HS
F 01494 784760
E helson1029@aol.com

EMPICA LTD   T 01275 394400
1 Lyons Court, Long Ashton Business Park
Yanley Lane, Bristol BS41 9LB
F 01275 393933
E info@empica.com
W www.empica.com

FIVEASH, Nick PR &
MANAGEMENT   T 07971 240987
4 Baxendale Street, London E2 7BY
E nickfiveash@me.com

GADABOUTS LTD   T 020 8445 5450
Theatre Marketing & Promotions
54 Friary Road, London N12 9PB
F 0870 7059140
E info@gadabouts.co.uk
W www.gadabouts.co.uk

GAYNOR, Avril ASSOCIATES   T 07958 623013
126 Brudenell Road
London SW17 8DE
E gaynorama@aol.com

GENERATE PR   T 07545 499254
Contact: Fran Walker
9 Winchester Way
Peterborough PE3 6HL
E fran@generatepr.co.uk

GOODMAN, Deborah
PUBLICITY (DGPR)   T 020 8959 9980
25 Glenmere Avenue, London NW7 2LT
F 020 8959 7875
E publicity@dgpr.co.uk
W www.dgpr.co.uk

GRIFFIN, Alison ASSOCIATES
3rd Floor, 146 Strand
London WC2R 1JD
E alison@alisongriffin.co.uk

HYMAN, Sue ASSOCIATES LTD   T 020 7379 8420
St Martin's House, 59 St Martin's Lane
London WC2N 4JS
T 07976 514449
E sue.hyman@btinternet.com
W www.suehyman.com

IMPACT AGENCY THE   T 020 7580 1770
3 Bloomsbury Place, London WC1A 2QL
F 020 7580 7200
E mail@impactagency.co.uk
W www.theimpactagency.com

KEAN LANYON LTD   T 020 7354 3574
Contact: Sharon Kean
Rose Cottage, The Aberdeen Centre
22 Highbury Grove, London N5 2EA
F 020 7359 0199
E sharon@keanlanyon.com
W www.keanlanyon.com

KELLER, Don   T 020 8800 4882
Arts Marketing
65 Glenwood Road
Harringay, London N15 3JS
E info@donkeller.co.uk

LEEP MARKETING & PR   T 020 7439 9777
Marketing. Press. Publicity
5 Nassau House, 122 Shaftesbury Avenue
London W1D 5ER
E philip@leep.biz
W www.leep.biz

MATTHEWS, Liz PR   T 020 7253 1639
8 Smokehouse Yard, 44-46 St John Street
London EC1M 4DF
E liz@lizmatthewspr.com
W www.lizmatthewspr.com

MAYER, Anne PR   T 020 7254 7391
82 Mortimer Road, London N1 4LH
T 07764 192842
E annemayer@btopenworld.com

McAULEY ARTS
MARKETING LTD   T 020 8676 4773
118 Broxholm Road
London SE27 0BT
E sam@mcauleyartsmarketing.co.uk
W www.mcauleyartsmarketing.co.uk

MITCHELL, Jackie T 01372 465041
JM Communications
4 Sims Cottages, The Green, Claygate, Surrey KT10 0JH
F 01372 471073
E pr@jackiem.com
W www.jackiem.com

MOBIUS T 020 7269 9929
The Crypt, St Georges Church
6-7 Little Russell Street, London WC1A 2HR
E info@mobiusindustries.com
W www.mobiusindustries.com

**MORGAN, Jane
ASSOCIATES (JMA)** T 020 7263 9867
Marketing. Media
8 Heathville Road, London N19 3AJ
E jma@janemorganassociates.com

NELSON BOSTOCK GROUP LTD T 020 7229 4400
Compass House, 22 Redan Place, London W2 4SA
F 020 7727 2025
E info@nelsonbostock.com
W www.nelsonbostock.com

**NICOLINA MARKETING &
COMMUNICATIONS** T 07729 757006
16 The Grange, London SW19 4PS
E consulting@nicolina-online.com
W www.lifestylemarketingcommunications.yolasite.com

PR OFFICE THE T 020 7284 6969
720 Highgate Studios, 53-79 Highgate Road
London NW5 1TL
F 020 7485 0345
E entertainment@theproffice.com
W www.theproffice.com

PR PEOPLE THE T 0161 976 2729
1 St James Drive, Sale, Cheshire M33 7QX
E graham@pr-people.uk.com
W www.pr-people.uk.com

PREMIER PR T 020 7292 8330
91 Berwick Street, London W1F 0NE
F 020 7734 2024
W www.premierpr.com

**PRESS COMPLAINTS
COMMISSION** T 020 7831 0022
Halton House, 20/23 Holborn, London EC1N 2JD
E complaints@pcc.org.uk
W www.pcc.org.uk

**PUBLIC EYE
COMMUNICATIONS LTD** T 020 7351 1555
Suite 313, Plaza
535 Kings Road, London SW10 0SZ
F 020 7351 1010
E assistant@publiceye.co.uk

**PURPLE REIGN
PUBLIC RELATIONS** T 07809 110982
28 Undercliff Road
Lewisham, London SE13 7TT
E info@purplereignpr.co.uk
W www.purplereignpr.co.uk

**RICHMOND TOWERS
COMMUNICATIONS LTD** T 020 7388 7421
26 Fitzroy Square, London W1T 6BT
F 020 7388 7761
W www.rt-com.com

RKM COMMUNICATIONS LTD T 020 3130 7090
London & Los Angeles
2nd Floor, 4 New Burlington Street
London W1S 2JG
F 020 7287 1704
E info@rkmcom.com
W www.rkmcom.com

S & X MEDIA T 0121 604 6366
Contact: Roulla Xenides
The Gatehouse, 2B Victoria Works
Vittoria Street, Birmingham B1 3PE
F 0121 694 6494
E roulla@sx-media.com
W www.sx-media.com

SAVIDENT, Paul T 020 8567 2089
Marketing. Press Management
The Office, 27 St Dunstan's Road, London W7 2EY
F 020 3287 0960
E info@savident.com
W www.savident.com

SEVEN COLOUR MEDIA LTD T 07572 107711
16 School Street, Leeds, Yorkshire LS28 8PN
E info@sevencolourmedia.co.uk
W www.sevencolourmedia.co.uk

**SHIPPEN, Martin
MARKETING & MEDIA** T 020 8968 1943
88 Purves Road, London NW10 5TB
T 07956 879165
E m.shippen@virgin.net

SNELL, Helen LTD T 020 7240 5537
4th Floor, 80-81 St Martin's Lane
London WC2N 4AA
F 020 7240 2947
E info@helensnell.com

SOCIETY OF LONDON THEATRE T 020 7557 6727
32 Rose Street
London WC2E 9ET
E alison@solttma.co.uk

STOTT, Barbara T 020 7350 1159
20 Sunbury Lane, London SW11 3NP
E b-stott@talktalk.net

TARGET LIVE LTD T 020 3372 0950
Design. Marketing. Media. Press
45-51 Whitfield Street, London W1T 4HB
F 020 3372 0951
E info@target-live.co.uk
W www.target-live.co.uk

**TAYLOR HERRING
PUBLIC RELATIONS** T 020 8206 5151
11 Westway Centre, 69 St Marks Road
London W10 6JG
F 020 8206 5155
E james.herring@taylorherring.com
W www.taylorherring.com

**THOMPSON, Peter
ASSOCIATES** T 020 7439 1210
Flat One, 12 Bourchier Street, London W1V 5HN
F 020 7439 1202

TRE-VETT, Eddie T 01425 475544
Brink House, Avon Castle
Ringwood, Hampshire BH24 2BL

**WILLIAMS, Tei PRESS
& ARTS MARKETING** T 01869 337940
Post Office Cottage, Clifton, Oxon OX15 0PD
T 07957 664116
E artsmarketing@btconnect.com

**WILSON, Stella PUBLICITY &
PERSONAL MANAGEMENT** T 07860 174301
293 Faversham Road, Seasalter
Whitstable, Kent CT5 4BN
E stella@stellawilson.com

**WINGHAM, Maureen PRESS &
PUBLIC RELATIONS** T 01449 771200
PO Box 125, Stowmarket, Suffolk IP14 1PB
E maureen.wingham@mwmedia.uk.com

R →

Radio
- BBC Radio
- BBC Local
- Independent

Rehearsal Rooms & Casting Suites

Role Play Companies / Theatre Skills in Business

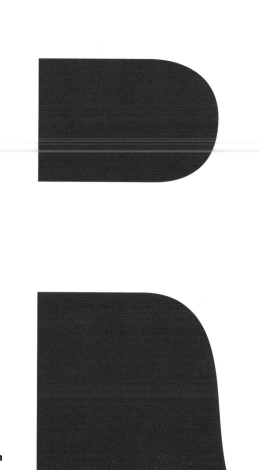

BBC RADIO
Broadcasting House
London W1A 1AA
T 020 7580 4468 (Main Switchboard)

In Autumn 2011, the BBC relocated a number of its departments to a new site at MediaCityUK, Salford Quays, Salford. Departments include BBC Children's, BBC Radio 5 live, parts of Future Media & Technology, BBC Learning, BBC Sport and BBC Breakfast. For further information about BBC North please contact the BBC's main London switchboard.

If you are interested in working for the BBC in a production role, you can submit your CV to the BBC Production Talent website at www.bbcproductiontalent.co.uk/main.aspx

• DRAMA
BBC Radio Drama
Broadcasting House
Portland Place, London W1A 1AA
T 020 7580 4468 (Main Switchboard)

Head of Audio Drama   Alison Hindell (BBC Wales)

Production
Editor   Toby Swift
Production Executive & RDC   Rebecca Wilmshurst

Executive Drama Producers – London
Sally Avens   Jeremy Mortimer
David Hunter   Marion Nancarrow

Drama Producers - London
Marc Beeby   Tracey Neale
Jessica Dromgoole   Jonquil Panting
Claire Grove   Mary Peate
Peter Kavanagh   Sasha Yevtushenko
Development   Abigail le Fleming

Readings Producers - London
Elizabeth Allard   Duncan Minshull
Emma Harding   Justine Willett
Gemma Jenkins
Editor   Di Speirs

Drama Producers - Manchester
Gary Brown   Nadia Molinari
Pauline Harris
Executive Drama Producer   Sue Roberts
Development   Charlotte Riches

Drama Producers - Birmingham
Julie Beckett   Rosemary Watts
Kim Greengrass
Executive Drama Producer   Vanessa Whitburn
Development   Fiona Kelcher

Drama Producer - BBC Wales
    Kate McAll

Drama Producers - BBC Scotland
Gaynor Macfarlane   Kirsty Williams
David Ian Neville
Editor   Bruce Young

Drama Producers - BBC Northern Ireland
    All enquiries to Gemma McMullan
Writersroom
Director   Kate Rowland

• RADIO COMEDY/RADIO PRODUCTION
Head, Radio Comedy   Jane Berthoud
Executive Producers
Steven Canny   Alison Vernon-Smith
Producers
Colin Anderson   Simon Mayhew-Archer
Sam Bryant   Julia McKenzie
Leanne Coop   Sam Michell

Tilusha Ghelani   Ed Morrish
Claire Jones   Katie Tyrrell
Victoria Lloyd
Production Executive   Sophie Taitt
Production Manager   Mel Almond

• NEWS AND CURRENT AFFAIRS
BBC News (Television & Radio)
Television Centre
Wood Lane, London W12 7RJ
T 020 8743 8000 (Main Switchboard)

Director, News   Helen Boaden
Deputy Director, BBC News & Head
  of Multimedia Programmes   Stephen Mitchell
Head of BBC Newsroom   Mary Hockaday
Head of Newsgathering   Fran Unsworth
Controller of BBC News Channel (incl. News at
  One) & Deputy Head of BBC Newsroom
    Kevin Bakhurst
Head of Editorial Development   Sam Taylor
Controller of Operations & Technology   Peter Coles
Head of Political Programmes,
  Analysis & Research   Sue Inglish
Executive Editor & Commissioning
  Editor for Current Affairs   Clive Edwards
Executive Editor, Radio
  Current Affairs   Nicola Meyrick
Editor, Six & Ten o'clock News   James Stephenson
Editor, Newsnight   Peter Rippon
Editor, Breakfast   Alison Ford
Editor, Panorama   Tom Giles
Editor, BBC News Website   Steve Herrmann

Radio Programmes
Editor, Today   Ceri Thomas
Editor, PM/Broadcasting House
The World This Weekend/
  The World at One   Joanna Carr
Editor, Newsbeat, Radio 1   Rod McKenzie

• RADIO SPORT
Deputy Controller/
  Commissioning Editor   Jonathan Wall

• CONTROLLERS
Director of Audio & Music   Tim Davie
RADIO 1
Controller   Andy Parfitt
RADIO 2
Controller   Bob Shennan
RADIO 3
Controller   Roger Wright
RADIO 4 & RADIO 7
Controller   Gwyneth Williams
RADIO 5 LIVE
Controller   Adrian Van Klaveren

• BBC NEW WRITING
BBC Writersroom
Brock House, Room 315
19 Langham Street, London W1A 1AA
T 020 8743 8000 (Main Switchboard)
E writersroom@bbc.co.uk
W www.bbc.co.uk/writersroom

Creative Director   Kate Rowland
Development Producer   Paul Ashton

Radio

Why should I work in radio?

To make a smooth transition from stage or camera to radio acting, everything that would otherwise be conveyed through body language and facial expressions must all be focused into the tone and pitch of the actor's voice.

If you have only ever considered visual acting work before, pursuing radio work would certainly enable you to expand your horizons and add additional skills to your CV. It is an opportunity to work in a different way and meet new requirements. Rehearsal and recording time is reduced in radio, which may allow you to pursue visual and radio acting alongside each other. Time constraints can be a pressure, and you have to get used to working without props (just sound effects), but this 'back to basics' existence is appealing to a lot of actors.

How can I become a radio presenter?

Presenting work in any medium comes under a different category as this is not classed as acting. It is a skill in its own right. Please refer to the 'Agents: Presenters' section for more information.

Do I need a voicereel?

This has to be your first and most important step into getting work as a radio actor. Your CV is not enough to get you a job without a professional-sounding voicereel. Voice-over work in commercial and corporate sectors requires a different type of reel. Please see the 'Promotional Services' section for more detailed voicereel advice.

Do I need an agent?

It is not strictly necessary to have an agent for radio work. The BBC is by far the main producer of radio drama and welcomes applications directly from actors, but some independent radio stations prefer using agents to put actors forward. It might be worth doing some research on your local radio stations and finding out their preferred method of contact and making a decision from there. If you are looking for a new agent and are interested in radio work as well as straight acting work, find out whether they deal with this area of the industry before signing up. If you only want to pursue radio and/or voice-over work, or are looking for a specialist agent in addition to your main agent, please see the 'Agents: Voice-over' section for further advice and listings.

How do I find work in radio?

You can send your CV and voicereel directly out to producers of radio drama, but make sure you target your search. Listen to radio plays and make a note of any producers whose work you particularly liked. This may also help you to identify what types of dramas you feel your voice would be most suited to. Once you have done your research and made a shortlist, send your voicereel with a personalised letter. Mention the plays you liked and explain that you feel he or she will be able to use your voice in productions like these. This method is likely to be much more effective than sending out a generic covering letter en masse, and will make you stand out. You don't need to send a headshot with your CV, but you could incorporate your photo in the body of your CV. It would be a good idea to have your name and contact details professionally printed onto your voicereel CD in case it becomes separated from your CV – see 'Promotional Services' for listings of companies that can do this for you.

CASE STUDY

Di Speirs is the Editor of Readings, BBC Radio, London. After five years in professional theatre, Di worked for ABC Australia before joining Woman's Hour on BBC Radio 4. She edited the Woman's Hour serial reading for five years and edited two collections of Woman's Hour short stories. Since 1997 she has produced readings and drama across Radio 4 and 3, particularly Book at Bedtime. She runs and judges the BBC National Short Story Award and was Chair of the Orange Award for New Writers in 2010.

The world of audio can be an overlooked one for actors, especially those starting out or who have perhaps come up through a screen route. And yet, on BBC Radio alone, there are hours of readings and radio drama every week and the commercial audiobook market is now taking advantage of the rapid growth of new media, from downloads to apps. For those whose voice is a strong part of their acting armoury there are opportunities, be they the most established of names and or at the beginning of their careers. And audio, particularly radio, is exciting and empowering for actors. It's a medium where they can take on roles they could never realistically hope to play in more visual mediums, stage or screen. The shortest actress can play that 'painted maypole', Helena, and in readings in particular, there's an unrivalled opportunity to not only give voice to both genders and all age ranges, but to people a whole cast.

As with anything in life, knowing the market is key to starting to work in it. In my area of radio readings, the bulk of the output is on BBC Radio 4, though Radio 3 also has proms and twenty minute interval slots, which are often stories, as well as The Essay. On Radio 4 there are three main strands: Book of the Week, 9.45am Monday to Friday, which is non-fiction; the Afternoon Reading, a mix of contemporary and classic commissioned and published stories and non-fiction; and Book at Bedtime, the original reading slot, which goes out at 10.45pm Monday to Friday and is usually a ten part abridgement of a new or classic novel.

Beyond this lie the riches of radio drama - with the Woman's Hour drama serial, the Afternoon Play at 2.45pm, the Saturday Play, and the Classic Serial on Sunday afternoons (repeated on Saturday evenings), not to mention The Archers. And then there are the plays on Radio 3 and occasional originations, often of science fiction, on Radio 7.

For many actors, radio has a special appeal, despite the smaller fees on offer. It is swift and frequently very convenient – a reading or a role in a radio drama can often be fitted in around the demands of a filming or a rehearsal schedule, or can be an ideal job once a play is running. BBC Radio has a devoted, loyal and large audience – often of over a million listeners – so you, and your talent, reaches many ears and may prompt other work. The variety of the work is enormous. Casting can be counter-intuitive and certainly allows a performer to explore areas they might not reach otherwise. If you still sound younger than your advancing years, you may yet get a coveted romantic lead; similarly the most able and versatile voice artists are able to adopt nationalities at will. Over two decades I have directed the same actress creating characters who were Welsh-Maltese, Ukrainian, Italian and Danish in different Book at Bedtimes.

The quality of the writing is, by and large, also extremely high. Radio is an unforgiving medium in that sense and poor writing shows. Given the wealth of literature on offer and the comparatively few slots available, the books that are chosen for broadcast are amongst the best of contemporary and classic writing and hopefully a pleasure to work on. Similarly the cost of dramatising a great classic, whilst still high in radio budget terms, remains feasible. And radio's ability to paint the best pictures through sound, part of which is of course through the performances, make it a challenging and satisfying environment to work in.

Beyond that, there is a magic about the intimacy of radio which is something actors, producers and directors relish. Listen out and you will hear the greatest British acting talent on our airwaves. It is always a small team – with readings a very small one – but that also means that there is a real sense of collaboration when working, and a real sense of connection, on a one-to-one basis, with that great unseen audience.

Getting your voice heard in the first place is the next question. I cast largely from theatre (which has some affinity) rather than film – and from other radio productions. BBC Radio maintains a unique theatrical institution – The Radio Drama Company – which began in the midst of the Blitz to keep a small company of actors safe and at hand for productions during the war. These days, while no longer 50 strong, the RDC consists of a group of actors on contract for a matter of months who appear in numerous dramas across the networks. Through its Soundstart programme, BBC Audio Drama also runs two major awards – The Carleton Hobbs and the Norman Beaton awards. For details on these and advice on how to get started in radio do look at the Soundstart webpages at www.bbc.co.uk/soundstart. There are many independent companies making productions for the audio market and for the BBC. It is worth sending demo tapes to them too.

If you are particularly interested in readings I would suggest including fairly long passages in any demo, which demonstrate not only the ability to create a host of characters (please don't over-characterise though – shading is usually more successful) but also that more elusive element – the narrator. Also take advantage of the useful facility on Spotlight to upload voice clips and include narration on the audio content. It's impossible to judge the ability of a potential reader or actor from an advertising voice-over. And if you are good at dialects, include a couple on your Spotlight page, as well as listing them. Listen to the output and get a sense of the tone of the network or outlet as well as the book. If sent the original book as well as the abridgement, try to read at least some of it. They tend to be sent because the background information will inform your performance. And prepare your scripts before either an audition or a job. There is nothing more disheartening than actors who clearly hope to sight read!

Great actors are not necessarily good readers – as we've all discovered. An empathy for storytelling and for literature, and an intelligence and interest in language does matter. It is quite an exposed place if you are used to working with a larger cast and there is nowhere to hide. It is tiring spending a day alone in a studio, often going over the same material for small nuances. But please don't let that put you off. I hope it's also one of the great unsung pleasures of a broad acting career.

Please visit www.bbc.co.uk/soundstart for further information and advice.

BBC RADIO BRISTOL   T 0117 974 1111
Contact: Tim Pemberton (Managing Editor),
Angela Frain (News Editor)
Bristol Broadcasting House
Whiteladies Road
Bristol BS8 2LR
F 0117 923 8323
E radio.bristol@bbc.co.uk
W www.bbc.co.uk/bristol

BBC RADIO CAMBRIDGESHIRE   T 01223 259696
Contact: Dave Harvey (Managing Editor)
Cambridge Business Park
Cowley Road
Cambridge CB4 0WZ
E cambs@bbc.co.uk
W www.bbc.co.uk/cambridgeshire

BBC RADIO CORNWALL   T 01872 275421
Contact: Pauline Causey (Managing Editor)
Phoenix Wharf, Truro
Cornwall TR1 1UA
F 01872 240679
W www.bbc.co.uk/cornwall

BBC COVENTRY & WARWICKSHIRE   T 024 7655 1000
Contact: Sue Curtis (News Desk Editor)
Priory Place
Coventry CV1 5SQ
F 024 7655 2000
E coventry.warwickshire@bbc.co.uk
W www.bbc.co.uk/coventry

BBC RADIO CUMBRIA   T 01228 592444
Contact: Nigel Dyson (Managing Editor)
Annetwell Street, Carlisle
Cumbria CA3 8BB
F 01228 511195
E radio.cumbria@bbc.co.uk
W www.bbc.co.uk/radiocumbria

BBC RADIO DERBY   T 01332 361111
Contact: Simon Cornes (Managing Editor)
56 St Helen's Street
Derby DE1 3HY
E radio.derby@bbc.co.uk
W www.bbc.co.uk/derby

BBC RADIO DEVON   T 01752 260323
Contact: Mark Grinnell (Managing Editor)
PO Box 1034
Plymouth PL3 5BD
F 01752 234595
E radio.devon@bbc.co.uk
W www.bbc.co.uk/devon

BBC ESSEX   T 01245 616000
Contact: Gerald Main (Managing Editor)
PO Box 765, Chelmsford
Essex CM2 9AB
F 01245 492983
E essex@bbc.co.uk
W www.bbc.co.uk/essex

BBC RADIO GLOUCESTERSHIRE   T 01452 308585
Contact: Mark Hurrell (Managing Editor)
London Road
Gloucester GL1 1SW
E radio.gloucestershire@bbc.co.uk
W www.bbc.co.uk/gloucestershire

BBC GUERNSEY   T 01481 200600
Contact: Robert Wallace (Managing Editor), Kay Langlois
(Assistant Editor), David Earl (Senior Broadcast Journalist)
Broadcasting House, Bulwer Avenue
St Sampsons, Guernsey GY2 4LA
F 01481 200361
E bbcguernsey@bbc.co.uk
W www.bbc.co.uk/guernsey

BBC HEREFORD & WORCESTER   T 01905 748485
Contact: James Coghill (Managing Editor)
Hylton Road, Worcester WR2 5WW
W www.bbc.co.uk/herefordandworcester

BBC RADIO HUMBERSIDE   T 01482 323232
Contact: Simon Pattern (Editor)
Queens Court, Queens Gardens, Hull HU1 3RH
F 01482 226409
E radio.humberside@bbc.co.uk
W www.bbc.co.uk/humberside

BBC RADIO JERSEY   T 01534 870000
Contact: Jon Gripton (Editor), Matthew Price
(Assistant Editor)
18 & 21 Parade Road, St Helier
Jersey JE2 3PL
F 01534 732569
E radiojersey@bbc.co.uk
W www.bbc.co.uk/jersey

BBC RADIO KENT   T 01892 670000
Contact: Paul Leaper (Managing Editor)
The Great Hall, Mount Pleasant Road
Tunbridge Wells, Kent TN1 1QQ
E radio.kent@bbc.co.uk
W www.bbc.co.uk/kent

BBC RADIO LANCASHIRE   T 01254 262411
Contact: John Clayton (Editor)
20-26 Darwen Street, Blackburn
Lancashire BB2 2EA
E radio.lancashire@bbc.co.uk
W www.bbc.co.uk/lancashire

BBC RADIO LEEDS   T 0113 244 2131
Contact: Rozina Breen (Managing Editor)
BBC Yorkshire, 2 St Peter's Square
Leeds LS9 8AH
F 0113 224 7316
E radioleeds@bbc.co.uk
W www.bbc.co.uk/leeds

BBC RADIO LEICESTER   T 0116 251 6688
Contact: Kate Squire (Managing Editor)
9 St Nicholas Place, Leicester LE1 5LB
F 0116 251 1463
E leicester@bbc.co.uk
W www.bbc.co.uk/leicester

BBC LINCOLNSHIRE   T 01522 511411
Contact: Charlie Partridge (Managing Editor)
Newport, Lincoln LN1 3XY
F 01522 511058
W www.bbc.co.uk/lincolnshire

BBC LONDON 94.9 FM   T 020 7224 2000
Contact: David Robey (Managing Editor)
Egton House, Portland Place
London W1A 1AA
E yourlondon@bbc.co.uk
W www.bbc.co.uk/london

BBC RADIO MANCHESTER T 0161 200 2000
Contact: John Ryan (Managing Editor)
PO Box 951, Oxford Road
Manchester M60 1SD
W www.bbc.co.uk/manchester

BBC RADIO MERSEYSIDE T 0151 708 5500
Contact: Mick Ord (Managing Editor)
PO Box 95.8
Liverpool L69 1ZJ
E radio.merseyside@bbc.co.uk
W www.bbc.co.uk/liverpool

BBC NEWCASTLE T 0191 232 4141
Contact: Andrew Robson (Editor)
Broadcasting Centre, Barrack Road
Newcastle upon Tyne NE99 1RN
F 0191 221 0796
E bbcnewcastle.news@bbc.co.uk
W www.bbc.co.uk/tyne

BBC RADIO NORFOLK T 01603 617411
Contact: David Clayton (Managing Editor)
The Forum, Millennium Plain
Norwich NR2 1BH
E norfolk@bbc.co.uk
W www.bbc.co.uk/norfolk

BBC NORTHAMPTON T 01604 239100
Contact: Laura Moss (Manager)
Broadcasting House
Abington Street
Northampton NN1 2BH
F 01604 230709
E northampton@bbc.co.uk
W www.bbc.co.uk/northamptonshire

BBC RADIO NOTTINGHAM T 0115 955 0500
Contact: Mike Bettison (Editor)
London Road
Nottingham NG2 4UU
F 0115 902 1984
E radio.notthingham@bbc.co.uk
W www.bbc.co.uk/nottingham

BBC RADIO SHEFFIELD T 0114 273 1177
Contact: Gary Keown (Managing Editor)
54 Shoreham Street
Sheffield S1 4RS
F 0114 267 5454
E radio.sheffield@bbc.co.uk
W www.bbc.co.uk/sheffield

BBC RADIO SHROPSHIRE T 01743 248484
Contact: Tim Beech (Editor), Sharon Simcock
(Senior Broadcast Journalist News)
2-4 Boscobel Drive, Shrewsbury
Shropshire SY1 3TT
F 01743 271702
E radio.shropshire@bbc.co.uk
W www.bbc.co.uk/shropshire

BBC RADIO SOLENT T 023 8063 1311
Contact: Chris Carnegy (Managing Editor)
Broadcasting House
10 Havelock Road
Southampton SO14 7PW
F 023 8033 9648
E radio.solent@bbc.co.uk
W www.bbc.co.uk/hampshire

BBC RADIO STOKE T 01782 208080
Contact: Sue Owen (Managing Editor)
Cheapside, Hanley
Stoke-on-Trent, Staffordshire ST1 1JJ
F 01782 289115
E radio.stoke@bbc.co.uk
W www.bbc.co.uk/stoke

BBC RADIO SUFFOLK T 01473 250000
Contact: Peter Cook (Editor)
Broadcasting House
St Matthews Street
Ipswich IP1 3EP
F 01473 210887
E radiosuffolk@bbc.co.uk
W www.bbc.co.uk/suffolk

BBC SURREY T 01273 320400
Contact: Nicci Holliday (Managing Editor),
Sara David (Assistant Editor)
Broadcasting Centre, Guildford
Surrey GU2 7AP
F 01483 304952
E sussex@bbc.co.uk
W www.bbc.co.uk/sussex

BBC SUSSEX T 01273 320400
Contact: Nicci Holliday (Managing Editor),
Sara David (Assistant Editor)
40-42 Queen's Road
Brighton BN1 3YB
F 01483 304952
E sussex@bbc.co.uk
W www.bbc.co.uk/sussex

BBC TEES T 01642 225211
Contact: Matthew Barraclough (Managing Editor)
Broadcasting House, Newport Road
Middlesbrough TS1 5DG
F 01642 211356
E tees.studios@bbc.co.uk
W www.bbc.co.uk/tees

BBC THREE COUNTIES RADIO T 01582 637400
Contact: Mark Norman (Managing Editor)
1 Hastings Street
Luton LU1 5XL
F 01582 401467
E 3cr@bbc.co.uk
W www.bbc.co.uk/threecounties

BBC WEST MIDLANDS T 0121 567 6767
Contact: Keith Beech (Editor Local Services)
The Mailbox, Birmingham B1 1RF
E bbcwm@bbc.co.uk
W www.bbc.co.uk/westmidlands

BBC WILTSHIRE T 01793 513626
Contact: Tony Worgan (Managing Editor)
Broadcasting House
56-58 Prospect Place
Swindon SN1 3RW
E wiltshire@bbc.co.uk
W www.bbc.co.uk/wiltshire

BBC RADIO YORK T 01904 641351
Contact: Sarah Drummond (Managing Editor)
20 Bootham Row, York YO30 7BR
E radio.york@bbc.co.uk
W www.bbc.co.uk/york

ABERDEEN: Northsound Radio   T 01224 337000
Abbotswell Road, West Tullos
Aberdeen AB12 3AJ
F 01224 400003
W www.northsound.com

AYR: West Sound Radio   T 01292 283662
Incorporating West Sound 1035 AM & West 96.7 FM
Radio House
54A Holmston Road
Ayr KA7 3BE
E carolyn.mcallister@westsound.co.uk
W www.westsound.co.uk

**BELFAST: City Beat
96.7 FM & 102.5 FM**   T 028 9023 4967
2nd Floor, Arena Building
85 Ormeau Road
Belfast BT7 1SH
F 028 9089 0100
E newsdesk@citybeat.co.uk
W www.citybeat.co.uk

BELFAST: Cool FM   T 028 9181 7181
Kiltonga Industrial Estate
Newtownards
Co Down BT23 4ES
E info@coolfm.co.uk
W www.coolfm.co.uk

BELFAST: Downtown Radio   T 028 9181 5555
Kiltonga Industrial Estate
Newtownards, Co Down BT23 4ES
E info@downtown.co.uk
W www.downtown.co.uk

**BERKSHIRE &
NORTH HAMPSHIRE: Heart**   T 0118 945 4400
PO Box 2020, Reading
Berkshire RG31 7FG
E thamesvalley.news@heart.co.uk
W www.heart.co.uk

**BIRMINGHAM:
BRMB 96.4 & Gold**   T 0121 566 5200
Nine Brindley Place, 4 Oozells Square
Birmingham B1 2DJ
W www.brmb.co.uk

BORDERS THE: Radio Borders   T 01896 759444
Tweedside Park, Galashiels TD1 3TD
F 0845 3457080
E info@radioborders.com
W www.radioborders.com

**BRADFORD:
Sunrise Radio Yorkshire**   T 01274 735043
55 Leeds Road, Bradford BD1 5AF
F 01274 728534
W www.sunriseradio.fm

**BRADFORD, HUDDERSFIELD, HALIFAX,
KEIGHLEY & DEWSBURY: Pulse 2**   T 01274 203040
Forster Square, Bradford BD1 5NE
E general@pulse.co.uk
W www.pulse2.net

**CAMBRIDGESHIRE &
PETERBOROUGH: Heart**   T 01733 281370
Queensgate Centre
Peterborough P1 1NS
E cambridgeshire.news@heart.co.uk
W www.heart.co.uk

**CARDIFF & NEWPORT:
Capital FM & Gold FM**   T 029 2066 2066
Global Radio
The Red Dragon Centre
Cardiff Bay, Cardiff CF10 4DJ
W www.capitalfm.com

**CHESTER, NORTH WALES
& WIRRAL: Heart**   T 01978 752202
Contact: Paul Holmes (Programme Controller)
The Studios, Mold Road
Wrexham LL11 4AF
E northwestwales.news@heart.co.uk
W www.heart.co.uk

COVENTRY: Mercia   T 024 7686 8200
Hertford Place, Coventry CV1 3TT
F 024 7686 8209
W www.mercia.co.uk

DUMFRIES: West Sound FM   T 01387 250999
Unit 40, The Loreburn Centre
High Street, Dumfries DG1 2BD
F 01387 265629
W www.westsoundradio.com

**DUNDEE & PERTH:
Radio Tay AM**   T 01382 200800
6 North Isla Street
Dundee DD3 7JQ
E tayam@radiotay.co.uk
W www.radiotay.co.uk

**DUNDEE & PERTH:
Radio Tay FM**   T 01382 200800
6 North Isla Street
Dundee DD3 7JQ
E tayfm@radiotay.co.uk
W www.radiotay.co.uk

**EAST MIDLANDS:
Capital East Midlands**   T 0115 873 1500
Incorporating Ram FM, Leicester Sound & Trent FM
Chapel Quarter, Maid Marian Way
Nottingham NG1 6HQ
W www.capitalfm.com

EDINBURGH: Radio Forth Ltd   T 0131 556 9255
Forth House, Forth Street
Edinburgh EH1 3LE
E info@radioforth.com
W www.radioforth.com

EXETER & TORBAY: Heart   T 01392 354200
Hawthorn House, Exeter Business Park
Exeter EX1 3QS
F 01392 354209
W www.heart.co.uk

FALKIRK: Central FM T 01324 611164
201-203 High Street, Falkirk FK1 1DU
F 01324 611168
W www.centralfm.co.uk

GLASGOW: Radio Clyde Ltd T 0141 565 2200
3 South Avenue, Clydebank Business Park
Glasgow G81 2RX
F 0141 565 2265
W www.clyde1.com

GLASGOW: Radio Clyde 2 T 0141 565 2200
3 South Avenue, Clydebank Business Park
Glasgow G81 2RX
F 0141 565 2265
W www.clyde2.com

**GLOUCESTER &
CHELTENHAM: Heart 102.4** T 01452 572400
Eastgate Shopping Centre
Gloucester GL1 1SS
F 01452 572409
W www.heart.co.uk

**GREAT YARMOUTH &
NORWICH: Heart** T 01603 630621
St Georges Plain, 47-49 Colegate
Norwich NR3 1DB
W www.heart.co.uk

GUILDFORD: 96.4 Eagle Radio T 01483 300964
Eagle Radio Ltd, Dolphin House, 3 North Street
Guildford, Surrey GU1 4AA
F 01483 454443
E onair@964eagle.co.uk
W www.964eagle.co.uk

**HEREFORD & WORCESTER:
Wyvern FM** T 01905 545500
1st Floor, Kirkham House
John Comyn Drive, Worcester WR3 7NS
W www.wyvernfm.co.uk

HOME COUNTIES: Heart T 01604 795600
*Bedford, Beds, Bucks, Herts, Milton Keynes
& Northamptonshire*
4th Floor, CVX11, 382-428 Midsummer Boulevard
Central Milton Keynes MK9 2EA
E hvnews@heart.co.uk
W www.heart.co.uk

INVERNESS: Moray Firth Radio T 01463 224433
PO Box 271, Scorguie Place
Inverness IV3 8UJ
F 01463 227714
E mfr@mfr.co.uk
W www.mfr.co.uk

**ISLE OF WIGHT:
Isle of Wight Radio** T 01983 822557
Dodnor Park, Newport
Isle of Wight PO30 5XE
F 01983 822109
E studio@iwradio.co.uk
W www.iwradio.co.uk

KENT: Heart T 01227 772004
Radio House
John Wilson Business Park
Whitstable, Kent CT5 3QX
E news.kent@heart.co.uk
W www.heart.co.uk

**LEEDS: Radio Aire
96.3 & Magic 828** T 0113 283 5500
51 Burley Road, Leeds LS3 1LR
F 0113 283 5501
W www.radioaire.com

LIVERPOOL: Radio City T 0151 472 6800
St Johns Beacon
1 Houghton Street
Liverpool L1 1RL
W www.radiocity.co.uk

LONDON: Absolute Radio T 020 7434 1215
1 Golden Square, London W1F 9DJ
F 020 7434 1197
W www.absoluteradio.co.uk

LONDON: Choice FM T 020 7766 6810
Global Radio
30 Leicester Square, London WC2H 7LA
F 020 7766 6100
W www.choicefm.com

LONDON: Classic FM T 020 7343 9000
Global Radio
30 Leicester Square, London WC2H 7LA
F 020 7344 2789
W www.classicfm.com

LONDON: Gold T 020 7054 8000
Global Radio
30 Leicester Square, London WC2H 7LA
F 020 7054 8019
W www.mygoldmusic.co.uk

**LONDON:
Independent Radio News** T 020 7182 8591
Mappin House, 4 Winsley Street
London W1W 8HF
E irn@bskyb.com
W www.irn.co.uk

LONDON: London Greek Radio T 020 8349 6950
437 High Road, Finchley
London N12 0AP
W www.lgr.co.uk

LONDON: Magic 105.4 FM T 020 7182 8233
Mappin House, 4 Winsley Street
London W1W 8HF
W www.magic.co.uk

LONDON: Smooth Radio T 020 7706 4100
26-27 Castlereagh Street
London W1H 5DL
T 0161 886 8800
E info@smoothradio.com
W www.smoothradio.co.uk

LUTON & BEDFORD: Heart T 01582 676200
Broadcast Centre, Chiltern Road
Dunstable LU6 1HQ
F 01582 676209
W www.heart.co.uk

MANCHESTER:
Key 103 FM & Magic 1152 T 0161 288 5000
Piccadilly Radio Ltd, Castle Quay
Castle Field, Manchester M15 4PR
F 0161 288 5071
W www.key103.co.uk

NORTHAMPTONSHIRE: Connect FM 97.2,
106.8 FM & 107.4 FM T 0844 8001769
55 Headlands, Kettering
Northampton NN15 7EU
T 01536 513664
W www.connectfm.com

OXFORD & BANBURY: Heart T 01865 871000
The Chase, Calcot
Reading RG31 7RB
W www.heart.co.uk

PETERBOROUGH: Heart T 01733 460460
PO Box 225, Queensgate Centre
Peterborough PE1 1XJ
W www.heart.co.uk

PLYMOUTH & DEVON: Heart T 01752 275600
Hawthorn House
Exeter Business Park EX1 3QS
W www.heart.co.uk

PORTSMOUTH &
SOUTHAMPTON: Gold T 01489 589911
Global Radio
Radio House, Whittle Avenue
Segensworth West, Fareham
Hampshire PO15 5SX
W www.mygoldmusic.co.uk

PORTSMOUTH &
SOUTHAMPTON: Heart T 01489 589911
Global Radio
Radio House, Whittle Avenue
Segensworth West, Fareham
Hampshire PO15 5SX
W www.heart.co.uk

PORTSMOUTH & SOUTHAMPTON:
Capital South Coast T 01489 589911
Global Radio
Radio House, Whittle Avenue
Segensworth West
Fareham, Hampshire PO15 5SX
W www.capitalfm.com

SOUTH MANCHESTER:
Imagine 104.9 FM T 0161 609 1400
Waterloo Place, Watson Square
Stockport, Cheshire SK1 3AZ
E sales@imaginefm.net
W www.imaginefm.net

STOKE-ON-TRENT &
STAFFORD: Signal Radio T 01782 441300
Stoke Road, Stoke-on-Trent
Staffordshire ST4 2SR
E info@signalradio.com
W www.signalone.co.uk

SUSSEX: Heart T 01273 430111
Radio House, Franklin Road
PO Box 2000
Brighton BN41 1AS
F 01273 316929
W www.heartsussex.co.uk

SWANSEA: The Wave 96.4 FM T 01792 511964
Victoria Road, Gowerton
Swansea SA4 3AB
W www.thewave.co.uk

TEESSIDE: Magic 1170 T 01642 888222
Yale Crescent, Teesdale
Thornaby, Stockton on Tees TS17 6AA
W www.magic1170.co.uk

TEESSIDE: TFM Radio T 01642 888222
Yale Crescent, Teesdale
Thornaby, Stockton on Tees TS17 6AA
W www.tfmradio.com

TYNE & WEAR, NORTHUMBERLAND
& DURHAM: Magic 1152 T 0191 230 6100
55 Degrees North, Pilgrim Street
Newcastle upon Tyne NE1 6BF
W www.magic1152.co.uk

TYNE & WEAR, NORTHUMBERLAND
& DURHAM: Metro Radio T 0191 230 6100
55 Degrees North, Pilgrim Street
Newcastle upon Tyne NE1 6BF
W www.metroradio.co.uk

WEST COUNTRY: Heart T 0117 984 3200
1 Passage Street
PO Box 2000
Bristol BS99 7SN
F 0117 984 3202
W www.heart.co.uk

WOLVERHAMPTON & BLACK COUNTRY/
SHREWSBURY &
TELFORD: Beacon Radio T 01902 461200
267 Tettenhall Road
Wolverhampton WV6 0DE
W www.beaconradio.co.uk

YORKSHIRE: Hallam FM
& Magic AM T 0114 209 1000
Radio House, 900 Herries Road
Hillsborough, Sheffield S6 1RH
W www.hallamfm.co.uk

YORKSHIRE & LINCOLNSHIRE: Viking 96.9 FM &
Magic 1161 AM T 01482 325141
Commercial Road, Hull HU1 2SG
W www.vikingfm.co.uk

101 IDENTITY REHEARSAL
& PERFORMANCE STUDIOS   T 020 7470 8711
73-75 Shacklewell Lane, London E8 2EB
E info@theidentitystudios.com
W www.theidentitystudios.com

3 MILLS STUDIOS   T 020 7363 3336
Three Mill Lane, London E3 3DU
F 0871 5944028
E info@3mills.com
W www.3mills.com

ABACUS ARTS   T 020 7277 2880
2A Browning Street, Southwark
London SE17 1LN
E info@abacus-arts.org.uk
W www.abacus-arts.org.uk

ACTORS CENTRE
(LONDON) THE   T 020 7632 8012
Auditioning. Casting. Rehearsals. Room Hire
1A Tower Street, London WC2H 9NP
T 020 7240 3940
E operations@actorscentre.co.uk
W www.actorscentre.co.uk

ACTORS STUDIO REHEARSAL &
CASTING SPACE   T 01753 650951
Pinewood Studios, Pinewood Road
Iver Heath, Bucks SL0 0NH
E info@actorsstudio.co.uk
W www.actorsstudio.co.uk

ACTOR'S TEMPLE THE   T 020 3004 4537
13-14 Warren Street, London W1T 5LG
E info@actorstemple.com
W www.actorstemple.com

AIRCRAFT CIRCUS   T 07951 896945
Hangar Arts Trust
Unit 7A, Mellish House
Harrington Way
London SE18 5NR
E alex@aircraftcircus.com
W www.aircraftcircus.com

ALBANY THE   T 020 8692 0231
Douglas Way, Deptford
London SE8 4AG
F 020 8469 2253
E hires@thealbany.org.uk
W www.thealbany.org.uk

ALFORD HOUSE   T 020 7735 1519
Aveline Street, London SE11 5DQ
E tim@alfordhouse.org.uk
W www.alfordhouse.org.uk

ALL TALENT,
THE SONIA SCOTT AGENCY   T 0141 418 1074
Unit 325, 95 Morrison Street
Glasgow G5 8BE
T 07971 337074
E enquiries@alltalentuk.co.uk
W www.alltalentuk.co.uk

ALRA (ACADEMY OF LIVE
& RECORDED ARTS)   T 020 8870 6475
The Royal Victoria Patriotic Building
John Archer Way
London SW18 3SX
F 020 8875 0789
E info@alra.co.uk
W www.alra.co.uk

Rehearsal Rooms & Casting Suites

How should I prepare for an audition?

When you are called to a casting you should make sure you are fully prepared with accurate information about the audition time, venue and format. Research the casting director too: look on his or her website and pay attention to media news. What productions have they worked on previously? What do they seem to look for and expect from the actors they cast?

For most auditions you will be given a script to learn, but you could be provided with a brief in advance and asked to find something suitable yourself. It would be advisable to have about five or six pieces ready to choose from that demonstrate your range before you are even called to a casting. You should select two relevant but contrasting pieces of about two to three minutes each for your audition, with the others as backups. If you can, read the whole play in addition to your speech.

It is generally best not to use 'popular' or very well-known pieces and instead to use original modern speeches, as this prevents the likelihood of the casting director comparing you, perhaps unfavourably, with anyone else. Having said this, however, you should still rehearse at least one Shakespeare piece. To find suitable speeches you should read widely for inspiration, or you could search online. If you are still struggling, think about who your favourite playwrights are and find out if they have written anything that is not too well-known.

What should I expect when I arrive at the audition?

Arrive early for your audition, but be prepared to wait! Time slots are allocated but auditions can overrun for various reasons. Be presentable and think about how your character might choose to dress, but overall you will feel more comfortable and confident if you don't differ too much from what you would normally wear. Don't come in costume unless specifically asked.

When you enter the audition room, you may have just the casting director in the room, or you could be confronted with a panel including the director and/or producer, and an editor and cameraman if you are being filmed. Don't let this disconcert you. Nerves are to be expected, but try to be positive and enjoy yourself. Remember, the casting director doesn't want to spend several days auditioning – they want you to get the job!

Take a few moments to work out where you should stand and where everything is. Don't ask too many questions as this can be irritating but you could ask whether to address your monologue to the casting director/camera, or whether to speak into the 'middle distance'. Make sure that your face, and in particular your eyes, can be seen as much as possible.

Once you have performed your monologue, pause and wait for the casting director to speak to you. Don't ask if they want to see a second speech. If they want another one, and if there's time, they will ask you. You may be asked your opinion on the speech so be prepared with possible answers. Never criticise previous productions you have worked on. At the end of the casting, remember to take your script away unless you are asked to leave it, otherwise it can look as if you're not interested.

Auditions are never a waste of time, even if you don't get the part. You may have performed well but you might not have been quite right for that particular role. Every audition is great practice and experience, and the casting director may very well keep you in mind for future productions.

Should I attend a casting in a house or flat?

Professional auditions are rarely held anywhere other than an official casting studio or venue. Be very wary if you are asked to go elsewhere. Trust your instincts. If something doesn't seem right to you, it probably isn't. Always take someone with you if you are in any doubt.

Rehearsal Spaces for hire

Two new, purpose built studios for hire just 15 minutes by tube from the West End. Suitable for dance, musicals, large scale rehearsals, meetings or intimate one on one work.

For full details visit our website:
www.losttheatre.co.uk
or call us on 020 7622 9208

Tube: Stockwell (Victoria & Northern Lines)
Vauxhall (Northern & Overground lines)

**AMERICAN CHURCH
IN LONDON THE**   T 020 7580 2791
Whitefield Memorial Church
79A Tottenham Court Road
London W1T 4TD
F 020 7580 5013
E latchcourt@amchurch.co.uk
W www.latchcourt.com

ARCH 468 THEATRE STUDIO   T 07973 302908
Arch 468
209A Coldharbour Lane
London SW9 8RU
E rebecca@arch468.com
W www.arch468.com

ARTEMIS STUDIOS LTD   T 01344 429403
30 Charles Square
Bracknell
Berkshire RG12 1AY
E info@artemis-studios.co.uk
W www.agency.artemis-studios.co.uk

ARTSADMIN   T 020 7247 5102
Toynbee Studios
28 Commercial Street
London E1 6AB
F 020 7247 5103
E admin@artsadmin.co.uk
W www.artsadmin.co.uk

BRIXTON COMMUNITY BASE

⁂ FORMERLY BRIXTON ST VINCENT'S COMMUNITY CENTRE ⁂

◀ **REHEARSAL STUDIO** 16 x 7.5 metres ▶

SECOND SPACE AVAILABLE

Piano / keyboards / showers / facility for aerial work / WiFi

Full Disabled Access

TEL - 020 7326 4417 / 020 7274 1190

Brixton Tube – Victoria line **www.bsvcc.org** Talma Road SW2 1AS

AVIV DANCE STUDIOS T/F 01923 250000
Watford Boys Grammar School
Rickmansworth Road, Watford WD18 7JF
E info@avivdance.com
W www.avivdance.com

**BAC
(BATTERSEA ARTS CENTRE)** T 020 7326 8211
Lavender Hill, London SW11 5TN
F 020 7978 5207
E venues@bac.org.uk
W www.bac.org.uk/hires

BIG CITY STUDIOS T 020 7241 6655
Montgomery House, 159-161 Balls Pond Road
Islington, London N1 4BG
F 020 7241 3006
W www.pineappleagency.com

**BLACK BOX CREATIVE
COMMUNITIES CIC LTD** T 0151 260 3000
The Black Box, 21 Hutchinson Walk, Liverpool L6 1JW
F 0151 260 3001
E admin@blackboxmerseyside.co.uk
W www.blackboxmerseyside.co.uk

BLOOMSBURY THEATRE THE T 020 7679 2777
15 Gordon Street, London WC1H 0AH
E admin@thebloomsbury.com
W www.thebloomsbury.com

BRIXTON COMMUNITY BASE T 020 7326 4417
Formerly Brixton St Vincent's Community Centre
Talma Road, London SW2 1AS
E info@brixtoncommunitybase.org
W www.bsvcc.org

**CALDER THEATRE
BOOKSHOP LTD THE** T 020 7620 2900
*Central London Rehearsal Space, Fringe Venue
& Theatre Bookshop*
51 The Cut, London SE1 8LF
E info@calderbookshop.com
W www.calderbookshop.com

CARDINBROOK LTD T 020 7373 1665
32 Barkston Gardens, London SW5 0EN
E info@ycbc.co.uk
W www.ycbc.co.uk/roomhire.htm

CAST IN SPACE T 020 7404 9637
Lupus House, 2nd Floor, 11-13 Macklin Street
Covent Garden, London WC2B 5NH
E castinspace@gmail.com W www.castinspace.tv

CASTING AT SWEET T 07905 120431
Sweet Studio, 1st Floor
42 Theobalds Road, London WC1X 8NW
E studio@sweet-uk.net

CECIL SHARP HOUSE T 020 7485 2206
2 Regent's Park Road, London NW1 7AY
F 020 7284 0534
E info@efdss.org
W www.efdss.org

**CENTRAL LONDON
GOLF CENTRE** T 020 8871 2468
Burntwood Lane, London SW17 0AT
F 020 8874 7447
E golf@clgc.co.uk
W www.clgc.co.uk

CENTRAL STUDIOS T 020 8698 8880
470 Bromley Road, Bromley, Kent BR1 4PQ
E bonnie@dandbmanagement.com
W www.dandbperformingarts.co.uk

CENTRE THE T 020 7286 1680
20 Cavendish Square, London W9 2JA
F 020 7266 1225
E amadeus@amadeuscentre.co.uk
W www.centreca.co.uk

CHARING CROSS THEATRE T 020 7930 5868
Formerly New Players Theatre
The Arches, Off Villiers Street
London WC2N 6NL
E info@charingcrosstheatre.co.uk
W www.charingcrosstheatre.co.uk

CHATS PALACE T 020 8533 0227
42-44 Brooksby's Walk, Hackney, London E9 6DF
E info@chatspalace.com
W www.chatspalace.co.uk

CHELSEA THEATRE T 020 7349 7811
Contact: Francis Alexander
World's End Place, King's Road, London SW10 0DR
F 020 7352 2024
E admin@chelseatheatre.org.uk
W www.chelseatheatre.org.uk

**CLAPHAM COMMUNITY
PROJECT** T/F 020 7720 8731
St Anne's Hall, 31-33 Bromells Road, London SW4 0BN
E admin@claphamcommunityproject.org.uk
W www.rehearseatccp.co.uk

CLEAN BREAK T 020 7482 8600
2 Patshull Road, London NW5 2LB
F 020 7482 8611
E general@cleanbreak.org.uk
W www.cleanbreak.org.uk

CLUB FOR ACTS & ACTORS T 020 7836 3172
Incorporating Concert Artistes Association
20 Bedford Street, London WC2E 9HP
E office@thecaa.org
W www.thecaa.org

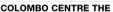

COLOMBO CENTRE THE   T 020 7261 1658
Audition & Rehearsal Space
34-68 Colombo Street, London SE1 8DP
E colombodm@jubileehalltrust.org
W www.colombo-centre.org

COPTIC STREET STUDIO LTD   T 020 7636 2030
9 Coptic Street, London WC1A 1NH
E studio@copticstreet.com

**COVENT GARDEN
DRAGON HALL TRUST**   T 020 7404 7274
17 Stukeley Street, London WC2B 5LT
E director@dragonhall.org.uk
W www.dragonhall.org.uk

CUSTARD FACTORY THE   T 0121 224 7777
Gibb Street, Digbeth, Birmingham B9 4AA
F 0121 604 8888
E info@custardfactory.co.uk
W www.custardfactory.co.uk

DANCE ATTIC STUDIOS   T 020 7610 2055
368 North End Road, London SW6
E danceattic@hotmail.com

DANCE COMPANY STUDIOS   T 020 8402 2424
76 High Street, Beckenham BR3 1ED
E hire@dancecompanystudios.co.uk
W www.dancecompanystudios.co.uk

DANCEWORKS   T 020 7318 4100
16 Balderton Street, London W1K 6TN
E info@danceworks.net
W www.danceworks.net

DAVIES Siobhan STUDIOS   T 020 7091 9650
85 St George's Road, London SE1 6ER
F 020 7091 9669
E info@siobhandavies.com
W www.siobhandavies.com

DRILL HALL THE   T 020 7307 5060
16 Chenies Street, London WC1E 7EX
F 020 7307 5062
E box.office@drillhall.co.uk
W www.drillhall.co.uk

EALING STUDIOS   T 020 8567 6655
Ealing Green, London W5 5EP
F 020 8758 8658
E bookings@ealingstudios.com
W www.ealingstudios.com

**ELMS LESTERS
PAINTING ROOMS**   T 020 7836 6747
1-3-5 Flitcroft Street, London WC2H 8DH
F 020 7379 0789
E info@elmslesters.co.uk
W www.elmslesters.co.uk

**ENGLISH FOLK DANCE &
SONG SOCIETY**   T 020 7485 2206
Cecil Sharp House, 2 Regent's Park Road
London NW1 7AY
F 020 7284 0534
E info@efdss.org
W www.efdss.org

ENGLISH NATIONAL OPERA   T 020 7624 7711
Lilian Baylis House
165 Broadhurst Gardens
London NW6 3AX
F 020 7625 3398
E receptionlbh@eno.org
W www.eno.org

ENGLISH TOURING THEATRE   T 020 7450 1990
25 Short Street, Waterloo, London SE1 8LJ
F 020 7633 0188
E admin@ett.org.uk
W www.ett.org.uk

ETCETERA THEATRE   T 020 7482 4857
(Above the Oxford Arms)
265 Camden High Street
London NW1 7BU
F 020 7482 0378
E etc@etceteratheatre.com
W www.etceteratheatre.com

EUROKIDS &
EKA CASTING STUDIOS   T 01925 761088
The Warehouse Studios, Glaziers Lane
Culcheth, Warrington, Cheshire WA3 4AQ
F 01925 767563
E castings@eka-agency.com
W www.eka-agency.com

EXCHANGE THE   T 01258 475137
Old Market Hill, Sturminster Newton DT10 1FH
E info@stur-exchange.co.uk
W www.stur-exchange.co.uk

EXPRESSIONS STUDIOS   T 020 7813 1580
Linton House, 39-51 Highgate Road
London NW5 1RT
F 020 7813 1582
E info@expressionsstudios.com
W www.expressionsstudios.com

FACTORY FITNESS &
DANCE CENTRE THE   T 020 7272 1122
407 Hornsey Road, London N19 4DX
E info@factorylondon.com
W www.factorylondon.com

FOREMAN, Giles
CENTRE FOR ACTING   T 020 8968 3772
Formerly CARAVANSERAI PRODUCTIONS
& ACTING STUDIO
Basement, Townsend House
22-25 Dean Street, London W1D 3RX
E info@gilesforeman.com
W www.gilesforeman.com

FSU LONDON STUDY CENTRE   T 020 7813 3223
99 Great Russell Street, London WC1B 3LA
F 020 7813 3270

GRAEAE THEATRE COMPANY   T 020 7613 6900
Bradbury Studios, 138 Kinsland Road, London E2 8DY
E info@graeae.org
W www.graeae.org

GREAT EASTERN DINING ROOM   T 020 7613 4545
54-56 Great Eastern Street, Shoreditch
London EC2A 3QR
E greateastern@rickerrestaurants.com
W www.rickerrestaurants.com

GREEN ROOM
CASTING STUDIO THE   T 020 7734 3057
7 D'Arblay Street, London W1F 8DW
E casting@thegreenroom.eu
W www.thegreenroom.eu

HAMPSTEAD THEATRE   T 020 7449 4200
Eton Avenue, Swiss Cottage, London NW3 3EU
F 020 7449 4201
E info@hampsteadtheatre.com
W www.hampsteadtheatre.com

HANGAR ARTS TRUST   T 020 8317 8401
Unit 7A, Mellish House
Harrington Way, London SE18 5NR
E afrith@hangarartstrust.org
W www.aircraftcircus.com

HEYTHROP COLLEGE   T 020 7795 6600
University of London, 23 Kensington Square
London W8 5HN
E conferences@heythrop.ac.uk
W www.heythrop.ac.uk

HOLLY LODGE
COMMUNITY CENTRE   T 020 8342 9524
2 Halls for Hire for Afternoons, Evenings & Weekends
30 Makepeace Avenue, London N6 6HL
E hollylodgelondon@hotmail.com
W www.hollylodge.org.uk

HOLY INNOCENTS CHURCH   T 07817 783051
Paddenswick Road, London W6 0UB
E bookings@hisj.co.uk
W www.hisj.co.uk

HOLY TRINITY W6   T 020 7603 3832
Holy Trinity Parish Centre, 41 Brook Green
London W6 7BL
E brookgreen@rcdow.org.uk
W www.holytrinityw6.org

HOMES FOR ISLINGTON   T 020 7527 8632
Highbury House, 5 Highbury Crescent
London N5 1RN
E service.development@homesforislington.org.uk
W www.homesforislington.org.uk

HOPE STREET LTD   T 0151 708 8007
13A Hope Street, Liverpool L1 9BQ
F 0151 709 3242
E peter@hope-street.org
W www.hope-street.org

**HOXTON HALL THEATRE &
YOUTH ARTS CENTRE**   T 020 7684 0060
130 Hoxton Street, London N1 6SH
E info@hoxtonhall.co.uk
W www.hoxtonhall.co.uk

IMT GALLERY   T 020 8980 5475
Unit 2, 210 Cambridge Heath Road, London E2 9NQ
E mail@imagemusictext.com
W www.imagemusictext.com

INC SPACE   T 020 7557 6650
9-13 Grape Street, Covent Garden, London WC2H 8ED
F 020 7557 6656
E debbie@internationalcollective.com
W www.inc-space.com

ISLINGTON ARTS FACTORY   T 020 7607 0561
2 Parkhurst Road, London N7 0SF
F 020 7700 7229
E info@islingtonartsfactory.org
W www.islingtonartsfactory.org

JACKSONS LANE   T 020 8340 5226
Various Spaces including Rehearsal Rooms & Theatre Hire
269A Archway Road, London N6 5AA
E reception@jacksonslane.org.uk
W www.jacksonslane.org.uk

JERWOOD SPACE   T 020 7654 0171
171 Union Street, London SE1 0LN
F 020 7654 0172
E space@jerwoodspace.co.uk
W www.jerwoodspace.co.uk

LIVE THEATRE   T 0191 261 2694
Broad Chare, Quayside
Newcastle upon Tyne NE1 3DQ
E info@live.org.uk
W www.live.org.uk

**LONDON BUBBLE
THEATRE COMPANY LTD**   T 020 7237 4434
5 Elephant Lane, London SE16 4JD
E admin@londonbubble.org.uk
W www.londonbubble.org.uk

**LONDON SCHOOL
OF CAPOEIRA**   T 020 7281 2020
Units 1 & 2 Leeds Place, Tollington Park
London N4 3RF
E studiohire@londonschoolofcapoeira.com
W www.londonschoolofcapoeira.com

LONDON STUDIO CENTRE   T 020 7837 7741
42-50 York Way, London N1 9AB
F 020 7837 3248
E info@london-studio-centre.co.uk
W www.london-studio-centre.co.uk

LONDON WELSH TRUST LTD   T 020 7837 3722
157-163 Gray's Inn Road, London WC1X 8UE
E administrator@lwcentre.demon.co.uk
W www.londonwelsh.org

LYRIC HAMMERSMITH   T 0871 2211722
King Street, London W6 0QL
F 020 8741 5965
E enquiries@lyric.co.uk
W www.lyric.co.uk

MACKINTOSH Cameron
REHEARSAL STUDIO　　　T 020 7372 6611
The Tricycle, 269 Kilburn High Road, London NW6 7JR
F 020 7328 0795
E admin@tricycle.co.uk
W www.tricycle.co.uk

MADDERMARKET THEATRE　　T 01603 626560
St John's Alley, Norwich, Norfolk NR2 1DR
E mmtheatre@btconnect.com
W www.maddermarket.co.uk

MENIER CHOCOLATE FACTORY　T 020 7378 1712
53 Southwark Street, London SE1 1RU
F 020 7234 0447
E office@menierchocolatefactory.com
W www.menierchocolatefactory.com

MHI STUDIO　　　　　　　　T 01746 787574
Burwarton, Near Bridgnorth, Shropshire WV16 6QJ
E meghawkins@btinternet.com
W www.meghawkins.com

MOBERLY SPORTS &
EDUCATION CENTRE　　　　T 020 7641 4807
101 Kilburn Lane, Kensal Rise, London W10 4AH
F 020 7641 5878
E moberly@westminster.gov.uk

MOVING EAST STUDIO　　　T 020 7503 3101
Harlequin Sprung Floor. Quadrophonic Sound System
St Matthias Church Hall, Wordsworth Road
London N16 8DD
E admin@movingeast.co.uk
W www.movingeast.co.uk

MUSIC ROOM AT
COLE KITCHENN　　　　　T 020 7427 5680
212 Strand, London WC2R 1AP
E info@colekitchenn.com

NATIONAL YOUTH THEATRE
OF GREAT BRITAIN　　　　T 020 7281 3863
443-445 Holloway Road, London N7 6LW
E info@nyt.org.uk
W www.nyt.org.uk

NEALS YARD
MEETING ROOMS　　　　T/F 020 7436 9875
14 Neals Yard, Covent Garden, London WC2H 9DP
E info@walkinbackrub.co.uk
W www.meetingrooms.org.uk

NETTLEFOLD THE　　　　　T 020 7926 8070
Theatre Hire only. No Casting Enquiries
West Norwood Library Centre, 1 Norwood High Street
London SE27 9JX
E thenettlefold@lambeth.gov.uk

NEW DIORAMA THEATRE THE　T 020 7916 5467
81 Seat Blackbox Theatre
15-16 Triton Street, Regents Place, London NW1 3BF
W www.newdiorama.com

NLPAC PERFORMING ARTS　T 020 8444 4544
Casting & Production Office Facilities
76 St James Lane
Muswell Hill, London N10 3DF
F 020 8444 4040
E nlpac@aol.com
W www.nlpac.co.uk

OBSERVATORY STUDIOS THE　T 020 7437 2823
45-46 Poland Street, London W1F 7NA
F 020 7437 2830
E info@theobservatorystudios.com
W www.theobservatorystudios.com

OCTOBER GALLERY　　　　T 020 7831 1618
24 Old Gloucester Street, London WC1N 3AL
F 020 7405 1851
E rentals@octobergallery.co.uk
W www.octobergallery.co.uk

OLD VIC THEATRE THE　　T 020 7928 2651
The Cut, London SE1 8NB
E hires@oldvictheatre.com
W www.oldvictheatre.com

ONLY CONNECT UK　　　　T 0845 3707990
32 Cubitt Street, London WC1X 0LR
E info@oclondon.org
W www.oclondon.org

OPEN DOOR
COMMUNITY CENTRE　　T/F 020 8871 8172
Beaumont Road, Wimbledon, London SW19 6TF
E dconstantinou@wandsworth.gov.uk
W www.wandsworth.gov.uk

OUT OF JOINT　　　　　　T 020 7609 0207
7 Thane Works, Thane Villas, London N7 7NU
F 020 7609 0203
E ojo@outofjoint.co.uk
W www.outofjoint.co.uk

OVAL HOUSE　　　　　　　T 020 7582 0080
52-54 Kennington Oval, London SE11 5SW
E info@ovalhouse.com
W www.ovalhouse.com

PAINES PLOUGH REHEARSAL
& AUDITION SPACE　　　　T 020 7240 4533
4th Floor, 43 Aldwych, London WC2B 4DN
F 020 7240 4534
E office@painesplough.com
W www.painesplough.com

PEOPLE SHOW   T 020 7729 1841
3 Rehearsal Rooms. Casting Suites. Set Building Workshop.
Sound & Lighting Equipment for Hire
People Show Studios, Pollard Row, London E2 6NB
F 020 7739 0203
E people@peopleshow.co.uk
W www.peopleshow.co.uk

PEREGRINES PIANOS   T 020 7242 9865
Auditioning. Casting. Filming. Piano Hire
137A Grays Inn Road, London WC1X 8TU
E info@peregrines-pianos.com
W www.peregrines-pianos.com

PHA CASTING SUITE   T 0161 273 4444
Tanzaro House, Ardwick Green North
Manchester M12 6FZ
F 0161 273 4567
E info@pha-agency.co.uk
W www.pha-agency.co.uk

PINEAPPLE DANCE STUDIOS T 020 7836 4004
7 Langley Street, Covent Garden, London WC2H 9JA
F 020 7836 0803
W www.pineapple.uk.com

PLACE THE   T 020 7121 1000
17 Duke's Road, London WC1H 9PY
F 020 7121 1142
E info@theplace.org.uk
W www.theplace.org.uk

PLAYGROUND STUDIO THE   T/F 020 8960 0110
Unit 8, Latimer Road, London W10 6RQ
E info@the-playground.co.uk
W www.the-playground.co.uk

POOR SCHOOL THE   T 020 7837 6030
242 Pentonville Road, London N1 9JY
E acting@thepoorschool.com
W www.thepoorschool.com

PRECINCT THEATRE THE   T 020 7359 3594
Units 2-3 The Precinct, Packington Square
London N1 7UP
F 020 7359 3660
E agency@breakalegman.com
W www.breakalegman.com

PRETZEL FILMS   T 020 7580 9595
11-12 Tottenham Mews, London W1T 4AG
F 020 7580 2232
E caroline@pretzelfilms.com
W www.pretzelfilms.com

QUESTORS THEATRE
EALING THE   T 020 8567 0011
12 Mattock Lane, London W5 5BQ
F 020 8567 2275
E alice@questors.org.uk
W www.questors.org.uk

RAG FACTORY THE   T 020 7183 3048
16-18 Heneage Street, London E1 5LJ
E hello@ragfactory.org.uk
W www.ragfactory.org.uk

RAMBERT DANCE COMPANY   T 020 8630 0600
94 Chiswick High Road, London W4 1SH
F 020 8747 8323
E rdc@rambert.org.uk
W www.rambert.org.uk

REALLY USEFUL
GROUP THEATRES   T 020 7240 0880
Contact: Michael Townsend
22 Tower Street, London WC2H 9TW
F 020 7240 1292
E mike.townsend@reallyuseful.co.uk
W www.reallyuseful.com

SOUTH LONDON DANCE STUDIOS

STUDIOS FOR HIRE
- 3 large dance studios for hire
- Sprung floors, mirrors, barres & piano
- Spacious changing & waiting facilities
- Suitable for auditions, castings & rehearsals

Herne Hill, SE London
10 mins from
Victoria by train
020 7978 8624

info@southlondondancestudios.co.uk

RIDGEWAY STUDIOS T 01992 633775
Office: 106 Hawkshead Road
Potters Bar, Herts EN6 1NG
E info@ridgewaystudios.co.uk

RITZ STUDIOS T 020 8870 1335
Provides Backline Hire for Musicians
110-112 Disraeli Road
London SW15 2DX
E lee@ritzstudios.com
W www.ritzstudios.com

RIVERSIDE STUDIOS T 020 8237 1000
Crisp Road, Hammersmith
London W6 9RL
T 020 8237 1007
E lornapaterson@riversidestudios.co.uk
W www.riversidestudios.co.uk

ROCHELLE SCHOOL T 020 7033 3539
Arnold Circus, London E2 7ES
E scott@rochelleschool.org
W www.rochelleschool.org

ROOFTOP STUDIO THEATRE T 01785 761233
Rooftop Studio, High Street Arcade
Stone, Staffordshire ST15 8AU
F 01785 818176
E elaine@pssa.co.uk
W www.rooftopstudio.co.uk

ROOMS ABOVE THE T 0845 6860802
Westheath Yard, (Opposite The Emmanuel School)
174 Mill Lane, West Hampstead, London NW6 1TB
F 020 8201 9464
E info@theroomsabove.org.uk
W www.theroomsabove.org.uk

ROSE STUDIO & GALLERY T 020 8546 6983
Rose Theatre
Kingston, 24-26 High Street
Kingston upon Thames, Surrey KT1 1HL
F 020 8546 8783
E hiresandevents@rosetheatrekingston.org
W www.rosetheatrekingston.org

Bloomsbury Theatre

REHEARSAL STUDIO

Attractive and modern, 11m x 8m (36ft x 26ft 4in)
Sprung dance floor, mirrored wall, piano,
kitchenette, adjustable lighting.
Shop and café on site.

Easily accessible central location

Available Mon through Sat, daytime and evening

Contact the Administration Officer
on **020 7679 2777**

15 Gordon Street, London WC1H 0AH
www.thebloomsbury.com

ROTHERHITHE STUDIOS T 020 7231 2209
82 St Marychurch Street, London SE16 4HZ
F 020 7231 2119
E ostockman@sandsfilms.co.uk
W www.sandsfilms.co.uk

ROYAL ACADEMY OF DANCE T 020 7326 8000
36 Battersea Square, London SW11 3RA
F 020 7924 3129
E info@rad.org.uk
W www.rad.org.uk

**ROYAL ACADEMY OF
DRAMATIC ART** T 020 7908 4822
62-64 Gower Street, London WC1E 6ED
E bookings@radaenterprises.org

**ROYAL SHAKESPEARE
COMPANY** T 020 7845 0500
35 Clapham High Street, London SW4 7TW
F 020 7819 8708
W www.rsc.org.uk

RTM STUDIOS T 0141 221 2258
Central Chambers, 93 Hope Street
Glasgow G2 6LD
F 0141 221 8622
E kay@resolutiontalentmanagement.com
W www.resolutiontalentmanagement.com

RUDEYE STUDIOS T 020 7014 3023
73 St John Street, Farringdon
London EC1M 4NJ
E info@rudeye.com
W www.rudeye.com

SADLER'S WELLS THEATRE T 020 7863 8065
Rosebery Avenue, London EC1R 4TN
F 020 7863 8061
E events@sadlerswells.com
W www.sadlerswells.com

SMA CENTRE T 020 7937 8885
Vicarage Gate, Kensington
London W8 4HN
F 020 7368 6505
E manager@smacentre.com
W www.smacentre.com

SOHO GYMS T 0845 6778890
Borough Gym, Empire Square
Long Lane, London SE1 4NA
F 020 7234 9397
W www.sohogyms.com

SOHO GYMS T 020 7482 4524
Camden Town Gym
193-199 Camden High Street, London NW1 7BT
F 020 7267 0500
W www.sohogyms.com

SOHO GYMS T 020 7720 0321
Clapham Common Gym, 95-97 Clapham High Street
London SW4 7TB
F 020 7720 6510
E clapham@sohogyms.com
W www.sohogyms.com

The Playground Studio
2,500sq.ft beautiful rehearsal space
London W10

Sprung Floor
Mirrored Wall
Natural Day Light

www.the-playground.co.uk
info@the-playground.co.uk
T: 020 8960 0110

SOHO GYMS   T 020 7242 1290
Covent Garden Gym
12 Macklin Street, London WC2B 5NF
F 020 7242 0899
W www.sohogyms.com

SOHO GYMS   T 020 7370 1402
Earl's Court Gym
254 Earl's Court Road, London SW5 9AD
F 020 7244 6893
W www.sohogyms.com

SOHO GYMS   T 020 7261 9798
Waterloo Gym, 11-15 Brad Street, London SE1 8TG
F 020 7928 8623
W www.sohogyms.com

SOHO THEATRE   T 020 7287 5060
21 Dean Street, London W1D 3NE
F 020 7287 5061
E hires@sohotheatre.com
W www.sohotheatre.com

SOUTH LONDON
DANCE STUDIOS   T 020 7978 8624
130 Herne Hill, London SE24 9QL
E info@southlondondancestudios.co.uk
W www.southlondondancestudios.co.uk

SPACE @ CLARENCE MEWS   T 020 8986 5260
40 Clarence Mews, London E5 8HL
E frith.salem@virgin.net
W www.movingarchitecture.com

RADA

ROYAL
ACADEMY OF
DRAMATIC ART

THREE THEATRES
FIFTEEN MULTI-PURPOSE REHEARSAL ROOMS
ONE MIRRORED DANCE STUDIO
ONE AUDIO RECORDING STUDIO
ONE BAR AND CABARET SPACE
CONSTRUCTION WORKSHOPS AND PAINTFRAME

All available for hire at RADA
62-64 Gower Street, London WC1E 6ED and
18-22 Chenies Street, London WC1E 7PA

Contact: +44 (0)20 7908 4754
bookings@rada.ac.uk, www.rada.org

St James's Church, Piccadilly Room Hire

Perfect rehearsal, casting and meeting space in the heart of the West End

For all enquiries or to arrange a viewing, please call: **020 7292 4860**

Conference Room:
10m x 7.5m (30ft x 25ft)

Meeting Room:
7.5m x 5m (26ft x 16ft)

St James's Church, 197 Piccadilly, London W1J 9LL
www.st-james-piccadilly.org • roomhire@st-james-piccadilly.org

"I would happily recommend St James's Conference Room to anyone needing rehearsal space in the West End."
- *Company Manager, Fiery Angel*

SPACE ARTS CENTRE THE   T 020 7515 7799
269 Westferry Road, London E14 3RS
E info@space.org.uk
W www.space.org.uk

SPACE CITY STUDIOS   T 020 7371 4000
79 Blythe Road, London W14 0HP
F 020 7371 4001
E info@spacecity.co.uk
W www.spacecitystudios.co.uk

SPOTLIGHT   T 020 7440 5041
Casting Studios. Room Hire
7 Leicester Place
London WC2H 7RJ
F 020 7287 1201
E rooms@spotlight.com
W www.spotlight.com/rooms

ST AGNES CHURCH   T 020 7735 3857
St Agnes Place, Kennington Park
London SE11 4BB
E keith.potter@talk21.com

ST ANDREW'S CHURCH   T 020 7633 9819
Casting Suites. Meetings. Rehearsal Room.
Workshops & Classes
Short Street, Southbank
London SE1 8LJ
E lorrainespenceley@hotmail.com
W www.stjohnswaterloo.co.uk

ST GEORGE'S
CHURCH BLOOMSBURY   T 020 7242 1979
Vestry Hall, 6 Little Russell Street
London WC1A 2HR
E hiring@stgeorgesbloomsbury.org.uk
W www.stgeorgesbloomsbury.org.uk

ST JAMES'S CHURCH
PICCADILLY   T 020 7292 4860
197 Piccadilly, London W1J 9LL
E secretary@st-james-piccadilly.org
W www.st-james-piccadilly.org

ST MARTINS-IN-THE-FIELDS   T 020 7766 1130
6 St Martins Place, London WC2N 4JJ
E jennifer.lang@smitf.org
W www.smitf.org

ST MARY NEWINGTON
CHURCH HALL   T 020 7735 1894
The Parish Office
57 Kennington Park Road
London SE11 4JQ

ST MARY'S CHURCH HALL
PADDINGTON   T 020 7446 6200
c/o Bill Kenwright Ltd,1 Venice Walk, London W2 1RR
F 020 7446 6222
E info@kenwright.com

ST SWITHUN'S CHURCH   T 020 8852 5088
Meetings. Workshops
Hither Green Lane, Lewisham SE13 6QE
W www.saintswithuns.org.uk

STUDIO THE   T 01746 787574
Burwarton, Nr Bridgnorth, Shropshire WV16 6QJ
E meghawkins@btinternet.com
W www.meghawkins.com

SUMMERS Mark
CASTING STUDIOS   T 020 7229 8413
1 Beaumont Avenue
West Kensington, London W14 9LP
E mark@marksummers.com
W www.marksummers.com

SUMMIT STUDIOS   T 020 8840 2200
2-4 Spring Bridge Mews
Spring Bridge Road, Ealing, London W5 2AB
F 020 8840 2446
E info@summitstudios.co.uk
W www.summitstudios.co.uk

SWEET CASTING
(See CASTING AT SWEET)

TAKE FIVE CASTING STUDIO   T 020 7287 2120
Casting Suite
37 Beak Street, London W1F 9RZ
F 020 7287 3035
E info@takefivestudio.com
W www.takefivestudio.com

THEATRO TECHNIS   T 020 3137 3879
26 Crowndale Road, London NW1 1TT
E info@theatrotechnis.com
W www.theatrotechnis.com

TREADWELL'S   T 020 7240 8906
33 Store Street, Bloomsbury, London WC1E 7BS
E info@treadwells-london.com
W www.treadwells-london.com/rehearsal_space.html

TRESTLE ARTS BASE   T 01727 850950
Home of Trestle Theatre Company
Russet Drive, St Albans, Herts AL4 0JQ
F 01727 855558
E admin@trestle.org.uk
W www.trestle.org.uk

The Old Finsbury Town Hall

The Old Finsbury Town Hall, Rosebery Avenue, EC1, the Central London home of **The Urdang Academy**, offers studios for castings, rehearsals and auditions. Sprung Harlequin floors, mirrors, pianos, sound system and WIFI.
T: 020 7713 7710 ext 2222 E: studiohire@theurdangacademy.com

TRICYCLE THE   T 020 7372 6611
269 Kilburn High Road, London NW6 7JR
F 020 7328 0795
E trish@tricycle.co.uk
W www.tricycle.co.uk

TT DANCE STUDIO   T 07904 771980
Parkwood Health & Fitness Centre, Darkes Lane
Potters Bar, Herts EN6 1AA
T 07930 400647
E ttdancestudio@aol.com
W www.talenttimetheatre.com

UNICORN THEATRE   T 020 7645 0500
147 Tooley Street, London SE1 2HZ
E sd.supervisor@unicorntheatre.com
W www.unicorntheatre.com

UNION CHAPEL PROJECT   T 020 7266 3750
Compton Avenue, London N1 2XD
F 020 7354 8343
E spacehire@unionchapel.org.uk
W www.unionchapel.org.uk

UR SPACE 4 U   T 020 8685 6193
Imperial Fields, Bishops Ford Road
Morden, Surrey SM4 6BF
F 020 8685 6190
E reception@urspace4u.com
W www.urspace4u.com

URDANG ACADEMY THE   T 020 7713 7710
The Old Finsbury Town Hall
Rosebery Avenue, London EC1R 4RP
F 020 7278 6727
E studiohire@theurdangacademy.com
W www.theurdangacademy.com

WALKING FORWARD LTD   T/F 020 7359 5249
Studio 6
Aberdeen Centre
22-24 Highbury Grove
London N5 2EA
E info@walkingforward.co.uk
W www.walkingforward.co.uk

WATERMANS   T 020 8232 1020
40 High Street
Brentford TW8 0DS
F 020 8232 1030
E info@watermans.org.uk
W www.watermans.org.uk

Y TOURING THEATRE COMPANY   T 020 7520 3090
One KX, 120 Cromer Street
London WC1H 8BS
E d.jackson@ytouring.org.uk
W www.theatreofdebate.com

YOUNG, Sylvia THEATRE SCHOOL   T 020 7258 2330
1 Nutford Place
London W1H 5YZ
F 020 7258 3915
E syoung@syts.co.uk
W www.syts.co.uk

YOUNG ACTORS THEATRE   T 020 7278 2101
70-72 Barnsbury Road
London N1 0ES
F 020 7833 9467
E info@yati.org.uk
W www.yati.org.uk

SPOTLIGHT
ROOMS & STUDIOS

Spacious, air-conditioned meeting rooms and casting studios in the heart of Central London

Large waiting rooms with free receptionist service

DVD-quality audition clips posted online within minutes

Ideal for TV, film and commercial castings, plus read-throughs, production meetings or theatre projects

www.spotlight.com/spaces

Spotlight   7 Leicester Place   London WC2H 7RJ   t 020 7440 5041   e studios@spotlight.com

ACT UP T 020 7924 7701
Unit 88, 99-109 Lavender Hill, London SW11 5QL
F 020 7924 6606
E info@act-up.co.uk
W www.act-up.co.uk

ACTIVATION T 020 8783 9494
Riverside House, Feltham Avenue
Hampton Court, Surrey KT8 9BJ
F 020 8783 9345
E info@activation.co.uk
W www.activation.co.uk

APROPOS PRODUCTIONS LTD T 020 7739 2857
PO Box 63581, London N6 9BH
E info@aproposltd.com
W www.aproposltd.com

**BROWNE, Michael
ASSOCIATES LTD** T/F 01462 812483
The Cloisters,168C Station Road
Lower Stondon, Bedfordshire SG16 6JQ
E enquiries@mba-roleplay.co.uk
W www.mba-roleplay.co.uk

CRAGRATS T 0844 8111184
Lawster House, 140 South Street
Dorking, Surrey RH4 2EU
E enquiries@cragrats.com W www.cragrats.com

DRAMANON LLP T 01753 647795
Langtons House, Templewood Lane
Farnham Common, Buckinghamshire SL2 3HD
F 01753 647783
E info@dramanon.co.uk W www.dramanon.co.uk

FRANK PARTNERS T 0117 908 5384
14 Brynland Avenue, Bishopton, Bristol BS7 9DT
E neil@frankpartners.co.uk W www.frankpartners.co.uk

GLOBAL7 T/F 020 7281 7679
PO Box 56232, London N4 4XP
T 07956 956652
E global7castings@gmail.com
W www.global7casting.com

INTERACT T 020 7793 7744
138 Southwark Bridge Road, London SE1 0DG
F 020 7793 7755
E cv@interact.eu.com W www.interact.eu.com

LADA PRODUCTIONS T 01522 837242
Sparkhouse Studios, Ropewalk, Lincoln, Lincs LN6 7DQ
F 01522 837201
E productions@lada.org.uk W www.lada.org.uk

NV MANAGEMENT LTD
E hello@nvmanagement.co.uk
W www.nvmanagement.co.uk

PERFORMANCE BUSINESS THE T 01932 888885
The Coach House, 78 Oatlands Drive
Weybridge, Surrey KT13 9HT
E lucy@theperformance.biz W www.theperformance.biz

ROLEPLAY UK T 01780 761960
2 St Mary's Hill, Stamford PE9 2DW
F 01780 764436 W www.roleplayuk.com

**STEPS DRAMA
LEARNING DEVELOPMENT** T 020 7403 9000
Suite 10, Baden Place, Crosby Row, London SE1 1YW
F 020 7403 0909
E mail@stepsdrama.com W www.stepsdrama.com

THEATRE& LTD T 01484 532967
Church Hall, St James Road
Marsh, Huddersfield HD1 4QA
F 01484 532962
E cmitchell@theatreand.com W www.theatreand.com

S →

**Set Construction, Lighting,
Sound & Scenery**

3D SET COMPANY LTD T 0161 273 8831
Construction. Exhibition Stands. Scenery Design. Sets
Unit 8 Temperance Street, Manchester M12 6HR
F 0161 273 6786
E twalsh@3dsetco.com
W www.3dsetco.com

ALBEMARLE SCENIC STUDIOS T 0845 6447021
Suppliers of Scenery & Costumes Construction/Hire
Admin: PO Box 240, Rotherfield TN6 9BN
E albemarle.productions@virgin.net
W www.albemarleproductions.com

ALL SCENE ALL PROPS T 01580 211121
CNC Routing Specialists. Prop Makers. Scenery Builders
Units 2 & 3, Spelmonden Farm
Goudhurst, Kent TN17 1HE
F 01580 211131
E info@allscene.net
W www.allscene.net

BRISTOL (UK) LTD T 01923 779333
Scenic Paint
Unit 3, Southerland Court
Tolpits Lane, Watford WD18 9SP
F 01923 779666
E tech.sales@bristolpaint.com
W www.bristolpaint.com

BRITISH HARLEQUIN PLC T 01892 514888
Festival House, Chapman Way
Tunbridge Wells, Kent TN2 3EF
F 01892 514222
E enquiries@harlequinfloors.com
W www.harlequinfloors.com

CAP PRODUCTION SOLUTIONS T 07973 432576
116 Wigmore Road, Carshalton, Surrey SM5 1RQ
E leigh@leighporter.com

CCT LIGHTING UK LTD T 0115 985 8919
Lighting. Dimmers. Sound & Stage Machinery
Unit 3, Ellesmere Business Park
Haydn Road, Sherwood, Nottingham NG5 1DX
F 0115 985 7091
E office@cctlighting.co.uk
W www.cctlighting.com

COD STEAKS T 0117 980 3910
Costume. Design. Exhibitions. Model Making.
Set Construction
2 Cole Road, Bristol BS2 0UG
E mail@codsteaks.com
W www.codsteaks.com

CREWCO T 0845 4589400
Stage & Technical Crew for London & Midlands
Admin Office: Unit 4, Old Road
Long Compton, Warwickshire CV36 5JS
F 0845 4589411
E contactus@crewco.net
W www.crewco.net

DAP STUDIO T/F 01892 730897
55 Longdown Lane North, Epsom, Surrey KT17 3JB
E info@dapstudio.co.uk
W www.dapstudio.co.uk

DISPLAY MAINTENANCE LTD T 0844 8711801
Unit 1, Calder Trading Estate, Lower Quarry Road
Bradley, Huddersfield HD5 0RR
E enquiries@dmnsolutions.co.uk
W www.dmnsolutions.co.uk

DOBSON SOUND PRODUCTION LTD T 020 8545 0202
Design. Installation. Sound Hire
66 Windsor Avenue, Merton, London SW19 2RR
F 020 8543 3636
E enquiries@dobsonsound.co.uk

FULL EFFECT THE T 020 7836 9562
Event Designers & Producers
30 Maiden Lane, London WC2E 7JS
F 020 7836 1044
E mark.harrison@tfe.co.uk
W www.thefulleffect.co.uk

FUTURIST SOUND & LIGHT LTD T 0113 279 0033
Unit 8, Brandon Street, Leeds LS12 2EB
F 0113 242 0088
E info@futurist.co.uk
W www.futurist.co.uk

GAUGE AUDIO VISUAL T 01243 641404
Gauge Theatre Sound. Consultancy.
Design. Hire. Installation. Sales
Tithe Barn Cottage, Rookery Lane
Sidlesham, West Sussex PO20 7ND
E jonathan@gauge-av.com
W www.gauge-av.com

GILL, Perry T 07815 048164
Installation. Production Management. Set Construction
E perry_gill100@hotmail.com

HALL STAGE LTD T 0845 3454255
Unit 4, Cosgrove Way, Luton, Beds LU1 1XL
F 0845 3454256
E sales@hallstage.com
W www.hallstage.com

HALO LIGHTING T 0844 8440484
98-124 Brewery Road, London N7 9PG
E info@halo.co.uk
W www.halo.co.uk

HAND & LOCK T 020 7580 7488
Embroidery for Costumes & Interiors
86 Margaret Street, London W1W 8TE
F 020 7580 7499
E enquiries@handembroidery.com
W www.handembroidery.com

HENSHALL, John T 01367 710191
Director of Lighting & Photography
68 High Street, Stanford in the Vale
Oxfordshire SN7 8NL
E john@epi-centre.com

HERON & DRIVER T 020 7394 8688
Scenic Furniture & Structural Prop Makers
Unit 7, Dockley Road Industrial Estate
Rotherhithe, London SE16 3SF
E mail@herondriver.co.uk
W www.herondriver.co.uk

LIGHT WORKS LTD T 020 7249 3627
2A Greenwood Road, London E8 1AB
F 020 7254 0306

MALTBURY STAGING T 0333 800 8881
Portable Staging Sales & Consultancy
Unit 9, Level 5 South, New England House
New England Street, Brighton BN1 4GH
F 0333 800 8882
E info@maltbury.com
W www.maltbury.com

MASSEY, Bob ASSOCIATES T/F 0115 926 3626
Electrical & Mechanical Stage Consultants
9 Worrall Avenue, Arnold
Nottinghamshire NG5 7GN
E bm.associates@virgin.net

MATT-LX LTD T 0845 6808693
Audio Visual. Health & Safety. Lighting. Production Design
Unit 3, Vinehall Business Centre
Vinehall Road, Robertsbridge
East Sussex TN32 5JW
E intray@mattlx.com
W www.mattlx.com

MODELBOX T 01837 54342
Computer Aided Design. Design Services
35 Mill Road, Okehampton, Devon EX20 1PS
E info@modelbox.co.uk
W www.modelboxplans.com

MODERNEON LONDON LTD T 020 8650 9690
Lighting. Signs
Cromwell House, 27 Brabourne Rise
Park Langley, Beckenham, Kent BR3 6SQ
F 020 8658 2770
E info@moderneon.co.uk
W www.moderneon.co.uk

MOUNSEY, Matthew T 07941 355450
Scenic Artist
E matthewmounsey@hotmail.com

NEED, Paul J. T 020 8659 2558
Lighting Designer
c/o 10 out of 10 Productions, 5 Orchard Business Centre
Kangley Bridge Road, London SE26 5AQ
F 020 8778 9217
E paul@10outof10.co.uk
W www.pauljneed.co.uk

NORTHERN LIGHT T 0131 622 9100
Communications, Lighting, Sound & Stage Equipment
Assembly Street, Leith, Edinburgh EH6 7RG
F 0131 622 9101
E info@northernlight.co.uk
W www.northernlight.co.uk

ORBITAL T 020 7501 6868
Sound Hire & Design
57 Acre Lane, Brixton, London SW2 5TN
F 020 7501 6869
E hire@orbitalsound.co.uk
W www.orbitalsound.co.uk

PANALUX T 020 8233 7000
12 Waxlow Road, London NW10 7NU
F 020 8233 7001
E info@panalux.biz
W www.panalux.biz

PMB THEATRE &
EXHIBITION SERVICES LTD T 01954 718227
The Barn, Kingston Wood Manor
Arrington, Royston, Herts SG8 0AP
F 01954 718032
E pmb@creatingtheimpossible.co.uk
W www.creatingtheimpossible.co.uk

PRODUCTION STORE T 0845 6808692
Consumables. Parts. Tapes. Tools
Unit 3, Vinehall Business Centre
Vinehall Road, Robertsbridge, East Sussex TN32 5JW
E sales@mattlx.com
W www.productionstore.net

REVOLVING STAGE
COMPANY LTD THE T 024 7668 7055
Unit F5, Little Heath Industrial Estate
Old Church Road, Coventry, Warwickshire CV6 7ND
F 024 7668 9355
E enquiries@therevolvingstagecompany.co.uk
W www.therevolvingstagecompany.co.uk

RK RESOURCE T 01233 750180
2 Wyvern Way, Henwood, Ashford, Kent TN24 8DW
F 01233 750133
E rkresource2007@aol.co.uk
W www.rk-resourcekent.com

S2 EVENTS T 020 7928 5474
Design, Equipment Hire, Production, Scenery/Set
Construction & Technical Services for Creative Live Events
3-5 Valentine Place, London SE1 8QH
F 020 7928 6082
E info@s2events.co.uk
W www.s2events.co.uk

We provide bespoke staging for all your event, exhibition, theatre, conference and product launch needs!

- Set Design & Build
- Technical Design Drafting
- Staging Solutions
- Print & Graphics
- Lightweight Aluminium Decks
- Lecterns
- Production Management
- Crewing

T: 020 7274 2044 F: 020 7738 3099 E: info@setcreations.com W: www.setcreations.com

SCENA PRODUCTIONS LLP T 020 7703 4444
Set Construction
240 Camberwell Road, London SE5 0DP
F 020 7703 7012
E info@scenapro.com
W www.scenapro.com

SCENIC WORKSHOPS LTD T 0151 933 6677
Baltic Road, Bootle, Liverpool L20 1AW
F 0151 933 6699
E info@scenicworkshops.co.uk
W www.scenicworkshops.co.uk

**SCOTT FLEARY
PRODUCTIONS LTD** T 0870 4441787
Unit 1-4, Vale Industrial Park
170 Rowan Road, London SW16 5BN
F 0870 4448322
E info@scottfleary.com

SET CREATIONS T 020 7274 2044
Unit 41, MG Industrial Estate
Milkwood Road, London SE24 0JF
F 020 7738 3099
E info@setcreations.com
W www.setcreations.com

SHOWSTORM LTD T 020 8123 3453
24 The Poplars, Littlehampton BN17 6GZ
E mark@showstorm.tv
W www.showstorm.tv

SMITH, Paul Don T 07949 710306
Graffiti Mural Artist. Graphics. Scenery
11A Cadogan Road, Surbiton, Surrey KT6 4DQ
E firedon_1@hotmail.com
W www.pauldonsmith.com

**STAGE MANAGEMENT
COMPANY** T 07731 429544
Unit 1 Accent Business Park, Barkerend Road
Bradford, West Yorkshire BD3 9BD
E info@stagemanagementcompany.co.uk
W www.stagemanagementcompany.co.uk

STAGE SYSTEMS T 01509 611021
*Designers & Suppliers of Modular Staging,
Tiering & Auditorium Seating*
Stage House, Prince William Road
Loughborough LE11 5GU
F 01509 233146
E info@stagesystems.co.uk
W www.stagesystems.co.uk

STAGE TEAM T 0844 8700497
2A Moorend Crescent, Cheltenham
Gloucestershire GL53 0EL
E info@stageteam.co.uk W www.stageteam.co.uk

**STAGECRAFT TECHNICAL
SERVICES LTD** T 0845 8382015
*Hire & Sales of Audio Visual, Lighting, Sound & Staging for
Conference & Live Events*
Porton Business Centre
Porton, Wiltshire SP4 0ND
F 0845 8382016
E hire@stagecraft.co.uk
W www.stagecraft.co.uk

**STAGEWORKS WORLDWIDE
PRODUCTIONS** T 01253 342426
Lighting. Props. Scenery. Sound
525 Ocean Boulevard
Blackpool FY4 1EZ
F 01253 342702
E info@stageworkswwp.com
W www.stageworkswwp.com

STEWART, Helen T 07887 682186
Theatre Designer
29C Hornsey Rise Gardens
London N19 3PP
E helen@helenstewart.co.uk
W www.helenstewart.co.uk

STORM LIGHTING LTD T 01483 757211
Warwick House, Monument Way West
Woking, Surrey GU21 5EN
F 01483 757710
E hire@stormlighting.co.uk
W www.stormlighting.co.uk

TITAN TOUR PRODUCTIONS T 07894 868750
55 Hereford Road, Eccles
Greater Manchester M30 9BX
E charlotte@titantourproductions.com
W www.titantourproductions.com

TMS THEATRICAL LTD T 020 7394 9519
Set Construction & Painting
306 St James's Road, London SE1 5JX
F 020 7232 2347
E administration@tmstheatrical.com
W www.tmstheatrical.com

TOP SHOW T 01904 750022
Props. Scenery. Conference Specialists
North Lane, Huntington, York YO32 9SU

WEST, John T/F 01527 516771
Art Director. Production Designer
103 Abbotswood Close, Winyates Green
Redditch, Worcestershire B98 0QF
T 07753 637451
E johnwest@blueyonder.co.uk
W www.johnwestartist.co.uk

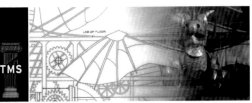

TMS Theatrical
Over 35 years of specialist construction.
Large & small scale installation for theatre,
opera, dance, events & display.

306 St James's Road, London SE1 5JX
+44 (0)20 7394 9519 production@tmstheatrical.com
www.tmstheatrical.com

TMS

T →

* A London Underground
  Map is included to
  assist with locating
  London venues

BBC TELEVISION
Wood Lane
London W12 7RJ
T 020 8743 8000

In Autumn 2011, the BBC relocated a number of its departments to a new site at MediaCityUK, Salford Quays, Salford. Departments include BBC Children's, BBC Radio 5 live, parts of Future Media & Technology, BBC Learning, BBC Sport and BBC Breakfast. For further information about BBC North please contact the BBC's main London switchboard.

If you are interested in working for the BBC in a production role, you can submit your CV to the BBC Production Talent website at www.bbcproductiontalent.co.uk/main.aspx

•TALENT & RIGHTS NEGOTIATION GROUP
Room 3400
201 Wood Lane
White City
London W12 7TS

Head of Talent Rights & Negotiation	Roger Leatham
Head of Copyright Contracting	Rob Kirkham
Head of Performance Contracting	Annie Thomas

LITERARY COPYRIGHT
Room 395 Drama Building
BBC Television Centre
London W12 7RJ

Manager	Neil Hunt

Senior Executives

Sue Dickson	Sally Millwood
Julie Gallagher	Hilary Sagar
David Knight	

MUSIC COPYRIGHT & MUSIC ENTERTAINMENT PERFORMANCE
Room 3370
BBC White City
London W12 7TS

Manager	Catherine Grimes
Executives	
Laura Amphlett	Celine Palavioux
Sally Dunsford	Natasha Pullin
Madeline Hennessy	Debbie Rogerson
Sam Nicholas	

BBC JOURNALISM, COMEDY & ENTERTAINMENT
Room 3029
BBC Television Centre
London W12 7RJ

Manager	Tessa Beckett
Rights Executives	
Mike Bickerdike	Jemma McGee
Gary Casey	Colette Robertson

LONDON FACTUAL & ARTS
Room 401, MC4 DI Media Centre
201 Wood Lane, London W12 7TQ

Rights Manager	Jane Armstrong
Executives	
Alice Brandon	Stuart Krelle
Selena Harvey	Shelagh Morrison
Matthew Hickling	
Classical Music Rights Manager	Simon Brown

TV DRAMA & RADIO DRAMA/COMEDY
Room 3370
BBC White City
London W12 7TS

Rights Manager	Nicola Hill
Executives – TV Drama	
Lorraine Clark	Candice Nichols
Fiona Dourado	
Executives – Radio Drama/Comedy	
Stephanie Beynon	Ian Heydon

PERFORMANCE CONTRACTING BBC NORTH
3rd Floor, Dock House
MediaCityUK
Salford M50 2HL

Rights Manager	Simon Ashwood
Executives	
Colleen Burrows	Sarah McHugh
Teresa Cordall	Collette Tanner

PERFORMANCE CONTRACTING BBC BIRMINGHAM
Level 10
The Mailbox
102-107 Wharfside Street
Birmingham B1 1AY

Rights Manager	Simon Ashwood
Executives	
Rachel Amos	Jill Ridley
Andrea Coles	

•DRAMA
BBC Drama Production
Lighthouse Building
Media Village
201 Wood Lane
London W12 7TQ
T 020 8743 8000 (Main Switchboard)

Director, Drama Production	Nicolas Brown
Controller, Series & Serials	Kate Harwood
Controller, Drama Production & New Talent	John Yorke
Head of Production	Susy Liddell
Creative Director, Drama Production	Manda Levin
Executive Producers - Drama Production	
Phillippa Giles	Hilary Salmon
Sue Hogg	Will Trotter
Anne Pivcevic	Jonathan Young
Jess Pope	
Executive Producer, EastEnders	Bryan Kirkwood

•COMMISSIONING

Director, BBC Vision	George Entwistle
Commissioning Editors, Drama	Sarah Brandist
	Polly Hill
Commissioning Editor, Independent Drama	Lucy Richer
Controller, Drama Production Studios	John Yorke
Controller, BBC Four	Richard Klein
Head of Knowledge Commissioning	Emma Swain
Controller, Series & Serials	Kate Harwood
Controller, Drama Commissioning	Ben Stephenson

•NEWS GROUP

BBC News (Television & Radio)
Television Centre
Wood Lane
London W12 7RJ
T 020 8743 8000 (Main Switchboard)

Director, News	Helen Boaden
Director, Global News	Peter Horrocks
Head of Programmes, News	Stephen Mitchell
Head of Newsgathering	Fran Unsworth
Head of Newsroom	Mary Hockaday
Head of Political Programmes, Research & Analysis	Sue Inglish
Controller of Production, News	Jenny Baxter
Controller, English Regions	David Holdsworth
Controller, BBC Parliament	Peter Knowles
Editor, BBC News Website	Steve Herrmann
Editor, Andrew Marr Show	Barney Jones
Editor, This Week & Daily Politics	Robbie Gibb
The Politics Show	Gavin Allen

London Factual Executive Producers

All based in the Media Centre at White City Media Village.
T 020 8743 8000 (Main Switchboard)

Arts	Basil Comely
	Jonty Claypole
Documentaries & Features	
Eamon Hardy	Nick Mirsky
Gary Hunter	Clare Sillery
Consumer	Lisa Ausden
Science	
Andrew Cohen	Tina Fletcher
Jonathan Renouf	
Horizon Editor	Aidan Laverty
Business & History	Dominic Crossley-Holland
	Eamon Hardy
Editor, The Culture Show	Janet Lee
Editor, The One Show	Sandy Smith

•CHILDREN

Director	Joe Godwin
Controller, CBBC	Damian Kavanagh
Controller, CBeebies	Kay Benbow
Head of In-house Production	Helen Bullough
Head of Children's Programmes, Scotland	Simon Parsons

•MUSIC

Head of Television, Classical Music & Performance	Peter Maniura
Managing Editor, Classical Music, Television	Caroline Speed
Editor Music Programmes, Television, Classical Music & Performance	Oliver Macfarlane
Talent Producer/Programme Development Manager	Victoria Jones
Executive Producer	Celina Parker
Producers/Directors	
Dominic Best	Andy King-Dabbs
Jonathan Haswell	Helen Mansfield
Francesca Kemp	
Production Executive	Ian Taitt

•SPORT

Director of Sport	Barbara Slater
Head of Major Events	Dave Gordon
Head of TV Sport	Philip Bernie
Head of Radio Sport	Gordon Turnbull
Head of Interactive & Formula 1	Ben Gallop
Head of Sports News	Richard Burgess
Head of Production	Jackie Myburgh
Head of HR Development	Pam Sikora
Head of Sports Rights	David Murray
Head of Marketing & Communications, Sports & Events	Louise Fyans
Finance Partner, Journalism, Sports	Daniel Chaffer

•NEW WRITING

BBC Writersroom
Brock House, Room 315
19 Langham Street
London W1A 1AA
T 020 8743 8000 (Main Switchboard)
E writersroom@bbc.co.uk
W www.bbc.co.uk/writersroom

Creative Director	Kate Rowland
Development Manager	Paul Ashton

BBC BRISTOL

Broadcasting House
Whiteladies Road
Bristol BS8 2LR   T 0117 973 2211

Network Television Features & Documentaries

Head of Bristol Factual	Ben Gale
Editor, Daytime	Kate Beetham
Head of Talent	Christopher Hutchins
Executive Producers	
Robi Dutta	Julian Mercer
Simon Knight	Michael Poole
Pete Lawrence	Simon Shaw
Series Producers	
Kate Broome	Alastair Laurence
Hannah Corneck	Ben Southwell
John Das	

BBC Audio & Musical Production Bristol (BBC Radio 4)

Managing Editor	Clare McGinn
Production Manager	Kate Chaney
Producers	
John Byrne	Chris Ledgard
Sara Davies	Beth O'Dea
Tim Dee	Mark Smalley
Christine Hall	Mary Ward-Lowery
Jolyon Jenkins	Miles Warde
Kirsten Lass	

Natural History Unit

Contact: Siobhan Lane
(Assistant to Head of Natural History Unit)

Head of Natural History Unit	Andrew Jackson
Executive Producers	
Wendy Darke	Julian Hector
Sara Ford	Brian Leith
Alastair Fothergill	Tim Martin
Mike Gunton	Tim Scoones

BBC WEST

Broadcasting House
Whiteladies Road
Bristol BS8 2LR   T 0117 973 2211

Head of Regional & Local Programmes,
including BBC West, Radio Bristol,
BBC Somerset, BBC Gloucestershire,
BBC Wiltshire   Lucio Mesquita

Editor, TV News   Neil Bennett

BBC SOUTH WEST

Seymour Road
Mannamead
Plymouth PL3 5BD   T 01752 229201

Head of BBC South West	Leo Devine
Editor, TV Current Affairs	Simon Willis
Output Editor	Simon Read

BBC SOUTH

Havelock Road
Southampton SO14 7PU   T 023 8022 6201

Head of Regional & Local Programmes	Jason Horton
TV News Editor	Lee Desty
Editor, BBC Oxford	Marianne Bell
Managing Editor, BBC Solent	Chris Carnegy
Managing Editor, BBC Radio Berkshire	Duncan McLarty

BBC LONDON

2nd Floor
Egton Wing Broadcasting House
10-22 Portland Place
London W1A 1AA   T 020 7224 2424

BBC London News

TV: The Politics Show
Radio: BBC London Radio 94.9FM
Online: BBC London online

Head of BBC London	Michael MacFarlane
TV Editor	Antony Dore
Editor, Inside Out	Dippy Chaudhary
Managing Editor, BBC Radio London 94.9FM	David Robey
Political Editor	Tim Donovan
Editor, BBC London Online	Claire Timms

BBC SOUTH EAST

The Great Hall Arcade
Mount Pleasant Road
Tunbridge Wells
Kent TN1 1QQ   T 01892 670000

Head of Regional & Local Programmes, BBC South East	Michael Rawsthorne
Managing Editor, BBC Radio Kent	Paul Leaper
Managing Editor, BBC Radio Surrey & BBC Radio Sussex	Nicci Holliday
Editor, BBC South East Today	Quentin Smith
Editor, Inside Out	Linda Bell
Assistant Editor, Politics Show	Dan Fineman

BBC NORTH WEST

New Broadcasting House
Oxford Road
Manchester M60 1SJ
W www.bbc.co.uk/manchester
W www.bbc.co.uk/liverpool
W www.bbc.co.uk/lancashire   T 0161 200 2020

Entertainment & Features

Editor, Entertainment & Features	Helen Bullough

Religion & Ethics

Head of Religion & Ethics &
  Commissioning Editor for Religion TV   Aaqil Ahmed
Executive Editor &
  Head of Radio, Religion & Ethnics   Christine Morgan
Head of Television Religion   Tommy Nagra

Regional & Local Programmes

Head of Regional & Local
  Programmes, North West   Aziz Rashid
Head of Regional & Local Programmes,
  North East & Cumbria   Phil Roberts

BBC BIRMINGHAM

BBC Birmingham
The Mailbox
Birmingham B1 1RF
F 0121 567 6875   T 0121 567 6767

English Regions

Controller, English Regions   David Holdsworth
Head of New Media Services,
  English Regions   Laura Ellis
Chief Operating Officer, English Regions   Ian Hughes
Senior Officer, Press & PR   Caroline Boots
Secretary, BBC Trust   Louise Hall
Head of Regional & Local
  Programmes, West Midlands   Cath Hearne
Vision Productions
Head of Birmingham &
  Manchester Factual   Nick Patten
Head of Production Talent, Birmingham
  & Manchester   Manjit Ahluwalia
Audio & Music Factual
Head of Rural Affairs & Audio &
  Music Production   Andrew Thorman
Deputy Editor   Fran Barnes

Drama

BBC Birmingham TV Drama Village
Archibald House
1059 Bristol Road, Selly Oak
Birmingham B29 6LT   T 0121 567 7417

Executive Producer   Will Trotter

BBC SCOTLAND

40 Pacific Quay
Glasgow G51 1DA
W www.bbc.co.uk/scotland   T 0141 422 6000

Scottish Executive Board

Director, Scotland   Ken MacQuarrie
Head of Programmes & Services Donalda MacKinnon
Head of Public Policy   Ian Small
Chief Operating Officer   Bruce Malcolm
Head of Talent Division   Donald-Iain Brown
Head of HR & Development   Wendy Aslett
Head of Marketing, Communications
  & Audiences   Mairead Ferguson
Head of Strategy   Catherine Smith

Genre Heads

Commissioning Editor,
  Television & Head of Sport   Ewan Angus
Head of News & Current Affairs   Atholl Duncan
Head of Radio, Scotland   Jeff Zycinski
Head of Service, BBC Alba   Margaret Mary Murray
Service Editor, BBC Alba   Marion MacKinnon
Head of Factual   Andrea Miller
Head of Drama, Television   Anne Mensah
Head of Drama, Radio   Bruce Young
Head of Children's   Simon Parsons
Executive Editor for CBBC Scotland   Sue Morgan
Editor for Cbeebies Scotland   Sara Harkins
Head of Entertainment & Events   Eileen Herlihy
Head of Learning   Nick Simons
Director, BBC Scottish Symphony
  Orchestra   Gavin Reid
Executive Editor, Entertainment
  Commissioning   Alan Tyler
Commissioning Executive, BBC Daytime, Scotland
  & Northern Ireland   Jo Street
Executive Producer, Scotland,
  Knowledge Commissioning   Sam Anthony

*BBC Scotland provides television and radio programmes
for Scotland and the UK networks as well as online and
interactive content. Based in the new digital headquarters
in Glasgow since 2007, there are also centres throughout
Scotland which includes City Halls, the home of the BBC
Scottish Symphony Orchestra.*

Aberdeen
Broadcasting House
Beechgrove Terrace
Aberdeen AB15 5ZT   T 01224 625233

Dumbarton
Dumbarton Studios,
Studio Way
Dumbarton G82 2AP   T 01389 736666

Dumfries
Elmbank, Lover's Walk
Dumfries DG1 1NZ   T 01387 268008

Dundee
Nethergate Centre
4th Floor, 66 Nethergate
Dundee DD1 4ER   T 01382 202481

Edinburgh
The Tun, 4 Jackson's Entry
111 Holyrood Road
Edinburgh EH8 8PJ   T 0131 557 5888

Glasgow
Glasgow City Halls
(BBC Scottish Symphony Orchestra)
87 Albion Street
Glasgow G1 1NQ   T 0141 552 0909

Inverness
7 Culduthel Road
Inverness IV2 4AD   T 01463 720720

Orkney
Castle Street, Kirkwall
Orkney KW15 1DF   T 01856 873939

Portree
Clydesdale Bank Buildings
Somerled Square

Portree
Isle of Skye IV51 9BT   T 01478 612005

Selkirk
Unit 1, Ettrick Riverside
Dunsdale Road
Selkirk TD7 5EB   T 01750 724567

Shetland
Pitt Lane, Lerwick
Shetland ZE1 0DW   T 01595 694747

Stornoway
Radio nan Gaidheal
Rosebank
52 Church Street

Stornoway
Isle of Lewis HS1 2LS   T 01851 705000

BBC CYMRU/WALES
Broadcasting House
Llandaff
Cardiff CF5 2YQ   T 029 2032 2000

Director	Keith Jones (Acting)
Head of Programmes (Welsh)	Sian Gwynedd (Acting
Head of Programmes (English)	Adrian Davies (Acting)
Head of Strategy & Communications	Rhodri Talfan Davies
Head of News & Current Affairs	Mark O'Callaghan
Head of HR & Development	Jude Gray
Chief Operating Officer	Gareth Powell
Head of Drama	Faith Penhale
Head of Broadcast Development	Cathryn Allen
Head of Sport	Geoff Williams
Head of Factual & Music	Judith Winnan (Acting)
Editor, Radio Wales	Steve Austins
Editor, Radio Cymru	Sian Gwynedd
Editor, New Media	Iain Tweedale

BBC NORTHERN IRELAND
Belfast
BBC Broadcasting House
Ormeau Avenue
Belfast BT2 8HQ   T 028 9033 8000
W www.bbc.co.uk/ni

Director, BBC Northern Ireland	Peter Johnston
Head of Programmes	Ailsa Orr
Head of Drama	Stephen Wright
Head of News	Kathleen Carragher
Chief Operating Officer	Mark Taylor
Head of Corporate & Community Affairs	Mark Adair
Head of Marketing, Communications & Audiences	Kathy Martin
Head of HR & Development	Lawrence Jackson
Head of TV Current Affairs	Jeremy Adams
Editor, Sport	Shane Glynn
Head of Multi-platform Commissioning	Susan Lovell
Managing Editor, Learning, Language & Social Action	Jane Cassidy
Head of Radio Ulster	Fergus Keeling
Editor, Radio Foyle	Michael Tumelty

BBC Radio Ulster
BBC Broadcasting House
Ormeau Avenue
Belfast BT2 8HQ   T 028 9033 8000
W www.bbc.co.uk/radioulster

BBC Radio Foyle
8 Northland Road
Londonderry BT48 7JD   T 028 7126 2244

ITV ANGLIA

Head Office
Anglia House
Norwich NR1 3JG
F 0844 5563931
E anglianews@itv.com
W www.itv.com/anglia   T 0844 8816900

East of England: Weekday & Weekend

Regional News Centres

Cambridge
Link House
Station Road
Great Shelford
Cambridge CB22 5LT   T 0844 8816985 (News)

Northampton
Portfolio Innovation Centre
University of Northampton
St George's Avenue
Northampton NN2 6JD   T 0844 8816974

Ipswich
Hubbard House
Civic Drive, Ipswich IP1 2QA   T 0844 8816999

CHANNEL TELEVISION LTD

Registered Office
The Television Centre
La Pouquelaye, St Helier
Jersey JE1 3ZD, Channel Islands
F 01534 816817
W www.channelonline.tv   T 01534 816816

Channel Islands: Weekday and Weekend

Managing Director (Broadcast)	Karen Rankine
Programme Producer	Laura Holgate
Managing Director (Commercial)	Mike Elsey
Director of Resource & Transmission	Kevin Banner
Programme Editor	Eric Blakeley

CHANNEL FOUR TELEVISION CORPORATION

London Office
124 Horseferry Road
London SW1P 2TX
Textphone 020 7396 8691   T 020 7396 4444

Members of the Board

Chairman	Lord Terry Burns
Deputy Chairman	Lord David Puttnam
Chief Executive	David Abraham
Chief Creative Officer	Jay Hunt
Chief Operating Officer	Anne Bulford

Non-Executive Directors

Monica Burch	Alicja Lesniak
Martha Lane Fox	Mark Price
Lord Tony Hall	Richard Rivers
Stephen Hill	

Executives

Director, Human Resources	Diane Herbert
Director, Audience Technology & Insight	Gill Whitehead
Director, Marketing & Communications	Dan Brooke

Heads of Department

Viewers Editor	Paula Carter
Controller, Research & Insight	Claire Grimmond
Director, Commercial Affairs	Martin Baker
Channel Manager, Channel 4	Richard Brent
Controller, Channel Management	George Dixon
Director, Commercial & Business Development	Sarah Rose
Head of Business Assurance	Jeff O'Sullivan
Director, Corporate Relations	Nick Toon
Director, Creative Diversity	Stuart Cosgrove
Head of Distribution & Broadcast Technology	David Dorans
Head of Documentaries	Hamish Mykura
Head of Comedy	Shane Allen
Head of Entertainment	Justin Gorman
Head of Corporate Services	Julie Kortens
Head of Features & Factual Entertainment	Sue Murphy
Head of Drama	Camilla Campbell
Controller, Film & Drama	Tessa Scantlebury
Director, Finance	Glyn Isherwood
Head of Online Sales	Errol Baran
Head of HR Operations	Rosie Ranganathan
Head of 4Talent & Learning	Joanna Taylor
Controller, Legal & Compliance	Prash Naik
Head of Marketing, New Media	Tracy Abraham
Group Marketing Manager	Steven Forde
Head of Network Marketing	Rufus Radcliffe
Head of Media Planning & Presentation	Greg Smith
Head of News & Current Affairs	Dorothy Byrne
Head of Online	Richard Davidson-Houston
Head of Portfolio & Airtime Management	Merlin Inkley
Head of Acquisitions	Gill Hay
Head of Specialist Factual	Ralph Lee
Head of Sponsorship	David Charlesworth
Head of Strategic Sales	Mike Parker
Director, Strategy	Keith Underwood
Chief Information Officer	Kevin Gallagher
Chief Technology Officer	Bob Harris
Head of Sales	Mick Perry
Controller, Press & Publicity	Jane Fletcher

CHANNEL 5 BROADCASTING LTD

The Northern & Shell Building
10 Lower Thames Street
London EC3R 6EN
W www.channel5.com   T 020 8612 7000

Chairman	Richard Desmond
Director of Programmes	Jeff Ford
Executive Assistant to Director of Programmes	Kelly Hornsby
Head of Scheduling	Craig Morris
Head of News & Factual	Andrew O'Connell
Head of Factual Entertainment & Head of Sport	Steve Gowans
Commissioning Editor, Entertainment, Daytime & Soaps	Greg Barnett
Commissioning Editor, Children's	Jessica Symons

Effingee Productions Ltd
www.effingee.com
PO Box 7615, G42 2FY Tel: 07946 586 939

Head of Digital Channels	Kate Barnes
Head of Acquisitions	Kate Keenan
Marketing Director	Zoe Harris
Creative Director	Rich Thrift
Head of Marketing	Iain Sawbridge
Commercial Sales Director	Nick Bampton
Director of Legal & Commercial Affairs	Marcus Lee
Group Finance Director	Rob Sanderson

Group Finance Director	Ian Griffiths
Managing Director, ITV Studios	Lee Bartlett
HR Director	Andy Doyle
Group Legal Director & Company Secretary	Andrew Garard
Managing Director, ITV Brand & Commercial	Rupert Howell

Casting Directors at ITV Studios

Manchester
Casting Director	Gennie Radcliffe
Assistant Casting Director	Katy Belshaw

Leeds
Casting Director	Faye Styring
Casting Assistant	Amy Hill

If you would like one of the casting teams to cover your performance in a stage production, please e-mail casting@itv.com including your name, the theatre and the dates.

ITV BREAKFAST
London Television Centre
Upper Ground, London SE1 9TT
F 020 7827 7001
W www.itv.com/daybreak   T 020 7827 7000

Editor	Ian Rumsey
Deputy Editor	Paul Connolly
Head of News	Alan Rook
Head of Features	Annemarie Leahy
Head of Planning	Caroline Sigley
Head of Entertainment	Corinne Bishop
Head of Graphics	Fiona Skinner
Director of Production & Resources	Diana Holmes
Director of Finance & Operations	Andy Whitaker

Lorraine
Creative Director	Emma Gormley
Series Editor	Pauline Haase
Series Producer	Lisa Armstrong

INDEPENDENT TELEVISION NEWS
200 Gray's Inn Road
London WC1X 8XZ   T 020 7833 3000

Chief Executive	John Hardie
Editor-in-Chief, ITV News	David Mannion
Editor, ITV News	Deborah Turness
Editor, Channel 4 News	Jim Gray

ITV PLC
Registered Office
The London Television Centre
London SE1 9LT
F 020 7849 9344
W www.itv.com   T 020 7157 3000

Management Board
Chairman	Archie Norman
Chief Executive	Adam Crozier
Director of Television, Channels & Online	Peter Fincham
Director of Strategy & Development	Carolyn Fairbairn
Group Director of Communications	Ruth Settle

ITV MERIDIAN
ITV Meridian is part of ITV Plc
Fusion 3
1200 Parkway
Whiteley, Hants PO15 7AD
F 0844 8812074   T 0844 8812000

Meridian Board
Regional Sales Manager	Matt Corse

Executives
Finance Manager	Malcolm Beasley
Head of News	Robin Britton

ITV WALES
Television Centre
Culverhouse Cross
Cardiff CF5 6XJ
E news@itvwales.com
W www.itv.com/wales   T 0844 8810100

Wales: All week

Head of News & Programmes	Phil Henfrey

ITV WEST & ITV WESTCOUNTRY
Bath Road
Bristol BS4 3HG   T 0844 8812345

Head of News	Liz Hannam

S4C

Parc Tŷ Glas, Llanishen
Cardiff CF14 5DU
F 029 2075 4444
E s4c@s4c.co.uk
W www.s4c.co.uk   T 029 2074 7444

The Welsh Fourth Channel Authority

Chair   Rheon Tomos

Authority Members

Bill Davies   Dr Glenda Jones
John Davies   Sir Roger Jones OBE
Cenwyn Edwards   Winston Roddick CB QC
Dyfrig Jones

Senior Staff

Chief Executive   Arwel Ellis Owen
Director of Commissioning   Meirion Davies
Director of Communications   Garffild Lloyd Lewis
Director of Finance &
    Human Resources   Kathryn Morris
Director of Broadcast & Distribution   Arshad Rasul
Director of Business Affairs   Delyth Wynne Griffiths
Director of Commercial &
    Corporate Policy   Elin Morris

STV

Glasgow Office
Pacific Quay, Glasgow G51 1PQ
F 0141 300 3030
W www.stv.tv   T 0141 300 3000

Aberdeen Office
Television Centre, Craigshaw Business Park
West Tullos, Aberdeen AB12 3QH
W www.stv.tv   T 01224 848848

London Office
21-25 St Anne's Court
London W1F OBJ
W www.stv.tv   T 020 7494 5747

Director of Channels   Bobby Hain
Head of News & Current Affairs   Gordon MacMillan
Chief Executive   Rob Woodward
Director of Content   Alan Clements
Head of Drama   Margaret Enefer
Head of Factual &
    Factual Entertainment   Paul Murray

ITV TYNE TEES & ITV BORDER

Television House, The Watermark
Gateshead NE11 9SZ   T 0844 8815000

Teesside News Gathering
20 Manor Way, Belasis Hall Technology Park
Billingham, Cleveland TS23 4HN
E tttvnews@itv.com   T 0844 8815000

North East and North Yorkshire: Weekday and Weekend

Executive Chair ITV   Adam Crozier
Head of News   Lucy West
Managing Director, SignPost   Malcolm Wright

UTV PLC

Ormeau Road
Belfast BT7 1EB
F 028 9024 6695
E info@u.tv
W www.utvmedia.com   T 028 9032 8122

Northern Ireland: Weekday and Weekend

Contact:
Sarah McCaffrey
Broadcast Marketing Executive   T 028 9026 2186

Chairman   J B McGuckian BSc (Econ)
Group Chief Executive   J McCann BSc, FCA
Group Financial Director   Jim Downey
Managing Director, Television   Michael Wilson
Head of Communications   Orla McKibbin
Head of News & Current Affairs   Rob Morrison
Sales Director   Paul Hutchinson

ITV YORKSHIRE

The Television Centre
Leeds LS3 1JS
F 0113 244 5107
W www.itv.com   T 0113 222 7000

London Office
London Television Centre
Upperground
London SE1 9LT   T 020 7620 1620

Executives
Head of News   Will Venters
Creative Director ITV Studios   John Whiston

SKY SATELLITE TELEVISION BRITISH SKY BROADCASTING LTD (BSkyB)

Grant Way, Isleworth
Middlesex TW7 5QD
F 0870 2403060
W www.sky.com/corporate   T 0844 8244100

Chief Executive   Jeremy Darroch
Chief Financial Officer   Andrew Griffith
Managing Director,
    Entertainment & News   Sophie Turner Laing
Director for People   Deborah Baker
Chief Operating Officer   Mike Darcey
Group Director of
    Corporate Affairs   Graham McWilliam
General Counsel   James Conyers
Managing Director, Sky Sports   Barney Francis
Managing Director, Product Design
    & Development   Alun Webber
Chief Technology Officer   Didier Lebrat
Group Director, Business Performance   William Mellis
Managing Director, Customer Group   Andrea Zappia
Group Director of Strategy   Mia Fyfield

10TH PLANET PRODUCTIONS T/F 020 8442 2659
75 Woodland Gardens, London N10 3UD
E admin@10thplanetproductions.com
W www.10thplanetproductions.com

30 BIRD PRODUCTIONS T 07970 960995
17 Emery Street, Cambridge CB1 2AY
E info@30birdproductions.org
W www.30birdproductions.org

A STAGE KINDLY LTD T 07947 074887
7 Northiam, Cromer Street
London WC1H 8LB
E mail@astagekindly.com
W www.astagekindly.com

ACORN ENTERTAINMENTS LTD T 01285 644622
PO Box 64, Cirencester, Glos GL7 5YD
F 01285 642291
E info@acornents.co.uk
W www.acornents.co.uk

ACT PRODUCTIONS LTD T 020 3077 8900
20-22 Stukeley Street, 3rd Floor, London WC2B 5LR
F 020 7242 3568
E info@actproductions.co.uk
W www.actproductions.co.uk

ACTORS PLATFORM LTD
Showcases for Professional Actors
Based in Central London
E melissa@actorsplatform.com
W www.actorsplatform.com

ACTOR'S TEMPLE THE T 020 3004 4537
13-14 Warren Street, London W1T 5LG
E info@actorstemple.com
W www.actorstemple.com

AJTC THEATRE COMPANY T/F 01483 232795
28 Rydes Hill Crescent, Guildford, Surrey GU2 9UH
W www.ajtctheatre.co.uk

AMBASSADOR THEATRE GROUP T 020 7534 6100
39-41 Charing Cross Road, London WC2H 0AR
F 020 7534 6109
E ccroffice@theambassadors.com
W www.ambassadortickets.com

ANTIC DISPOSITION T 020 7284 0760
4A Oval Road, London NW1 7EB
E info@anticdisposition.co.uk
W www.anticdisposition.co.uk

AOD (ACTORS OF DIONYSUS) T/F 01273 692604
14 Cuthbert Road, Brighton BN2 0EN
E info@actorsofdionysus.com
W www.actorsofdionysus.com

ARCADE PRODUCTIONS LTD T 020 7100 1123
Contact: Henry Filloux-Bennett, Stephen Makin,
Kellie Spooner, Nick Rogers (Producers)
271-273 City Road, London EC1V 1LA
E info@arcadeproductions.co.uk
W www.arcadeproductions.co.uk

ARDEN ENTERTAINMENT T 020 7263 9193
7 Maiden Place, London NW5 1HZ
E douglas@arden-entertainment.co.uk
W www.arden-entertainment.co.uk

ARTS MANAGEMENT (REDROOF ASSOCIATES)
Contact: By Post
Novello Theatre, High Street
Sunninghill, Ascot SL5 9NE

ASHTON GROUP THEATRE THE T 01229 430636
The Old Fire Station, Abbey Road
Barrow-in-Furness, Cumbria LA14 1XH
E theashtongroup@btconnect.com
W www.ashtongroup.co.uk

ATC T 020 7033 7360
Contact: Nick Williams (Executive Director)
The Tab Centre, 3 Godfrey Place
London E2 7NT
E atc@atctheatre.com
W www.atctheatre.com

ATTIC THEATRE COMPANY (LONDON) LTD T 020 8640 6800
Mitcham Library, 157 London Road
Mitcham CR4 2YR
E info@attictheatrecompany.com
W www.attictheatrecompany.com

BARNES, Andy PRODUCTIONS T 020 7839 9003
5A Irving Street, London WC2H 7AT
E andy@andybarnesproductions.com
W www.andybarnesproductions.com

BEE & BUSTLE ENTERPRISES T 020 8450 0371
32 Exeter Road, London NW2 4SB
F 020 8450 1057
E info@beeandbustle.co.uk
W www.beeandbustle.co.uk

BIRMINGHAM STAGE COMPANY THE T 020 7437 3391
Suite 228, The Linen Hall
162 Regent Street, London W1B 5TB
F 020 7437 3395
E info@birminghamstage.com
W www.birminghamstage.com

BLUE BOX ENTERTAINMENT LTD T 020 7395 7520
Top Floor, 80-81 St Martin's Lane, London WC2N 4AA
F 020 3292 1699
E info@newbluebox.com
W www.newbluebox.com

BLUE STAR PRODUCTIONS T 020 7836 6220
Contact: Barrie Stacey, Keith Hopkins
7-8 Shaldon Mansions, 132 Charing Cross Road
London WC2H 0LA
T 020 7836 4128
E hopkinstacey@aol.com

BORDER CROSSINGS T 020 8829 8928
13 Bankside, Enfield EN2 8BN
F 020 8366 5239
E info@bordercrossings.org.uk
W www.bordercrossings.org.uk

BOTELLO, Catalina T 020 7935 1360
48 New Cavendish Street, London W1G 8TG
T 07939 060434
E contact@catalinabotello.com
W www.outoftheboxproductions.org

BRIT-POL THEATRE LTD T 020 7266 0323
10 Bristol Gardens, London W9 2JG
E admin@britpoltheatre.com
W www.britpoltheatre.com

BRITISH THEATRE SEASON IN MONACO T 020 8455 3278
1 Hogarth Hill, London NW11 6AY
E mail@montecarlotheatre.co.uk
W www.montecarlotheatre.com

BROADHOUSE PRODUCTIONS LTD T 01984 640773
Lodge Rocks House, Bilbrook
Minehead, Somerset TA24 6RD
F 01984 641027
E admin@broadhouse.co.uk

BROOKE, Nick LTD T 020 7240 3901
2nd Floor, 80-81 St Martin's Lane, London WC2N 4AA
F 020 7240 2947
E nick@nickbrooke.com
W www.nickbrooke.com

Theatre Producers

What is a theatre producer?

A theatre producer is someone who oversees and organises a theatre show. He or she will find, or arrange for other professionals to find, a suitable script, design, director and cast for each production, while also managing all finances and marketing.

How should I use these listings?

Theatre producers tend to use casting directors to put forward suitable actors for the parts in forthcoming productions, but you could also try approaching them yourself. Rather than sending your CV and headshot to every producer listed, it would be best to do some research first in order to target your search. You need to decide what type of work you want to do first, as there is no need to waste your time and the producer's time sending your CV to unsuitable companies. Then find out what each company has produced in the past, what they are currently working on, and if possible what they are considering producing in the future, and only send your CV to those most relevant to the roles you want to play. Don't forget to include a covering letter which states why you are contacting this producer in particular: this could be because you feel you are perfect for a particular role in their next production, for example. Personalising and targeting your correspondence in this way gives you the best chance of your CV being considered in a favourable light.

How should I approach theatre producers?

You should contact theatre producers by post or e-mail only. We would advise against calling them, especially when approaching them for the first time. Address your correspondence to an individual within the company, as this demonstrates that you have done your research. If you are unsure as to the best method of applying to theatre producers, as with other casting professionals it is safest to post your CV and headshot in the traditional way rather than e-mailing it. Remember to put your name and telephone number on the back of the photo in case it gets separated from your CV. It would be a good idea to include a SAE big enough to contain your 10 x 8 photo and with sufficient postage to increase your chances of getting a reply. Do not enclose your showreel but you can mention that you have one available in your covering letter, and if the producer is interested in viewing it they will contact you.

When should I approach theatre producers?

Listen to industry news and have a look at theatre producers' websites for forthcoming production details. The casting process usually takes place around three months prior to rehearsals, so bear this in mind when you are writing your covering letter.

How do I become a theatre producer?

The best way to learn about producing is to work in producing. Internships are a good way to get to grips with the industry; research the theatre producers listed over the following pages by checking their websites' jobs sections for vacancies. Remember to make sure they actually work in the area you are interested in before making contact. You should also try to build up a good general knowledge of the industry by going to see as many theatrical productions as you can and keeping track of which producers work on which types of shows.

Theatre Producers

James Quaife is an award-winning commercial theatre producer who has produced on the London Fringe, in the West End and in New York. He has produced critically-successful productions such as Molière and the London première of Precious Little Talent at Trafalgar Studios, which won the Best New Play award at The London Theatre Festival Awards 2011. He has also produced numerous well-received plays and musicals at the award-winning Finborough Theatre.

He has also worked as the Project Manager for Old Vic New Voices at The Old Vic where he has produced and general managed The 24 Hour Plays: Old Vic New Voices, The TS Eliot US/UK Exchange and Time Warner IGNITE. He was also the Associate Producer on PLATFORM at The Old Vic Tunnels.

What is a producer?

For me (and there is no set description for this) a producer is the person who selects a play or musical they wish to bring to life on stage and fundamentally believe that an audience should pay to see that production. They are the person at the top and ultimately responsible for overseeing all aspects of mounting a theatrical production.

Once the production has been chosen a producer will begin the process of bringing a strong team around them, often starting with the selection of a director and then working with them to bring a team of designers and other creatives onboard and then beginning the process of casting that production.

Producing is a practical thing as are many crafts within the arts, such as writing and directing, which you can only learn and develop if you are actually physically doing it.

The producer will then have to play the balancing game of coordinating the business and financial aspects of mounting a production with the creative realisation of what the director would like and what the production needs. As a commercial producer my main goal is for the production to make a

profit or at least not make a loss. This is not to say that all choices of productions are driven by the possibility of them making money; you have to have a desire and passion to want to put that production on. The real skill and intelligence of a producer is working out how that production could then make money and become the hottest ticket in town!

How to produce?

Before I started working at The Old Vic I was lucky enough to be a participant in The 24 Hour Plays: Old Vic New Voices, 2009. This gave me a fantastic opportunity for networking with other young producers but also with writers, directors and actors. I then went on to complete a producing course with Stage One who offer bursaries and apprentice schemes for new producers.

Producing is a practical thing as are many crafts within the arts, such as writing and directing, which you can only learn and develop if you are actually physically doing it. I think this is most true of producing and I have learnt the most from having a hands-on approach and taking a play and getting it up on its feet. It is in this way that I have developed my skill as a producer.

How did you become a producer?

Originally I trained as a theatre director and after directing a few productions I felt that this was not the correct role for me and made the decision to become a theatre producer. From that moment I formed my company JQ Productions and a few months later I was staging my first play which suddenly snowballed into producing four productions in one year each running for four weeks and gaining national press attention.

I became a theatre producer because it is now the only thing I can see myself ever doing. I have a great passion for innovative and exciting theatre and the development of new writing and musical theatre. My company is also committed to producing high quality theatre and is dedicated to staging ambitious productions which contribute to the vibrancy and development of the theatre industry.

Please visit www.jamesquaife.com for further information.

BUDDY WORLDWIDE LTD   T 020 7240 9941
PO Box 293
Letchworth Garden City, Herts SG6 9EU
F 01462 684851
E info@buddyshow.com
W www.buddythemusical.com

BUSH THEATRE   T 020 8743 3584
7 Uxbridge Road, Shepherd's Bush
London W12 8LJ
E info@bushtheatre.co.uk
W www.bushtheatre.co.uk

CAHOOTS THEATRE COMPANY   T 020 8743 7777
Contact: Denise Silvey
St Martin's Theatre, West Street
London WC2N 9NH
E ds@denisesilvey.com

**CAP PRODUCTION
SOLUTIONS LTD**   T 07973 432576
116 Wigmore Road
Carshalton, Surrey SM5 1RQ
F 07970 763480
E leigh@leighporter.com

CENTRELINE PRODUCTIONS   T 07710 522438
41 Beresford Road, London N8 0AL
E jenny@centrelinenet.com
W www.centrelinenet.com

**CHAIN REACTION
THEATRE COMPANY**   T/F 020 8534 0007
Three Mills Studios, Sugar House Yard
Sugar House Lane, London E15 2QS
E mail@chainreactiontheatre.co.uk
W www.chainreactiontheatre.co.uk

**CHANNEL THEATRE
PRODUCTIONS LTD**   T 01843 587950
Penistone House, 5 High Street
St Lawrence, Ramsgate, Kent CT11 0QH
E info@channel-theatre.co.uk
W www.channel-theatre.co.uk

**CHAPMAN, Duggie
ASSOCIATES**   T/F 01253 403177
Concerts. Musicals. Pantomime
Clifton House
106 Clifton Drive, Blackpool FY4 1RR
E info@duggiechapmanassociates.co.uk
W www.duggiechapman.co.uk

CHEEK BY JOWL   T 020 7382 7304
Contact: Griselda Yorke
Stage Door, Barbican Centre
Silk Street, London EC2Y 8DS
E info@cheekbyjowl.com
W www.cheekbyjowl.com

CHICHESTER FESTIVAL THEATRE T 01243 784437
Oaklands Park, Chichester
West Sussex PO19 6AP
F 01243 787288
E admin@cft.org.uk
W www.cft.org.uk

CHICKENSHED   T 020 8351 6161
Chase Side, Southgate, London N14 4PE
E info@chickenshed.org.uk
W www.chickenshed.org.uk

CHOL THEATRE   T 01484 536008
Contact: Susan Burns (Director)
Lawrence Batley Theatre, 8 Queen Street
Huddersfield, West Yorkshire HD1 2SP
F 01484 425336
E info@choltheatre.co.uk
W www.choltheatre.co.uk

**CHURCHILL THEATRE
BROMLEY LTD**   T 020 8464 7131
Producing Theatre
The Churchill, High Street, Bromley, Kent BR1 1HA
F 020 8290 6968
W www.ambassadortickets.com/churchill

CLEAN BREAK   T 020 7482 8600
Theatre Education. New Writing
2 Patshull Road, London NW5 2LB
F 020 7482 8611
E general@cleanbreak.org.uk
W www.cleanbreak.org.uk

CODRON, Michael PLAYS LTD   T 020 7240 8291
Aldwych Theatre Offices, London WC2B 4DF
F 020 7240 8467

COLE KITCHENN LTD   T 020 7427 5682
212 Strand, London WC2R 1AP
F 020 7353 9639
E guy@colekitchenn.com
W www.colekitchenn.com

COMPLICITE   T 020 7485 7700
14 Anglers Lane, London NW5 3DG
F 020 7485 7701
E email@complicite.org
W www.complicite.org

CONCORDANCE   T 020 7244 7439
Contact: Neil McPherson
Finborough Theatre, 118 Finborough Road
London SW10 9ED
E admin@concordance.org.uk
W www.concordance.org.uk

CONTEMPORARY STAGE COMPANY
9 Finchley Way, London N3 1AG
E contemp.stage@hotmail.co.uk
W www.contemporarystage.co.uk

**CONWAY, Clive
CELEBRITY PRODUCTIONS LTD**   T 01865 514830
32 Grove Street, Oxford OX2 7JT
F 01865 514409
E info@celebrityproductions.org

**CREATIVE BLAST
PRODUCTIONS**   T 07545 009830
The Training Centre, Radford Way
Billericay, Essex CM12 0DX
E info@creativeblastcompany.com
W www.creativeblastcompany.com

**CREATIVE MANAGEMENT
& PRODUCTIONS (CMP) LTD**   T 020 7240 3033
1st Floor, 26-28 Neal Street, London WC2H 9QQ
F 020 7240 3037
E mail@cmplimited.com
W www.cmplimited.com

CROI8 PRODUCTIONS   T 00 353 85 1420683
Town Hall Theatre, Galway, Co. Galway, Ireland
E croiproductions@yahoo.co.uk

DEAD EARNEST THEATRE   T 0114 321 0450
Sheffield Design Studio, 40 Ball Street, Sheffield S3 8DB
E info@deadearnest.co.uk
W www.deadearnest.co.uk

DEAN, Lee   T 020 7497 5111
PO Box 10703, London WC2H 9ED
E admin@leedean.co.uk

DEBUT PRODUCTIONS   T 07505 677994
Actor Showcases in London's West End & Manchester
65 Norton Way North, Letchworth, Herts SG6 1BH
E submissions@debutproductions.co.uk
W www.debutproductions.co.uk

DISNEY THEATRICAL PRODUCTIONS (UK)　T 020 7845 0900
Lyceum Theatre, 21 Wellington Street
London WC2E 7RQ
F 020 7845 0999

DONEGAN, David LTD　T 07957 358909
PO Box LB689, London W1A 9LB
E daviddonegan@hotmail.co.uk

DRAMATIS PERSONAE LTD　T 020 7834 9300
Contact: Nathan Silver, Nicolas Kent
19 Regency Street, London SW1P 4BY
E ns@nathansilver.com

EASTERN ANGLES THEATRE COMPANY　T 01473 218202
Hiring The Sir John Mills Theatre
Gatacre Road, Ipswich, Suffolk IP1 2LQ
F 01473 384999
E admin@easternangles.co.uk
W www.easternangles.co.uk

EASY TIGER PRODUCTIONS LTD　T 020 7731 2826
Hurlingham Studios, London SW6 3PA
F 020 7371 8656
E mail@easytigerproductions.com
W www.easytigerproductions.com

ELLIOTT, Paul　T 020 7379 4870
18 Exeter Street, London WC2E 7DU
E pre@paulelliott.ltd.uk

ENGLISH NATIONAL OPERA　T 020 7836 0111
London Coliseum, St Martin's Lane, London WC2N 4ES
F 020 7845 9277
W www.eno.org

ENGLISH STAGE COMPANY LTD　T 020 7565 5050
Royal Court Theatre, Sloane Square, London SW1W 8AS
F 020 7565 5001
E info@royalcourttheatre.com
W www.royalcourttheatre.com

ENGLISH TOURING THEATRE (ETT)　T 020 7450 1990
25 Short Street, London SE1 8LJ
F 020 7633 0188
E admin@ett.org.uk
W www.ett.org.uk

ENTERTAINMENT BUSINESS LTD THE　T 020 7766 5274
Cameo House, 11 Bear Street, London WC2H 7AS
F 020 7766 5275
E info@entbiz.co.uk
W www.entbiz.co.uk

EUROPEAN THEATRE COMPANY THE
15 Beverley Avenue, London SW20 0RL
E admin@europeantheatre.co.uk
W www.europeantheatre.co.uk

EXCESS ALL AREAS LTD　T/F 020 7737 5300
1st & 2nd Floors, 20 Stansfield Road
Stockwell, London SW9 9RZ
E paul@excessallareas.co.uk
W www.excessallareas.co.uk

FACADE　T 020 8291 7079
Musicals
43A Garthorne Road, London SE23 1EP
F 020 8291 4969
E facade@cobomedia.com

FAIRBANK PRODUCTIONS　T/F 020 8555 3085
Contact: Gerald Armin
27 Harcourt Road, London E15 3DX
E info@fairbankproductions.co.uk
W www.fairbankproductions.co.uk

|Richard Jordan
|Productions Ltd

- Producing
- General Management
  UK and International Productions,
  and International Festivals
- Consultancy
- Richard Jordan Productions Ltd
  Mews Studios, 16 Vernon Yard
  London W11 2DX

  Tel:　　020 7243 9001
  Fax:　　020 7313 9667
  e-mail:　richard.jordan@virgin.net

FEATHER PRODUCTIONS LTD　T 020 8940 2335
Unit 3, Blade House
77 Petersham Road, Richmond
E anna@featherproductions.com
W www.featherproductions.com

FELL, Andrew LTD
E hq@andrewfell.co.uk

FERGUSON, Jason LTD　T 020 8876 2707
Contact: By e-mail
5 The Gallery, 6 North Road
Richmond, London TW9 4HA
F 020 8711 5662
E info@fergandco.com
W www.jason-ferguson.com

FIELD, Anthony ASSOCIATES LTD　T 020 7240 5453
Top Floor, 80-81 St Martin's Lane
London WC2N 4AA
F 020 7240 2947
E anthonyfieldassociates.com
W www.anthonyfieldassociates.com

FIERY ANGEL LTD　T 020 7907 7040
22-24 Torrington Place, London WC1E 7HJ
F 020 7436 6287
E mail@fiery-angel.com
W www.fiery-angel.com

FLYING ANGEL PRODUCTIONS LTD
277C Eastern Road, Brighton BN2 5TA
E info@pauldufer.com
W www.flyingangelproductions.com

FORBIDDEN THEATRE COMPANY　T 0845 0093084
20 Rupert Street, London W1D 6DF
E info@forbidden.org.uk
W www.forbidden.org.uk

FORD, Vanessa PRODUCTIONS LTD　T 01483 278203
Upper House Farm, Upper House Lane
Shamley Green, Surrey GU5 0SX
E vanessa@vanessafordproductions.co.uk
W www.thehobbittour.co.uk

FOSTER, Sharon PRODUCTIONS　T 0121 443 4865
15A Hollybank Road, Birmingham B13 0RF
E mail@sharonfoster.co.uk
W www.sharonfosterproductions.co.uk

FOX, Robert LTD　T 020 7584 6855
6 Beauchamp Place, London SW3 1NG
F 020 7225 1638
E info@robertfoxltd.com
W www.robertfoxltd.com

FRANK, Lina B. / AUSFORM
Circus. Dance. Live Arts. Theatre
Cube Cinema, Bristol BS2 8NQ
E lina@ausform.co.uk
W www.ausform.co.uk

FRANKLIN, Neil PRODUCTIONS   T 020 7720 3718
187 Drury Lane, London WC2B 5QD
E office@franklinproductions.co.uk

FREEDMAN, Bill LTD   T 020 7226 5554
Colebrooke House
10-12 Gaskin Street, London N1 2RY

FRESH GLORY PRODUCTIONS   T 020 7240 1941
59 St Martin's Lane, London WC2N 4JS
E info@freshglory.com
W www.freshglory.com

FRICKER, Ian (THEATRE) LTD   T 020 7836 3090
3rd Floor, 146 Strand, London WC2R 1JD
F 020 7836 3078
E mail@ianfricker.com
W www.ianfricker.com

**FRIEDMAN, Sonia
PRODUCTIONS**   T 020 7845 8750
Duke of York's Theatre
104 St Martin's Lane, London WC2N 4BG
F 020 7845 8759
E office@soniafriedman.com
W www.soniafriedman.com

**GALLEON THEATRE
COMPANY LTD**   T 020 8858 9256
Contact: Alice De Sousa
Greenwich Playhouse
Greenwich BR Station Forecourt
189 Greenwich High Road, London SE10 8JA
F 020 8310 7276
E boxoffice@galleontheatre.co.uk
W www.galleontheatre.co.uk

GBM PRODUCTIONS LTD   T 01837 871522
Bidlake Toft, Roadford Lake
Germansweek, Devon EX21 5BD
E gbm@bidlaketoft.com
W www.musicaltheatrecreations.com

GIANT STEPS LTD   T/F 020 8741 2446
41 Parfrey Street, London W6 9EW
T 07808 742307
E giantstepstheatre@googlemail.com
W www.rolandjaquarello.com

GINGERBEE PRODUCTIONS LTD   T 01522 837233
Sparkhouse Studios
Ropewalk, Lincoln, Lincs LN6 7DQ
F 01522 837201
E info@gingerbee.co.uk
W www.gingerbee.co.uk

GOOD NIGHT OUT PRESENTS   T 020 7226 8561
115 Upper Street
Islington, London N1 1QN
T 020 3286 8788
E info@kingsheadtheatre.com
W www.kingsheadtheatre.com

**GOODNIGHTS
ENTERTAINMENT LTD**   T 01908 672077
74 Pannier Place
Milton Keynes MK14 7QP
E goodnights@talk21.com
W www.goodnights.org

GOUCHER, Mark LTD   T 020 7438 9570
3rd Floor, 20-22 Stukeley Street, London WC2B 5LR
F 020 7438 9577
E jess@markgoucher.com

GRAEAE THEATRE COMPANY   T 020 7613 6900
Bradbury Studios
138 Kingsland Road, London E2 8DY
E info@graeae.org
W www.graeae.org

**GRAHAM, David
ENTERTAINMENT LTD**   T 0870 3211600
72 New Bond Street, London W1S 1RR
F 0870 3211700
E info@davidgraham.co.uk
W www.davidgrahamentertainment.com

**HAMPSTEAD THEATRE
PRODUCTIONS LTD**   T 020 7449 4200
Eton Avenue, Swiss Cottage
London NW3 3EU
F 020 7449 4201
E info@hampsteadtheatre.com
W www.hampsteadtheatre.com

HANDSTAND PRODUCTIONS   T 0151 708 7441
13 Hope Street, Liverpool L1 9BH
F 0151 709 3515
E info@handstand-uk.com
W www.handstand-uk.com

HARLEY PRODUCTIONS   T 020 7580 3247
68 New Cavendish Street, London W1G 8TE
F 020 8202 8863
E harleyprods@aol.com

HAYMARKET THE   T 01256 819797
c/o The Anvil Trust, Wote Street
Basingstoke, Hampshire RG21 7NW
F 01256 814845
E christine.bradwell@anvilarts.org.uk
W www.anvilarts.org.uk

HEADLONG THEATRE LTD   T 020 7478 0270
3rd Floor, 34-35 Berwick Street
London W1F 8RP
F 020 7438 1749
E info@headlongtheatre.co.uk
W www.headlongtheatre.co.uk

**HENDERSON, Glynis
PRODUCTIONS LTD**   T 020 7580 9644
69 Charlotte Street, London W1T 4PJ
F 020 7436 1489
E info@ghmp.co.uk
W www.ghmp.co.uk

**HENDRY, Jamie
PRODUCTIONS LTD**   T/F 020 7183 5630
20-22 Stukeley Street, 2nd Floor
Covent Garden, London WC2B 5LR
E office@jamiehendryproductions.com
W www.jamiehendryproductions.com

HENNEGAN, Nicholas LTD   T 020 8582 7506
33A Prebend Mansions
Chiswick High Road
London W4 2LU
E info@nicholashennegan.com
W www.nicholashennegan.com

HESTER, John PRODUCTIONS   T/F 020 8393 5705
Intimate Mysteries Theatre Company
105 Stoneleigh Park Road, Epsom
Surrey KT19 0RF
E hjohnhester@aol.com

HISS & BOO COMPANY LTD THE   T 01444 881707
Contact: Ian Liston. By Post (SAE). No unsolicited scripts
Nyes Hill, Wineham Lane
Bolney, West Sussex RH17 5SD
F 01444 882057
E email@hissboo.co.uk
W www.hissboo.co.uk

HISTORIA THEATRE COMPANY T 020 7837 8008
8 Cloudesley Square, London N1 0HT
T 07811 892079
E kateprice@lineone.net
W www.historiatheatre.com

HOIPOLLOI T 01223 322748
Office F, Dale's Brewery
Gwydir Street, Cambridge CB1 2LJ
E info@hoipolloi.org.uk
W www.hoipolloi.org.uk

HOLLOW CROWN T 07930 530948
2 Old Hall Farm, Halesworth Road
Reydon, Suffolk IP18 6SG
E enquiries@hollowcrown.co.uk
W www.hollowcrown.co.uk

HOLMAN, Paul
ASSOCIATES LTD T 020 8845 9408
Morritt House, 58 Station Approach
South Ruislip, Middlesex HA4 6SA
F 020 8839 3124
E enquiries@paulholmanassociates.co.uk
W www.paulholmanassociates.co.uk

HOLT, Thelma LTD T 020 7812 7455
Noel Coward Theatre, 85 St Martin's Lane
London WC2N 4AU
F 020 7812 7550
E thelma@dircon.co.uk
W www.thelmaholt.co.uk

HUGHES, Steve PRODUCTIONS T 07816 844024
70 Merrifield Court, Welwyn Garden City
Hertfordshire AL7 4SH
E info@hughes-productions.com
W www.hughes-productions.com

HULL TRUCK THEATRE T 01482 224800
50 Ferensway, Hull HU2 8LB
F 01482 581182
E admin@hulltruck.co.uk
W www.hulltruck.co.uk

HUMBLE THEATRE COMPANY LTD THE
24 Salisbury Close, Stotfold, Hitchin SG5 4FL
E info@humbletheatre.com
W www.humbletheatre.com

IAN, David PRODUCTIONS T 020 7257 6380
Third Floor, 33 Henrietta Street, London WC2E 8NA
F 020 7257 6381
E enquiries@davidianproductions.com
W www.davidianproductions.com

IBSEN STAGE COMPANY T 07958 566274
Flat 1, 1 Thurleigh Road, London SW12 8UB
E ask@ibsenstage.com
W www.ibsenstage.com

ICARUS THEATRE COLLECTIVE T 020 7998 1562
32 Portland Place, London W1B 1NA
E info@icarustheatre.co.uk
W www.icarustheatre.co.uk

IMAGE MUSICAL THEATRE T 020 8743 9380
23 Sedgeford Road, Shepherd's Bush, London W12 0NA
F 020 8749 9294
E brian@imagemusicaltheatre.co.uk
W www.imagemusicaltheatre.co.uk

INCISOR T 07979 498450
41 Edith Avenue, Peacehaven, East Sussex BN10 8JB
E sarahmann7@hotmail.co.uk
W www.theatre-company-incisor.com

INDIGO ENTERTAINMENTS T 01978 790211
Tynymynydd, Bryneglwys
Corwen, Denbighshire LL21 9NP
E info@indigoentertainments.com
W www.indigoentertainments.com

INGRAM, Colin LTD T 020 7038 3906
Suite 526, Linen Hall
162-168 Regent Street, London W1B 5TE
F 020 7038 3907
E info@coliningramltd.com
W www.coliningramltd.com

INSIDE INTELLIGENCE T/F 020 8986 8013
Theatre. Contemporary Opera. Music Theatre
13 Athlone Close, London E5 8HD
E admin@inside-intelligence.org.uk
W www.inside-intelligence.org.uk

INSTANT WIT T 0117 974 5734
Comedy Improvisation Theatre Show.
Corporate/Conference Entertainment Show.
Drama Based Training
6 Worrall Place, Worrall Road, Clifton, Bristol BS8 2WP
T 07711 644094
E info@instantwit.co.uk
W www.instantwit.co.uk

INTERNATIONAL THEATRE
& MUSIC LTD T 020 7470 8786
Contact: Piers Chater Robinson
Garden Studios, 11-15 Betterton Street
Covent Garden, London WC2H 9BP
F 020 7379 0801
E info@it-m.co.uk
W www.it-m.co.uk

JAM THEATRE COMPANY T 01628 487773
21 Beechtree Avenue, Marlow, Bucks SL7 3NH
E office@jamtheatre.co.uk
W www.jamtheatre.co.uk

JAMES, Bruce
PRODUCTIONS LTD T 07850 369018
10 Tillingham Way, Rayleigh, Essex SS6 9HF
E info@brucejamesproductions.co.uk
W www.brucejamesproductions.co.uk

JOHNSON, David T 020 7284 3733
85B Torriano Avenue, London NW5 2RX
E david@johnsontemple.co.uk

JOHNSON, Gareth LTD T 01239 891368
Plas Hafren, Eglwyswrw
Crymych, Pembrokeshire SA41 3UL
T 07700 225227
E gjltd@mac.com

JORDAN, Andy
PRODUCTIONS LTD T 07775 615205
Studio D, 413-419 Harrow Road
Maida Vale, London W9 3QJ
E andy@andyjordanproductions.co.uk

JORDAN, Richard
PRODUCTIONS LTD T 020 7243 9001
Mews Studios, 16 Vernon Yard, London W11 2DX
F 020 7313 9667
E richard.jordan@virgin.net

JORDAN PRODUCTIONS LTD T 01323 417745
Phoenix Auction Rooms, 142 Langney Road
Eastbourne, East Sussex BN22 8AQ
F 01323 417766
E info@jordanproductionsltd.co.uk

JQ PRODUCTIONS
Contact: James Quaife
E jamesquaife@gmail.com
W www.jamesquaife.com

KEAN PRODUCTIONS T 020 3151 2710
Communications House, 26 York Street
London W1U 6PZ
E info@keanprods.com
W www.keanprods.com

KELLY, Robert C. LTD T 0141 229 1444
The Alhambra Suite, 82 Mitchell Street
Glasgow G1 3NA
E office@robertckelly.co.uk
W www.robertckelly.co.uk

KENWRIGHT, Bill LTD T 020 7446 6200
BKL House, 1 Venice Walk, London W2 1RR
F 020 7446 6222
E info@kenwright.com
W www.kenwright.com

**LANGUAGE LAID BARE
PRODUCTIONS** T 07545 704016
Top Floor, 298 Brockley Road, London SE4 2RA
E languagelaidbare@yahoo.co.uk

LATCHMERE THEATRE T 020 7978 2620
Contact: Chris Fisher
Unit 5A, Spaces Business Centre
Ingate Place, London SW8 3NS
F 020 7978 2631
E latchmere@fishers.org.uk

LEIGH-PEMBERTON, David T 07814 726452
12 Tannery House, 6 Deal Street, London E1 5AG
E david@leigh-pemberton.co.uk
W www.davidleigh-pemberton.co.uk

LHP LTD T 07973 938634
PO Box 60231, London EC1P 1FL
E lhpltd@msn.com

LIMELIGHT PRODUCTIONS T 020 8853 9570
Unit 13, The io Centre, The Royal Arsenal
Seymour Street, London SE18 6SX
F 020 8853 9579
E enquiries@thelimelightgroup.co.uk

LINNIT PRODUCTIONS LTD T 020 7352 7722
123A King's Road, London SW3 4PL
F 020 7352 3450

LIVE THEATRE T 0191 261 2694
Broad Chare, Quayside
Newcastle upon Tyne NE1 3DQ
E info@live.org.uk
W www.live.org.uk

**LONDON BUBBLE
THEATRE COMPANY LTD** T 020 7237 4434
5 Elephant Lane, London SE16 4JD
E admin@londonbubble.org.uk
W www.londonbubble.org.uk

LONDON CLASSIC THEATRE T 020 8395 2095
The Production Office, 63 Shirley Avenue
Sutton, Surrey SM1 3QT
E admin@londonclassictheatre.co.uk
W www.londonclassictheatre.co.uk

LONDON PRODUCTIONS LTD T 020 7497 5111
PO Box 10703, London WC2H 9ED
F 020 7836 6968
E admin@leedean.co.uk

**LONDON REPERTORY
COMPANY** T/F 020 7258 1944
PO Box 59385, London NW8 1HL
E info@londonrepertorycompany.com
W www.londonrepertorycompany.com

MACKINTOSH, Cameron LTD T 020 7637 8866
Contact: Paul Wooller (Casting Assistant)
1 Bedford Square, London WC1B 3RB
F 020 7436 2683
E paul@camack.co.uk

MACNAGHTEN PRODUCTIONS T 01223 577974
19 Grange Court, Grange Road
Cambridge CB3 9BD

**MALCOLM, Christopher
PRODUCTIONS LTD** T 01225 832038
The Old Vicarage, South Stoke, Bath BA2 7DU
T 07850 555042
E cm@christophermalcolm.co.uk
W www.christophermalcolm.co.uk

MANS, Johnny PRODUCTIONS T 01992 470907
PO Box 196, Hoddesdon, Herts EN10 7WG
T 07974 755997
E johnnymansagent@aol.com
W www.johnnymansproductions.co.uk

**MASTERSON, Guy
PRODUCTIONS** T/F 01707 330360
The Hawthorne Auditorium, Campus West, The Campus
Welwyn Garden City, Herts AL8 6BX
E admin@theatretoursinternational.com
W www.theatretoursinternational.com

MEADOW, Jeremy LTD T 020 7436 2244
73 Great Titchfield Street, London W1W 6RD
F 0870 7627882
E info@jeremymeadow.com

MENZIES, Lee LTD T 020 7611 0050
2nd Floor, 20-22 Stukeley Street, London WC2B 5LR
F 020 7681 3670
E leemenzies@leemenzies.co.uk
W www.leemenzies.co.uk

**MIDDLE GROUND
THEATRE CO LTD** T 01684 577231
3 Gordon Terrace, Malvern Wells
Malvern, Worcestershire WR14 4ER
F 01684 574472
E middleground@middlegroundtheatre.co.uk
W www.middlegroundtheatre.co.uk

MITCHELL, Matthew LTD T/F 01273 842572
New Barn Farm, London Road
Hassocks, West Sussex BN6 9ND
E info@matthewmitchell.org

MJE PRODUCTIONS LTD T 020 7395 0260
Contact: Carole Winter, Michael Edwards
1st Floor, 18 Exeter Street
London WC2E 7DU
F 020 7395 0261
E info@mjeproductions.com
W www.mjeproductions.com

MMP T 020 7494 4007
4 D'Arblay Street, Soho, London W1F 8DJ
E mailbox@michaelmccabe.net
W www.michaelmccabe.net

MOKITAGRIT T 07980 564849
6 Addington Road, London N4 4RP
E mail@mokitagrit.com
W www.mokitagrit.com

MOVING THEATRE T 01323 815726
16 Laughton Lodge, Nr Lewes
East Sussex BN8 6BY
F 01323 815736
E info@movingtheatre.com
W www.movingtheatre.com

MUSIC THEATRE LONDON T 07831 243942
c/o Capriol Films, The Old Reading Room
The Street, Brinton
Melton Constable, Norfolk NR24 2QF
E info@capriolfilms.co.uk
W www.capriolfilms.co.uk

NADINE'S WINDOW
Theatre Company
E nadineswindow@yahoo.co.uk
W www.nadineswindow.com

NATIONAL ANGELS   T 020 7376 4878
123A Kings Road, London SW3 4PL
F 020 7352 3450
E admin@nationalangels.com

NATIONAL THEATRE   T 020 7452 3333
Upper Ground, South Bank
London SE1 9PX
F 020 7452 3344
W www.nationaltheatre.org.uk

NEAL STREET
PRODUCTIONS LTD   T 020 7240 8890
1st Floor, 26-28 Neal Street
London WC2H 9QQ
F 020 7240 7099
E post@nealstreetproductions.com

NEWPALM PRODUCTIONS   T 020 8349 0802
26 Cavendish Avenue, London N3 3QN
F 020 8346 8257
E newpalm@btopenworld.com
W www.newpalm.co.uk

NEW PERSPECTIVES
THEATRE COMPANY   T 0115 927 2334
Regional & National New Writing Touring Theatre
Park Lane Business Centre, Park Lane
Basford, Nottinghamshire NG6 0DW
E info@newperspectives.co.uk
W www.newperspectives.co.uk

NICHOLAS, Paul &
IAN, David ASSOCIATES LTD   T 020 7257 6380
c/o Third Floor, 33 Henrietta Street
London WC2E 8NA
F 020 7257 6381
E enquiries@davidianproductions.com

NITRO   T 020 7609 1331
6 Brewery Road, London N7 9NH
F 020 7609 1221
E info@nitro.co.uk
W www.nitro.co.uk

NORDIC NOMAD PRODUCTIONS   T 07980 619165
Contact: Tanja Raaste (Creative Producer). Specialising in New Writing, Site Specific & Interactive Work and Tango & Dance Events. Training & Workshops: Business Skills for Performers
64 Tulse Hill, London SW2 2PT
E info@nordicnomad.com
W www.nordicnomad.com

NORTHERN BROADSIDES
THEATRE COMPANY   T 01422 369704
Dean Clough, Halifax HX3 5AX
E sue@northern-broadsides.co.uk
W www.northern-broadsides.co.uk

NORTHERN STAGE (THEATRICAL
PRODUCTIONS) LTD   T 0191 242 7200
Barras Bridge, Newcastle upon Tyne NE1 7RH
F 0191 242 7257
E info@northernstage.co.uk
W www.northernstage.co.uk

NORTHUMBERLAND
THEATRE COMPANY (NTC)   T 01665 602586
The Playhouse, Bondgate Without
Alnwick, Northumberland NE66 1PQ
F 01665 605837
E admin@northumberlandtheatre.co.uk
W www.northumberlandtheatre.co.uk

OLD VIC PRODUCTIONS PLC   T 020 7928 2651
The Old Vic Theatre, The Cut
Waterloo, London SE1 8NB
F 020 7981 0991
E becky.barber@oldvictheatre.com

ONE NIGHT BOOKING
COMPANY THE   T 020 8455 3278
1 Hogarth Hill, London NW11 6AY
E mail@onenightbooking.com
W www.onenightbooking.com

OPERATING THEATRE
COMPANY   T 020 7419 2476
22 Burghley Road, London NW5 1UE
E info@operating-theatre.co.uk
W www.operating-theatre.co.uk

OUT OF JOINT   T 020 7609 0207
7 Thane Works, Thane Villas
London N7 7PH
F 020 7609 0203
E ojo@outofjoint.co.uk
W www.outofjoint.co.uk

OVATION   T 020 8340 4256
Upstairs at The Gatehouse, The Gatehouse
Highgate Village, London N6 4BD
F 020 8340 3466
E events@ovationproductions.com
W www.ovationtheatres.com

PAINES PLOUGH   T 020 7240 4533
4th Floor, 43 Aldwych, London WC2B 4DN
F 020 7240 4534
E office@painesplough.com
W www.painesplough.com

PAPATANGO THEATRE
COMPANY   T 07834 958804
37A Harold Road, London SE19 3PL
E papatango.theatre@gmail.com
W www.papatango.co.uk

PAPER MOON
THEATRE COMPANY   T/F 020 8873 1901
Specialising in Traditional Victorian Music Hall
6 Thames Meadow, West Molesey
Surrey KT8 1TQ
E jan@papermoontheatre.co.uk

PASSWORD PRODUCTIONS LTD   T 020 7284 3733
Contact: John Mackay
85B Torriano Avenue, London NW5 2RX
E johnmackay2001@aol.com

PENDLE PRODUCTIONS LTD   T 01253 839375
Bridge Farm, 249 Hawes Side Lane
Blackpool FY4 4AA
F 01253 792930
E admin@pendleproductions.co.uk
W www.pendleproductions.co.uk

PENTABUS THEATRE   T 01584 856564
Bromfield, Ludlow, Shropshire SY8 2JU
E john@pentabus.co.uk
W www.pentabus.co.uk

PEOPLE SHOW   T 020 7729 1841
People Show Studios, Pollard Row
London E2 6NB
F 020 7739 0203
E people@peopleshow.co.uk
W www.peopleshow.co.uk

PERFECT PITCH
MUSICALS LTD   T 020 7839 9003
5A Irving Street, London WC2H 7AT
E wendy@perfectpitchmusicals.com
W www.perfectpitchmusicals.com

PERFORMANCE BUSINESS THE   T 01932 888885
78 Oatlands Drive, Weybridge
Surrey KT13 9HT
E info@theperformance.biz
W www.theperformance.biz

PILOT THEATRE　　　　T 01904 635755
Performance Work Across Platforms & National Touring
York Theatre Royal, St Leonard's Place
York YO1 7HD
F 01904 656378
E info@pilot-theatre.com
W www.pilot-theatre.com

PLANTAGENET PRODUCTIONS　T 01635 253322
Drawing Room Recitals
Westridge Open Centre, Star Lane
Highclere, Nr Newbury RG20 9PJ

PLAYFUL PRODUCTIONS　　T 020 7811 4600
Haymarket House, 1 Oxendon Street
London SW1Y 4EE
F 020 7811 4622
E aboutus@playfuluk.com

**PLAYHOUSE ENTERTAINMENT
GROUP THE**　　　　T/F 01323 638980
Playhouse Studios
1st Floor, 104 Cavendish Place
Eastbourne, East Sussex BN21 3TZ
E enquiries@playhousecostumes.co.uk
W www.playhousecostumes.co.uk

PLUTO PRODUCTIONS LTD　T 020 7472 5800
New End Theatre, 27 New End
Hampstead, London NW3 1JD
F 020 7794 4044
E briandaniels@newendtheatre.co.uk
W www.newendtheatre.co.uk

POLKA THEATRE　　　　T 020 8545 8323
240 The Broadway, Wimbledon SW19 1SB
F 020 8545 8365
E stephen@polkatheatre.com
W www.polkatheatre.com

POPULAR PRODUCTIONS LTD　T 020 8347 0221
8A High Street, London N8 7PD
E info@popularproductions.com
W www.popularproductions.com

PORTER, Richard LTD　　T 07884 183404
214 Grange Road, London SE1 3AA
E office@richardporterltd.com
W www.richardporterltd.com

POSTER, Kim　　　　T 020 7240 3098
4th Floor, 80-81 St Martin's Lane
London WC2N 4AA
F 020 7504 8656
E admin@stanhopeprod.com

PROMENADE PRODUCTIONS　T 020 7240 3407
71 Endell Street, London WC2H 9AT
E mat@promenadeproductions.com
W www.promenadeproductions.com

PUGH, David & ROGERS Dafydd　T 020 7292 0390
Wyndhams Theatre, Charing Cross Road
London WC2H 0DA
F 020 7292 0399
E dpl@davidpughltd.com

**PURSUED BY A BEAR
PRODUCTIONS**　　　　T 01252 745445
Farnham Maltings, Bridge Square
Farnham GU9 7QR
E pursuedbyabear@yahoo.co.uk
W www.pursuedbyabear.co.uk

PW PRODUCTIONS LTD　　T 020 7395 7580
2nd Floor, 80-81 St Martin's Lane
London WC2N 4AA
F 020 7240 2947
E info@pwprods.co.uk
W www.pwprods.co.uk

QDOS ENTERTAINMENT　　T 01723 500038
Qdos House, Queen Margaret's Road
Scarborough, North Yorkshire YO11 2YH
F 01723 361958
E info@qdosentertainment.co.uk
W www.qdosentertainment.com

QUANTUM THEATRE　　　T 020 8317 9000
The Old Button Factory, 1-11 Bannockburn Road
Plumstead, London SE18 1ET
E office@quantumtheatre.co.uk
W www.quantumtheatre.co.uk

**RAGS & FEATHERS
THEATRE COMPANY**　　T 020 8224 2203
80 Summer Road, Thames Ditton
Surrey KT7 0QP
T 07958 724374
E jilldowning.tls@gmail.com

**RAIN OR SHINE
THEATRE COMPANY**　　T/F 01452 521575
25 Paddock Gardens, Longlevens
Gloucester GL2 0ED
E theatre@rainorshine.co.uk
W www.rainorshine.co.uk

**RATTLING TONGUE
THEATRE COMPANY**　　T 07817 697510
44 Fairfield South, Kingston Upon Thames
Surrey KT1 2UW
E info@rattlingtongue.com
W www.rattlingtongue.com

REAL CIRCUMSTANCE THEATRE COMPANY
22 Erle Harvard Road, West Bergholt
Colchester CO6 3BW
E info@realcircumstance.com
W www.realcircumstance.com

**REALLY USEFUL THEATRE
COMPANY THE**　　　T 020 7240 0880
22 Tower Street, London WC2H 9TW
F 020 7240 1293

RED ROOM THE　　　　T 020 7470 8790
The Garden Studios, 11-15 Betterton Street
Covent Garden, London WC2H 9BP
E info@theredroom.org.uk
W www.theredroom.org.uk

RED ROSE CHAIN　　　T 01473 603388
Gippeswyk Hall, Gippeswyk Avenue
Ipswich, Suffolk IP2 9AF
E info@redrosechain.co.uk
W www.redrosechain.co.uk

**RED SHIFT THEATRE
COMPANY**　　　　T/F 020 8540 1271
PO Box 60151, London SW19 2TB
E jane@redshifttheatreco.co.uk
W www.redshifttheatreco.co.uk

REGENT'S PARK THEATRE LTD　T 0844 3753460
Open Air Theatre
The Iron Works, Inner Circle
Regent's Park, London NW1 4NR
W www.openairtheatre.com

REVEAL THEATRE COMPANY LTD T 01782 294871
The Creative Village
Staffordshire University Business Village
72 Leek Road, Stoke on Trent ST4 2AR
E enquiries@revealtheatre.co.uk
W www.revealtheatre.co.uk

RGC PRODUCTIONS　　　T 07740 286727
260 Kings Road, Kingston, Surrey KT2 5HX
E info@rgcproductions.com
W www.rgcproductions.com

RHO DELTA LTD   T 020 7436 1392
Contact: Greg Ripley-Duggan
26 Goodge Street, London W1T 2QG
E info@ripleyduggan.com

ROCKET THEATRE   T 0161 969 1444
32 Baxter Road, Sale, Manchester M33 3AL
T 07788 723570
E martin@rockettheatre.co.uk
W www.rockettheatre.co.uk

ROGERS, Nick LTD   T 020 7100 1123
212 Strand, London WC2R 1AP
E info@nickrogerslimited.com
W www.nickrogerslimited.com

ROSE, Michael LTD   T 01202 522711
The Old Dairy, Throop Road
Holdenhurst, Bournemouth, Dorset BH8 0DL
F 01202 522311
E nicky@michaelroseltd.com

ROSE THEATRE, KINGSTON   T 020 8546 6983
Contact: Stephen Unwin (Artistic Director),
Lisa Lepki (PA to Artistic Director)
24-26 High Street
Kingston Upon Thames, Surrey KT1 1HL
F 020 8546 8783
E admin@rosetheatrekingston.org
W www.rosetheatrekingston.org

ROSENTHAL, Suzanna LTD   T/F 020 8340 4421
61 Talbot Road, London N6 4QX
E admin@suzannarosenthal.com

ROYAL COURT THEATRE
PRODUCTIONS LTD   T 020 7565 5050
Sloane Square, London SW1W 8AS
F 020 7565 5001
E info@royalcourttheatre.com
W www.royalcourttheatre.com

ROYAL EXCHANGE THEATRE   T 0161 833 9333
St Ann's Square, Manchester M2 7DH
W www.royalexchange.co.uk

ROYAL SHAKESPEARE
COMPANY   T 020 7845 0500
1 Earlham Street, London WC2H 9LL
F 020 7845 0505
W www.rsc.org.uk

ROYAL SHAKESPEARE
COMPANY   T 01789 296655
Royal Shakespeare Theatre, Waterside
Stratford-upon-Avon CV37 6BB
F 01789 272509
W www.rsc.org.uk

RUBINSTEIN, Mark LTD   T 020 7021 0787
25 Short Street, London SE1 8LJ
F 0870 7059731
E info@mrluk.com

SCAMP THEATRE LTD   T 01462 734843
Sutherland Callow Arts Management & Production
44 Church Lane, Arlesey, Beds SG15 6UX
T 07710 491111
E admin@scamptheatre.com
W www.scamptheatre.com

SCARLET THEATRE   T 020 8441 9779
Studio 4, The Bull, 68 High Street, Barnet, Herts EN5 5SJ
E admin@scarlettheatre.co.uk
W www.scarlettheatre.co.uk

SEABRIGHT PRODUCTIONS LTD   T 020 7439 1173
Palace Theatre, Shaftesbury Avenue, London W1D 5AY
F 020 7183 6023
E office@seabrightproductions.co.uk
W www.seabrightproductions.co.uk

SHAKESPEARE'S MEN   T 01708 222938
10 Dee Close, Upminster
Essex RM14 1QD
E terence@terencemustoo.com
W www.terencemustoo.com

SHARED EXPERIENCE   T 01865 305321
National & International Touring
13 Riverside House
27-29 Vauxhall Grove
London SW8 1SY
E admin@sharedexperience.org.uk
W www.sharedexperience.org.uk

SHOW OF STRENGTH   T 0117 902 0235
74 Chessel Street
Bedminster, Bristol BS3 3DN
E info@showofstrength.org.uk
W www.showofstrength.org.uk

SHOWCASE ENTERTAINMENTS
INTERNATIONAL LTD   T 01325 316224
Contact: Geoffrey J.L. Hindmarch (Executive Producer)
2 Lumley Close, Newton Aycliffe
Co Durham DL5 5PA
E gjl@showcaseproductions.co.uk
W www.showcaseproductions.co.uk

SIMPLY THEATRE   T 00 41 22 8600518
Chemin des Couleuvres 8B, 1295 Tannay
Switzerland 1295
E info@simplytheatre.com
W www.simplytheatre.com

SINDEN, Marc PRODUCTIONS   T 020 8455 3278
1 Hogarth Hill, London NW11 6AY
E mail@sindenproductions.com
W www.sindenproductions.com

SIXTEENFEET PRODUCTIONS   T 020 7326 4417
25 Rattray Road, London SW2 1AZ
T 07958 448690
E info@sixteenfeet.co.uk
W www.sixteenfeet.co.uk

SOHO THEATRE COMPANY   T 020 7287 5060
21 Dean Street, London W1D 3NE
F 020 7287 5061
W www.sohotheatre.com

SPARROW, Daniel &
WALSH, Mike PRODUCTIONS   T 020 7240 2720
1A Neal's Yard, London WC2H 9AW
T 07879 897900
E info@danielsparrowproductions.com
W www.danielsparrowproductions.com

SPHINX THEATRE COMPANY   T 01865 306321
13 Riverside House
27-29 Vauxhall Grove, London SW8 1SY
E info@sphinxtheatre.co.uk
W www.sphinxtheatre.co.uk

SPLATS ENTERTAINMENT   T 07944 283659
5 Denmark Street, London WC2H 8LP
E admin@splatsentertainment.co.uk
W www.splatsentertainment.co.uk

SPLITMOON THEATRE   T 020 7252 8126
PO Box 58891, London SE15 9DE
E info@splitmoontheatre.org
W www.splitmoontheatre.org

SQUAREDEAL
PRODUCTIONS LTD   T 020 7249 5966
Contact: Jenny Topper
24 De Beauvoir Square
London N1 4LE
F 020 7275 7553
E jenny@jennytopper.com

SQUIRES & JOHNS
PRODUCTIONS LTD   T 0871 2003343
Sullon Lodge, Sullon Side Lane
Garstang PR3 1GH
F 01253 407715
E info@squiresjohns.com
W www.squiresjohns.com

STAGE ENTERTAINMENT
UK LTD   T 020 7025 6970
6th Floor, Swan House, 52 Poland Street
London W1F 7NQ
F 020 7025 6971
W www.stage-entertainment.co.uk

STAGE FURTHER
PRODUCTIONS LTD   T 01323 739478
Westgate House, Stansted Road
Eastbourne, East Sussex BN22 8LG
F 01323 736127
E garthsfp@hotmail.co.uk

STANHOPE PRODUCTIONS LTD   T 020 7240 3098
4th Floor, 80-81 St Martin's Lane, London WC2N 4AA
F 020 7504 8656
E admin@stanhopeprod.com

STEPHENSON, Ian
PRODUCTIONS LTD   T 07960 999374
E soholondon@aol.com

STRAIGHT LINE PRODUCTIONS   T 020 8393 4220
58 Castle Avenue, Epsom, Surrey KT17 2PH
F 020 8393 8079
E hilary@straightlinemanagement.co.uk

TALAWA THEATRE COMPANY   T 020 7251 6644
Ground Floor, 53-55 East Road, London N1 6AH
F 020 7251 5969
E hq@talawa.com
W www.talawa.com

TAMASHA THEATRE COMPANY   T 020 7633 2270
Unit 220, Great Guildford Business Square
30 Great Guildford Street, London SE1 0HS
F 020 7021 0421
E info@tamasha.org.uk
W www.tamasha.org.uk

TBA MUSIC   T 0845 1203722
1 St Gabriels Road, London NW2 4DS
F 0700 607 0808
E peter@tbagroup.co.uk

TEG PRODUCTIONS LTD   T 020 7436 2244
73 Great Titchfield Street, London W1W 6RD
F 0870 7627882
E info@tegproductions.com

THAT'S ENTERTAINMENT
PRODUCTIONS   T 01903 263454
PO Box 4766, Worthing BN11 9NY
E info@thatsentertainmentproductions.co.uk
W www.thatsentertainmentproductions.co.uk

THEATRE ABSOLUTE   T 07799 292957
Shop Front Theatre, 38 City Arcade, Coventry
E info@theatreabsolute.co.uk
W www.theatreabsolute.co.uk

THEATRE ALIVE!
13 St Barnabas Road, London E17 8JZ
E theatrealive@tiscali.co.uk
W www.theatrealive.org.uk

THEATRE NORTH   T 01273 542518
22 Port Hall Place, Brighton BN1 5PN
T 07837 878732
E info@theatrenorth.co.uk
W www.theatrenorth.co.uk

THEATRE OF COMEDY
COMPANY LTD   T 020 7379 3345
Shaftesbury Theatre, 210 Shaftesbury Avenue
London WC2H 8DP
F 020 7836 8181
E info@shaftesburytheatre.com

THEATRE ROYAL HAYMARKET
PRODUCTIONS   T 020 7389 9669
Theatre Royal Haymarket, 18 Suffolk Street
London SW1Y 4HT
E nigel@trh.co.uk

THEATRE ROYAL
STRATFORD EAST   T 020 8534 0310
Gerry Raffles Square, Stratford
London E15 1BN
F 020 8534 8381
E theatreroyal@stratfordeast.com
W www.stratfordeast.com

THEATRE SANS FRONTIERES   T 01434 652484
Queen's Hall Arts Centre, Beaumont Street
Hexham NE46 3LS
F 01434 607206
E info@tsf.org.uk
W www.tsf.org.uk

THEATRE TOURS
INTERNATIONAL   T/F 01707 330360
Contact: Guy Masterson
The Hawthorne Auditorium
Campus West, The Campus
Welwyn Garden City, Herts AL8 6BX
E admin@theatretoursinternational.com
W www.theatretoursinternational.com

THEATRE WORKOUT LTD   T 020 8144 2290
13A Stratheden Road, Blackheath
London SE3 7TH
E enquiries@theatreworkout.co.uk
W www.theatreworkout.com

THEATREWORKS   T 01684 578342
2 Hanley Road, Malvern Wells
Worcs WR14 4PQ
E info@theatreworks.info
W www.theatreworks.info

TIATA FAHODZI   T/F 020 3538 6257
The Africa Centre, 38 King Street
London WC2E 8JT
E info@tiatafahodzi.com
W www.tiatafahodzi.com

TOLD BY AN IDIOT   T 020 7407 4123
Unit LF 1.7 Lafone House, The Leathermarket
11-13 Weston Street, London SE1 3ER
F 020 7407 9002
E info@toldbyanidiot.org
W www.toldbyanidiot.org

TOPPER, Jenny   T 020 7249 5966
SquaredDeal Productions Ltd
24 De Beauvoir Square
London N1 4LE
F 020 7275 7553
E jenny@jennytopper.com

TOWER THEATRE COMPANY   T/F 020 7353 5700
Full-time non-professional
St Bride Foundation, Bride Lane
London EC4Y 8EQ
E info@towertheatre.freeserve.co.uk
W www.towertheatre.org.uk

TREAGUS, Andrew ASSOCIATES LTD
32-33 St James's Place, London SW1A 1NR
E admin@at-assoc.co.uk

TRESTLE THEATRE COMPANY   **T** 01727 850950
Visual/Physical Theatre. Music. Choreography. New Writing
Trestle Arts Base, Russet Drive
Herts, St Albans AL4 0JQ
F 01727 855558
E admin@trestle.org.uk
W www.trestle.org.uk

TRICYCLE LONDON PRODUCTIONS   **T** 020 7372 6611
269 Kilburn High Road, London NW6 7JR
F 020 7328 0795
E admin@tricycle.co.uk
W www.tricycle.co.uk

TRIUMPH PROSCENIUM PRODUCTIONS LTD   **T** 020 7207 1301
18 Exeter Street, London WC2E 7DU
T 020 7379 4870

TURTLE KEY ARTS   **T** 020 8964 5060
Ladbroke Hall, 79 Barlby Road
London W10 6AZ
F 020 8964 4080
E admin@turtlekeyarts.org.uk
W www.turtlekeyarts.org.uk

TWO'S COMPANY   **T** 020 8299 4593
244 Upland Road, London SE22 0DN
F 020 8299 3714
E graham@2scompanytheatre.co.uk

UK ARTS INTERNATIONAL   **T** 01905 26424
1st Floor, 6 Shaw Street
Worcester WR1 3QQ
F 01905 22868
E janryan@ukarts.com
W www.ukarts.com

UK PRODUCTIONS LTD   **T** 01483 423600
Churchmill House, Ockford Road
Godalming, Surrey GU7 1QY
F 01483 418486
E mail@ukproductions.co.uk
W www.ukproductions.co.uk

UNRESTRICTED VIEW   **T** 020 7704 2001
Above Hen & Chickens Theatre Bar
109 St Paul's Road
London N1 2NA
E henandchickens@aol.com
W www.henandchickens.com

VANDER ELST Anthony PRODUCTIONS   **T** 020 8466 5580
The Studio, 14 College Road
Bromley, Kent BR1 3NS

VAYU NAIDU COMPANY   **T** 020 7720 0707
Storytellers & Actors
Unit C16, The Old Imperial Laundry
71 Warriner Gardens
Battersea, London SW11 4XW
E vayunaidu@vayunaiducompany.org.uk
W www.vayunaiducompany.org.uk

VOLCANO THEATRE COMPANY LTD   **T** 01792 464790
229 High Street, Swansea SA1 1NY
E mail@volcanotheatre.co.uk
W www.volcanotheatre.co.uk

WALKING FORWARD LTD   **T/F** 020 7359 5249
Studio 6, Aberdeen Centre
22-24 Highbury Grove
London N5 2EA
E info@walkingforward.co.uk
W www.walkingforward.co.uk

WALLACE Kevin LTD   **T** 020 7812 7238
27B Floral Street, London WC2E 9DP
F 020 7836 9587
E info@kevinwallace.co.uk

WAREHOUSE THEATRE COMPANY   **T** 020 8681 1257
Dingwall Road, Croydon CR0 2NF
F 020 8688 6699
E info@warehousetheatre.co.uk
W www.warehousetheatre.co.uk

WAX, Kenny LTD   **T** 020 7437 1736
3rd Floor, 25 Lexington Street
London W1F 9AG
F 020 3214 6063
W www.kennywax.com

WELDON, Duncan C. PRODUCTIONS LTD   **T** 020 7207 1301
1 Lumley Court, Off 402 The Strand
London WC2R 0NB

WEST END PROPERTY PRODUCTIONS   **T** 023 9263 7067
29 Creek Road, Hayling Island
Hampshire PO11 9QZ
F 023 9263 7264
E directaccounts@btconnect.com
W www.soultraders-themusical.com

WHITALL, Keith   **T** 01323 844882
25 Solway, Hailsham
East Sussex BN27 3HB

WHITEHALL, Michael   **T** 020 8785 3737
10 Lower Common South, London SW15 1BP
F 020 8788 2340
E mwhitehall@msn.com

WILLS, Newton MANAGEMENT   **T** 07989 398381
12 St Johns Road, Isleworth, Middlesex TW7 6NN
F 00 33 4 68218685
E newtoncttg@aol.com
W www.newtonwills.com

WORD & MUSIC COMPANY THE   **T** 020 8237 1080
Riverside Studios, Crisp Road
London W6 9RL
E info@associatedstudios.co.uk
W www.wordandmusiccompany.co.uk

WORK THE ROOM ENTERTAINMENTS LTD   **T** 020 7635 7083
Unit 2, The Wheelwright Building
125 Pomeroy Street, London SE14 5BT
E info@worktherooments.co.uk
W www.worktherooments.co.uk

WORTMAN UK / POLESTAR PICTURES   **T** 020 8994 8886
Theatre & Film Productions
48 Chiswick Staithe, London W4 3TP
T 07976 805976
E neville@speakwell.co.uk
W www.speakwell.co.uk

YELLOW EARTH THEATRE   **T** 020 7734 5988
3rd Floor, 20 Rupert Street
London W1D 6DF
E artisticdirector@yellowearth.org
W www.yellowearth.org

YOUNG VIC THEATRE   **T** 020 7922 2800
66 The Cut, London SE1 8LZ
F 020 7922 2801
E info@youngvic.org
W www.youngvic.org

1623 THEATRE COMPANY   T 01332 285434
See Shakespeare Differently
QUAD, Market Place
Cathedral Quarter, Derby DE1 3AS
E messages@1623theatre.co.uk
W www.1623theatre.co.uk

ABERYSTWYTH ARTS CENTRE   T 01970 621512
Penglais, Aberystwyth
Ceredigion SY23 3DE
F 01970 622883
E ggo@aber.ac.uk
W www.aber.ac.uk/artscentre

ADMIRATION THEATRE   T 07010 041579
Based in London E1
E email@admirationtheatre.com
W www.admirationtheatre.com

**AGE EXCHANGE
THEATRE TRUST**   T 020 8318 9105
*Contact: Suzanne Lockett (Director of
Training & Support Services)*
The Reminiscence Centre
11 Blackheath Village
London SE3 9LA
E administrator@age-exchange.org.uk
W www.age-exchange.org.uk

ALTERNATIVE ARTS   T 020 7375 0441
Top Studio, Montefiore Centre
Hanbury Street, London E1 5HZ
F 020 7375 0484
E info@alternativearts.co.uk
W www.alternativearts.co.uk

ANGLES THEATRE THE   T 01945 585587
Alexandra Road, Wisbech
Cambridgeshire PE13 1HQ
F 01945 581967
E ratz@anglestheatre.co.uk

ARUNDEL JAILHOUSE   T/F 01903 889821
Arundel Town Hall, Arundel
West Sussex BN18 9AP
E info@arundeljailhouse.co.uk
W www.arundeljailhouse.co.uk

ASHTON GROUP THEATRE THE   T 01229 430636
The Old Fire Station, Abbey Road
Barrow-in-Furness, Cumbria LA14 1XH
E theashtongroup@btconnect.com
W www.ashtongroup.co.uk

ATTIC THEATRE COMPANY   T 020 8640 6800
Mitcham Library, 157 London Road
Mitcham CR4 2YR
E info@attictheatrecompany.com
W www.attictheatrecompany.com

BANNER THEATRE   T 0845 4581909
Oaklands New Church Centre, Winleigh Road
Handsworth Wood, Birmingham B20 2HN
E info@bannertheatre.co.uk

BECK THEATRE   T 020 8561 7506
Grange Road, Hayes
Middlesex UB3 2UE
T 020 8561 8371
E enquiries@becktheatre.org.uk
W www.becktheatre.org.uk

**BENT BACK TULIPS
THEATRE COMPANY**   T 07971 159940
59B Crystal Palace Road
Crystal Palace, London SE26 6UT
E info@bentbacktulips.com
W www.bentbacktulips.com

BISHOPS GREAVES THEATRE   T 01522 583761
Bishop Grosseteste University College, Newport
Lincoln, Lincolnshire, LN1 3DY
E theatre@bishopg.ac.uk
W www.bishopg.ac.uk/theatre

BLANK PAGES
Double-bills of New Writing put on in Feb, May, Aug & Nov
89 Birchanger Lane, Bishop Stortford CM23 5QF
E contactblankpages@gmail.com
W www.wix.com/blankpages1/blankpages

**BLUEYED THEATRE
PRODUCTIONS**   T 07799 137487
59B Crystal Palace Park Road, London SE26 6UT
T 07971 159940
E info@blueyedtheatreproductions.co.uk
W www.blueyedtheatreproductions.co.uk

**BLUNDERBUS THEATRE
COMPANY LTD**   T 01636 678900
The Studio, The Palace Theatre
Appletongate, Newark, Notts NG24 1JY
E admin@blunderbus.co.uk
W www.blunderbus.co.uk

**CAPITAL ARTS YOUTH
THEATRE**   T/F 020 8449 2342
Wyllyotts Centre, Darkes Lane
Potters Bar, Herts EN6 2HN
T 07885 232414
E capitalarts@btconnect.com
W www.capitalarts.org.uk

CARIB THEATRE COMPANY   T/F 020 8903 4592
73 Lancelot Road, Wembley
Middlesex HA0 2AN
E antoncarib@yahoo.co.uk

**CENTRE FOR PERFORMANCE
RESEARCH**   T 01970 622133
The Foundry, Parry Williams, Penglais Campus SY23 3AJ
F 01970 622132
E info@thecpr.org.uk
W www.thecpr.org.uk

**CHAIN REACTION
THEATRE COMPANY**   T/F 020 8534 0007
Three Mills Studios, Sugar House Yard
Sugar House Lane, London E15 2QS
E mail@chainreactiontheatre.co.uk
W www.chainreactiontheatre.co.uk

CHALKFOOT THEATRE ARTS
c/o Channel Theatre Productions Ltd
Penistone House, 5 High Street
St Lawrence, Ramsgate, Kent CT11 0QH
E info@chalkfoot.org.uk
W www.chalkfoot.org.uk

CHATS PALACE   T 020 8533 0227
42-44 Brooksby's Walk, Hackney, London E9 6DF
E info@chatspalace.com
W www.chatspalace.co.uk

CHICKENSHED   T 020 8351 6161
Chase Side, Southgate, London N14 4PE
F 020 8292 0202
E susanj@chickenshed.org.uk
W www.chickenshed.org.uk

CHOL THEATRE   T 01484 536008
Contact: Susan Burns (Director)
Lawrence Batley Theatre, 8 Queen Street
Huddersfield, West Yorkshire HD1 2SP
F 01484 425336
E info@choltheatre.co.uk
W www.choltheatre.co.uk

Theatre

There are hundreds of theatres in the UK, varying dramatically in size and type. The theatre sections are organised under headings which best indicate a theatre's principal area of work. A summary of each of these is below.

Alternative & Community

Many of these companies tour to Arts Centres, small and middle-scale theatres, and non-theatrical venues which do not have a resident company, or they may be commissioned to develop site-specific projects. The term 'alternative' is sometimes used to describe work that is more experimental in style and execution.

Children's, Young People's & TIE

The primary focus of these theatre companies is to reach younger audiences. They often tour to smaller theatres, schools and non-theatrical venues. Interactive teaching - through audience participation and workshops - is often a feature of their work.

English Speaking Theatre Companies in Europe

These work principally outside of the UK. Some are based in one venue whilst others are touring companies. Their work varies enormously and includes Young People's Theatre, large scale musicals, revivals of classics and dinner theatre. Actors are employed either for an individual production or a 'season' of several plays.

London Theatres

Larger theatres situated in the West End and Central London. A few are producing houses, but most are leased to Theatre Producers who take responsibility for putting together a company for a run of a single show. In such cases it is they and not the venue who cast productions (often with the help of Casting Directors). Alternatively, a production will open outside London and tour to Provincial Theatres, then subsequently, if successful, transfer to a London venue.

Outer London, Fringe & Venues

Small and middle-scale theatres in Outer London and around the country. Some are producing houses, others are only available for hire. Many of the London venues have provided useful directions on how they may be reached by public transport.

Provincial / Touring

Theatre Producers and other companies sell their ready-made productions to the Provincial/Touring Theatres, a list of larger venues outside London. A run in each theatre varies between a night and several weeks, but a week per venue for tours of plays is usual. Even if a venue is not usually a producing house, most Provincial Theatres and Arts Centres put on a family show at Christmas.

Puppet Theatre Companies

Some Puppet Theatres are one-performer companies who literally create their own work from scratch. The content and style of productions varies enormously. For example, not all are aimed at children, and some are more interactive than others. Although we list a few theatres with Puppet Companies in permanent residence, this kind of work often involves touring. As with all small and middle scale touring, performers who are willing, and have the skills, to involve themselves with all aspects of company life are always more valuable.

Repertory (Regional) Theatres

Theatres situated outside London which employ a resident company of actors (i.e. the 'repertory company') on a play-by-play basis or for a season of several plays. In addition to the main auditorium (usually the largest acting space) these theatres may have a smaller studio theatre attached, which will be home to an additional company whose focus is education or the production of new plays (see 'Theatre: Children's, Young People's & TIE'). In recent years the length of repertory seasons has become shorter; this means that a number of productions are no longer in-house. It is common for gaps in the performance calendar to be filled by tours mounted by Theatre Producers, other Repertory (Regional) Theatres and non-venue based production companies.

**CLOSE FOR COMFORT
THEATRE COMPANY**   T 07710 258290
34 Boleyn Walk, Leatherhead, Surrey KT22 7HU
T 01372 378613
E close4comf@aol.com
W www.closeforcomforttheatre.co.uk

**COMPLETE WORKS
CREATIVE COMPANY LTD THE**   T 020 7377 0280
The Old Truman Brewery, 91 Brick Lane
London E1 6QL
F 020 7247 7405
E jacinta@tcw.org.uk
W www.tcw.org.uk

**CORNELIUS & JONES
ORIGINAL PRODUCTIONS**   T/F 01908 612593
49 Carters Close, Sherington
Newport Pagnell, Buckinghamshire MK16 9NW
E admin@corneliusjones.com
W www.corneliusjones.com

CUT-CLOTH THEATRE   T 020 7503 4393
41 Beresford Road, Highbury
London N5 2HR
T 07950 542346

EALDFAEDER   T 01787 238257
Anglo Saxon Living History & Re-enactment
12 Carleton Close, Great Yeldham
Essex CO9 4QJ
E pete@gippeswic.demon.co.uk
W www.ealdfaeder.org

ELAN WALES   T/F 029 2019 0077
European Live Arts Network
17 Douglas Buildings, Royal Stuart Lane
Cardiff CF10 5EL
E elanwales@ntlbusiness.com
W www.elanwales.org

ELECTRIC CABARET   T 01280 700956
107 High Street, Brackley, Northants NN13 7BN
T 07714 089763
E richard@electriccabaret.co.uk
W www.electriccabaret.co.uk

EUROPEAN THEATRE COMPANY THE
15 Beverley Avenue, London SW20 0RL
E admin@europeantheatre.co.uk
W www.europeantheatre.co.uk

**FEMME FATALE
THEATRE COMPANY**   T 07779 611414
30 Creighton Avenue, Muswell Hill
London N10 1NU
E dianelefley@yahoo.com
W www.femmefataletheatrecompany.com

**FOREST FORGE
THEATRE COMPANY**   T 01425 470188
The Theatre Centre, Endeavour Park, Crow Arch Lane
Ringwood, Hampshire BH24 1SF
F 01425 471158
E info@forestforge.co.uk
W www.forestforge.co.uk

FOUND THEATRE   T 01629 813083
The Byways, Church Street
Monyash, Derbyshire DE45 1JH
E found_theatre@yahoo.co.uk
W www.foundtheatre.org.uk

FOURSIGHT THEATRE LTD   T 01902 714257
Newhampton Arts Centre, Dunkley Street
Wolverhampton WV1 4AN
F 01902 428413
E admin@foursighttheatre.co.uk
W www.foursighttheatre.co.uk

FRANTIC THEATRE COMPANY   T/F 0870 1657350
32 Woodlane, Falmouth TR11 4RF
E bookings@frantictheatre.com
W www.frantictheatre.com

**GALLEON THEATRE
COMPANY LTD**   T 020 8858 9256
Greenwich Playhouse, Greenwich BR Station Forecourt
189 Greenwich High Road, London SE10 8JA
F 020 8310 7276
E alice@galleontheatre.co.uk
W www.galleontheatre.co.uk

GOOD NIGHT OUT PRESENTS   T 020 7226 8561
Contact: Adam Spreadbury-Maher (Artistic Director)
115 Upper Street, Islington, London N1 1QN
T 020 3286 8788
E info@kingsheadtheatre.com
W www.kingsheadtheatre.com

GRANGE ARTS CENTRE   T 0161 785 4239
Rochdale Road, Oldham
Greater Manchester OL9 6EA
F 0161 785 4263
E grangearts@oldham.ac.uk
W www.grangeartsoldham.co.uk

GREASEPAINT ANONYMOUS   T 020 8886 2263
Youth Theatre Company
4 Gallus Close, Winchmore Hill
London N21 1JR
F 020 8882 9189
E info@greasepaintanonymous.co.uk

HALL FOR CORNWALL   T 01872 321970
Contact: Suzanne Death (Creative Learning Administrator)
Back Quay, Truro
Cornwall TR1 2LL
E admin@hallforcornwall.org.uk
W www.hallforcornwall.co.uk

HIJINX THEATRE   T 029 2030 0331
*Touring Theatre Company. Community.
Adults with Learning Disabilities*
Wales Millennium Centre, Bute Place
Cardiff CF10 5AL
F 029 2063 5621
E info@hijinx.org.uk
W www.hijinx.org.uk

HISTORIA THEATRE COMPANY   T 020 7837 8008
8 Cloudesley Square, London N1 0HT
T 07811 892079
E kateprice@lineone.net
W www.historiatheatre.com

ICON THEATRE   T 01634 813179
The Brook Theatre, Old Town Hall
Chatham, Kent ME4 4SE
E nancy@icontheatre.org.uk
W www.icontheatre.org.uk

IMAGE MUSICAL THEATRE   T 020 8743 9380
23 Sedgeford Road, Shepherd's Bush
London W12 0NA
F 020 8749 9294
E brian@imagemusicaltheatre.co.uk
W www.imagemusicaltheatre.co.uk

IMMEDIATE THEATRE   T 020 7012 1677
1.2 Hoxton Works, 128 Hoxton Street
London N1 6SH
E info@immediate-theatre.com
W www.immediate-theatre.com

INOCENTE ART & FILM LTD   T 07973 518132
Film. Multimedia. Music Videos. Two Rock 'n' Roll Musicals
Flat 2, 76 Highdown Road, Hove BN3 6EB
E tarascas@btopenworld.com

ISOSCELES T 020 8946 3905
7 Amity Grove, Raynes Park
London SW20 0LQ
E patanddave@isosceles.biz
W www.isosceles.biz

KNUTSFORD CIVIC CENTRE T 01565 633005
Cheshire East Council
Toft Road, Knutsford
Cheshire WA16 0PE
E knutsfordcinema@cheshireeast.gov.uk
W www.cheshireeast.gov.uk/cinemas

KOMEDIA T 01273 647101
44-47 Gardner Street, Brighton BN1 1UN
F 01273 647102
E info@komedia.co.uk
W www.komedia.co.uk

KORU THEATRE T 020 8579 1029
11 Clovelly Road, London W5 5HF
E info@korutheatre.com
W www.korutheatre.com

**LADDER TO THE
MOON ENTERTAINMENT** T 020 7228 9700
Unit 105, Battersea Business Centre
99-109 Lavender Hill, London SW11 5QL
E info@laddertothemoon.co.uk

LIVE THEATRE T 0191 261 2694
New Writing
Broad Chare, Quayside
Newcastle upon Tyne NE1 3DQ
F 0191 232 2224
E info@live.org.uk
W www.live.org.uk

**LONDON ACTORS
THEATRE COMPANY** T 020 7978 2620
Unit 5A, Imex Business Centre
Ingate Place, London SW8 3NS
F 020 7978 2631
E latchmere@fishers.org.uk

**LONDON BUBBLE
THEATRE COMPANY LTD** T 020 7237 4434
5 Elephant Lane, London SE16 4JD
E admin@londonbubble.org.uk
W www.londonbubble.org.uk

**LONG OVERDUE
THEATRE COMPANY THE** T 07870 832562
16 Butterfield Drive, Amesbury
Wiltshire SP4 7SJ
E admin@longoverdue.co.uk
W www.longoverdue.co.uk

LSW JUNIOR INTER-ACT T/F 020 7793 9755
PO Box 31855, London SE17 3XP
E londonswo@hotmail.com
W www.londonshakespeare.org.uk

LSW PRISON PROJECT T/F 020 7793 9755
PO Box 31855, London SE17 3XP
E londonswo@hotmail.com
W www.lswproductions.co.uk

LSW SENIOR RE-ACTION T/F 020 7793 9755
PO Box 31855, London SE17 3XP
E londonswo@hotmail.com
W www.lswproductions.co.uk

M6 THEATRE COMPANY T 01706 355898
Studio Theatre, Hamer CP School
Albert Royds Street, Rochdale OL16 2SU
F 01706 712601
E info@m6theatre.co.uk
W www.m6theatre.co.uk

MADDERMARKET THEATRE T 01603 626560
*Resident Community Theatre Company. Small-Scale
Producing & Receiving House*
St John's Alley, Norwich NR2 1DR
E mmtheatre@btconnect.com
W www.maddermarket.co.uk

MAGIC HAT PRODUCTIONS T 07769 560991
Brookslee, Brookshill Drive
Harrow HA3 6SB
E general@magichat-productions.com
W www.magichat-productions.com

**MANCHESTER
ACTORS COMPANY** T 0161 227 8702
PO Box 54, Manchester M60 7AB
E dramaticnights@aol.com
W www.manactco.org.uk

**MAVERICK THEATRE
COMPANY LTD** T 0121 444 0933
12 Lydney Grove, Northfield
Birmingham, West Midlands B31 1RB
T 07531 138248
E info@mavericktheatre.co.uk
W www.mavericktheatre.co.uk

**MIKRON THEATRE
COMPANY LTD** T 01484 843701
Marsden Mechanics, Peel Street
Marsden, Huddersfield HD7 6BW
E admin@mikron.org.uk
W www.mikron.org.uk

MONTAGE THEATRE ARTS T 020 8692 7007
Contact: Judy Gordon (Artistic Director)
The Albany, Douglas Way
London SE8 4AG
E office@montagetheatre.com
W www.montagetheatre.com

NATURAL THEATRE COMPANY T 01225 469131
Street Theatre. Touring. Corporate
Widcombe Institute
Widcombe Hill, Bath BA2 6AA
E info@naturaltheatre.co.uk
W www.naturaltheatre.co.uk

**NET CURTAINS
THEATRE COMPANY** T 07968 564687
Contact: Claire Farrington (Artistic Director)
Scurms, Rye Road, Sandhurst, Kent TN18 5PQ
E claire@netcurtains.org
W www.netcurtains.org

NETTLEFOLD THE T 020 7926 8070
West Norwood Library Centre
1 Norwood High Street, London SE27 9JX
E thenettlefold@lambeth.gov.uk

**NEW PERSPECTIVES
THEATRE COMPANY** T 0115 927 2334
Regional/National New Writing Touring Theatre
Park Lane Business Centre, Park Lane
Basford, Nottinghamshire NG6 0DW
E info@newperspectives.co.uk
W www.newperspectives.co.uk

NEWFOUND THEATRE COMPANY
Contact: By Post/e-mail
E newfoundtheatre@gmail.com
W www.newfoundtheatre.com

NORTH COUNTRY THEATRE T 01748 825288
3 Rosemary Lane, Richmond
North Yorkshire DL10 4DP
E office@northcountrytheatre.com
W www.northcountrytheatre.com

**NORTHERN STAGE (THEATRICAL
PRODUCTIONS) LTD**   T 0191 242 7200
Barras Bridge, Newcastle upon Tyne NE1 7RH
F 0191 242 7257
E info@northernstage.co.uk
W www.northernstage.co.uk

**NORTHUMBERLAND
THEATRE COMPANY (NTC)**   T 01665 602586
Touring Regionally & Nationally
The Playhouse, Bondgate Without
Alnwick, Northumberland NE66 1PQ
F 01665 605837
E admin@northumberlandtheatre.co.uk
W www.northumberlandtheatre.co.uk

NUDGE PRODUCTIONS LTD   T 07525 939250
32A Stradbroke Road, Pakefield
Lowesloft, Suffolk NR33 7HT
E info@nudge-productions.com
W www.nudge-productions.com

NUFFIELD THEATRE   T 023 8031 5500
Projects. Touring
University Road, Southampton SO17 1TR
F 023 8031 5511
E annie.reilly@nuffieldtheatre.co.uk
W www.nuffieldtheatre.co.uk

**OLD TYME PLAYERS
THEATRE COMPANY**   T 01425 612830
Music Hall. Revues. Locally Based
35 Barton Court Avenue
Barton on Sea, Hants BH25 7EP
E oldetymeplayers@tiscali.co.uk
W www.oldtymeplayers.co.uk

OPEN STAGE PRODUCTIONS   T/F 0121 777 9086
49 Springfield Road, Moseley
Birmingham B13 9NN
E info@openstage.co.uk
W www.openstage.co.uk

**OXFORDSHIRE THEATRE
COMPANY**   T 01865 249444
The Annexe, SS Mary & John School
Meadow Lane, Oxford OX4 1TJ
F 01865 247266
E info@oxfordshiretheatrecompany.co.uk
W www.oxfordshiretheatrecompany.co.uk

PASCAL THEATRE COMPANY   T 020 7383 0920
35 Flaxman Court, Flaxman Terrace
Bloomsbury, London WC1H 9AR
E pascaltheatreco@aol.com
W www.pascal-theatre.com

PENS PEOPLE   T 01708 457443
75 Victor Walk, Hornchurch
Essex RM12 4XQ
E penny@penspeople.co.uk
W www.penspeople.co.uk

**PEOPLE'S THEATRE
COMPANY THE**   T 01784 470439
12E High Street, Egham
Surrey TW20 9EA
E admin@ptc.org.uk
W www.ptc.org.uk

PHANTOM CAPTAIN THE   T 020 8455 4564
618B Finchley Road, London NW11 7RR
E lambhorn@gmail.com
W www.phantomcaptain.netfirms.com

PLAYTIME THEATRE COMPANY   T 01227 266272
18 Bennells Avenue, Whitstable, Kent CT5 2HP
F 01227 266648
E playtime@dircon.co.uk
W www.playtimetheatre.co.uk

**POWERHOUSE
THEATRE COMPANY**   T 01483 444787
Contact: Geoff Lawson (Artistic Director)
The Electric Theatre, Onslow Street, Guildford GU1 4SZ
T 07949 821567
E powerhousetheatre@hotmail.co.uk
W www.powerhousetheatre.co.uk

POWYS ART   T 01597 824444
The Drama Centre, Tremont Road
Llandrindod Wells, Powys LD1 5EB
F 01597 824381
E lucy.bevan@powys.gov.uk
W www.theatrpowys.co.uk

PRIME PRODUCTIONS   T/F 0131 449 4055
54 Hermiston Village, Currie EH14 4AQ
E primeproductions@talktalk.net
W www.primeproductions.co.uk

PROTEUS THEATRE COMPANY   T 01256 354541
Multimedia & Cross-art Form Work
Queen Mary's College, Cliddesden Road
Basingstoke, Hampshire RG21 3HF
E info@proteustheatre.com
W www.proteustheatre.com

**PURSUED BY A
BEAR PRODUCTIONS**   T 01252 745445
Farnham Maltings, Bridge Square, Farnham GU9 7QR
E pursuedbyabear@yahoo.co.uk
W www.pursuedbyabear.co.uk

Q20 THEATRE LTD   T 0845 1260632
Dockfield Road, Shipley, West Yorkshire BD17 7AD
E info@q20theatre.co.uk

**RIDING LIGHTS
THEATRE COMPANY**   T 01904 655317
Friargate Theatre, Lower Friargate, York YO1 9SL
F 01904 651532
E info@rltc.org
W www.ridinglights.org

SALTMINE THEATRE COMPANY   T 01384 454807
61 The Broadway, Dudley DY1 3EB
E creative@saltmine.org
W www.saltminetrust.org.uk

SCRATCH PRODUCTIONS   T/F 01278 458253
20 Sandpiper Road, Blakespool Park
Bridgwater, Somerset TA6 5QU
E info@bluemoontheatre.co.uk

SPANNER IN THE WORKS   T 020 7193 7995
PO Box 239, Sidcup DA15 0DP
T 07850 313986
E info@spannerintheworks.org.uk
W www.spannerintheworks.org.uk

SPARE TYRE   T/F 020 7061 6454
*Contact: Bonnie Mitchell (General Manager). Theatre
Without Prejudice. For performers who are female, older or
have learning disabilities*
Unit 3.22, Canterbury Court, Kennington Park
1-3 Brixton Road, London SW9 6DE
E info@sparetyre.org
W www.sparetyre.org

SPECTACLE THEATRE T 01443 430700
Coleg Morgannwg Rhondda
Llwynypia, Tonypandy CF40 2TQ
F 01443 439640
E info@spectacletheatre.co.uk
W www.spectacletheatre.co.uk

SPONTANEITY SHOP THE T 020 7788 4080
85-87 Bayham Street, London NW1 0AG
E info@the-spontaneity-shop.com
W www.the-spontaneity-shop.com

ST JOHN'S CHURCH T 020 7633 9819
Hosts Classical Concerts, Conferences,
Large Meetings & Lectures
Waterloo Road, Southbank
London SE1 8TY
E lorrainespenceley@hotmail.com
W www.stjohnswaterloo.co.uk

TAG CITIZENS T 0141 429 5561
Citizens' Theatre, 119 Gorbals Street
Glasgow G5 9DS
F 0141 429 7374
E info@citz.co.uk
W www.citz.co.uk

**TAKING FLIGHT
THEATRE COMPANY** T 029 2022 6072
31 Brunswick Street
Canton, Cardiff CF5 1LH
E takingflighttheatre@yahoo.co.uk
W www.takingflighttheatre.com

TARA ARTS GROUP T 020 8333 4457
356 Garratt Lane, London SW18 4ES
F 020 8870 9540
E tara@tara-arts.com
W www.tara-arts.com

THEATRE& LTD T 01484 532967
Church Hall, St James Road
Marsh, Huddersfield HD1 4QA
F 01484 532962
E cmitchell@theatreand.com
W www.theatreand.com

THEATRE & FILM WORKSHOP T 0131 555 3854
Out of the Blue Drill Hall
36 Dalmeny Street, Edinburgh EH6 8RG
W www.theatre-workshop.com

THEATRE IS... T 01582 481221
The Hat Factory, 65-67 Bute Street
Luton, Bedfordshire LU1 2EY
E info@theatreis.org
W www.theatreis.org

THEATRE OF LITERATURE THE T 020 7633 0599
Dramatised Readings
51 The Cut, London SE1 8LF
E info@calderpublications.com

THEATRE PECKHAM T 020 7708 5401
Havil Street, London SE5 7SD
E admin@theatrepeckham.co.uk
W www.theatrepeckham.co.uk

TOBACCO FACTORY THEATRE T 0117 902 0345
Raleigh Road
Southville, Bristol BS3 1TF
E theatre@tobaccofactory.com
W www.tobaccofactorytheatre.com

**TRAFFORD
MARGARETIANS AOS** T 0161 718 5398
2 Shows per year. Monday Rehearsals
5 Newgate Road, Sale, Cheshire M33 4NQ
T 07980 931345
E tmaos@hotmail.co.uk
W www.tmaos.co.uk

TRICYCLE THEATRE T 020 7372 6611
269 Kilburn High Road, London NW6 7JR
F 020 7328 0795
E admin@tricycle.co.uk
W www.tricycle.co.uk

**WAREHOUSE THEATRE
COMPANY** T 020 8681 1257
Dingwall Road, Croydon CR0 2NF
F 020 8688 6699
E info@warehousetheatre.co.uk
W www.warehousetheatre.co.uk

**WINCHESTER HAT FAIR, FESTIVAL
OF STREET THEATRE** T 01962 849841
5A Jewry Street, Winchester, Hampshire SO23 8RZ
E info@hatfair.co.uk
W www.hatfair.co.uk

**WOMEN & THEATRE
BIRMINGHAM LTD** T 0121 449 7117
The Old Lodge, Uffculme, 50 Queensbridge Road
Moseley, Birmingham B13 8QY
F 0121 449 0785
E info@womenandtheatre.co.uk

**Y TOURING THEATRE
COMPANY** T 020 7520 3090
One KX, 120 Cromer Street, London WC1H 8BS
E d.jackson@ytouring.org.uk
W www.theatreofdebate.com

YELLOW EARTH THEATRE T 020 7734 5988
3rd Floor, 20 Rupert Street, London W1D 6DF
E admin@yellowearth.org
W www.yellowearth.org

**YELLOWCHAIR
PERFORMANCE EXPERIENCE THE**
First Breaks on the London Fringe for New Talent
89 Birchanger Lane
Bishop Stortford CM23 5QF
E contacttype@gmail.com
W www.wix.com/yellowchair/type

**YORICK INTERNATIONALIST
THEATRE ENSEMBLE** T/F 020 7836 7637
Yorick Theatre & Film
4 Duval Court, 36 Bedfordbury
Covent Garden, London WC2N 4DQ
E yorickx@hotmail.com

YOUNG VIC THEATRE T 020 7922 2800
66 The Cut, London SE1 8LZ
BO 020 7922 2922
E info@youngvic.org
W www.youngvic.org

ZIP THEATRE T 01902 572250
Newhampton Arts Centre, Dunkley Street
Wolverhampton WV1 4AN
F 01902 572251
E admin@ziptheatre.co.uk
W www.ziptheatre.co.uk

A THOUSAND CRANES   **T** 07801 269772
48 Brunswick Crescent, London N11 1EB
F 020 8994 7674
E kumiko@athousandcranes.org.uk
W www.athousandcranes.org.uk

ACTION STATION UK LTD THE   **T** 0870 7702705
33 Victorian Heights, Thackeray Road, London SW8 3TE
E info@theactionstation.co.uk
W www.theactionstation.co.uk

ACTION TRANSPORT THEATRE   **T** 0151 357 2120
New Writing. Professional Production for,
by & with Young People
Whitby Hall, Stanney Lane
Ellesmere Port, Cheshire CH65 9AE
E info@actiontransporttheatre.org
W www.actiontransporttheatre.org

ACTIONWORK   **T** 01934 815163
Theatre & Film Productions with Young People
PO Box 433, Weston-super-Mare
Somerset BS24 0WY
E admin@actionwork.com
W www.actionwork.com

**ARTY-FACT THEATRE
COMPANY LTD**   **T** 07020 962096
18 Weston Lane, Crewe, Cheshire CW2 5AN
F 07020 982098
W www.arty-fact.co.uk

ASHCROFT YOUTH THEATRE   **T** 0844 8005328
Ashcroft Academy of Dramatic Art
Malcolm Primary School
Malcolm Road, Penge, London SE20 8RH
T 07799 791586
E info@ashcroftacademy.com
W www.ashcroftacademy.com

**BARKING DOG
THEATRE COMPANY**   **T** 020 8883 0034
14 Leaside Mansions, Fortis Green, London N10 3EB
E mike@barkingdog.co.uk
W www.barkingdog.co.uk

BECK THEATRE   **T** 020 8561 7506
Grange Road, Hayes, Middlesex UB3 2UE
T 020 8561 8371
E enquiries@becktheatre.org.uk
W www.becktheatre.org.uk

BIG WOODEN HORSE   **T** 020 8567 8431
30 Northfield Road, West Ealing
London W13 9SY
E info@bigwoodenhorse.com
W www.bigwoodenhorse.com

**BIRMINGHAM STAGE
COMPANY THE**   **T** 020 7437 3391
Contact: Neal Foster (Actor/Manager),
Philip Compton (Executive Producer)
Suite 228, The Linen Hall
162 Regent Street, London W1B 5TB
F 020 7437 3395
E info@birminghamstage.com
W www.birminghamstage.com

BITESIZE THEATRE COMPANY   **T** 01978 358320
8 Green Meadows, New Broughton, Wrexham LL11 6SG
F 01978 756308
E admin@bitesizetheatre.co.uk
W www.bitesizetheatre.co.uk

**BLAH BLAH BLAH
THEATRE COMPANY THE**   **T** 0113 274 0030
The West Park Centre, Spen Lane
Leeds LS16 5BE
E admin@blahs.co.uk
W www.blahs.co.uk

**BLUE MOON THEATRE
COMPANY**   **T/F** 01278 458253
20 Sandpiper Road, Blakespool Park
Bridgwater, Somerset TA6 5QU
E info@bluemoontheatre.co.uk
W www.bluemoontheatre.co.uk

**BLUNDERBUS THEATRE
COMPANY LTD**   **T** 01636 678900
The Studio, The Palace Theatre
Appletongate, Newark, Notts NG24 1JY
E admin@blunderbus.co.uk
W www.blunderbus.co.uk

**BOOSTER CUSHION
THEATRE LTD**   **T** 01727 873874
75 How Wood, Park Street, St Albans, Herts AL2 2RW
F 01727 872597
E admin@booster-cushion.co.uk
W www.booster-cushion.co.uk

BRIDGE HOUSE THEATRE   **T** 01926 776437
Professional & School Productions. Visiting Companies
Warwick School Site, Myton Road, Warwick CV34 6PP
E info@bridgehousetheatre.co.uk
W www.bridgehousetheatre.co.uk

BRIEF CANDLE THEATRE   **T** 01246 556161
Chesterfield Studios, 44 Newbold Road
Chesterfield, Derbyshire S41 7PL
E office@briefcandle.co.uk
W www.briefcandle.co.uk

**CAMBRIDGE TOURING
THEATRE**   **T/F** 01223 246533
29 Worts Causeway, Cambridge CB1 8RJ
E info@cambridgetouringtheatre.co.uk
W www.cambridgetouringtheatre.co.uk

CAUGHT IN THE ACT   **T** 01608 659555
Conygree House, Church Street
Kingham, Oxfordshire OX7 6YA
E cita@caughtintheact.co.uk
W www.caughtintheact.co.uk

**CHAIN REACTION
THEATRE COMPANY**   **T/F** 020 8534 0007
Three Mills Studios, Sugar House Yard
Sugar House Lane, London E15 2QS
E mail@chainreactiontheatre.co.uk
W www.chainreactiontheatre.co.uk

CHALKFOOT THEATRE ARTS
Contact: Philip Dart (Artistic Director)
c/o Channel Theatre Productions Ltd
Penistone House, 5 High Street
St Lawrence, Ramsgate, Kent CT11 0QH
E info@chalkfoot.org.uk
W www.chalkfoot.org.uk

CHICKENSHED   **T** 020 8351 6161
Contact: Mary Ward MBE (Artistic Director)
Chase Side, Southgate, London N14 4PE
BO 020 8292 9222
E susanj@chickenshed.org.uk
W www.chickenshed.org.uk

**CLWYD THEATR CYMRU
THEATRE FOR YOUNG PEOPLE**   **T** 01352 701575
Contact: Neryf (Education Administrator)
Raikef Lane, Mold, Flintshire CH7 1YA
F 01352 701558
E education@clwyd-theatr-cymru.co.uk
W www.ctctyp.co.uk

COMPLETE WORKS LTD THE   **T** 020 7377 0280
Contact: Phil Evans (Artistic Director)
The Old Truman Brewery, 91 Brick Lane, London E1 6QL
F 020 7247 7405
E jacinta@tcw.org.uk
W www.tcw.org.uk

CRAGRATS　　　　　　　　T 0844 8111184
Lawster House, 140 South Street
Dorking, Surrey RH4 2EU
E enquiries@cragrats.com
W www.cragrats.com

CREATIVE PERFORMANCE
LABORATORY　　　　　　　T 07902 396618
E creativeperformancelab@googlemail.com

DAYLIGHT THEATRE　　　　T 01453 763808
66 Middle Street, Stroud
Gloucestershire GL5 1EA

DONNA MARIA COMPANY　　T 020 8670 7814
16 Bell Meadow, Dulwich, London SE19 1HP
E info@donnamariasworld.co.uk
W www.donna-marias-world.co.uk

DRAGON DRAMA　　　　　　T 020 8617 3141
Theatre Company. Parties. Tuition. Workshops.
1B Station Road, Hampton Wick
Surrey KT1 4HG
E askus@dragondrama.co.uk
W www.dragondrama.co.uk

EUROPA CLOWN
THEATRE SHOW　　　　　　T 01892 537964
36 St Lukes Road, Tunbridge Wells, Kent TN4 9JH
E mike@heypresto.orangehome.co.uk
W www.clownseuropa.co.uk

EUROPEAN THEATRE COMPANY THE
Contact: By Post/e-mail
15 Beverley Avenue, London SW20 0RL
E admin@europeantheatre.co.uk
W www.europeantheatre.co.uk

FUSE: NEW THEATRE
FOR YOUNG PEOPLE CO LTD　T 0151 708 0877
Contact: Michael Quirke (General Manager), Andrew Raffle
(Artistic Producer)
13 Hope Street, Liverpool L1 9BH
F 0151 707 9950
E info@fusetheatre.com
W www.fusetheatre.co.uk

FUTURES THEATRE COMPANY　T 020 7928 2832
St John's Crypt, 73 Waterloo Road, London SE1 8UD
F 020 7928 6724
E info@futurestheatrecompany.co.uk
W www.futurestheatrecompany.co.uk

GAZEBO THEATRE COMPANY　T 01902 497222
The Town Hall, Church Street
Bilston, West Midlands WV14 0AP
F 01902 497244
E admin@gazebotie.org
W www.gazebotie.org

GRANT, Derek
ORGANISATION LTD　　　　T 01202 855777
13 Beechwood Road
West Moors, Dorset BH22 0BN
E admin@derekgrant.co.uk
W www.derekgrant.co.uk

GREENWICH & LEWISHAM YOUNG PEOPLE'S
THEATRE (GLYPT)　　　　　T 020 8854 1316
The Tramshed
51-53 Woolwich New Road, London SE18 6ES
F 020 8317 8595
E postbox@glypt.co.uk
W www.glypt.co.uk

GROUP 64 YOUTH THEATRE　T 020 8788 6935
Putney Arts Theatre, Ravenna Road, London SW15 6AW
F 020 8788 6940
E info@putneyartstheatre.org.uk
W www.putneyartstheatre.org.uk

GWENT THEATRE　　　　　　T 01873 853167
The Drama Centre Pen-y-pound
Abergavenny, Monmouthshire NP7 5UD
F 01873 853910
E gwenttie@uwclub.net

HALF MOON YOUNG
PEOPLE'S THEATRE　　　　T 020 7265 8138
43 White Horse Road, London E1 0ND
F 020 7709 8914
E admin@halfmoon.org.uk
W www.halfmoon.org.uk

HOXTON HALL　　　　　　　T 020 7684 0060
130 Hoxton Street, London N1 6SH
E getcreative@hoxtonhall.co.uk
W www.hoxtonhall.co.uk

IMAGE MUSICAL THEATRE　T 020 8743 9380
23 Sedgeford Road, Shepherd's Bush
London W12 0NA
F 020 8749 9294
E brian@imagemusicaltheatre.co.uk
W www.imagemusicaltheatre.co.uk

INDIGO MOON THEATRE　　T 07855 328552
35 Waltham Court, Beverley
East Yorkshire HU17 9JF
E info@indigomoontheatre.com
W www.indigomoontheatre.com

INTERPLAY THEATRE　　　　T 0113 263 8556
Armley Ridge Road, Leeds LS12 3LE
E info@interplayleeds.co.uk
W www.interplayleeds.co.uk

KINETIC THEATRE
COMPANY LTD　　　　　　T 020 8286 2613
Suite H, The Jubilee Centre
Lombard Road, Wimbledon, London SW19 3TZ
F 020 8286 2645
E paul@kinetictheatre.co.uk
W www.kinetictheatre.co.uk

KOMEDIA　　　　　　　　　T 01273 647101
44-47 Gardner Street, Brighton BN1 1UN
E info@komedia.co.uk
W www.komedia.co.uk

LEAVENERS YOUTH
THEATRE THE　　　　　　T 0121 414 0099
Ground Floor, 1 The Lodge
1046 Bristol Road, Birmingham B29 6LJ
F 0121 414 0090
E enquiries@leaveners.org
W www.leaveners.org

LEIGHTON BUZZARD
YOUTH THEATRE　　　　　T 01525 377222
6 Hillside Road, Leighton Buzzard LU7 3BU
E sarah.cavender@tesco.net
W www.lbyt.org

LITTLE ACTORS
THEATRE COMPANY　　　　T 0151 336 4302
9 Carlton Close Road, Parkgate, Cheshire CH64 6TD
E mail@littleactorstheatre.com

M6 THEATRE COMPANY　　T 01706 355898
Studio Theatre, Hamer CP School
Albert Royds Street, Rochdale OL16 2SU
F 01706 712601
E info@m6theatre.co.uk
W www.m6theatre.co.uk

MAGIC CARPET THEATRE　T 01482 709939
18 Church Street, Sutton-on-Hull HU7 4TS
F 01482 787362
E admin@magiccarpettheatre.com
W www.magiccarpettheatre.com

**NATIONAL ASSOCIATION OF
YOUTH THEATRES (NAYT)**   T 01325 363330
Arts Centre, Vane Terrace
Darlington, County Durham DL3 7AX
F 01325 363313
E nayt@btconnect.com
W www.nayt.org.uk

**NATIONAL STUDENT
DRAMA FESTIVAL**   T 020 7036 9027
Woolyard, 54 Bermondsey Street, London SE1 3UD
E info@nsdf.org.uk
W www.nsdf.org.uk

**NATIONAL YOUTH
MUSIC THEATRE**   T 020 7802 0386
Adrian House, 27 Vincent Square, London SW1P 2NN
F 020 7821 0458
E enquiries@nymt.org.uk
W www.nymt.org.uk

**NATIONAL YOUTH
THEATRE OF GREAT BRITAIN**   T 020 7281 3863
Woolyard, 52 Bermondsey Street, London SE1 3UD
F 020 7036 9031
E info@nyt.org.uk
W www.nyt.org.uk

NETTLEFOLD THE   T 020 7926 8070
West Norwood Library Centre, 1 Norwood High Street
London SE27 9JX
E thenettlefold@lambeth.gov.uk

**NOTTINGHAM PLAYHOUSE
TOURING (SCHOOLS)**   T 0115 947 4361
Nottingham Playhouse, Wellington Circus
Nottingham NG1 5AF
F 0115 947 5759
E roundabout@nottinghamplayhouse.co.uk

OILY CART   T 020 8672 6329
*Create work for the under 6s and for young people 3-19
with profound & multiple disabilities (PMLD) or ASD*
Smallwood School Annexe, Smallwood Road
London SW17 0TW
F 020 8672 0792
E oilies@oilycart.org.uk
W www.oilycart.org.uk

ONATTI PRODUCTIONS LTD   T 07710 886805
Contact: Andrew Bardwell (Artistic Director)
The Old Chapel, Yorkley, Gloucestershire GL15 4SB
F 0870 1643629
E info@onatti.co.uk
W www.onatti.co.uk

OUTLOUD PRODUCTIONS LTD   T 07946 357521
Drama Workshops
PO Box 2183, Leigh on Sea, Essex SS9 3RQ
E info@outloudproductions.co.uk
W www.outloudproductions.co.uk

**PANDEMONIUM
TOURING PARTNERSHIP**   T 029 2047 2060
228 Railway Street, Cardiff CF24 2NJ
E paul@pandemoniumtheatre.com

**PANDORA'S BOX
THEATRE COMPANY**   T/F 020 8769 8710
National Touring Young Children's Theatre
43 Fallsbrook Road, London SW16 6DU
E info@pandorasboxtheatre.co.uk
W www.pandorasboxtheatre.co.uk

PENS PEOPLE   T 01708 457443
75 Victor Walk, Hornchurch, Essex RM12 4XQ
E penny@penspeople.co.uk
W www.penspeople.co.uk

**PIED PIPER
THEATRE COMPANY**   T/F 01428 684022
1 Lilian Place, Coxcombe Lane
Chiddingfold, Surrey GU8 4QA
E twpiedpiper@aol.com
W www.piedpipertheatre.co.uk

PILOT THEATRE   T 01904 635755
Performance Work across Platforms. National Touring
York Theatre Royal, St Leonard's Place, York YO1 7HD
F 01904 656378
E info@pilot-theatre.com
W www.pilot-theatre.com

PLAY HOUSE THE   T 0121 464 5712
Language Alive!
Longmore Street, Birmingham B12 9ED
F 0121 464 5713
E info@theplayhouse.org.uk
W www.theplayhouse.org.uk

PLAYTIME THEATRE COMPANY   T 01227 266272
18 Bennells Avenue, Whitstable, Kent CT5 2HP
F 01227 266648
E playtime@dircon.co.uk
W www.playtimetheatre.co.uk

POLKA THEATRE   T 020 8545 8323
240 The Broadway, Wimbledon SW19 1SB
F 020 8545 8365
E stephen@polkatheatre.com
W www.polkatheatre.com

Q20 THEATRE COMPANY   T 0845 1260632
Dockfield Road, Shipley, West Yorkshire BD17 7AD
E info@q20theatre.co.uk

QUANTUM THEATRE   T 020 8317 9000
*Contact: Michael Whitmore, Jessica Selous
(Artistic Directors)*
The Old Button Factory, 1-11 Bannockburn Road
Plumstead, London SE18 1ET
E office@quantumtheatre.co.uk
W www.quantumtheatre.co.uk

**RAINBOW BIGBOTTOM
& CO LTD**   T 01494 771029
Parkview 1A, Stanley Avenue, Chesham, Bucks HP5 2JF
T 07778 106552
E lorrainebmays@aol.com
W www.mrpanda.co.uk

**RAINBOW THEATRE
LONDON EAST**   T 020 8856 5023
56 Sutlej Road, Charlton, London SE7 7DB
F 07092 315384
E rainbowtheatrelondoneast@yahoo.co.uk
W www.rainbow-theatre.com

REDROOFS THEATRE COMPANY
Contact: By Post
The Novello Theatre, Sunninghill
Nr Ascot, Berkshire SL5 9NE
W www.novellotheatre.co.uk

ROYAL & DERNGATE   T 01604 626222
19-21 Guildhall Road, Northampton NN1 1DP
E alex.soulsby@royalandderngate.co.uk
W www.royalandderngate.co.uk

ROYAL COURT THEATRE   T 020 7565 5050
Royal Court Theatre, Sloane Square, London SW1W 8AS
F 020 7565 5001
E info@royalcourttheatre.com
W www.royalcourttheatre.com

SCOTTISH YOUTH THEATRE   T 0141 552 3988
The Old Sheriff Court, 105 Brunswick Street
Glasgow G1 1TF
E info@scottishyouththeatre.org
W www.scottishyouththeatre.org

SHAKESPEARE 4 KIDZ
THEATRE COMPANY THE   T 01342 894548
Drewshearne Barn, Crowhurst Lane End
Oxted, Surrey RH8 9NT
F 01342 893754
E theatre@shakespeare4kidz.com
W www.shakespeare4kidz.com

SHAKESPEAREWORKS   T/F 01865 241281
22 Chilswell Road, Oxford OX1 4PJ
E info@shakespeareworks.co.uk
W www.shakespeareworks.co.uk

SHARED EXPERIENCE
YOUTH THEATRE   T 01865 305321
13 Riverside House, 27-29 Vauxhall Grove
London SW8 1SY
F 020 7735 0374
E admin@sharedexperience.org.uk
W www.sharedexperience.org.uk

SHEFFIELD THEATRES TRUST   T 0114 249 5999
*Contact: Sue Burley (Education Administrator), Dan Bates
(Chief Executive)*
55 Norfolk Street, Sheffield S1 1DA
F 0114 249 6003
E info@sheffieldtheatres.co.uk
W www.sheffieldtheatres.co.uk/creativedevelopmentprogramme

SOLOMON THEATRE COMPANY T/F 01725 518760
Penny Black, High Street
Damerham, Fordingbridge, Hants SP6 3EU
E office@solomon-theatre.co.uk
W www.solomon-theatre.co.uk

SPECTACLE THEATRE   T 01443 430700
Coleg Morgannwg, Rhondda
Llwynypia, Tonypandy CF40 2TQ
F 01443 439640
E info@spectacletheatre.co.uk
W www.spectacletheatre.co.uk

STOPWATCH THEATRE
COMPANY   T 023 8078 3800
Unit 318 Solent Business Centre, Millbrook Road West
Southampton SO15 0HW
E info@stopwatchtheatre.com
W www.stopwatchtheatre.com

STORYTELLERS THEATRE
COMPANY THE   T 01253 839375
Bridge Farm, 249 Hawes Side Lane, Blackpool FY4 4AA
F 01253 792930
E admin@pendleproductions.co.uk
W www.pendleproductions.co.uk

SUPPORT ACT PRODUCTIONS   T 07980 300927
Contact: Ian McCracken
197 Church Road, Northolt UB5 5BE
E info@supportact.co.uk
W www.supportact.co.uk

TALEGATE THEATRE   T 01777 708333
5 Station Road, Retford, Nottinghamshire DN22 7DE
E info@talegatetheatre.co.uk
W www.talegatetheatre.co.uk

THEATR IOLO LTD   T 029 2061 3782
The Old School Building, Cefn Road
Mynachdy, Cardiff CF14 3HS
F 029 2052 2225
E info@theatriolo.com
W www.theatriolo.com

THEATRE& LTD   T 01484 532967
Church Hall, St James Road
Marsh, Huddersfield HD1 4QA
F 01484 532962
E cmitchell@theatreand.com
W www.theatreand.com

THEATRE ALIBI   T/F 01392 217315
Adults & Young People
Emmanuel Hall
Emmanuel Road, Exeter EX4 1EJ
E info@theatrealibi.co.uk
W www.theatrealibi.co.uk

THEATRE CENTRE   T 020 7729 3066
National Touring. New Writing for Young Audiences
Shoreditch Town Hall
380 Old Street, London EC1V 9LT
F 020 7739 9741
E admin@theatre-centre.co.uk
W www.theatre-centre.co.uk

THEATRE HULLABALOO   T 01325 352004
Arts Centre, Vane Terrace
Darlington, County Durham DL3 7AX
F 01325 369404
E info@theatrehullabaloo.org.uk
W www.theatrehullabaloo.org.uk

THEATRE IS...   T 01582 481221
The Hat Factory, 65-67 Bute Street
Luton, Bedfordshire LU1 2EY
E info@theatreis.org
W www.theatreis.org

THEATRE NA N'OG   T 01639 641771
Unit 3, Millands Road Industrial Estate, Neath SA11 1NJ
F 01639 647941
E drama@theatr-nanog.co.uk
W www.theatr-nanog.co.uk

THEATRE WORKOUT LTD   T 020 8144 2290
13A Stratheden Road
Blackheath, London SE3 7TH
E enquiries@theatreworkout.co.uk
W www.theatreworkout.com

TICKLISH ALLSORTS SHOW   T/F 01722 744949
57 Victoria Road, Wilton
Salisbury, Wiltshire SP2 0DZ
E garynunn@ntlworld.com
W www.ticklishallsorts.co.uk

TRICYCLE THEATRE   T/F 020 7372 6611
Contact: Gillian Christie (Education Director)
269 Kilburn High Road, London NW6 7JR
E education@tricycle.co.uk
W www.tricycle.co.uk

UNICORN THEATRE   T 020 7645 0500
147 Tooley Street, London SE1 2HZ
F 020 7645 0550
E admin@unicorntheatre.com
W www.unicorntheatre.com

WEST YORKSHIRE PLAYHOUSE   T 0113 213 7225
Touring Company
Playhouse Square, Quarry Hill, Leeds LS2 7UP
E gail.mcintyre@wyp.org.uk
W www.wyp.org.uk

WIZARD THEATRE   T 0800 5832373
*Contact: Leon Hamilton (Director), Emmy Bradbury
(Company Manager), Oliver Gray (Associate Producer)*
175 Royal Crescent
Ruislip, Middlesex HA4 0PN
E admin@wizardtheatre.co.uk
W www.wizardtheatre.co.uk

YOUNG SHAKESPEARE
COMPANY   T 020 8368 4828
*Contact: Christopher Geelan, Sarah Gordon
(Artistic Directors)*
213 Fox Lane, Southgate, London N13 4BB
E youngshakespeare@mac.com
W www.youngshakespeare.org.uk

AUSTRIA, VIENNA:
Vienna's English Theatre   T/F 01304 813330
Main House Representative:
VM Theatre Productions Ltd
16 The Street, Ash
Canterbury, Kent CT3 2HJ
E vanessa@vmtheatre.demon.co.uk
W www.englishtheatre.at

AUSTRIA, VIENNA:
Vienna's English Theatre   T 020 8946 3400
School Tours Representative:
The European Production Co
15 Beverley Avenue, London SW20 0RL
E europeanproductions@virginmedia.com
W www.englishtheatre.at

DENMARK, COPENHAGEN:
The London Toast Theatre   T 00 45 33228686
Contact: Vivienne McKee (Artistic Director),
Soren Hall (Administrator)
London Toast Theatre, Kochsvej 18
DK-1812 Frb. C, Denmark
E mail@londontoast.dk
W www.londontoast.dk

FRANCE, LYON: Theatre From Oxford (Touring
Europe & Beyond)
Contact: Robert Southam. By Post
B.P. 10, F-42750 St-Denis-de-Cabanne
France
E theatre.oxford@virgin.net

FRANCE, PARIS:
ACT Company   T 00 33 1 46562050
Contact: Andrew Wilson (Artistic Director), Anne Wilson
(Administrator)
25 Avenue Mal Leclerc, 92240 Malakoff, France
E andrew@acttheatre.com
W www.acttheatre.com

GERMANY, FRANKFURT AM MAIN: The English
Theatre Frankfurt   T 00 49 69 24231615
Contact: Daniel Nicolai (Artistic & Managing Director),
Amy Rycroft (Casting, See RYCROFT CASTING)
Gallusanlage 7, 60329, Frankfurt am Main, Germany
F 00 49 69 24231645
E mail@english-theatre.de
W www.english-theatre.de

GERMANY, HAMBURG: The English Theatre of
Hamburg   T 00 49 40 2277089
Contact: Robert Rumpf, Clifford Dean
Lerchenfeld 14, 22081 Hamburg, Germany
F 00 49 40 2277927
W www.englishtheatre.de

GERMANY, TOURING GERMANY:
White Horse Theatre   T 00 49 29 21339339
Contact: Peter Griffith, Michael Dray
Boerdenstrasse 17, 59494 Soest-Muellingsen, Germany
F 00 49 29 21339336
E theatre@white-horse-theatre.eu
W www.whitehorse.de

HUNGARY, BUDAPEST:
Merlin International Theatre   T 00 36 1 3179338
Contact: Laszlo Magacs
Gerloczy Utca 4, 1052 Budapest, Hungary
F 00 36 1 2660904
E info@merlinszinhaz.hu
W www.merlinszinhaz.hu

ICELAND, REYKJAVIK: Light Nights -
The Summer Theatre   T 00 354 5519181
Contact: Kristine G. Magnus (Artistic Director)
The Travelling Theatre
Baldursgata 37, IS-101 Reykjavik, Iceland
E info@lightnights.com
W www.lightnights.com

ITALY, SANREMO: Theatrino & Melting Pot
Theatre - ACLE   T 00 39 0184 506070
Via Roma 54, 18038 Sanremo (IM), Italy
F 00 39 0184 509996
E info@acle.org
W www.acle.org

SWITZERLAND, TANNAY:
Simply Theatre   T 00 41 22 8600518
Chemin des Couleuvres 8B, 1295 Tannay, Switzerland
F 00 41 22 8600519
E info@simplytheatre.com
W www.simplytheatre.com

UNITED KINGDOM, YORKLEY:
Onatti Productions Ltd   T 07710 886805
Contact: Andrew Bardwell
The Old Chapel, Yorkley, Gloucestershire GL15 4SB
F 0870 1643629
E info@onatti.co.uk
W www.onatti.co.uk

ADELPHI T 020 7836 1166
411-412 Strand, London WC2R 0NS
BO 0844 4124651

ALDWYCH T 020 7836 5537
Aldwych, London WC2B 4DF
BO 020 7379 3367
W www.aldwychtheatre.co.uk

ALMEIDA T 020 7288 4900
Almeida Street, London N1 1TA
BO 020 7359 4404

AMBASSADORS T 020 7395 5410
West Street, London WC2H 9ND
BO 0844 8112334
E enquiries@theambassadorstheatre.co.uk
W www.theambassadorstheatre.co.uk

APOLLO T 020 7494 5834
Shaftesbury Avenue, London W1D 7EZ
BO 0844 4124658
E enquiries@nimaxtheatres.com
W www.nimaxtheatres.com

APOLLO VICTORIA T 020 7834 6318
17 Wilton Road, London SW1V 1LG
BO 0870 4000650
W www.apollovictorialondon.org.uk

ARTS T 020 3174 0960
6-7 Great Newport Street, London WC2H 7JB
BO 0845 0175584
E info@artstheatrewestend.co.uk
W www.artstheatrewestend.co.uk

BARBICAN T 020 7628 3351
Barbican, London EC2Y 8DS
BO 0845 1207511
W www.barbican.org.uk

BLOOMSBURY T 020 7679 2777
15 Gordon Street, London WC1H 0AH
BO 020 7388 8822
E admin@thebloomsbury.com
W www.thebloomsbury.com

BUSH T 020 8743 3584
7 Uxbridge Road, London W12 8LJ
BO 020 8743 5050
E info@bushtheatre.co.uk
W www.bushtheatre.co.uk

CAMBRIDGE T 020 7850 8710
Earlham Street, Seven Dials
Covent Garden, London WC2H 9HU
BO 020 7850 8715
W www.reallyuseful.com

CHARING CROSS T 020 7930 5868
Formerly New Players Theatre
The Arches, Off Villiers Street, London WC2N 6NL
E info@charingcrosstheatre.co.uk
W www.charingcrosstheatre.co.uk

COLISEUM
(ENGLISH NATIONAL OPERA) T 020 7836 0111
St Martin's Lane, London WC2N 4ES
BO 0870 1450200
W www.eno.org

CRITERION T 020 7839 8811
2 Jermyn Street, Piccadilly, London SW1Y 4XA
BO 0844 8471778
E admin@criterion-theatre.co.uk
W www.criterion-theatre.co.uk

DOMINION T 020 7927 0900
268-269 Tottenham Court Road, London W1T 7AQ
BO 0870 7490587
W www.dominiontheatrelondon.com

DONMAR WAREHOUSE T 020 7240 4882
41 Earlham Street, London WC2H 9LX
BO 0870 060 6624
E office@donmarwarehouse.com
W www.donmarwarehouse.com

DRURY LANE T 020 7850 8790
Theatre Royal, Catherine Street, London WC2B 5JF
BO 020 7494 5060
W www.rutheatres.com

DUCHESS T 020 7632 9601
Catherine Street, London WC2B 5LA
BO 020 7632 9602
E enquiries@nimaxtheatres.com

DUKE OF YORK'S T 020 7565 6500
St Martin's Lane, London WC2N 4BG
BO 0870 0606623

FORTUNE T 020 7010 7901
Russell Street, Covent Garden
London WC2B 5HH
BO 0870 0606626

GARRICK T 020 7520 5692
2 Charing Cross Road, London WC2H 0HH
BO 020 7520 5693
E enquiries@nimaxtheatres.com

GIELGUD T 020 7292 1320
Shaftesbury Avenue, London W1D 6AR
BO 0844 4825130

HACKNEY EMPIRE T 020 8510 4500
291 Mare Street, London E8 1EJ
BO 020 8985 2424
E info@hackneyempire.co.uk
W www.hackneyempire.co.uk

HAMMERSMITH APOLLO BO 0844 8444748
Queen Caroline Street, London W6 9QH
BO 0844 4999999
W www.hammersmithapollo.net

HAMPSTEAD T 020 7449 4200
Eton Avenue, Swiss Cottage, London NW3 3EU
BO 020 7722 9301
E info@hampsteadtheatre.com
W www.hampsteadtheatre.com

HAROLD PINTER T 020 7321 5310
Formerly Comedy Theatre. Ambassador Theatre Group
Panton Street, London SW1Y 4DN
BO 0870 0606637
E juliethayes@theambassadors.com

HER MAJESTY'S T 020 7850 8750
Haymarket, London SW1Y 4QL
BO 0844 4122707

LONDON PALLADIUM T 020 7850 8770
Argyll Street, London W1F 7TF
BO 0870 8901108

LYCEUM T 020 7420 8100
21 Wellington Street, London WC2E 7RQ
BO 0844 8440005

LYRIC T 020 7494 5840
29 Shaftesbury Avenue, London W1D 7ES
BO 0844 4124661
E enquiries@nimaxtheatres.com

LYRIC HAMMERSMITH T 0871 2211722 (T/BO)
Lyric Square, King Street, London W6 0QL
E enquiries@lyric.co.uk
W www.lyric.co.uk

NATIONAL T 020 7452 3333
South Bank, Upper Ground, London SE1 9PX
BO 020 7452 3000
W www.nationaltheatre.org.uk

NEW LONDON   T 020 7242 9802
Drury Lane, London WC2B 5PW
BO 0844 4124654
E cuqui.rivera@reallyuseful.co.uk

NOEL COWARD   T 020 7759 8011
Formerly Albery. A Delfont Mackintosh Theatre
St Martin's Lane, London WC2N 4AU
BO 0844 4825140

NOVELLO   T 020 7759 9611
Formerly Strand
5 Aldwych, London WC2B 4LD
BO 0844 4825171

OLD VIC   T 020 7928 2651
The Cut, London SE1 8NB
BO 0844 8717628
E ovtcadmin@oldvictheatre.com
W www.oldvictheatre.com

PALACE   T 020 7434 0088
Shaftesbury Avenue, London W1D 5AY
BO 0844 7550016
E info@reallyuseful.co.uk
W www.rutheatres.com

PEACOCK   T 020 7863 8268
For Administration see SADLER'S WELLS
Portugal Street, Kingsway, London WC2A 2HT
BO 0844 4124322
E info@sadlerswells.com
W www.sadlerswells.com

PHOENIX   T 020 7438 9610
110 Charing Cross Road, London WC2H 0JP
BO 020 7438 9605
E phoenixtheatremanagement@theambassadors.com

PICCADILLY   T 020 7478 8800
Denman Street, London W1D 7DY
BO 020 7478 8805
E piccadillymanager@theambassadors.com

PLAYHOUSE   T 020 7839 4292
Northumberland Avenue, London WC2N 5DE
BO 0844 8717631

PRINCE EDWARD   T 020 7440 3021
28 Old Compton Street, London W1D 4HS
BO 0844 4825151
W www.delfont-mackintosh.com

PRINCE OF WALES   T 020 7766 2100
Coventry Street, London W1D 6AS
BO 0844 4825115
E powmanagers@delmack.co.uk
W www.delfontmackintosh.co.uk

QUEEN'S   T 020 7292 1350
Contact: Nicolas Shaw (Manager)
51 Shaftesbury Avenue, London W1D 6BA
BO 0844 4825160

REGENT'S PARK OPEN AIR   T 0844 3753460
Inner Circle, Regent's Park, London NW1 4NR
BO 0844 8264242
W www.openairtheatre.com

RIVERSIDE STUDIOS   T 020 8237 1000
Crisp Road, Hammersmith, London W6 9RL
BO 020 8237 1111
E info@riversidestudios.co.uk
W www.riversidestudios.co.uk

ROYAL COURT   T 020 7565 5050
Sloane Square, London SW1W 8AS
BO 020 7565 5000
E info@royalcourttheatre.com
W www.royalcourttheatre.com

ROYAL OPERA HOUSE   T 020 7240 1200
Bow Street
Covent Garden, London WC2E 9DD
BO 020 7304 4000

SADLER'S WELLS   T 020 7863 8034
Rosebery Avenue, London EC1R 4TN
BO 0844 4124300
E info@sadlerswells.com
W www.sadlerswells.com

SAVOY   T 020 7845 6050
Strand, London WC2R 0ET
BO 0844 8717687
E savoymanager@theambassadors.com
W www.ambassadortickets.com

SHAFTESBURY   T 020 7379 3345
Theatre of Comedy Company
210 Shaftesbury Avenue
London WC2H 8DP
BO 020 7379 5399
E info@shaftesburytheatre.com

SHAKESPEARE'S GLOBE   T 020 7902 1400
21 New Globe Walk
Bankside, London SE1 9DT
BO 020 7401 9919
E info@shakespearesglobe.com
W www.shakespeares-globe.org

SHAW   T 020 7666 9037
Contact: Artistic Director
100-110 Euston Road, London NW1 2AJ
BO 0844 2485075
E info@shaw-theatre.com
W www.shaw-theatre.com

SOHO   T 020 7287 5060
21 Dean Street, London W1D 3NE
BO 020 7478 0100
E box1@sohotheatre.com
W www.sohotheatre.com

ST MARTIN'S   T 020 7497 0578
West Street, London WC2H 9NZ
BO 0844 4991515
E enquiries@stmartinstheatre.co.uk

THEATRE ROYAL   T 020 7930 8890
Haymarket, London SW1Y 4HT
BO 0845 4811870

TRICYCLE   T 020 7372 6611
269 Kilburn High Road
London NW6 7JR
BO 020 7328 1000
E info@tricycle.co.uk
W www.tricycle.co.uk

VAUDEVILLE   T 020 7632 9538
404 Strand, London WC2R 0NH
BO 0870 8900511

VICTORIA PALACE   T 020 7828 0600
Victoria Street, London SW1E 5EA
BO 0844 8110055
E enquiries@victoriapalace.co.uk

WYNDHAM'S   T 020 7759 8077
Charing Cross Road
London WC2H 0DA
BO 0870 9500925

YOUNG VIC   T 020 7922 2800
66 The Cut, London SE1 8LZ
BO 020 7922 2922
E info@youngvic.org
W www.youngvic.org

ALBANY THE   T 020 8692 0231
Douglas Way, Deptford, London SE8 4AG
BO 020 8692 4446
E boxoffice@thealbany.org.uk
W www.thealbany.org.uk

ARCH 468 THEATRE STUDIO   T 07973 302908
Arch 468, 209A Coldharbour Lane, London SW9 8RU
E rebecca@arch468.com
W www.arch468.com

ARCOLA THEATRE   T 020 7503 1645
*Contact: Mehmet Ergen (Artistic Director), Leyla Nazli
(Executive Producer). Route: Victoria Line to Highbury &
Islington, then North London Line to Dalston Kingsland
(Main Line) - 5 min walk. Buses: 38 or 242 from West End,
149 from London Bridge or 30, 67, 76, 243*
24 Ashwin Street, Dalston, London E8 3DL
BO 020 7503 1646
E info@arcolatheatre.com
W www.arcolatheatre.com

ARTSDEPOT   T 020 8369 5454
5 Nether Street, Tally Ho Corner
North Finchley, London N12 0GA
E info@artsdepot.co.uk
W www.artsdepot.co.uk

**BAC
(BATTERSEA ARTS CENTRE)**   T 020 7223 6557
*Route: Victoria or Waterloo (Main Line) to Clapham Junction
then 5 min walk or Northern Line to Clapham Common then
20 min walk*
Lavender Hill, London SW11 5TN
BO 020 7223 2223
E mailbox@bac.org.uk
W www.bac.org.uk

BARONS COURT THEATRE   T 020 8932 4747
*'The Curtain's Up'
Route: West Kensington or Barons Court tube, Piccadilly &
District Lines*
28A Comeragh Road, West Kensington
London W14 9HR
E londontheatre@gmail.com
W www.offwestend.com

BATES, Tristan THEATRE   T 020 7632 8010
Contact: Laura Kriefman (Creative Producer)
1A Tower Street, London WC2H 9NP
BO 020 7240 6283
E tbt@tristanbatestheatre.co.uk
W www.tristanbatestheatre.co.uk

BECK THEATRE   T 020 8561 7506
*Route: Metropolitan Line to Uxbridge then buses 427 or
607 to Theatre or Paddington (Main Line) to Hayes
Harlington then buses 90, H98 or 195 (10 min)*
Grange Road, Hayes, Middlesex UB3 2UE
BO 020 8561 8371
E enquiries@becktheatre.org.uk
W www.becktheatre.org.uk

BEDLAM THEATRE   T 0131 225 9873
11B Bristo Place, Edinburgh EH1 1EZ
BO 0131 225 9893
E info@bedlamtheatre.co.uk
W www.bedlamtheatre.co.uk

BIKE SHED THEATRE THE   T 01392 434169
162/3 Fore Street, Exeter EX4 3AT
E info@bikeshedtheatre.co.uk
W www.bikeshedtheatre.co.uk

BLACKHEATH HALLS   T 020 8318 9758
23 Lee Road, Blackheath, London SE3 9RQ
BO 020 8463 0100
E programming@blackheathhalls.com
W www.blackheathhalls.com

BLOOMSBURY THEATRE   T 020 7679 2777
Route: Tube to Euston, Euston Square or Warren Street
15 Gordon Street, Bloomsbury, London WC1H 0AH
BO 020 7388 8822
E admin@thebloomsbury.com
W www.thebloomsbury.com

BRENTWOOD THEATRE   T 01277 230833
*Contact: David Zelly (Production Manager). Route: Liverpool
Street (Main Line) to Shenfield, then 15 min walk*
15 Shenfield Road, Brentwood
Essex CM15 8AG
BO 01277 200305
E david@brentwood-theatre.org
W www.brentwood-theatre.org

BRIDEWELL THEATRE THE   T 020 7353 3331
*Route: Circle Line to St Paul's. City Thameslink Capital
Connect. 15 different bus routes*
St Bride Foundation, Bride Lane
Fleet Street, London EC4Y 8EQ
E info@stbridefoundation.org
W www.bridewelltheatre.org

BROADWAY THE   T 020 8507 5610
Broadway, Barking IG11 7LS
BO 020 8507 5607
E admin@thebroadwaybarking.com
W www.thebroadwaybarking.com

**BROADWAY STUDIO
THEATRE THE**   T 020 8690 1000
*Contact: Martin Costello (Director). Route: Charing Cross to
Catford Bridge*
Catford, London SE6 4RU
BO 020 8690 0002
E martin@broadwaytheatre.org.uk
W www.broadwaytheatre.org.uk

**CALDER THEATRE
BOOKSHOP LTD**   T 020 7620 2900
*40 seat theatre venue. Wide selection of plays on sale in
bookshop. Rehearsal space for hire*
51 The Cut, London SE1 8LF
E info@calderbook.com

CAMDEN PEOPLE'S THEATRE   T 020 7419 4841
*Route: Victoria or Northern Line to Euston or Warren Street,
Metropolitan or Circle Line to Euston Square (2 min walk
either way)*
58-60 Hampstead Road, London NW1 2PY
E admin@cptheatre.co.uk
W www.cptheatre.co.uk

CANAL CAFE THEATRE THE   T 020 7289 6056
Contact: Emma Taylor (Artistic Director)
The Bridge House, Delamere Terrace
Little Venice, London W2 6ND
BO 020 7289 6054
E mail@canalcafetheatre.com
W www.canalcafetheatre.com

CHARING CROSS THEATRE   T 020 7930 5868
Formerly New Players Theatre
The Arches, Villiers Street, London WC2N 6NL
E info@charingcrosstheatre.co.uk
W www.charingcrosstheatre.co.uk

CHATS PALACE   T 020 8533 0227
42-44 Brooksby's Walk, Hackney, London E9 6DF
E info@chatspalace.com
W www.chatspalace.co.uk

CHELSEA THEATRE   T 020 7349 7811
*Route: District or Circle Line to Sloane Square then short
bus ride 11 or 22 down King's Road*
World's End Place, King's Road, London SW10 0DR
E admin@chelseatheatre.org.uk
W www.chelseatheatre.org.uk

CHICKENSHED T 020 8351 6161
Contact: Mary Ward MBE (Artistic Director). Route: Piccadilly Line to Oakwood, turn left outside tube & walk 8 min down Bramley Road or take 307 bus. Buses 298, 299, 699 or N19. Car parking available & easy access parking by reservation
Chase Side, Southgate
London N14 4PE
BO 020 8292 9222
E susanj@chickenshed.org.uk
W www.chickenshed.org.uk

CHRIST'S HOSPITAL THEATRE T 01403 247435
Contact: Dave Saunders (Director)
Horsham, West Sussex RH13 7LW
BO 01403 247434
E dps@christs-hospital.org.uk

CHURCHILL THE T 020 8464 7131
Contact: John Bartliff (Administrator)
High Street, Bromley
Kent BR1 1HA
BO 0844 8717620
W www.ambassadortickets.com/bromley

CLUB FOR ACTS & ACTORS THE T 020 7836 3172
Contact: Malcolm Knight (Concert Artistes Association). Route: Piccadilly or Northern Line to Leicester Square then few mins walk
20 Bedford Street, London WC2E 9HP
E office@thecaa.org
W www.thecaa.org

COCHRANE THEATRE T 020 7269 1600
Contact: Deirdre Malynn. Route: Central or Piccadilly Line to Holborn then 3 min walk
Southampton Row, London WC1B 4AP
BO 020 7269 1606
E info@cochranetheatre.co.uk

COCKPIT THE T 020 7258 2920
Route: Tube to Marylebone/Edgware Road then short walk or bus 139 or 189 to Lisson Grove & 6, 8, 16, 18, 98, 332 or 414 to Edgware Road
Gateforth Street, Paddington
London NW8 8EH
BO 020 7258 2925
E mail@thecockpit.org.uk
W www.thecockpit.org.uk

COLOUR HOUSE THEATRE THE T 020 8542 5511
Merton Abbey Mills, Watermill Way
London SW19 2RD
E info@colourhousetheatre.co.uk
W www.colourhousetheatre.co.uk

CORBETT THEATRE T 020 8508 5983
Route: Central Line (Epping Branch) to Debden then 6 min walk
East 15 Acting School, Hatfields
Rectory Lane, Loughton IG10 3RY
E east15@essex.ac.uk
W www.east15.ac.uk

COURTYARD THEATRE THE T 020 7739 6868
Contact: June Abbott, Tim Gill (Joint Artistic Directors)
Bowling Green Walk, 40 Pitfield Street
London N1 6EU
BO 020 7729 2202
E info@thecourtyard.org.uk
W www.thecourtyard.org.uk

CROYDON CLOCKTOWER T 020 8253 1030
Katharine Street, Croydon CR9 1ET
E conference&hires@croydon.gov.uk
W www.croydonclocktower.org.uk

CUSTARD FACTORY T 0121 224 7777
Gibb Street, Digbeth, Birmingham B9 4AA
E info@custardfactory.co.uk
W www.custardfactory.co.uk

DARTFORD ORCHARD THEATRE T 01322 220099
Contact: Andy Hill (Theatre Director). Route: Charing Cross (Main Line) to Dartford
Home Gardens, Dartford, Kent DA1 1ED
BO 01322 220000
W www.orchardtheatre.co.uk

DRILL HALL THE BO 020 7307 5060
Route: Northern Line to Goodge Street then 1 min walk
16 Chenies Street, London WC1E 7EX
E box.office@drillhall.co.uk
W www.drillhall.co.uk

EDINBURGH FESTIVAL FRINGE SOCIETY T 0131 226 0026
180 High Street, Edinburgh EH1 1QS
E admin@edfringe.com
W www.edfringe.com

EDINBURGH UNIVERSITY THEATRE COMPANY
See BEDLAM THEATRE

EMBASSY THEATRE & STUDIOS T 020 7722 8183
Route: Jubilee Line to Swiss Cottage then 1 min walk
The Central School of Speech & Drama, 64 Eton Avenue
Swiss Cottage, London NW3 3HY
E enquiries@cssd.ac.uk
W www.cssd.ac.uk

EPSOM PLAYHOUSE THE T 01372 742226
Contact: Trevor Mitchell (General Manager & Artistic Director). Main Auditorium seats 450. Myers Studio seats 80
Ashley Avenue, Epsom, Surrey KT18 5AL
BO 01372 742555
E tmitchell@epsom-ewell.gov.uk
W www.epsomplayhouse.co.uk

ETCETERA THEATRE CLUB T 020 7482 4857
Contact: Michelle Flower (Director)
Oxford Arms, 265 Camden High Street
London NW1 7BU
E etc@etceteratheatre.com
W www.etceteratheatre.com

FAIRFIELD HALLS T 020 8681 0821
Route: Victoria & London Bridge (Main Line) to East Croydon then 5 min walk
Ashcroft Theatre & Concert Hall, Park Lane
Croydon CR9 1DG
BO 020 8688 9291
E info@fairfield.co.uk
W www.fairfield.co.uk

FINBOROUGH THEATRE T 020 7244 7439
Contact: Neil McPherson (Artistic Director). Route: District or Piccadilly Line to Earls Court then 5 min walk. Buses 74, 328, C1, C3, 74 then 3 min walk
118 Finborough Road, London SW10 9ED
BO 0844 8471652
E admin@finboroughtheatre.co.uk
W www.finboroughtheatre.co.uk

GATE THEATRE T 020 7229 5387
Route: Central, Circle or District Line to Notting Hill Gate then 1 min walk. Buses 23, 27, 28, 31, 52, 70, 94, 148, 328, 390, 452
11 Pembridge Road
Above Prince Albert Pub
Notting Hill, London W11 3HQ
BO 020 7229 0706
E gate@gatetheatre.co.uk
W www.gatetheatre.co.uk

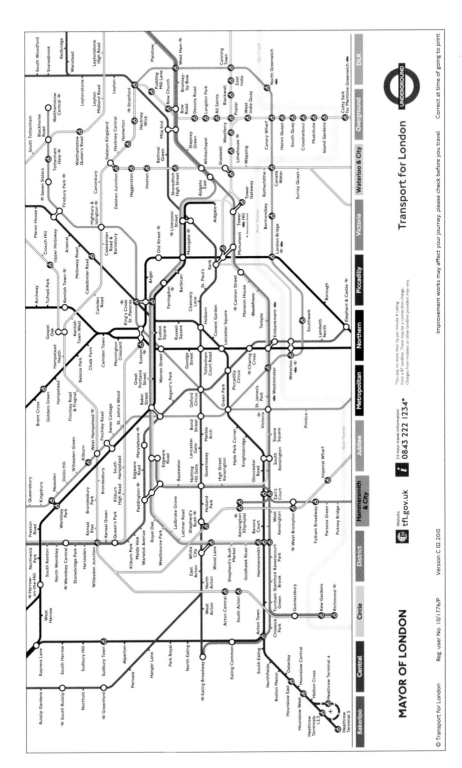

**GBS THEATRE
(GEORGE BERNARD SHAW)**   T 020 7908 4822
Malet Street, London WC1E 7JN
BO 020 7908 4800
E bookings@radaenterprises.org
W www.radaenterprises.org

GIELGUD, John THEATRE   T 020 7908 4822
Malet Street, London WC1E 7JN
BO 020 7908 4800
E bookings@radaenterprises.org
W www.radaenterprises.org

GOOD NIGHT OUT PRESENTS   T 020 7226 8561
*Contact: Adam Spreadbury-Maher (Artistic Director). Route:
Northern Line to Angel then 5 min walk. Approx halfway
between Angel and Highbury & Islington tube stations*
115 Upper Street, Islington
London N1 1QN
T 020 3286 8788
E info@kingsheadtheatre.com
W www.kingsheadtheatre.com

GREENWICH PLAYHOUSE   T 020 8858 9256
*Contact: Alice de Sousa. Route: Main Line from Charing
Cross, Waterloo East or London Bridge, DLR to Greenwich*
Greenwich BR Station Forecourt
189 Greenwich High Road
London SE10 8JA
E alice@galleontheatre.co.uk
W www.galleontheatre.co.uk

GREENWICH THEATRE   T 020 8858 4447
*Contact: James Haddrell (Executive Director). Route: Jubilee
Line (change Canary Wharf) then DLR to Greenwich Cutty
Sark, 3 min walk or Charing Cross (Main Line) to
Greenwich, 5 min walk*
Crooms Hill, Greenwich
London SE10 8ES
BO 020 8858 7755
E info@greenwichtheatre.org.uk
W www.greenwichtheatre.org.uk

**GUILDHALL SCHOOL OF
MUSIC & DRAMA**   T 020 7628 2571
*Route: Hammersmith & City, Circle or Metropolitan line to
Barbican or Moorgate (also served by Northern line) then
5 min walk*
Silk Street, Barbican
London EC2Y 8DT
E info@gsmd.ac.uk
W www.gsmd.ac.uk

HACKNEY EMPIRE THEATRE   T 020 8510 4500
Route: North London Line to Hackney Central
291 Mare Street, Hackney
London E8 1EJ
BO 020 8985 2424
E info@hackneyempire.co.uk
W www.hackneyempire.com

HEN & CHICKENS THEATRE   T 020 7704 2001
*Route: Victoria Line or Main Line to Highbury & Islington
directly opposite station*
Unrestricted View
Above Hen & Chickens Theatre Bar
109 St Paul's Road, Islington, London N1 2NA
E henandchickens@aol.com
W www.henandchickens.com

ICA THEATRE   T 020 7930 0493
*No CVs. Venue only. Route: Nearest stations Piccadilly &
Charing Cross*
The Mall, London SW1Y 5AH
BO 020 7930 3647
W www.ica.org.uk

IVY ARTS CENTRE THE   T 01483 684040
Stag Hill, Guildford GU2 7XH
BO 01483 444789
E gsaenquiries@gsa.surrey.ac.uk
W www.gsauk.org

JACKSONS LANE   T 020 8340 5226
269A Archway Road, London N6 5AA
E reception@jacksonslane.org.uk
W www.jacksonslane.org.uk

JACK STUDIO THEATRE THE   T 020 8291 1206
410 Brockley Road, London SE4 2DH
E admin@brockleyjack.co.uk
W www.brockleyjack.co.uk

JERMYN STREET THEATRE   T 020 7434 1443
*Contact: Gene David Kirk (Artistic Director), Penny Horner
(General Manager)*
16B Jermyn Street
London SW1Y 6ST
BO 020 7287 2875
E info@jermynstreettheatre.co.uk
W www.jermynstreettheatre.co.uk

**JERWOOD VANBRUGH
THEATRE**   T 020 7908 4822
Malet Street, London WC1E 7JN
BO 020 7908 4800
E bookings@radaenterprises.org
W www.radaenterprises.org

KING'S LYNN CORN EXCHANGE   T 01553 765565
Tuesday Market Place, King's Lynn
Norfolk PE30 1JW
BO 01553 764864
E entertainment_admin@west-norfolk.gov.uk
W www.kingslynncornexchange.co.uk

KOMEDIA   T 01273 647101
Contact: Marina Kobler (Programmer)
44-47 Gardner Street, Brighton BN1 1UN
BO 01273 647100
E info@komedia.co.uk
W www.komedia.co.uk

LANDMARK ARTS CENTRE   T 020 8977 7558
Ferry Road, Teddington, Middlesex TW11 9NN
E info@landmarkartscentre.org
W www.landmarkartscentre.org

LANDOR THEATRE THE   T 020 7737 7276
*Contact: Robert McWhir (Artistic Director), Andrew Keates
(Theatre Manager). Route: Northern Line Clapham North
then 2 min walk*
70 Landor Road, London SW9 9PH
E info@landortheatre.co.uk
W www.landortheatre.co.uk

LEICESTER SQUARE THEATRE   T 020 7534 1740
6 Leicester Place, London WC2H 7BX
BO 0844 8733433
E info@leicestersquaretheatre.com
W www.leicestersquaretheatre.com

LEIGHTON BUZZARD THEATRE   T 0300 3008130
Lake Street, Leighton Buzzard, Bedfordshire LU7 1RX
BO 0300 3008125
E lbtboxoffice@centralbedfordshire.gov.uk
W www.leightonbuzzardtheatre.co.uk

LIBRARY THEATRE THE   T 0114 273 4102
*260 Seat Civic Theatre for Hire.
Traditional 1930s Art Deco Style*
Central Library, Tudor Square
Sheffield, South Yorkshire S1 1XZ
E philip.repper@sheffield.gov.uk
W www.sheffield.gov.uk/libraries/librarytheatre

LILIAN BAYLIS THEATRE   T 020 7863 8065
For information see Sadler's Wells Theatre
Rosebery Avenue, London EC1R 4TN
BO 0844 48710090
E info@sadlerswells.com
W www.sadlerswells.com

LIVE THEATRE   T 0191 261 2694
Broad Chare, Quayside
Newcastle upon Tyne NE1 3DQ
BO 0191 232 1232
E info@live.org.uk
W www.live.org.uk

LOST THEATRE   T 020 7622 9208
208 Wandsworth Road, London SW8 2JU
E losttheatre@yahoo.co.uk
W www.losttheatre.co.uk

MACOWAN THEATRE   T 020 7244 8744
*LAMDA. Route: District or Piccadilly Line to
Earl's Court then 6 min walk*
1-2 Logan Place, London W8 6QN
W www.lamda.org.uk

MADDERMARKET THEATRE   T 01603 626560
Contact: Michael Lyas (General Manager)
St John's Alley, Norwich NR2 1DR
BO 01603 620917
E mmtheatre@btconnect.com
W www.maddermarket.co.uk

MENIER CHOCOLATE FACTORY   T 020 7378 1712
53 Southwark Street, London SE1 1RU
BO 020 7378 1713
E office@menierchocolatefactory.com
W www.menierchocolatefactory.com

MILLFIELD ARTS CENTRE   T 020 8887 7301
*Route: Liverpool Street (Main Line) to Silver Street or tube
to Turnpike Lane then bus 144 (15 min to Cambridge
Roundabout)*
Silver Street, London N18 1PJ
BO 020 8807 6680
E boxoffice@enfield.gov.uk
W www.millfieldartscentre.co.uk

NETTLEFOLD THE   T 020 7926 8070
*Route: Victoria, West Croydon or London Bridge (Main Line)
to West Norwood then 2 min walk, or tube to Brixton then
buses 2, 196, 322, 432, or buses 68, 468*
West Norwood Library Centre, 1 Norwood High Street
London SE27 9JX
E thenettlefold@lambeth.gov.uk

NEW DIORAMA THEATRE THE   T 020 7916 5467
*Hire Venue. Route: Circle & District Line to Great Portland
Street then 1 min walk, or Victoria/Northern line to Warren
Street then 5 min walk*
15-16 Triton Street, Regents Place
London NW1 3BF
W www.newdiorama.com

NEW END THEATRE   T 020 7472 5800
*Route: Northern Line to Hampstead then 2 min
walk off Heath Street*
27 New End, Hampstead, London NW3 1JD
BO 0870 0332733
E info@newendtheatre.co.uk
W www.newendtheatre.co.uk

NEW RED LION THEATRE   T 020 7833 3053
*Contact: Henry Filloux-Bennett, Nicholas Thompson (Artistic
Directors). Route: Northern Line to Angel or Old Street then
5 min walk*
271-273 City Road, London EC1V 1LA
BO 0844 4124307
E info@oldredliontheatre.co.uk

**NEW WIMBLEDON
THEATRE & STUDIO**   T 020 8545 7900
*Route: Main Line or District Line to Wimbledon, then 3 min
walk. Buses 57, 93, 155*
The Broadway, Wimbledon
London SW19 1QG
BO 0844 8717646
W www.newwimbledontheatre.co.uk

NORTHBROOK THEATRE THE   BO 01903 606162
Contact: Neil Tiplady (Theatre Co-ordinator)
Littlehampton Road
Goring-by-Sea
Worthing, West Sussex BN12 6NU
E box.office@nbcol.ac.uk
W www.stacatnorthbrook.com

NORWICH PUPPET THEATRE   T 01603 615564
St James, Whitefriars
Norwich NR3 1TN
BO 01603 629921
E info@puppettheatre.co.uk
W www.puppettheatre.co.uk

NOVELLO THEATRE THE   T 01344 620881
*Redroofs Theatre Company. Route: Waterloo (Main Line) to
Ascot then 1 mile from station*
2 High Street, Sunninghill
Nr Ascot, Berkshire SL5 9NE

OLD RED LION THEATRE PUB   T 020 7833 3053
*Contact: Henry Filloux-Bennett, Nicholas Thompson (Artistic
Directors). Route: Northern Line to Angel, then 1 min walk*
418 St John Street, Islington
London EC1V 4NJ
BO 0844 4124307
E info@oldredliontheatre.co.uk

ORANGE TREE   T 020 8940 0141
*Contact: Sam Walters (Artistic Director). Route: District Line,
Waterloo (Main Line) or North London Line then virtually
opposite station*
1 Clarence Street
Richmond TW9 2SA
BO 020 8940 3633
E admin@orangetreetheatre.co.uk

OVAL HOUSE THEATRE   T 020 7582 0080
*Route: Northern Line to Oval then 1 min walk, Victoria Line &
Main Line to Vauxhall then 10 min walk*
52-54 Kennington Oval, London SE11 5SW
BO 020 7582 7680
E info@ovalhouse.com
W www.ovalhouse.com

OVATION THEATRES LTD   T 020 8340 4256
*Route: Northern Line to Highgate then 10 min walk. Buses
143, 210, 214, 271*
Upstairs at the Gatehouse
Corner of Hampstead Lane/North Road
Highgate, London N6 4BD
BO 020 8340 3488
E events@ovationproductions.com
W www.upstairsatthegatehouse.com

PAVILION THEATRE   T 00 353 1 2312929
Marine Road, Dun Laoghaire
County Dublin, Ireland
E info@paviliontheatre.ie
W www.paviliontheatre.ie

PENTAMETERS   T 020 7435 3648
*Route: Northern Line to Hampstead then 1 min walk.
Buses 268, 46*
(Theatre Entrance in Oriel Place)
28 Heath Street
London NW3 6TE
W www.pentameters.co.uk

PLACE THE T 020 7121 1101
Main London Venue for Contemporary Dance.
Route: Northern or Victoria Lines to Euston; Circle,
Hammersmith & City, Metropolitan, Northern, Piccadilly and
Victoria Lines to King's Cross St Pancras; Circle,
Hammersmith & City, Metropolitan lines to Euston Square;
Piccadilly Line to Russell Square are all within easy walking
distance
17 Duke's Road, London WC1H 9PY
BO 020 7121 1100
E theatre@theplace.org.uk
W www.theplace.org.uk

PLEASANCE ISLINGTON T 020 7619 6868
Contact: Anthony Alderson. Route: Piccadilly Line to
Caledonian Road, turn left, walk 50 yds, turn left into North
Road, 2 min walk. Buses 17, 91, 259, N91, 393
Carpenters Mews, North Road
(Off Caledonian Road), London N7 9EF
BO 020 7609 1800
E info@pleasance.co.uk
W www.pleasance.co.uk

POLKA THEATRE T 020 8545 8323
Route: Waterloo (Main Line) or District Line to Wimbledon
then 10 min walk. Northern Line to South Wimbledon then
10 min walk. Tram to Wimbledon, Buses 57, 93, 219, 493
240 The Broadway
Wimbledon SW19 1SB
BO 020 8543 4888
E stephen@polkatheatre.com
W www.polkatheatre.com

**PRINCESS THEATRE
HUNSTANTON** T 01485 532252 (T/BO)
The Green, Hunstanton
Norfolk PE36 5AH
E theprincesshunstanton@hotmail.co.uk
W www.princesstheatrehunstanton.co.uk

PRINT ROOM THE T 020 7221 6036
34 Hereford Road, Notting Hill
London W2 5AJ
E mail@the-print-room.org

PUTNEY ARTS THEATRE T 020 8788 6943
Ravenna Road, Putney SW15 6AW
E info@putneyartstheatre.org.uk
W www.putneyartstheatre.org.uk

QUEEN'S THEATRE T 01708 462362
Contact: Bob Carlton (Artistic Director). Route: District Line
to Hornchurch, Main Line to Romford/Gidea Park. 15 miles
from West End take A13, A1306 then A125 or
A12 then A127
Billet Lane, Hornchurch
Essex RM11 1QT
BO 01708 443333
E info@queens-theatre.co.uk
W www.queens-theatre.co.uk

**QUESTORS THEATRE
EALING THE** T 020 8567 0011
Route: Central or District Line to Ealing Broadway then 5 min
walk. Buses 207, 83, 65, 427, 607, E2, E7, E8, E11
12 Mattock Lane, London W5 5BQ
BO 020 8567 5184
E jane@questors.org.uk
W www.questors.org.uk

**RED LADDER THEATRE
COMPANY LTD** T 0113 245 5311
3 St Peter's Buildings, York Street
Leeds LS9 8AJ
E rod@redladder.co.uk
W www.redladder.co.uk

RICHMOND THEATRE T 020 8332 4500
Contact: Kate Wrightson (General Manager). Route: 20
minutes from Waterloo (South West Trains) or District Line to
Richmond then 2 min walk
The Green, Richmond
Surrey TW9 1QJ
BO 0844 8717651
E richmondstagedoor@theambassadors.com
W www.ambassadortickets.com/richmond

RIDWARE THEATRE T 01889 504380
Contact: Alan & Margaret Williams. Venue only. No resident
performing company
Wheelwright's House, Pipe Ridware
Rugeley, Staffs WS15 3QL
E al@christmas-time.com
W www.ridwares.co.uk

RIVERSIDE STUDIOS T 020 8237 1000
Route: District, Piccadilly or Hammersmith & City Line to
Hammersmith then 5 min walk. Buses 9, 10, 27, 33, 72,
190, 209, 211, 266, 267, 283, 295, 391, 419
Crisp Road, London W6 9RL
BO 020 8237 1111
E info@riversidestudios.co.uk
W www.riversidestudios.co.uk

ROSE THEATRE, KINGSTON T 020 8546 6983
Contact: Stephen Unwin (Artistic Director), Lisa Lepki (PA to
Artistic Director)
24-26 High Street, Kingston upon Thames
Surrey KT1 1HL
E admin@rosetheatrekingston.org
W www.rosetheatrekingston.org

ROSEMARY BRANCH THEATRE T 020 7704 6665
Route: Tube to Bank, Moorgate or Old Street (exit 5), then
No 21, 76 or 141 bus to Baring Street, or 271 bus from
Highbury and Islington
2 Shepperton Road, London N1 3DT
E cecilia@rosemarybranch.co.uk
W www.rosemarybranch.co.uk

**SCOTTISH STORYTELLING
CENTRE** T 0131 556 9579
Netherbow Theatre
43-45 High Street, Edinburgh EH1 1SR
E reception@scottishstorytellingcentre.com
W www.scottishstorytellingcentre.co.uk

**SHAW THEATRE @ NOVOTEL
LONDON ST PANCRAS** T 020 7666 9037
Contact: John-Jackson Almond (Artistic Director)
100-110 Euston Road, London NW1 2AJ
BO 0844 2485075
E info@shaw-theatre.com

**SOUTH HILL PARK
ARTS CENTRE** T 01344 484858
Route: Waterloo (Main Line) to Bracknell then 10 min bus
ride or taxi rank at station
Bracknell, Berkshire RG12 7PA
BO 01344 484123
E admin@southhillpark.org.uk
W www.southhillpark.org.uk

SOUTH LONDON THEATRE T 020 8670 3474
Route: Victoria or London Bridge (Main Line) to West
Norwood then 2 min walk, or Victoria Line to Brixton then
buses 2, 68, 196, 322
Bell Theatre & Prompt Corner
2A Norwood High Street
London SE27 9NS
E southlondontheatre@yahoo.co.uk
W www.southlondontheatre.co.uk

SOUTHWARK PLAYHOUSE   T 020 7407 0234
Contact: Chris Smyrnios (Chief Executive). Route: Trains to London Bridge, Jubilee/Northern Line to London Bridge. Buses 47, 381, RV1, N47, N381. River service to London Bridge City
Shipwright Yard
Corner of Tooley Street & Bermondsey Street
London SE1 2TF
E admin@southwarkplayhouse.co.uk
W www.southwarkplayhouse.co.uk

SPACE ARTS CENTRE THE   T 020 7515 7799
269 Westferry Road, London E14 3RS
E info@space.org.uk
W www.space.org.uk

TABARD THEATRE   T 020 8995 6035
Contact: Collin Hilton, Fred Perry (Artistic Directors), Simon Reilly (Theatre Manager)
2 Bath Road, London W4 1LW
E info@tabardtheatre.co.uk
W www.tabardtheatre.co.uk

THEATRE 503   T 020 7978 7040
Route: Victoria or Waterloo (Main Line) to Clapham Junction then 10 min walk or buses 44, 319, 344, 345 or tube to South Kensington then buses 49 or 345 or tube to Sloane Square then bus 319
The Latchmere Pub, 503 Battersea Park Road
London SW11 3BW
E info@theatre503.com
W www.theatre503.com

THEATRE ALIBI   T 01392 217315
Emmanuel Hall, Emmanuel Road
Exeter EX4 1EJ
E info@theatrealibi.co.uk
W www.theatrealibi.co.uk

THEATRE ROYAL STRATFORD EAST   T 020 8534 7374
Contact: Kerry Michael (Artistic Director). Route: Central or Jubilee Lines, DLR, Overground or National Express trains to Stratford then 2 min walk
Gerry Raffles Square, London E15 1BN
BO 020 8534 0310
E theatreroyal@stratfordeast.com
W www.stratfordeast.com

THEATRO TECHNIS   T 020 7387 6617
Contact: George Eugeniou (Artistic Director). Route: Northern Line to Mornington Crescent then 3 min walk
26 Crowndale Road, London NW1 1TT
E info@theatrotechnis.com
W www.theatrotechnis.com

TOBACCO FACTORY THEATRE   T 0117 902 0345
Raleigh Road, Southville, Bristol BS3 1TF
E theatre@tobaccofactory.com
W www.tobaccofactorytheatre.com

TRICYCLE THEATRE   T 020 7372 6611
Contact: Nicolas Kent (Artistic Director), Mary Lauder (General Manager. Route: Jubilee Line to Kilburn then 5 min walk or buses 16, 189, 32 pass the door, 98, 31, 206, 316, 332 pass nearby
269 Kilburn High Road, London NW6 7JR
BO 020 7328 1000
E admin@tricycle.co.uk
W www.tricycle.co.uk

TRON THEATRE   T 0141 552 3748
63 Trongate, Glasgow G1 5HB
BO 0141 552 4267
E casting@tron.co.uk
W www.tron.co.uk

UNION THEATRE THE   T 020 7261 9876
Contact: Sasha Regan (Artistic Director), Ben De Wynter (Associate Director), Steve Miller (Technical Director), Paul Flynn (All Casting Enquiries). Route: Jubilee Line to Southwark then 2 min walk
204 Union Street, Southwark
London SE1 0LX
E sasha@uniontheatre.freeserve.co.uk
W www.uniontheatre.biz

WAREHOUSE THEATRE   T 020 8681 1257
Contact: Ted Craig (Artistic Director). Route: Adjacent to East Croydon (Main Line). Direct from Victoria (15 min), Clapham Junction (10 min) or by First Capital Connect from West Hampstead, Kentish Town, Kings Cross (25 Mins) & London Bridge (10 mins)
Dingwall Road
Croydon CR0 2NF
BO 020 8680 4060
E info@warehousetheatre.co.uk
W www.warehousetheatre.co.uk

WATERLOO EAST THEATRE   T 020 7928 0060
Entrance Brad Street
3 Wooton Street, London SE1 8TG
E info@waterlooeast.co.uk
W www.waterlooeast.co.uk

WATERMANS   T 020 8232 1019
Route: Buses: 237, 267, 65, N9. Tube: Gunnersbury or South Ealing. Main Line: Kew Bridge then 5 min walk, Gunnersbury then 10 min walk, or Brentford
40 High Street, Brentford TW8 0DS
BO 020 8232 1010
E info@watermans.org.uk
W www.watermans.org.uk

WESTRIDGE (OPEN CENTRE)   T 01635 253322
Drawing Room Recitals
Star Lane, Highclere
Nr Newbury, Berkshire RG20 9PJ

WHITE BEAR THEATRE   T 020 7793 9193
Favours New Writing
Route: Northern Line to Kennington (2 min walk)
138 Kennington Park Road
London SE11 4DJ
E info@whitebeartheatre.co.uk
W www.whitebeartheatre.co.uk

WILTON'S MUSIC HALL   T 020 7702 9555
Route: Tube: Under 10 minutes walk from Aldgate East (exit for Leman Street)/Tower Hill. DLR: Shadwell or Tower Gateway. Car: Follow the yellow AA signs to Wiltons Music Hall from the Highway, Aldgate or Tower Hill
Graces Alley, Off Ensign Street
London E1 8JB
W www.wiltons.org.uk

WIMBLEDON STUDIO THEATRE
See NEW WIMBLEDON THEATRE & STUDIO

WYCOMBE SWAN   T 01494 514444
St Mary Street, High Wycombe
Buckinghamshire HP11 2XE
BO 01494 512000
E enquiries@wycombeswan.co.uk
W www.wycombeswan.co.uk

WYVERN THEATRE   T 01793 535534
Theatre Square, Swindon
Wiltshire SN1 1QN
BO 01793 524481
E info@wyverntheatre.org.uk
W www.wyverntheatre.org.uk

ABERDEEN:
His Majesty's Theatre   T 0845 2708200
Rosemount Viaduct, Aberdeen AB25 1GL
BO 01224 641122
E hmtinfo@aberdeenperformingarts.com
W www.boxofficeaberdeen.com

ABERYSTWYTH:
Aberystwyth Arts Centre   T 01970 622882
University of Wales, Aberystwyth SY23 3DE
BO 01970 623232
E ggo@aber.ac.uk
W www.aber.ac.uk/artscentre

BACUP: Royal Court Theatre   BO 01706 874080
Rochdale Road, Bacup OL13 9NR
E bacuproyalcourttheatre@googlemail.com
W www.brct.co

BASINGSTOKE:
The Haymarket Theatre   T 01256 819797
Wote Street, Basingstoke RG21 7NW
BO 01256 844244
E box.office@anvilarts.org.uk
W www.anvilarts.org.uk

BATH: Theatre Royal   T 01225 448815
Sawclose, Bath BA1 1ET
BO 01225 448844
E forename.surname@theatreroyal.org.uk
W www.theatreroyal.org.uk

BELFAST: Grand Opera House   T 028 9024 0411
Great Victoria Street, Belfast BT2 7HR
BO 028 9024 1919
E info@goh.co.uk
W www.goh.co.uk

BILLINGHAM: Forum Theatre   T 01642 551389
Town Centre, Billingham TS23 2LJ
E forumtheatre@btconnect.com
W www.forumtheatrebillingham.co.uk

BIRMINGHAM: Hippodrome   T 0870 7305555
Hurst Street, Birmingham B5 4TB
BO 0844 3385000
W www.birminghamhippodrome.com

BIRMINGHAM:
New Alexandra Theatre   T 0121 643 5536
Station Street, Birmingham B5 4DS
BO 0844 8713011
W www.newalexandratheatre.co.uk

BLACKPOOL: Grand Theatre   T 01253 290111
33 Church Street, Blackpool FY1 1HT
BO 01253 290190
E admin@blackpoolgrand.co.uk
W www.blackpoolgrand.co.uk

BLACKPOOL: Opera House   T 01253 625252
Church Street, Blackpool FY1 1HW
BO 0844 8561111
W www.blackpoollive.com

BOURNEMOUTH:
Pavilion Theatre   T 01202 456400
Westover Road, Bournemouth BH1 2BU
BO 0844 5763000
W www.bic.co.uk

BRADFORD: Alhambra Theatre   T 01274 432375
Morley Street, Bradford BD7 1AJ
BO 01274 432000
E administration@ces.bradford.gov.uk
W www.bradford-theatres.co.uk

BRADFORD: Theatre in The Mill   T 01274 233185
University of Bradford, Shearbridge Road
Bradford BD7 1DP
BO 01274 233200
E theatre@bradford.ac.uk
W www.bradford.ac.uk/theatre

BRIGHTON: Brighton Dome
& Festivals Ltd   T 01273 700747
The Dome, Corn Exchange & Pavilion Theatres
12A Pavilion Buildings, Castle Square, Brighton BN1 1EE
BO 01273 709709
E info@brightondome.org
W www.brightondome.org

BRIGHTON:
Theatre Royal Brighton   T 01273 764400
New Road, Brighton BN1 1SD
BO 0844 8717650
E timwarren@theambassadors.com
W www.ambassadortickets.com/brighton

BRISTOL: Bristol Hippodrome   T 0117 302 3310
St Augustines Parade, Bristol BS1 4UZ
BO 0844 8472325
W www.bristolhippodrome.org.uk

BROXBOURNE:
Broxbourne Civic Hall   T 01992 441931
High Street, Hoddesdon, Herts EN11 8BE
BO 01992 441946
E civic.leisure@broxbourne.gov.uk
W www.broxbourne.gov.uk/whatson

BURY ST EDMUNDS:
Theatre Royal   T 01284 755127
Westgate Street, Bury St Edmunds IP33 1QR
BO 01284 769505
E admin@theatreroyal.org
W www.theatreroyal.org

BUXTON: Buxton Opera House   T 01298 72050
Water Street, Buxton SK17 6XN
BO 0845 1272190
E admin@boh.org.uk
W www.buxtonoperahouse.org.uk

CAMBERLEY:
The Camberley Theatre   BO 01276 707600
Knoll Road, Camberley, Surrey GU15 3SY
E camberley.theatre@surreyheath.gov.uk
W www.camberleytheatre.biz

CAMBRIDGE: Cambridge Arts
Theatre Trust Ltd   T 01223 578904
6 St Edward's Passage, Cambridge CB2 3PJ
BO 01223 503333
E info@cambridgeartstheatre.com
W www.cambridgeartstheatre.com

CAMBRIDGE: Mumford Theatre   T 01223 417748
Anglia Ruskin University, East Road, Cambridge CB1 1PT
BO 0845 1962320
E mumford@anglia.ac.uk

CANTERBURY:
Gulbenkian Theatre   T 01227 827861
University of Kent, Canterbury CT2 7NB
BO 01227 769075
E gulbenkian@kent.ac.uk
W www.gulbenkiantheatre.co.uk

CANTERBURY:
The Marlowe Theatre   BO 01227 787787
The Friars, Canterbury, Kent CT1 2AS
E info@marlowetheatre.com
W www.marlowetheatre.com

CARDIFF: New Theatre   T 029 2087 8787
Park Place, Cardiff CF10 3LN
BO 029 2087 8889
E ntmailings@cardiff.gov.uk
W www.newtheatrecardiff.co.uk

CARDIFF:
Wales Millennium Centre   T 029 2063 6400
Bute Place, Cardiff CF10 5AL
BO 029 2063 6464
E stagedoor@wmc.org.uk   W www.wmc.org.uk

CHELTENHAM: Everyman Theatre T 01242 512515
Regent Street, Cheltenham GL50 1HQ
BO 01242 572573
E admin@everymantheatre.org.uk
W www.everymantheatre.org.uk

CHICHESTER: Festival Theatre T 01243 784437
Oaklands Park, Chichester PO19 6AP
BO 01243 781312
E admin@cft.org.uk
W www.cft.org.uk

CRAWLEY: The Hawth T 01293 552941
Hawth Avenue, Crawley, West Sussex RH10 6YZ
BO 01293 553636
E info@hawth.co.uk
W www.hawth.co.uk

CREWE: Lyceum Theatre T 01270 537243
Heath Street, Crewe CW1 2DA
BO 01270 537333
E lyceum.theatre@cheshireeast.gov.uk

DARLINGTON: Civic Theatre T 01325 387775
Parkgate, Darlington DL1 1RR
BO 01325 486555
E artscentre.info@darlington.gov.uk
W www.darlingtonarts.co.uk

DUBLIN: Gaiety Theatre T 00 353 1 6795622
South King Street, Dublin 2
BO 00 353 1 6771717
E info@gaietytheatre.com
W www.gaietytheatre.com

DUBLIN: Gate Theatre T 00 353 1 8744368
1 Cavendish Row, Dublin 1
BO 00 353 1 8744045
E info@gate-theatre.ie
W www.gate-theatre.ie

DUBLIN: Olympia Theatre T 00 353 1 6725883
72 Dame Street, Dublin 2
BO 00 353 1 6793323
E info@olympia.ie
W www.olympia.ie

EASTBOURNE: Congress Theatre T 01323 415500
Admin Office: Winter Garden
Compton Street, Eastbourne BN21 4BP
BO 01323 412000
E theatres@eastbourne.gov.uk
W www.eastbournetheatres.co.uk

EASTBOURNE:
Devonshire Park Theatre T 01323 415500
Admin Office: Winter Garden, Compton Street
Eastbourne BN21 4BP
BO 01323 412000
E theatres@eastbourne.gov.uk
W www.eastbournetheatres.co.uk

EDINBURGH: King's Theatre T 0131 662 1112
2 Leven Street, Edinburgh EH3 9LQ
BO 0131 529 6000
E empire@eft.co.uk
W www.fctt.co.uk

EDINBURGH: Playhouse Theatre T 0131 524 3333
18-22 Greenside Place, Edinburgh EH1 3AA
BO 0844 8471660
E edinburghadministrators@theambassadors.com
W www.edinburghplayhouse.org.uk

GLASGOW: King's Theatre T 0141 240 1300
297 Bath Street, Glasgow G2 4JN
BO 0844 8717648
E glasgowstagedoor@theambassadors.com
W www.ambassadortickets.com

GLASGOW: Theatre Royal T 0141-332 3321
282 Hope Street, Glasgow G2 3QA
BO 0844 8717647
W www.ambassadortickets.com/glasgow

GRAYS THURROCK:
Thameside Theatre T 01375 413981
Orsett Road, Grays Thurrock RM17 5DX
BO 0845 3005264
E thameside.theatre@thurrock.gov.uk
W www.thurrock.gov.uk/theatre

HARLOW: Harlow Playhouse T 01279 446704
Playhouse Square, Harlow CM20 1LS
BO 01279 431945
E playhouse@harlow.gov.uk
W www.playhouseharlow.com

HARROGATE: Harrogate
International Centre T 01423 500500
Kings Road, Harrogate HG1 5LA
BO 0845 1308840
E sales@harrogateinternationalcentre.co.uk
W www.harrogateinternationalcentre.co.uk

HASTINGS: White Rock Theatre T 01424 462283
White Rock, Hastings TN34 1JX
BO 01424 462288
E enquiries@whiterocktheatre.org.uk
W www.whiterocktheatre.org.uk

HAYES: Beck Theatre T 020 8561 7506
Grange Road, Hayes, Middlesex UB3 2UE
BO 020 8561 8371
E enquiries@becktheatre.org.uk
W www.becktheatre.org.uk

HIGH WYCOMBE:
Wycombe Swan T 01494 514444
St Mary Street, High Wycombe HP11 2XE
BO 01494 512000
E enquiries@wycombeswan.co.uk
W www.wycombeswan.co.uk

HUDDERSFIELD:
Lawrence Batley Theatre T 01484 425282
Queen's Square, Queen Street, Huddersfield HD1 2SP
BO 01484 430528
E theatre@thelbt.org
W www.thelbt.org

HULL: Hull New Theatre T 01482 613818
Kingston Square, Hull HU1 3HF
BO 01482 300300
E theatre.management@hullcc.gov.uk
W www.hullcc.gov.uk

HULL: Hull Truck Theatre T 01482 224800
50 Ferensway, Hull HU2 8LB
BO 01482 323638
E admin@hulltruck.co.uk
W www.hulltruck.co.uk

ILFORD: Kenneth More Theatre T 020 8553 4464
Oakfield Road, Ilford IG1 1BT
BO 020 8553 4466
E kmtheatre@aol.com   W www.kmtheatre.co.uk

IPSWICH: Sir John Mills Theatre T 01473 218202
Eastern Angles Theatre Company
Sir John Mills Theatre, Gatacre Road, Ipswich IP1 2LQ
BO 01473 211498
E admin@easternangles.co.uk
W www.easternangles.co.uk

JERSEY: Jersey Opera House T 01534 511100
Gloucester Street, St Helier, Jersey JE2 3QR
BO 01534 511115
E admin@jerseyoperahouse.co.uk
W www.jerseyoperahouse.co.uk

KINGSTON: Rose Theatre   T 020 8546 6983
24-26 High Street
Kingston Upon Thames, Surrey KT1 1HL
F 020 8546 8783
E admin@rosetheatrekingston.org
W www.rosetheatrekingston.org

KIRKCALDY: Adam Smith Theatre T 01592 583301
Bennochy Road, Kirkcaldy KY1 1ET
BO 01592 583302

LEATHERHEAD:
The Leatherhead Theatre   T 01372 365130
7 Church Street, Leatherhead
Surrey KT22 8DN
BO 01372 365141
E info@the-theatre.org
W www.the-theatre.org

LEEDS: City Varieties Music Hall T 0113 391 7777
Swan Street, Leeds LS1 6LW
BO 0113 243 0808
E info@cityvarieties.co.uk
W www.cityvarieties.co.uk

LEEDS: Grand Theatre
& Opera House   T 0113 245 6014
46 New Briggate, Leeds LS1 6NZ
BO 0844 8482705
E boxoffice@leedsgrandtheatre.com
W www.leedsgrandtheatre.com

LICHFIELD: The Lichfield Garrick T 01543 412110
Castle Dyke, Lichfield WS13 6HR
BO 01543 412121
E garrick@lichfieldgarrick.com
W www.lichfieldgarrick.com

LINCOLN: Theatre Royal   T 01522 519999
Clasketgate, Lincoln LN2 1JJ
BO 01522 525555
E trl@dial.pipex.com
W www.lincolntheatreroyal.com

LIVERPOOL: Empire Theatre   T 0151 702 7320
Lime Street, Liverpool L1 1JE
BO 0844 8713017
W www.liverpoolempire.org.uk

LLANDUDNO: Venue Cymru   T 01492 879771
Promenade, Llandudno
Conwy, North Wales LL30 1BB
BO 01492 872000
E info@venuecymru.co.uk
W www.venuecymru.co.uk

MALVERN: Malvern Theatres   T 01684 569256
Festival & Forum Theatres
Grange Road, Malvern WR14 3HB
BO 01684 892277
E post@malvern-theatres.co.uk
W www.malvern-theatres.co.uk

MANCHESTER:
O2Apollo Manchester   T 0161 273 6921
Stockport Road, Ardwick Green
Manchester M12 6AP
BO 0844 4777677
E o2apollomanchester@livenation.co.uk
W www.o2apollomanchester.co.uk

MANCHESTER: Opera House   T 0161 828 1700
Quay Street, Manchester M3 3HP
BO 0844 8472484
W www.palaceandoperahouse.org.uk

MANCHESTER: Palace Theatre   T 0161 245 6600
Oxford Street, Manchester M1 6FT
BO 0844 8472484
W www.palaceandoperahouse.org.uk

MARGATE:
Theatre Royal Margate   T 01843 293397
Addington Street, Margate, Kent CT9 1PW
BO 0845 1301786
W www.theatreroyalmargate.com

MILTON KEYNES:
Milton Keynes Theatre   T 01908 547500
500 Marlborough Gate, Central Milton Keynes MK9 3NZ
BO 0844 8717652
W www.ambassadortickets.com/miltonkeynes

NEWARK: Palace Theatre   T 01636 655750
Appletongate, Newark NG24 1JY
BO 01636 655755
E kevan.jackson@nsdc.info
W www.palacenewark.com

NEWCASTLE UPON TYNE:
NORTHERN STAGE (THEATRICAL
PRODUCTIONS) Ltd   T 0191 242 7200
Barras Bridge, Newcastle upon Tyne NE1 7RH
BO 0191 230 5151
E info@northernstage.co.uk
W www.northernstage.co.uk

NEWCASTLE UPON TYNE:
Theatre Royal   T 0191 244 2500
100 Grey Street, Newcastle upon Tyne NE1 6BR
BO 0844 8112121
W www.theatreroyal.co.uk

NORTHAMPTON: Royal &
Derngate Theatres   T 01604 626222
19-21 Guildhall Road, Northampton NN1 1DP
BO 01604 624811
E postbox@royalandderngate.co.uk
W www.royalandderngate.co.uk

NORWICH:
Norwich Theatre Royal   T 01603 598500
Theatre Street, Norwich NR2 1RL
BO 01603 630000
W www.theatreroyalnorwich.co.uk

NOTTINGHAM: Royal Centre   T 0115 989 5500
Theatre Royal & Royal Concert Hall
Theatre Square, Nottingham NG1 5ND
BO 0115 989 5555
E enquiry@royalcentre-nottingham.co.uk
W www.royalcentre-nottingham.co.uk

OXFORD: New Theatre   T 01865 320760
George Street, Oxford OX1 2AG
BO 0844 8713020
E oxfordstagedoor@theambassadors.com

OXFORD: Oxford Playhouse   T 01865 305300
11-12 Beaumont Street, Oxford OX1 2LW
BO 01865 305305
E admin@oxfordplayhouse.com
W www.oxfordplayhouse.com

POOLE: Lighthouse, Poole's
Centre for the Arts   BO 0844 4068666
Kingland Road, Poole BH15 1UG
W www.lighthousepoole.co.uk

READING: The Hexagon   T 0118 937 2123
Queen's Walk, Reading RG1 7UA
BO 0118 960 6060
E boxoffice@readingarts.com
W www.readingarts.com

RICHMOND, N YORKS:
Georgian Theatre Royal   T 01748 823710
Victoria Road, Richmond, North Yorkshire DL10 4DW
BO 01748 825252
E admin@georgiantheatreroyal.co.uk
W www.georgiantheatreroyal.co.uk

RICHMOND, SURREY:
Richmond Theatre   T 020 8332 4500
The Green, Richmond, Surrey TW9 1QJ
BO 0844 8717651
E richmondstagedoor@theambassadors.com
W www.ambassadortickets.com/richmond

ROCHDALE:
Gracie Fields Theatre   T 01706 716689
Hudsons Walk
Rochdale, Lancashire OL11 5EF
E enquiries@graciefieldstheatre.com
W www.graciefieldstheatre.com

SHEFFIELD:
Sheffield Theatres Trust   T 0114 249 5999
Crucible, Lyceum & Crucible Studio
55 Norfolk Street, Sheffield S1 1DA
BO 0114 249 6000
E info@sheffieldtheatres.co.uk
W www.sheffieldtheatres.co.uk

SHERINGHAM:
The Little Theatre   T 01263 822117
2 Station Road, Sheringham
Norfolk NR26 8RE
BO 01263 822347
E enquiries@sheringhamlittletheatre.com
W www.sheringhamlittletheatre.com

SOUTHAMPTON:
The Mayflower Theatre   T 023 8071 1800
Empire Lane, Southampton SO15 1AP
BO 023 8071 1811
E info@mayflower.org.uk
W www.mayflower.org.uk

SOUTHEND: Southend Theatres   T 01702 390657
Cliffs Pavilion, Palace Theatre & Dixon Studio
Cliffs Pavilion, Station Road
Westcliff-on-Sea, Essex SS0 7RA
BO 01702 351135
E info@southendtheatres.org.uk
W www.southendtheatres.org.uk

ST ALBANS: Abbey Theatre   T 01727 847472
Holywell Hill, St Albans AL1 2DL
BO 01727 857861
E manager@abbeytheatre.org.uk
W www.abbeytheatre.org.uk

ST ALBANS: Alban Arena   T 01727 861078
Civic Centre, St Albans AL1 3LD
BO 01727 844488
E alban.arena@leisureconnection.co.uk
W www.alban-arena.co.uk

ST HELENS: Theatre Royal   T 01744 756333
Corporation Street
St Helens WA10 1LQ
BO 01744 756000
E info@sthelenstheatreroyal.co.uk
W www.sthelenstheatreroyal.com

STAFFORD:
Stafford Gatehouse Theatre   T 01785 253595
Eastgate Street, Stafford ST16 2LT
BO 01785 254653
E gatehouse@staffordbc.gov.uk
W www.staffordgatehousetheatre.co.uk

STEVENAGE:
Gordon Craig Theatre   T 01438 242679
Arts & Leisure Centre
Lytton Way, Stevenage SG1 1LZ
BO 01438 363200
E gordoncraig@stevenage-leisure.co.uk
W www.gordon-craig.co.uk

SUNDERLAND:
Sunderland Empire   T 0191 566 1040
High Street West
Sunderland SR1 3EX
BO 0844 8713022
E sunderlandboxoffice@theambassadors.com
W www.sunderlandempire.org.uk

SWANAGE: Mowlem Theatre   BO 01929 422239
Shore Road, Swanage BH19 1DD
E mowlem.box@googlemail.com

TAMWORTH: Assembly Rooms   T 01827 709619
Corporation Street
Tamworth B79 7DN
BO 01827 709618
E assemblyrooms@tamworth.gov.uk
W www.tamworthassemblyrooms.gov.uk

TEWKESBURY: The Roses   T 01684 290734
Sun Street, Tewkesbury GL20 5NX
BO 01684 295074
E admin@rosestheatre.org
W www.rosestheatre.org

TORQUAY:
Babbacombe Theatre   T 01803 322233
Babbacombe Downs
Torquay TQ1 3LU
BO 01803 328385
E info@babbacombe-theatre.com
W www.babbacombe-theatre.com

TORQUAY: Princess Theatre   T 01803 290288
Torbay Road
Torquay TQ2 5EZ
BO 0844 8713023
E wendybennett@theambassadors.com
W www.princesstheatre.org.uk

TRURO: Hall For Cornwall   T 01872 262465
Black Quay, Truro, Cornwall TR1 2LL
BO 01872 262466
E admin@hallforcornwall.org.uk
W www.hallforcornwall.co.uk

WINCHESTER: Theatre Royal   T 01962 844600
21-23 Jewry Street
Winchester SO23 8SB
BO 01962 840440
E comms@theatreroyalwinchester.co.uk
W www.theatreroyalwinchester.co.uk

WORCESTER: Swan Theatre   T 01905 726969
The Moors, Worcester WR1 3ED
BO 01905 611427
E chris@worcesterlive.co.uk
W www.worcesterlive.co.uk

WORTHING: Connaught Theatre, Pavilion
Theatre & The Assembly Hall   T 01903 231799
Union Place
Worthing BN11 1LG
BO 01903 206206
E theatres@worthing.gov.uk
W www.worthingtheatres.co.uk

YEOVIL: Octagon Theatre   T 01935 845900
Hendford, Yeovil BA20 1UX
BO 01935 422884
E octagontheatre@southsomerset.gov.uk
W www.octagon-theatre.co.uk

YORK: Grand Opera House   T 01904 678700
Cumberland Street, York YO1 9SW
BO 0844 8713024
E yorkboxoffice@theambassadors.com
W www.grandoperahouseyork.org.uk

AUTHENTIC PUNCH & JUDY T/F 020 8300 3579
Contact: John Styles. Booths. Presentations. Puppets
42 Christchurch Road
Sidcup, Kent DA15 7HQ
W www.johnstylesentertainer.co.uk

BUCKLEY, Simon
Freelance Puppeteer/Presenter
E simon@simonbuckley.co.ukl
W www.simonbuckley.co.uk

COMPLETE WORKS LTD THE T 020 7377 0280
Contact: Phil Evans (Artistic Director)
The Old Truman Brewery
91 Brick Lane, London E1 6QL
F 020 7247 7405
E jacinta@tcw.org.uk
W www.tcw.org.uk

CORNELIUS & JONES
ORIGINAL PRODUCTIONS T/F 01908 612593
49 Carters Close, Sherington
Newport Pagnell
Buckinghamshire MK16 9NW
E admin@corneliusjones.com
W www.corneliusjones.com

DYNAMIC NEW ANIMATION T 0161 408 1720
Unit 13, The Watermark
Ribbleton Lane, Preston PR1 5EZ
E info@dynamicnewanimation.co.uk
W www.dynamicnewanimation.co.uk

INDIGO MOON THEATRE T 07855 328552
35 Waltham Court, Beverley
East Yorkshire HU17 9JF
E info@indigomoontheatre.com
W www.indigomoontheatre.com

JACOLLY PUPPET THEATRE T 01822 852346
Kirkella Road, Yelverton
West Devon PL20 6BB
E theatre@jacolly-puppets.co.uk
W www.jacolly-puppets.co.uk

LITTLE ANGEL THEATRE T 020 7226 1787
14 Dagmar Passage
Cross Street, London N1 2DN
E info@littleangeltheatre.com
W www.littleangeltheatre.com

MAJOR MUSTARD'S
TRAVELLING SHOW T 0121 426 4329
1 Carless Avenue, Harborne, Birmingham B17 9EG
E mm@majormustard.com

NORWICH PUPPET THEATRE T 01603 615564
St James, Whitefriars, Norwich NR3 1TN
F 01603 617578
E info@puppettheatre.co.uk
W www.puppettheatre.co.uk

PEKKO'S PUPPETS T 020 8575 2311
Contact: Stephen Novy (Director)
92 Stanley Avenue, Greenford
Middlesex UB6 8NP
E enquiries@pekkospuppets.co.uk

PROFESSOR PATTEN'S
PUNCH & JUDY T 01707 873262
Magic. Puppetry
14 The Crest, Goffs Oak, Herts EN7 5NP
W www.dennispatten.co.uk

PUPPET THEATRE WALES T 01446 790634
22 Starling Road, St Athan
Vale of Glamorgan CF62 4NJ
E info@puppettheatrewales.co.uk
W www.puppettheatrewales.co.uk

TALK TO THE HAND
PRODUCTIONS T 07855 421454
Custom Characters Created & Performed
Studio 277, Wimbledon Art Studios
Riverside Yard, Earlsfield, London SW17 0BB
T 07813 682293
E info@talktothehandpuppets.com
W www.talktothehandpuppets.com

TICKLISH ALLSORTS SHOW T/F 01722 744949
57 Victoria Road, Wilton
Salisbury, Wiltshire SP2 0DZ
E garynunn@ntlworld.com
W www.ticklishallsorts.co.uk

TOPPER Chris PUPPETS T 0151 424 8692
Puppets & Costume Characters. Created & Performed
75 Barrows Green Lane, Widnes
Cheshire WA8 3JH
E christopper@ntlworld.com
W www.christopperpuppets.co.uk

ALDEBURGH: Summer Theatre (July & August)
The Jubilee Hall T 01502 724462
Crabbe Street, Aldeburgh IP15 5BN
W www.southwoldtheatre.org

BELFAST: Lyric Theatre T 028 9038 5685
Contact: Richard Croxford (Artistic Director),
Conor McGivern (Head of Production & Technical Services),
Clare Gault (Theatre Administrator), Ciaran McAuley
(Chief Executive), Deirdre Ferguson (Finance Manager)
55 Ridgeway Street, Belfast BT9 5FB
E info@lyrictheatre.co.uk
W www.lyrictheatre.co.uk

BIRMINGHAM:
Birmingham Stage Company T 0121 245 4455
Contact: Neal Foster (Actor/Manager)
The Old Rep Theatre, Station Street, Birmingham B5 4DY
BO 0121 303 2323
E info@birminghamstage.com
W www.birminghamstage.com

BIRMINGHAM:
Birmingham Stage Company T 020 7437 3391
Contact: Neal Foster (Actor/Manager), Philip Compton
(Executive Producer)
London Office: Suite 228 The Linen Hall
162 Regent Street, London W1B 5TB
E info@birminghamstage.com
W www.birminghamstage.com

BIRMINGHAM:
Repertory Theatre T 0121 245 2000
Contact: Roxana Silbert (Artistic Director), Stuart Rogers
(Executive Director)
St George's Court, 1 Albion Street, Birmingham B1 3AH
BO 0121 236 4455
E info@birmingham-rep.co.uk

BOLTON: Octagon Theatre T 01204 529407
Contact: David Thacker (Artistic Director), John Blackmore
(Executive Director), Lesley Etherington (Head of
Administration), Oliver Seviour (Head of Production)
Howell Croft South, Bolton BL1 1SB
BO 01204 520661
E info@octagonbolton.co.uk
W www.octagonbolton.co.uk

BRISTOL:
Theatre Royal & Studio T 0117 949 3993
Contact: Tom Morris (Artistic Director), Emma Stenning
(Executive Director)
Bristol Old Vic, King Street, Bristol BS1 4ED
BO 0117 987 7877
E admin@bristololdvic.org.uk
W www.bristololdvic.org.uk

CARDIFF: Sherman Cymru T 029 2064 6901
Contact: Chris Ricketts (Director), Margaret Jones
(General Manager)
Senghennydd Road, Cardiff CF24 4YE
T 029 2064 6900
E kate.perridge@shermancymru.co.uk

CHICHESTER:
Chichester Festival Theatre T 01243 784437
Contact: Jonathan Church (Artistic Director), Alan Finch
(Executive Director), Janet Bakose (Theatre Manager)
Oaklands Park, Chichester
West Sussex PO19 6AP
BO 01243 781312
E admin@cft.org.uk
W www.cft.org.uk

CHICHESTER: Minerva Theatre at Chichester
Festival Theatre T 01243 784437
Contact: Jonathan Church (Artistic Director), Alan Finch
(Executive Director), Janet Bakose (Theatre Manager)
Oaklands Park, Chichester
West Sussex PO19 6AP
BO 01243 781312
E admin@cft.org.uk
W www.cft.org.uk

COLCHESTER: Mercury Theatre T 01206 577006
Contact: Dee Evans (Chief Executive), Adrian Grady
(Executive Director)
Balkerne Gate, Colchester
Essex CO1 1PT
BO 01206 573948
E info@mercurytheatre.co.uk
W www.mercurytheatre.co.uk

COVENTRY: Belgrade Main Stage &
B2 Auditorium T 024 7625 6431
Contact: Hamish Glen (Artistic Director/CEO), Joanna Reid
(Executive Director), Nicola Young (Director of
Communications)
Belgrade Square, Coventry
West Midlands CV1 1GS
BO 024 7655 3055
E admin@belgrade.co.uk
W www.belgrade.co.uk

DERBY: Derby Live BO 01322 255800
Market Place, Derby
Derbyshire DE1 3AH
E derbylive@derby.gov.uk
W www.derbylive.co.uk

DUBLIN: Abbey Theatre Amharclann na
Mainistreach T 00 353 1 8872200
Contact: Fiach MacConghail (Director)
26 Lower Abbey Street
Dublin 1, Ireland
BO 00 353 1 8787222
E info@abbeytheatre.ie
W www.abbeytheatre.ie

DUNDEE:
Dundee Repertory Theatre T 01382 227684
Contact: James Brining (Artistic Director/Chief Executive),
Jemima Levick (Associate Director), Ian Alexander
(General Manager)
Tay Square, Dundee DD1 1PB
BO 01382 223530
E info@dundeereptheatre.co.uk
W www.dundeerep.co.uk

EDINBURGH: Royal Lyceum
Theatre Company T 0131 248 4800
Contact: Mark Thomson (Artistic Director)
30B Grindlay Street
Edinburgh EH3 9AX
BO 0131 248 4848
E info@lyceum.org.uk
W www.lyceum.org.uk

EDINBURGH: Traverse Theatre T 0131 228 3223
Contact: Dominic Hill (Artistic Director), Linda Crooks
(Administrative Director). New Writing. Own Productions.
Touring & Visiting Companies
10 Cambridge Street
Edinburgh EH1 2ED
BO 0131 228 1404
E admin@traverse.co.uk
W www.traverse.co.uk

EXETER:
Exeter Northcott Theatre   T 01392 223999
Contact: Kate Tyrrell (Chief Executive)
Stocker Road, Exeter
Devon EX4 4QB
BO 01392 493493
E info@exeternorthcott.co.uk
W www.exeternorthcott.co.uk

FRINTON:
Frinton Summer Theatre
July-Sept   T 07905 589792
The McGrigor Hall, Fourth Avenue
Frinton-on-Sea, Essex CO13 9EB

GLASGOW: Citizens Theatre   T 0141 429 5561
Contact: Dominic Hill (Artistic Director), Anna Stapleton
(Administrative Director)
Gorbals, Glasgow G5 9DS
BO 0141 429 0022
E info@citz.co.uk
W www.citz.co.uk

GUILDFORD:
Yvonne Arnaud Theatre   T 01483 440077
Contact: James Barber (Director)
Millbrook, Guildford, Surrey GU1 3UX
BO 01483 440000
E yat@yvonne-arnaud.co.uk
W www.yvonne-arnaud.co.uk

HARROGATE: Harrogate Theatre   T 01423 502710
Contact: David Bown (Chief Executive).
Mainly Co-productions. Touring & Visiting Companies
Oxford Street, Harrogate HG1 1QF
BO 01423 502116
E info@harrogatetheatre.co.uk
W www.harrogatetheatre.co.uk

HULL: Hull Truck Theatre   T 01482 224800
Contact: Andrew Smaje (Chief Executive), Paul Marshall
(Executive Director), Nick Lane (Literary Manager)
50 Ferensway, Hull HU2 8LB
E admin@hulltruck.co.uk
W www.hulltruck.co.uk

IPSWICH:
The New Wolsey Theatre   T 01473 295911
Contact: Peter Rowe (Artistic Director), Sarah Holmes
(Chief Executive)
Civic Drive, Ipswich IP1 2AS
BO 01473 295900
E info@wolseytheatre.co.uk
W www.wolseytheatre.co.uk

KESWICK: Theatre by The Lake   T 01768 772282
Contact: Ian Forrest (Artistic Director), Patric Gilchrist
(Executive Director)
Lakeside, Keswick
Cumbria CA12 5DJ
BO 01768 774411
E enquiries@theatrebythelake.com
W www.theatrebythelake.com

LANCASTER: The Dukes   T 01524 598505
Contact: Joe Sumsion (Director)
Moor Lane, Lancaster
Lancashire LA1 1QE
BO 01524 598500
E info@dukes-lancaster.org
W www.dukes-lancaster.org

LEEDS:
West Yorkshire Playhouse   T 0113 213 7800
Contact: Ian Brown (Artistic Director/Chief Executive),
Sheena Wrigley (Joint Chief Executive),
Henrietta Duckworth (Producer)
Playhouse Square
Quarry Hill, Leeds LS2 7UP
W www.wyp.org.uk

LEICESTER: Curve   T 0116 242 3560
Contact: Juliette Stark (Assistant Producer), Paul Kerryson
(Artistic Director), Stella McCabe (Deputy Chief Executive),
Iain Gillie (Executive Producer)
Rutland Street, Leicester LE1 1SB
E j.stark@curvetheatre.co.uk
W www.curveonline.co.uk

LIVERPOOL: Everyman &
Playhouse Theatres   T 0151 708 3700
Contact: Gemma Bodinetz (Artistic Director),
Deborah Aydon (Executive Director)
Everyman: 13 Hope Street, Liverpool L1 9BH
Playhouse: Williamson Square, Liverpool L1 1EL
BO 0151 709 4776
E info@everymanplayhouse.com
W www.everymanplayhouse.com

MANCHESTER:
Contact Theatre Company   T 0161 274 0623
Contact: Baba Israel (Chief Executive/Artistic Director)
Oxford Road
Manchester M15 6JA
BO 0161 274 0600
E info@contact-theatre.org
W www.contact-theatre.org

MANCHESTER:
Library Theatre Company   T 0161 234 1913
Contact: Chris Honer (Artistic Director), Paul Clay
(Executive Director)
Zion Arts, 335 Stretford Road
Manchester M15 5ZA
E ltcadmin@manchester.gov.uk
W www.librarytheatre.com

MANCHESTER:
Royal Exchange Theatre   T 0161 833 9333
Contact: Braham Murray, Gregory Hersov, Sarah Frankcom
(Artistic Directors), Richard Morgan (Producer/Studio),
Jerry Knight-Smith (Casting Director)
St Ann's Square
Manchester M2 7DH
BO 0161 833 9833
W www.royalexchange.co.uk

MILFORD HAVEN: Torch Theatre   T 01646 694192
Contact: Peter Doran (Artistic Director)
St Peter's Road, Milford Haven
Pembrokeshire SA73 2BU
BO 01646 695267
E info@torchtheatre.co.uk
W www.torchtheatre.co.uk

MOLD: Clwyd Theatr Cymru   T 01352 756331
Repertoire. 4 Weekly. Also touring
Mold, Flintshire
North Wales CH7 1YA
BO 0845 3303565
E admin@clwyd-theatr-cymru.co.uk
W www.clwyd-theatr-cymru.co.uk

MUSSELBURGH:
The Brunton Theatre   T 0131 665 9900
Contact: Lesley Smith (General Manager).
Annual programme of Theatre, Dance, Music,
Comedy & Children's Work
Ladywell Way, Musselburgh EH21 6AA
BO 0131 665 2240
W www.bruntontheatre.co.uk

NEWBURY: Watermill Theatre   T 01635 45834
Contact: Hedda Beeby (Artistic & Executive Director),
Clare Lindsay (General Manager). 4-8 Weekly. Feb-Jan
Bagnor, Nr Newbury, Berkshire RG20 8AE
BO 01635 46044
E admin@watermill.org.uk
W www.watermill.org.uk

NEWCASTLE UNDER LYME:
New Vic Theatre   T 01782 717954
Contact: Theresa Heskins (Artistic Director), Fiona Wallace
(Executive Director)
Etruria Road, Newcastle-under-Lyme
Staffordshire ST5 0JG
BO 01782 717962
E casting@newvictheatre.org.uk
W www.newvictheatre.org.uk

NEWCASTLE UPON TYNE: Northern Stage
(Theatrical Productions) Ltd   T 0191 232 3366
Contact: Erica Whyman (Chief Executive)
Barras Bridge, Newcastle upon Tyne NE1 7RH
BO 0191 230 5151
E info@northernstage.co.uk
W www.northernstage.co.uk

NORTHAMPTON:
Royal & Derngate   T 01604 626222
Contact: Martin Sutherland (Chief Executive), Laurie Sansom
(Artistic Director), Dani Parr (Associate Director)
19-21 Guildhall Road, Northampton
Northamptonshire NN1 1DP
BO 01604 624811
E postbox@royalandderngate.co.uk
W www.royalandderngate.co.uk

NOTTINGHAM:
Nottingham Playhouse   T 0115 947 4361
Contact: Stephanie Sirr (Chief Executive),
Giles Croft (Artistic Director), Andrew Breakwell (Director,
Roundabout and Education)
Nottingham Playhouse Trust Ltd
Wellington Circus, Nottingham NG1 5AL
BO 0115 941 9419
E enquiry@nottinghamplayhouse.co.uk
W www.nottinghamplayhouse.co.uk

OLDHAM: Coliseum Theatre   T 0161 624 1731
Contact: Kevin Shaw (Chief Executive). 3-4 Weekly
Fairbottom Street, Oldham, Lancashire OL1 3SW
BO 0161 624 2829
E mail@coliseum.org.uk
W www.coliseum.org.uk

PERTH: Perth Theatre   T 01738 472700
Contact: Rachel O'Riordan (Artistic Director), Paul Hackett
(Head of Planning & Resources), Jane Spiers
(Chief Executive). 2-3 Weekly
Horsecross Arts, 185 High Street
Perth PH1 5UW
BO 01738 621031
E info@horsecross.co.uk
W www.horsecross.co.uk

PETERBOROUGH: Key Theatre   T 01733 207237
Touring & Occasional Seasonal
Embankment Road, Peterborough
Cambridgeshire PE1 1EF
BO 01733 207239
E key.theatre@vivacity-peterborough.com

PITLOCHRY:
Pitlochry Festival Theatre   T 01796 484600
Contact: John Durnin (Chief Executive/Artistic Director)
Pitlochry, Perthshire PH16 5DR
BO 01796 484626
E admin@pitlochryfestivaltheatre.org.uk
W www.pitlochryfestivaltheatre.org.uk

PLYMOUTH: Theatre
Royal & Drum Theatre   T 01752 668282
Contact: Simon Stokes (Artistic Director), Adrian Vinken
(Chief Executive)
Royal Parade, Plymouth, Devon PL1 2TR
BO 01752 267222
E info@theatreroyal.com
W www.theatreroyal.com

READING: The Mill at
Sonning Theatre   T 0118 969 6039
Contact: Sally Hughes (Artistic Director), Ann Seymour
(Assistant Administrator). 5-6 Weekly
Sonning Eye, Reading RG4 6TY
BO 0118 969 8000
W www.millatsonning.com

SALISBURY:
Playhouse & Salberg Studio   T 01722 320117
Contact: Gareth Machin (Artistic Director),
Michelle Carwardine-Palmer (Executive Director).
3-4 Weekly
Malthouse Lane, Salisbury
Wiltshire SP2 7RA
BO 01722 320333
E info@salisburyplayhouse.com
W www.salisburyplayhouse.com

SCARBOROUGH:
Stephen Joseph Theatre   T 01723 370540
Contact: Chris Monks (Artistic Director), Stephen Wood
(Executive Director). Repertoire/Repertory
Westborough, Scarborough, North Yorkshire YO11 1JW
BO 01723 370541
E enquiries@sjt.uk.com
W www.sjt.uk.com

SHEFFIELD: Crucible, Studio
& Lyceum Theatres   T 0114 249 5999
Contact: Dan Bates (Chief Executive)
55 Norfolk Street, Sheffield S1 1DA
BO 0114 249 6000
E info@sheffieldtheatres.co.uk
W www.sheffieldtheatres.co.uk

SHERINGHAM:
Sheringham Little Theatre   T 01263 822347
Contact: Debbie Thompson (Artistic Director)
2 Station Road, Sheringham, Norfolk NR26 8RE
E enquiries@sheringhamlittletheatre.com
W www.sheringhamlittletheatre.com

SIDMOUTH:
Manor Pavilion Theatre   T 01395 579977
Weekly. July-Sept
Manor Road, Sidmouth, Devon EX10 8RP

SOUTHAMPTON:
Nuffield Theatre   T 023 8031 5500
Contact: Patrick Sandford (Artistic Director), Kate Anderson (Executive Director). Sept-July. Tours
University Road, Southampton SO17 1TR
BO 023 8067 1771
E info@nuffieldtheatre.co.uk
W www.nuffieldtheatre.co.uk

SOUTHWOLD: Summer Theatre   T 01502 724462
Contact: The Jill Freud Company (Producer). July-Sept
St Edmund's Hall, Cumberland Road
Southwold IP18 6JP
E enquiries@southwoldtheatre.org
W www.southwoldtheatre.org

SOUTHWOLD: Summer Theatre   T 01502 724462
Contact: The Jill Freud Company (Producer)
4 Foster Close, Southwold, Suffolk IP18 6LE
E enquiries@southwoldtheatre.org
W www.southwoldtheatre.org

ST ANDREWS: Byre Theatre T 01334 475000 (T/BO)
Contact: Jacqueline McKay (Chief Executive).
Not producing. Co-productions only
Abbey Street, St Andrews KY16 9LA
E enquiries@byretheatre.com
W www.byretheatre.com

STRATFORD-UPON-AVON:
Royal Shakespeare
Company   T 0844 8001110 (T/BO)
Waterside, Stratford-upon-Avon
Warwickshire CV37 6BB
E info@rsc.org.uk
W www.rsc.org.uk

WATFORD:
Watford Palace Theatre   T 01923 235455
Contact: Brigid Larmour (Artistic Director/Chief Executive), Mathew Russell (Executive Director)
20 Clarendon Road
Watford
Hertfordshire WD17 1JZ
BO 01923 225671
E enquiries@watfordpalacetheatre.co.uk
W www.watfordpalacetheatre.co.uk

WINDSOR: Theatre Royal   T 01753 863444
Contact: Simon Pearce (Director)
Thames Street
Windsor
Berkshire SL4 1PS
BO 01753 853888
E info@theatreroyalwindsor.co.uk
W www.theatreroyalwindsor.co.uk

WOKING: New Victoria Theatre,
The Ambassadors   T 01483 545999
Peacocks Centre
Woking GU21 6GQ
BO 0844 8717645
E wokingboxoffice@theambassadors.com
W www.theambassadors.com/woking

YORK: Theatre Royal   T 01904 658162
Contact: Damian Cruden (Artistic Director), Liz Wilson (Chief Executive)
St Leonard's Place
York YO1 7HD
BO 01904 623568
E admin@yorktheatreroyal.co.uk
W www.yorktheatreroyal.co.uk

U →

Unions, Professional Guilds & Associations

Unions

What are performers' unions?

The unions listed in this section exist to protect and improve the rights, interests and working conditions of performers. They offer very important services to their members, such as advice on pay and conditions, help with contracts and negotiations, legal support and welfare advice. To join a performers' union there is usually a one-off joining fee and then an annual subscription fee calculated in relation to an individual's total yearly earnings. Equity is the main actors' union in the UK. See www.equity.org.uk and their case study in this section for more details.

Do similar organisations exist for other sectors of the entertainment industry?

In addition to representation by trade unions, some skills also have professional bodies, guilds and associations which complement the work of trade unions. These include directors, producers, stage managers, designers and casting directors. These can also be found in the following listings.

What is the FIA?

The FIA (International Federation of Actors) www.fia-actors.com is an organisation which represents performers' trade unions, guilds and associations from all around the world. It tackles the same issues as individual actors' unions, but on an international rather than local level. Please see their case study in this section for further information.

I'm a professionally trained actor from overseas and I want to work in the UK. How do I get started?

As with all forms of employment, to work as an actor in the UK you will need to have a relevant work permit/working visa. You might want to visit www.bia.homeoffice.gov.uk/workingintheuk for full information. You may also wish to join the UK's actors' union, Equity. For more information please visit their website www.equity.org.uk. If you can prove that you have relevant professional acting training and/or experience, you can also apply to join Spotlight to promote yourself to casting opportunities.

I am a UK resident and I want to work as an actor elsewhere in Europe. Where do I start?

A good starting point would be to contact the actors' union in the country in which you are hoping to work for information on their employment legislation. Contact details for performers' unions in Europe can be found in the following listings or obtained from the FIA www.fia-actors.com, who in most cases will be able to advise on what criteria you need to fulfil to be eligible for work.

As a UK national, you have the right to work in any country which is a member of the European Union (EU) without a work permit. You will be given the same employment rights as nationals of the country you are working in, but these rights will change according to the country you choose to work in and may not be the same as the UK.

For more general advice, the Foreign and Commonwealth Office (FCO) offers advice on living overseas and provides information on contacting the UK embassy in and relevant entry requirements for the country of your choice. Please see www.fco.gov.uk/en/travelling-and-living-overseas for details. You could also visit Directgov's website www.direct.gov.uk/en/BritonsLivingAbroad/index.htm for further useful guidance for British citizens living abroad.

You should also go further and start researching agents, casting directors, production companies and so on which are based in the country you wish to live and work in. Begin your search online and then decide whether to approach a person or company for further information once you have found out more about them. Learning the culture and becoming as fluent as possible in the language of your chosen country would be advisable, as this opens up a far wider range of job opportunities.

What are English Speaking Theatres?

English Speaking Theatres can provide British actors with an opportunity to work abroad in theatre. These companies vary greatly in terms of the plays they put on and the audiences they attract: they may aim to teach English to schoolchildren; help audiences develop an appreciation of English plays; or may exist simply because there is a demand for English speaking entertainment. Some are based in one venue while others tour round the country. Actors may be employed for an individual production or, especially if touring, for a series of plays. Performers interested in the possibility of working for this type of theatre company should refer to the 'Theatre: English Speaking in Europe' section for listings.

I am a UK resident and I want to work as an actor in the USA. Where do I start?

To work in America you will need a Green Card – a visa which entitles the holder to live and work there permanently as an immigrant – but you will not qualify for one unless you are sponsored by a prospective employer in the US or a relative who is a US citizen. It would be worth visiting the US Embassy's website http://london.usembassy.gov/visas.html or the US Department of State's Bureau of Consular Affairs' website http://travel.state.gov/visa/visa_1750.html for information about the criteria you must meet and the fees you will have to pay. Relocation companies and legal services tailored to helping performers move to America can be found in the 'Accountants, Insurance & Law' section of Contacts.

Don't expect to be granted immediate entry to the USA. There is a limit to the number of people who can apply for immigrant status every year, so you could be on the waiting list for several years depending on the category of your application. You could enter the Green Card Lottery at www.greencard.co.uk for a chance to fast-track the processing of your application, although your visa will still have to be approved.

Finding employment from outside the USA will be difficult. You might want to try signing with an American talent agent to submit you for work, although there is huge competition for agents. Try the Association of Talent Agents (ATA) www.agentassociation.com for US agent details. The most effective way to gain an American agent's interest would be to get a personal referral from an industry contact, such as a casting director or acting coach. You should also promote yourself as you would with Spotlight by signing up with casting directories such as www.breakdownservices.com.

Acting employment in America is divided into union work and non-union work. The major actors' unions are SAG www.sag.org, AEA www.actorsequity.org, and AFTRA www.aftra.com. As with any other union they protect and enhance the rights of their members and offer various services and benefits. You will only become eligible for membership once you have provided proof of a contract for a job which comes under a particular union's jurisdiction. Non-members can work on union jobs if a producer is willing to employ them. You can join more than one union, but once you have joined at least one you will be unable to accept any non-union work.

You may have to begin your career in America with non-union work, as experience or union membership in the UK does not make you eligible to join a union in the US. Work ungoverned by the unions could include student and independent films, small stage productions, commercials, voice-overs, extra work, and so on. You are unlikely to be paid well as non-union contracts are not governed by the minimum wages set by the unions, but you will be able to build on your CV and begin making yourself known in the US acting industry.

Unions

CASE STUDY

Phil Pemberton is the Campaigns & Publications Officer at Equity, the trade union for the UK entertainment industry. He works to provide a voice of authority for performers and the industry in general.

There are lots of good reasons to join a performers' union. The issues that impact most upon you as a performer will depend on your personal circumstances and your career, amongst other things, but the one thing that performers can be sure of is that Equity is the union that best represents your interests.

So, why should you join Equity? Here are ten good reasons to get you thinking…

1. Pay: Equity contracts set the minimum rates for employment throughout the entertainment industry and the provisions in our contracts protect members from exploitation and deliver minimum standards. The stronger we become, the more we push for improved deals. When members come together we can make real progress. In the last twelve months we've achieved a minimum wage of £500 in West End theatres.

2. Decent Treatment At Work: On everything from holiday entitlement to meal breaks and from health and safety protection to maximum working time, Equity has negotiated agreements across the industry to protect you from exploitation by unscrupulous employers and to increase awareness of best practice.

3. Equal Treatment: Regardless of your gender, your race or your sexuality, Equity works for equal opportunities across the entertainment industry and to end discrimination. Recent campaigns for greater opportunities for older women and for a media that is more representative of all sectors of the community have been high profile and continue to attract considerable support.

4. Protection: If your employers, managers or agents are treating you unfairly, Equity will be by your side to ensure that your rights are protected. Equity has a team of specialist organisers working full-time to represent your needs and we have strong legal support for when you need it.

5. Public Liability: For many performers, Equity's public liability insurance (which provides coverage of up to £10million) is an essential protection for their working lives and provides unbeatable value. If someone gets hurt during your act or if something gets damaged, then the knowledge that full insurance comes with your membership can help take the drama out of a crisis.

6. Compensation: If you are injured or get ill because of your working conditions our legal services can ensure you get proper compensation. We have specialist legal support and a 24 hour helpline if you need to make a personal injury claim.

7. Belonging: By becoming an Equity member you make a statement about your commitment to your vocation and your place within our industry. For almost 80 years Equity membership has been a symbol of unity in an industry where work is often transitory and geographically diverse. Your Equity card is a symbol of your professionalism.

8. Contribute: If you are serious about making a contribution to improving conditions for yourself and those you work with, the best way to help is to get involved in your union. In Equity our democratic structures mean your voice can be heard and that you can genuinely make a difference to your own working life and that of your fellow performers.

9. Influence: Equity is a major voice in the entertainment industry, contributing to public debate at local, regional, national and international levels. Our influence comes from the strength of our membership. Although we are not affiliated to any political party, we work with other entertainment unions to influence politicians and to protect your interests and the interests of the arts and media in general.

10. Pride: By being part of Equity you can be proud of your contribution to making your industry a safer and more rewarding place for everyone who works. Your membership makes our union stronger; your involvement gives your union greater influence. Working together we can make Equity a union we can all be proud of.

For more information about Equity contact:
Post: Equity, Guild House
Upper St Martin's Lane
London WC2H 9EG
T 020 7379 6000
W www.equity.org.uk
E info@equity.org.uk

Unions

CASE STUDY

The International Federation of Actors (FIA) is the umbrella organisation representing performers' unions, guilds and professional associations beyond national borders. Set up in 1952 by Equity and the French Actors' Union (SFA), it has spread to gather more than 100 affiliates in about 80 countries around the world. Together with its sister federation FIM (International Federation of Musicians) it is the only international trade body voicing the professional interests of performers at global level. It enjoys consultative status with the World Intellectual Property Organisation, the International Labour Organisation, UNESCO and the Council of Europe.

Increasingly, decisions are taken at supranational level that may have serious repercussions for the daily lives of hundreds of thousands of professional performers. Our remit at FIA is to anticipate change and ensure that performers' legitimate concerns are duly taken into account. Whether the focus is on intellectual property, core labour rights, cultural diversity, mobility, new media or any other issue that is relevant to them, we bring performers and their livelihoods right to the heart of the decision-making process. As other industrial players also actively foster their own interests at international level, our presence is essential to preserve an equitable level playing field for all. We work closely with other interested parties and their trade bodies across the industry to seek solutions to common problems, wherever possible, through dialogue and negotiation.

Our ability to speak with an authoritative voice relies on the collective strength of our members. To this aim, we relentlessly work to help performers around the world build knowledgeable and effective trade unions. Unions are a vital tool for performers as they secure them decent working conditions and a minimum safety net for them to make a living. They are resourceful contributors to the entertainment industry, as they structure dialogue, help prevent and solve conflicts, raise professional standards, promote excellence and campaign for the industry to continue to be successful and fairly reward its creative talent. Our committed work carries us to countries where our knowledge can truly make a difference and bring local performers hope for a better future. To this end, FIA is particularly active in Africa, Latin America and Asia where we organise regular workshops and grow partnerships to reduce the divide between creative industries in developed and developing countries. We organise several regional meetings each year where unions in North America and in Europe can share experience, coordinate policies and respond to industrial developments.

We always strongly encourage performers to join and support their unions and offer our services to strengthen their network.

We are committed to raising professional standards in the industry and regularly publish researches, guidelines and basic advice for performers. With the cooperation of the International Labour Organisation, we recently completed a Health & Safety brief for performers working in live shows as well as in television and film production. We also released a collection of minimum terms of reference for dancers working in countries where there are no collective agreements in place as well as a pan-European study on gender portrayal in the entertainment industry.

We always strongly encourage performers to join and support their unions and offer our services to strengthen their network. We channel solidarity and expertise to our members and create mechanisms to extend assistance to performers when their work brings them far from their union's jurisdiction. Active membership in one of our affiliated unions gives performers privileged access to advice and counselling in many other countries where FIA affiliates are established.

FIA is the voice of performers in the world. By joining local unions, they can help us protect their interests more effectively beyond national borders. They can also help us make a real difference to many other fellow performers who still face very difficult conditions as they struggle to live by their creative work in less fortunate countries.

For more information about FIA contact:
Post: International Federation of Actors (FIA), 31, rue de l'Hôpital, Box 9 1000 Brussels, Belgium
T +32 2 234 5653
F +32 2 235 0861
W www.fia-actors.com
E office@fia-actors.com

UNITED KINGDOM: BECTU - Broadcasting Entertainment, Cinematograph & Theatre Union   T 020 7346 0900
373-377 Clapham Road, London SW9 9BT
F 020 7346 0901
E info@bectu.org.uk
W www.bectu.org.uk

UNITED KINGDOM: CDG - Casting Directors' Guild
PO Box 64973, London SW20 2AW
E info@thecdg.co.uk
W www.thecdg.co.uk

UNITED KINGDOM: DGGB - Directors Guild of Great Britain   T 020 8871 1660
Studio 24, The Royal Victoria Patriotic Building
John Archer Way, London SW18 3SX
F 020 8870 3585
E info@dggb.org
W www.dggb.org

UNITED KINGDOM: EQUITY inc Variety Artistes' Federation   T 020 7379 6000
Guild House, Upper St Martin's Lane, London WC2H 9EG
F 020 7240 6341
E info@equity.org.uk
W www.equity.org.uk

UNITED KINGDOM: EQUITY inc Variety Artistes' Federation (Midlands)   T/F 024 7655 3612
Office 1, Steeple House, Percy Street, Coventry CV1 3BY
E tjohnson@midlands-equity.org.uk

UNITED KINGDOM: EQUITY inc Variety Artistes' Federation (North West & Isle of Man)   T 0161 244 5995
Express Networks, 1 George Leigh Street
Manchester M4 5DL
F 0161 244 5971
E info@manchester-equity.org.uk

UNITED KINGDOM: EQUITY inc Variety Artistes' Federation (Scotland & Northern Ireland)   T 0141 248 2472
114 Union Street, Glasgow G1 3QQ
F 0141 248 2473
E mcurren@glasgow.equity.org.uk
W www.equity.org.uk

UNITED KINGDOM: EQUITY inc Variety Artistes' Federation (Wales & South West)   T 029 2039 7971
Transport House, 1 Cathedral Road, Cardiff CF11 9SD
F 029 2023 0754
E info@cardiff-equity.org.uk

UNITED KINGDOM: FAA - Film Artistes' Association   T 020 7346 0900
Amalgamated with BECTU
373-377 Clapham Road, London SW9 9BT
F 020 7346 0925
W www.bectu.org.uk

UNITED KINGDOM: Musicians' Union   T 020 7582 5566
60-62 Clapham Road, London SW9 0JJ
F 020 7582 9805
E info@themu.org   W www.themu.org

UNITED KINGDOM: NAAA - North American Actors Association   T 07873 371891
Contact: By e-mail/Telephone only
E admin@naaa.org.uk   W www.naaa.org.uk

UNITED KINGDOM: PMA - Personal Managers' Association Ltd   T 0845 6027191
PO Box 63819, London N1P 1HL
E info@thepma.com   W www.thepma.com

UNITED KINGDOM: Writers' Guild of Great Britain   T 020 7833 0777
40 Rosebery Avenue, London EC1R 4RX
E admin@writersguild.org.uk
W www.writersguild.org.uk

BELGIUM: ACV/TRANSCOM - Cultuur   T 00 32 2 2890830
Galerij Agora, Grasmarkt 105 bus 40, 1000 Brussels
E info@acvcultuur.be
W www.acvcultuur.be

BELGIUM: Centrale Générale des Services Publics   T 00 32 2 5085811
Place Fontainas 9-11, 1000 Brussels
F 00 32 2 5085902
W www.acod.be

BELGIUM: FIA - International Federation of Actors   T 00 32 2 2345653
31 rue de l'Hôpital, Box 9, 1000 Brussels
F 00 32 2 2350861
E office@fia-actors.com
W www.fia-actors.com

DENMARK: DAF - Dansk Artist Forbud   T 00 45 33326677
Dronningensgade 68, 1420 Copenhagen K
F 00 45 33337330
E artisten@artisten.dk
W www.artisten.dk

DENMARK: Dansk Skuespillerforbund   T 00 45 33242200
Sankt Knuds Vej 26, 1903 Frederiksberg C
F 00 45 33248159
E dsf@skuespillerforbundet.dk
W www.skuespillerforbundet.dk

FINLAND: SNL - Suomen Näyttelijäliitto   T 00 353 9 25112135
Meritullinkatu 33, 00170 Helsinki
F 00 358 9 25112139
E toimisto@nayttelijaliitto.fi
W www.nayttelijaliitto.fi

FRANCE: Syndicat Français des Artistes-Interprètes   T 00 33 1 53250909
1 rue Janssen, 75019 Paris
F 00 33 1 53250901
E contact@sfa-cgt.fr
W www.sfa-cgt.fr

GERMANY: GDBA - Genossenschaft Deutscher Bühnen-Angehöriger   T 00 49 40 445185
Feldbrunnenstrasse 74, 20148 Hamburg
F 00 49 40 459352
E gdba@buehnengenossenschaft.de
W www.buehnengenossenschaft.de

GREECE: HAU - Hellenic Actors' Union   T 00 30 210 3833742
33 Kanigos, 106 82 Athens
F 00 30 210 3808651
E sei@sei.gr
W www.sei.gr

IRELAND: IEG - Irish Equity Group   T 00 353 1 8586403
SIPTU
Liberty Hall, Dublin 1
F 00 353 1 8743691
E equity@siptu.ie
W www.irishequity.ie

ITALY: Sindicato Attori Italiano   T 00 39 06 8417303
Via Ofanto 18, 00198 Rome
F 00 39 06 8546780
E sai@slc.cgil.it   W www.cgil.it/sai-slc

LUXEMBOURG: OGBL - Onofhnagege Gewerk-schaftbond Letztbuerg　T 00 352 64543777
60 bd. J.F. Kennedy, B.P. 149, L-4002 Esch/Alzette
F 00 352 541620
E info@ogbl.lu　　　　W www.ogb-l.lu

NETHERLANDS: FNV - Kunsten Informatie en Media　T 00 31 20 3553636
Jan Tooropstraat 1, Postbus 9354, 1006 AJ Amsterdam
F 00 31 20 3553737
E algemeen@fnv-kiem.nl　　W www.fnv.nl/kiem

NORWAY: NSF - Norsk Skuespillerforbund　T 00 47 21027190
Welhavensgate 1, 0166 Oslo
F 00 47 21027191
E nsf@skuespillerforbund.no
W www.skuespillerforbund.no

PORTUGAL: STE - Sindicato dos Trabalhadores de Espectáculos　T 00 351 21 8852728
Rua da Fé 23, 2do piso, 1150-149 Lisbon
F 00 351 21 8853787
E sind.trab.espect@mail.telepac.pt

SPAIN: CC.OO. - Comisiones Obreras Servicios a La Ciudadanaia Sector de Medios, Artes, Cultura y Deporte　T 00 34 91 5409295
Plaza Cristino Martos 4, 6A Planta, 28015 Madrid
F 00 34 91 5481613
E medios@fsc.ccoo.es　　W www.fsc.ccoo.es/medios

SPAIN: FAEE - Federación de Artistas del Estado Español　T 00 34 91 5222804
C/ Montera 34, 1ro Piso, 28013 Madrid
F 00 34 91 5226055
E federaciondeartistas@faee.es　　W www.faee.es

SWEDEN: TF - Teaterförbundet　T 00 46 8 4411300
Kaplansbacken 2A
Box 12 710, 112 94 Stockholm
F 00 46 8 6539507
E info@teaterforbundet.se
W www.teaterforbundet.se

UNITED STATES OF AMERICA: AFTRA - American Federation of Television & Radio Artists　T 001 212 532 0800
260 Madison Avenue
New York, NY 10016-2401
F 001 212 532 2242
W www.aftra.com

UNITED STATES OF AMERICA: AFTRA - American Federation of Television & Radio Artists　T 001 323 634 8100
5757 Wilshire Boulevard, 9th Floor
Los Angeles CA 90036
F 001 323 634 8246
W www.aftra.com

UNITED STATES OF AMERICA: S A G - Screen Actors Guild　T 001 323 954 1600
7th Floor, 5757 Wilshire Boulevard
Los Angeles, CA 90036-3600
W www.sag.org

UNITED STATES OF AMERICA: S A G - Screen Actors Guild　T 001 212 944 1030
360 Madison Avenue
12th Floor, New York NY 10017
F 001 212 944 6774
E nymember@sag.org　　W www.sag.org

Index To Advertisers

Alphabetical Listing Of Advertisers

PROPERTIES & TRADES

PUBLICATIONS & PUBLISHERS

REHEARSAL/AUDITION ROOMS/ CASTING SUITES

REPRO COMPANIES & PHOTOGRAPHIC RETOUCHING

ROLE PLAY COMPANIES

SET CONSTRUCTION

SHOWREELS, VOICE TAPES, CVS, PRODUCTION & WEB DESIGN

Alphabetical Listing Of Advertisers Contacts 2012

V

W

Y

N →

Notes

Notes